Evaluation Guide for *Chemistry: A Modern Course*

Chemistry: A Modern Course presents the most modern ideas in chemistry. It is an integrated chemistry program which is both vital and basic. Concepts and principles of chemistry are developed in a logical yet flexible order to make the student's study of chemistry both challenging and interesting. To strengthen the presentation of the text material with the intent of increasing the student's understanding and also his interest in chemistry, the authors and editors have included many *special features.*

To examine examples of the features of *Chemistry: A Modern Course* please turn to the following pages:

(p. 2)   A **thought-provoking paragraph and photo** many in full color, introduce each chapter.

(p. 3)   A **Goal statement** at the beginning of each chapter lets the student know what he is expected to learn from the chapter.

(pp. 8-9,   Accurate **diagrams** along with **photographs** and **line drawings,** many in full color, help the student visualize ideas presented in the text.
118-121)

(pp. 170-171)   **Margin notes** throughout the text emphasize important ideas and direct the student's review.

(p. 229)   **New terms** and important concepts are presented in italic type, are defined in context, are spelled phonetically, and are often emphasized in the margin notes.

(pp. 263-4)   **Problems** are presented within the chapter to encourage the student to develop his understanding of the material presented in the section being studied.

(p. 304)   A brief **biography** of a scientist who contributed to principles to be discussed is included in each chapter.

(p. 335)   The **factor-label method** of problem solving is used throughout the text.

(pp. 434)   **Tables** appear within the context of related material.

(pp. 481-83)   A **Summary** of the main ideas, comprehensive **Problems,** and further questions and problems in **One More Step** appear at the end of each chapter.

(pp. 571-588)   The **Appendices** include supplementary information and tables for general reference.

(pp. 589-608)   The **Index**

International Atomic Masses

Element	Symbol	Atomic number	Atomic mass	Element	Symbol	Atomic number	Atomic mass
Actinium	Ac	89	227*	Mercury	Hg	80	200.59
Aluminum	Al	13	26.98154	Molybdenum	Mo	42	95.94
Americium	Am	95	243*	Neodymium	Nd	60	144.24
Antimony	Sb	51	121.75	Neon	Ne	10	20.179
Argon	Ar	18	39.948	Neptunium	Np	93	237.0482*
Arsenic	As	33	74.9216	Nickel	Ni	28	58.70
Astatine	At	85	210*	Niobium	Nb	41	92.9064
Barium	Ba	56	137.34	Nitrogen	N	7	14.0067
Berkelium	Bk	97	247*	Nobelium	No	102	255*
Beryllium	Be	4	9.01218	Osmium	Os	76	190.2
Bismuth	Bi	83	208.9804	Oxygen	O	8	15.9994
Boron	B	5	10.81	Palladium	Pd	46	106.4
Bromine	Br	35	79.904	Phosphorus	P	15	30.97376
Cadmium	Cd	48	112.40	Platinum	Pt	78	195.09
Calcium	Ca	20	40.08	Plutonium	Pu	94	244*
Californium	Cf	98	251*	Polonium	Po	84	209*
Carbon	C	6	12.011	Potassium	K	19	39.098
Cerium	Ce	58	140.12	Praseodymium	Pr	59	140.9077
Cesium	Cs	55	132.9054	Promethium	Pm	61	145*
Chlorine	Cl	17	35.453	Protactinium	Pa	91	231.0359*
Chromium	Cr	24	51.996	Radium	Ra	88	226.0254
Cobalt	Co	27	58.9332	Radon	Rn	86	222*
Copper	Cu	29	63.546	Rhenium	Re	75	186.207
Curium	Cm	96	247*	Rhodium	Rh	45	102.9055
Dysprosium	Dy	66	162.50	Rubidium	Rb	37	85.4678
Einsteinium	Es	99	254*	Ruthenium	Ru	44	101.07
Erbium	Er	68	167.26	Samarium	Sm	62	150.4
Europium	Eu	63	151.96	Scandium	Sc	21	44.9559
Fermium	Fm	100	257*	Selenium	Se	34	78.96
Fluorine	F	9	18.99840	Silicon	Si	14	28.086
Francium	Fr	87	223*	Silver	Ag	47	107.868
Gadolinium	Gd	64	157.25	Sodium	Na	11	22.98977
Gallium	Ga	31	69.72	Strontium	Sr	38	87.62
Germanium	Ge	32	72.59	Sulfur	S	16	32.06
Gold	Au	79	196.9665	Tantalum	Ta	73	180.9479
Hafnium	Hf	72	178.49	Technetium	Tc	43	98.9062*
Helium	He	2	4.00260	Tellurium	Te	52	127.60
Holmium	Ho	67	164.9304	Terbium	Tb	65	158.9254
Hydrogen	H	1	1.0079	Thallium	Tl	81	204.37
Indium	In	49	114.82	Thorium	Th	90	232.0381
Iodine	I	53	126.9045	Thulium	Tm	69	168.9342
Iridium	Ir	77	192.22	Tin	Sn	50	118.69
Iron	Fe	26	55.847	Titanium	Ti	22	47.90
Krypton	Kr	36	83.80	Tungsten	W	74	183.85
Lanthanum	La	57	138.9055	Uranium	U	92	238.029
Lawrencium	Lr	103	256*	Vanadium	V	23	50.9414
Lead	Pb	82	207.2	Xenon	Xe	54	131.30
Lithium	Li	3	6.941	Ytterbium	Yb	70	173.04
Lutetium	Lu	71	174.97	Yttrium	Y	39	88.9059
Magnesium	Mg	12	24.305	Zinc	Zn	30	65.38
Manganese	Mn	25	54.9380	Zirconium	Zr	40	91.22
Mendelevium	Md	101	258*	Element 104†		104	257*
				Element 105†		105	260*

* The mass number of the isotope with the longest known half-life.

† Names for elements 104 and 105 have not yet been approved by the IUPAC. The USSR has proposed Kurchatovium (Ku) for element 104 and Bohrium (Bh) for element 105. The United States has proposed Rutherfordium (Rf) for element 104 and Hahnium (Ha) for element 105.

CHEMISTRY
A Modern Course

ROBERT C. SMOOT
Chairman, Science Department
McDonogh School
McDonogh, Maryland

JACK PRICE
San Diego City Schools
San Diego, California

CHARLES E. MERRILL PUBLISHING CO.
A Bell & Howell Company   Columbus, Ohio

PREFACE

The *Teacher's Annotated Edition and Solutions Manual* for the fourth edition of *CHEMISTRY: A Modern Course* is an integral part of the revised Merrill Chemistry Program. In one book, you have at your fingertips all of these important features: complete solutions to all problems in the text — suggested teaching aids and demonstrations — interesting approaches to new material — correlation of important sections and ideas throughout the text.

Using this Annotated Edition you will find that it is not necessary to carry with you two or more easily-misplaced supplementary books. All of the material you need is in the Annotated Text at the place you will need it. The Annotated Edition eliminates the time-consuming, frustrating, and often fruitless search for usable supplementary material.

The comments, notes, and suggestions are concise and written with an awareness of the classroom situation. The Teacher's Annotated Edition is provided with the intention of making your teaching of chemistry effective. It is a book that you will want to use.

The teacher's materials consist of:

1. *Annotations*. The annotations are concise sentences or paragraphs overprinted in red on the student text. Each annotation is directly applicable to the section, paragraph, or problem near which it is located.

2. *Solutions Manual*. The solutions manual appears at the front of the book. It is a compilation of the complete problem solutions together with additional explanations and comments arranged in consecutive order as they appear in the text. This arrangement makes it possible to quickly locate supplementary material and check assignments. It also includes literature references to use in exploring selected topics related to chemistry.

New Features of the Teacher's Edition. *Performance Objectives* are included at the beginning of each chapter in the solutions manual at the front of this book. The introduction to the teacher's edition includes a discussion of performance objectives and ideas for using them.

Suggested Readings for each chapter have been expanded to include both resource materials for the instructor and interesting reading for the student.

The Authors

ISBN O-675-07529-7

Published by
CHARLES E. MERRILL PUBLISHING CO.
A Bell & Howell Company

Columbus, Ohio 43216

INTRODUCTION

Flexibility in Teaching

CHEMISTRY: A Modern Course is designed for maximum flexibility in teaching. The text is divided into 24 chapters. Each chapter is divided into subheadings which are divided into numbered sections. The numbering and headings of the sections aid the student in locating specific topics and assist the teacher in arranging class and homework assignments. Further, the teacher may cover the number of sections per week that paces the progress of the class.

CHEMISTRY: A Modern Course follows a logical, sequential development of major chemistry principles. The text begins with the "mechanics" of chemistry, the structure of matter, and the mole concept. The text then deals with the behavior of matter in terms of acidity, oxidation-reduction, and electric potential. It concludes with descriptive material in nuclear, organic, colloid, coordinate, and analytic chemistry.

Alternate Teaching Plans

Time allotments, school schedules, and curricula vary greatly from school system to school system. With this in mind, the authors and editors of the Merrill Chemistry Program have provided for ease in adapting CHEMISTRY: A Modern Course to a variety of school scheduling plans, such as two-semester, trimester, or quarter plans.

Laboratory Work

Laboratory Chemistry provides the student with a variety of laboratory work to introduce or reinforce his discovery of chemical principles. Quantitative aspects of chemistry laboratory procedures are emphasized. Laboratory experiments are designed to fit differing laboratory schedules and equipment set-ups.

Problems

Learning to solve chemistry problems involves four learning principles — introduction, example and illustration, practice, and review. These principles are incorporated in solutions to problems in the text.

Student Notes

Student notes placed in the margin aid in review as well as serve as a reading aid. They provide a ready outline of concepts discussed within the chapter besides giving concise statements about those concepts.

Photographs, Illustrations, and Captions

This edition of CHEMISTRY: A Modern Course has greatly expanded the use of material to provide the student with visual links between chemistry principles and real-world happenings. Captions do not merely repeat the evident, but incorporate additional information which can be used as valuable teaching aids.

PERFORMANCE OBJECTIVES

What Is a Performance Objective?

Pick up almost any book on science education and you'll find reasons for teaching science:

> "For students to acquire habits of critical thinking . . . ."
> "To instill an appreciation for their natural environment . . . ."
> "To learn scientific terms, concepts, and principles . . . ."
> "So that students will sustain and enhance their natural curiosity . . . . "

This list could go on and on, and no doubt you could add your own reasons as to why you teach chemistry or some other science course. Statements of what science teaching intends to accomplish are no doubt valid and justifiable. The question is: How do you know that you are succeeding in achieving the goals of science education?

> What would you look for if students really were thinking critically?
> What would students be doing if they are appreciating their natural environment?
> How could you tell whether or not a student has learned a scientific term, concept, or principle?

How would you know if your teaching enhanced or extinguished a student's natural curiosity?

Therein lies the value of performance objectives — the behaviors which you, the teacher, can observe and which seem to indicate that students are actually achieving the lofty goals of science education.

For example, let's take the first one: "For students to acquire habits of critical thinking. . . ." Now what can you think of that students might do if they are thinking critically? Here are some behaviors which you might observe:

Students ask questions related to the topic being discussed.

They gather data or share evidence which supports their answers.

They question or express doubt about the theories posed by others.

They suggest alternate solutions to a problem.

They reject their ideas when the evidence they gather does not support their theories.

Perhaps you could think of other behaviors which would indicate that students are thinking critically. This list is not exhaustive by any means. It only serves as an example of what you might look for if you were accomplishing that goal.

Let's try another one: "To learn scientific terms, concepts, and principles. . . ." How could a student demonstrate to you that he has learned something? For example, when discussing chemical bonding does he use the terms covalent and ionic correctly? If he does, you might think that he has learned them.

Or, when he is asked to define them orally, does he say something like: "Ionic bonding assumes that electron transfer has taken place while covalent bonding occurs when the total energy required to hold the electrons near the nuclei is less when the bonded atoms are sharing the electrons than when the atoms are separate." If he does, you might think that he has learned them.

Or, when he is asked to give examples of ionic and covalent bonds, he names sodium chloride and hydrogen molecules.

Or, when he is presented with diagrams of ionic and covalent bonds, he is able to distinguish between them.

Or, given the definitions of the two bonds, he matches the term with the correct definition.

An unlimited number of behaviors could be cited which indicate a student has learned something. Basically, a performance objective is a description of the behavior you might observe in a student if he is achieving an educational goal.

What Is a Good Performance Objective?

Statements of performance objectives can usually be divided into three distinct parts. First is a description of the conditions under which the desired behavior will be observed. Here are some examples which describe the condition:

"When presented with models of crystal structures . . . ."

"When asked to draw electron dot diagrams for . . . ."

"When presented with the materials suggested on page . . . ."

"After having read and discussed . . . ."

"In groups of three students, given conductivity apparatus and several solutions . . . ."

A good performance objective includes a condition which tells what causes, stimulates, or motivates the student to perform the behaviors or under what circumstances those behaviors will be performed.

The second part of a well-stated performance objective is a clear description of exactly what behavior you're looking for. A good performance objective would avoid using such terms as "know about," "appreciate," or "sense the relationship between." Rather, a good performance objective will include terms which describe what you could observe students doing if they do "know about" or "appreciate." It's almost impossible to observe a student "appreciating," but you can gather some evidence that he is appreciating science if he is:

reading science books instead of comic books;

staying late or coming to class early to work in the laboratory;

requesting that you repeat a demonstration or wanting to do it himself;

expressing to you a liking for chemistry.

In other words, a good performance objective uses verbs which express some type of observable action. Here are some examples of action verbs which describe observable behaviors:

states orally	manipulates
matches	measures
distinguishes between	expresses
	watches
constructs	states hypotheses
identifies	recalls
lists	

The third part of a well-stated performance objective is a description of some level of performance or criteria which may help you to know if the student or class has performed to the degree which you hoped for.

For example, if you were teaching students to use a balance, would you want all of your class to be able to accurately measure the mass of a solid or liquid? Would you feel satisfied if 90% of your class could perform this skill? 80%? 50%? Would you be happy if just one student did it? Obviously, this level of performance would vary for each class, each student, each teacher, and each task. In some classrooms, a teacher might think that all students should be able to measure accurately. In other classrooms, a teacher would be elated if even a few students could measure accurately.

What do we mean by accurately? Would you be satisfied if students could measure a mass to the nearest centigram? Half-centigram? Milligram? More accurately than that? Just how accurately would be acceptable to you? Here then, is another aspect of a level of performance: A well-stated performance objective might also include some description of how precise, how accurate, how well the behavior should be performed in order for you to know that the student has really achieved the objective.

Another kind of a criterion measure or performance level which might be included in a performance objective is a statement of how often or how many times a student must perform the behavior in order to demonstrate that he has learned something. For example, if he measured a mass with a balance accurately just one time, would you conclude that he has learned how to measure? What if you asked him to measure the mass of 5 objects with a balance, and you were looking for his ability to measure them correctly to the nearest centigram? Would you be satisfied if he measured four of them correctly? Three out of five? Or would you only be satisfied if he measured all five of them correctly?

Again, this decision will have to be made on the basis of what you know about the student's ability, and the task at hand. For some students, you'd be happy if they could do it just once; for other students, you might expect perfection four out of five trials.

Now let's put all these parts together and see what a well-stated performance objective looks like:

Conditions
(tell you how to plan and organize your class and what materials you'll need)

Working individually, when presented with a laboratory balance, beaker, liquid, solid, and graduated cylinder,

Performance
(tells you what behaviors of students to look for)

students will measure the masses of the liquid and solid to the nearest 0.01 g, measure the volume of liquid to the nearest 0.01 ml, measure the volume of the solid by liquid displacement. Students will be able to calculate the density of the solid and liquid to correct number of significant digits.

Criterion Measure
(tells you how many of the students or to what degree the objective should be achieved)

Of all the students, 95% will achieve 100% of the above objectives.

Why Should You Use Performance Objectives?

A performance objective cannot and should not tell you how to teach. Your teaching strategy is a product of your own creativity as a professional teacher, your knowledge of science and teaching methodology, suggestions from teacher's guides and textbooks, and immediate clues from your students. A performance objective is only a suggested outcome of what students will be able to do after or during your teaching.

Planning instruction is one use of a performance objective. It can help you decide what materials, classroom conditions, grouping and teaching strategies you must acquire or develop prior to meeting with your students. This description of conditions is part of the well-stated objective. It helps you think through what you, the teacher, must do to cause the desired behavior to happen.

Another use of a performance objective is to help you gather and provide evidence that students in your class are learning. It allows you to become accountable for time and energy you spend teaching science. It means, however, that you have to evaluate and keep records of student progress. If you do keep records, then, you or anyone else —parent, teacher, administrator, or supervisor—could observe and evaluate your teaching of science. If anyone were to ask you how you know your students are learning something, you could provide them with some performance evidence that the goals of your science program were being achieved. Of course, students may not exhibit the desired behaviors. If they don't, you have a basis for examining your own teaching, the instructional materials, the classroom, and the school environment and changing them to make them more conducive to learning. But you wouldn't know what changes to make unless you knew what performance outcomes you desired. Part of the well-stated performance objective describes the performance. A precise description tells you what behaviors you should be able to observe if students are achieving the goals of science.

Diagnosing a student's abilities is another use of performance objectives. When you can observe and evaluate certain behaviors, it is easier to determine what a student is capable of doing, or what he has accomplished in the past, and what he has yet to master. It more clearly defines the boundaries between what he knows and what he doesn't know. With this information, you can provide a better individualized learning situation for each student. If the students already have demonstrated to you that, for example, they can distinguish between physical and chemical changes around them, why dwell on that? Go on to another objective. Or, perhaps some of your students can do this while others cannot. If it is an important goal, then you'll need to provide some individual or small group activities for some of your students while others might be pursuing other goals. An effective teacher will provide for these individual differences. It is the criterion measure part of the well-stated performance objective that allows you to diagnose which students have accomplished the objective and to what degree they have achieved it.

In addition, performance objectives are helpful because they tune students in to what it is you're trying to achieve. When it is apparent to students what it is you and they are trying to accomplish, when it is clear to all what is meant by successful completion, then students may use their energies to achieve the objective rather than try to "psych-out" what the teacher wants them to do. Many teachers have found that when they share with students what objectives are sought (if they are reasonable), much of the teaching job is accomplished. Most students will accept the challenge rather than try to "play games" with the teacher.

Where Do Performance Objectives Come From?

Statements of performance objectives come in many forms, and no given number of them constitute a science curriculum. You could never say that students, having achieved the objectives contained in this guide, will then "know" chemistry. The performance objectives for each school, class, group of students, or individual student will vary according to the students, the teacher, the resources available in the learning environment, and the task at hand.

Books are available which contain performance objectives for science. Several are listed in the Bibliography on p. 9 T. There is even an Instructional Objectives Exchange to which you can subscribe.* It

---

*Information and a catalog of objective collections can be obtained from: Instructional Objectives Exchange, Center for the Study of Evaluation, Graduate School of Education, University of California, Los Angeles, California 90024.

is difficult for teachers in New York or Washington or Los Angeles to write adequate performance objectives for teachers to use with their students in Centerville, Garden City, or Westberg. Even school districts which employ science curriculum specialists cannot decide what objectives are appropriate for you and your students in your situation with the materials and resources you have available.

Ultimately, the task of selecting, composing, and evaluating performance objectives is up to you. You should draw upon the performance objectives in this guide and upon other sources or other people who could help you. Students are good, if not the best, sources of performance objectives. When they can express to you their questions, their interests, and their goals, then you can cooperatively decide what objectives shall be reached. The next section of this guide and any other list of performance objectives provides a basis for selecting what is appropriate for your students. Select from these lists, objectives from other teachers and consultants, and create some of your own. The ultimate decision of what to teach is yours; the decision of what to learn is the student's.

Any performance objective for teaching science should be based upon one or more of the goals of science education. You should be able to say that the reason you're working to accomplish this particular objective is because it's one step or one part of a long range goal of science education. For example, if one of the goals of science education is to develop the student's ability to utilize some of the methods and processes by which problems are solved scientifically, then one of the purposes of a lesson might be to develop an understanding of what an experiment is. If a student does understand what an experiment is:

When asked to define an experiment, he will state that it is a test or a way of proving some theory or principle.
When asked what he would do to find out if food coloring diffuses faster in warm water than in cold water, he will describe what he would do and uses the term "experiment" in his description.

When asked for examples of experiments which have been conducted so far this semester, he will cite at least three.

Specific performance objectives such as the above are only examples of one small part of that large, broader goal for science education. However, each performance objective should be consistent with one or more of those goals so that you can justify what you are teaching, and so that you can see students progress toward that goal.

How Do You Use the Performance Objectives in This Teacher's Guide?

Performance objectives are listed for each chapter of *CHEMISTRY: A Modern Course*. They are related to four broad goals of science education.

A 1. Attitudes: To develop students' attitudes of curiosity, of wonderment about and involvement with phenomena in their natural environment; to develop an appreciation for the contributions of science to daily living; and to develop the value and inclinations toward solving problems in a scientific manner.

P 2. Processes: To develop those intellectual processes of inquiry by which scientific problems and phenomena are explained, predicted, and/or controlled.

K 3. Knowledge: To develop knowledge of facts, terminology, concepts, generalizations, and principles which help the students confront and interpret their environment.

S 4. Skills: To develop the student's ability to handle, construct, and manipulate materials and equipment in a productive and safe manner, and to develop his ability to measure, organize, and communicate scientific information.

Next to each performance objective you will find one or more of the following capital letters: A, P, K, S. They indicate the goal on which the objective is based — Attitudes, Processes, Knowledge, Skills. Designed to help you see a consistency between the specific objectives and the goals of science education, it may serve to help you keep in mind a balance among these four goals since they are all of equal priority.

1. The statements of performance objectives which are identified as "A" — developing Attitude goals — are behaviors which you might observe as students increase their enjoyment of science activities, and as they demonstrate an interest in the scientific objects and events in their environment. You will find such statements as:

Students will request that the demonstration be repeated.

Students will volunteer to conduct the activity at home.

Students will request the use of the chemistry laboratory during free periods.

When given a choice between study hall and working at a chemistry experiment, students will choose the chemistry activity.

Students will volunteer to do research and report their findings in class.

As you can see, few of these behaviors are prompted by the teacher. They are voluntary behaviors which indicate an affinity for, an inclination toward, and a preference for science. You will find suggested attitudinal behaviors throughout the list and particularly at the end of each area or chapter when students may have an opportunity to go beyond the information presented in the text.

2. The statements of performance objectives which are identified as "P" — developing Process goals — are behaviors which you might observe as students use the thinking processes of analyzing, experimenting, applying, hypothesizing, theorizing, comparing and contrasting, classifying, observing, etc. You will find such statements as:

When presented with various objects, students will compare and contrast their similarities and differences and place them in groups of metallic and nonmetallic.

Given data from Appendices A and C, students will calculate the amount of heat needed to raise the temperature of 1000 kg of iron from 20°C to 1000°C.

Given percentage composition, students can find the empirical formula of a compound.

Given a skeleton equation, students will balance a redox equation by the half-reaction method.

3. The statements of performance objectives which are identified as 'K" — developing knowledge goals — are behaviors which you might observe as students demonstrate they have gained an understanding and use of certain terms, concepts, and generalizations of science. You will find such statements as:

When asked, students will define the term "ionization" correctly.

Students will explain the reason reaction rate varies as temperature changes.

Students will correctly identify the triple point on a phase diagram.

Students will describe the effects of a catalyst on reaction rate.

Generally, a knowledge objective is one which calls upon the student to recall or explain information, concepts, or principles which he has learned in the past or which have been presented in the text and other materials.

4. The statements of performance objectives which are identified as "S" — developing Skills goals — are behaviors which you might observe as students gain skill in using scientific equipment correctly, and organizing, recording, or reporting information accurately. Some examples of such statements are:

Students will use a pipette to transfer a solution from one container to another.

While observing the demonstration, students will record their observations in their notebooks.

Using a laboratory balance, students will measure and reheat a substance to constant mass.

Using styrofoam spheres and toothpicks, students will construct models of crystal lattice types.

In the Teacher's Guide that follows, a specific statement of the goal for each chapter is given. A goal statement is also given at the beginning of each chapter in the student's text. Following the goal statement in the Teacher's Guide, the specific performance objectives for each section of the chapter are listed. There may be several objectives in each section. Each objective is numbered to correspond to that section of the chapter. For example, 22:5 is Chapter 22, section 5. From these objectives you should be able to determine and plan for the achievement of the objectives for each section of a chapter.

Remember, these performance objectives are not meant to be all inclusive. You should supplement them with objectives from other sources and with those you create yourself.

As you examine these objectives, you will find many of them include a description of the conditions. Feel free to alter these conditions according to your own classroom situation. For example, the objectives may state a condition: "When presented with three halide solutions . . . ." You may not have these solutions in your classroom. Change the statement of conditions to reflect those particular materials you have available. Another example: "When asked to state . . . ." Maybe you would prefer your students to write or to demonstrate a certain response. Make adjustments as required.

You will also find that the criterion or level of performance for each objective is not included. The intent was to create guidelines and not to state levels of expectancies for you. Only you can decide if 100% or only 50% of your students should be able to accomplish each task. You will need to develop and insert these criterion levels for your own students based upon your materials, and your own situation.

How Do You Know You've Achieved Your Objectives?

When you try to find out if students have learned anything, you probably give some form of written test — true-false, completion, matching, or essay type of examination. All of these forms of evaluation are important in determining whether or not students have achieved their objectives. Other evaluation materials are available to accompany the Merrill Science Programs. These include Spirit Duplicating Masters Evaluation Programs for *CHEMISTRY: A Modern Course*, *BIOLOGY: Living Systems*, and *PHYSICS: Principles and Problems*.

Performance Objectives

GOAL: Students will gain an understanding of the nature of chemistry through relationships ranging from science-mankind to matter-energy.

Bibliography

Bloom, Benjamin, Hastings, J. Thomas, and Madaus, George, *Handbook on Formative and Summative Evaluation of Student Learning.* McGraw-Hill Book Co., New York, 1971.

Bloom, Benjamin and others, *Taxonomy of Educational Objectives, Handbook I: Cognitive Domain.* David McKay, New York, 1956.

California State Department of Education, *Science Framework for California Public Schools.* Sacramento, Calif., 1970.

Eiss, Albert F., and Harbeck, Mary B., *Behavioral Objectives in the Affective Domain.* National Science Teachers Association, National Education Association, Washington, D. C., 1969.

Krathwohl, D. R., Bloom, Benjamin, and Masia, Bertram R., *Taxonomy of Educational Objectives, Handbook II: Affective Domain.* David McKay, New York, 1956.

Lindvall, C. M., ed., *Defining Educational Objectives.* University of Pittsburgh Press, Pittsburgh, 1964.

Mager, Robert, *Preparing Instructional Objectives.* Fearon Publishers, Inc., Palo Alto, Calif., 1962.

Picard, Anthony, and Sund, Robert, *Behavioral Objectives and Evaluational Measures for Science and Mathematics.* Charles E. Merrill Publishing Co., Columbus, Ohio, 1971.

Plowman, Paul, *Behavioral Objectives in Science.* Science Research Associates, Chicago, 1969.

Popham, W. James, *The Teacher-Empiricist.* Aegeus Publishing Co., Los Angeles, 1965.

Popham, W. James, and Baker, Eva L., *Establishing Instructional Goals.* Prentice Hall, Inc., Englewood Cliffs, N. J., 1970.

Walbesser, Henry H., *Constructing Behavioral Objectives.* Bureau of Educational Research and Field Services, University of Maryland, College Park, Md., 1970.

Chapter 1

Objectives: Upon completion of the reading and activities, and when asked to diagram, demonstrate, or respond either orally or on a written test, students will:

1:1	P	list some major problems facing today's world.
1:2	P	differentiate between facts and value judgments.
1:2	K	explain differences between processes and products of science.
1:3	K	define chemistry.
1:4	K	explain inertia as a property of matter.
1:5	K	list various forms of energy.
1:6	K,P	state the law of conservation of matter and energy and give examples of its application.

Upon completion of the reading and activities, students will exhibit an interest in science by:

A	voluntarily completing one or more of the One More Step activities listed at the end of the chapter on their own time.
A	reading unassigned literature related to the ideas presented in the chapter.

Page 12. End of Chapter

1. potential, kinetic, electrical, mechanical, thermal, radiant

2. potential—energy due to position
   kinetic—energy due to motion
   mechanical—composed of potential and kinetic
   electrical — energy due to electrical charge
   thermal—form of kinetic energy (or radiant energy)
   radiant—energy due to electromagnetic property of a wave
   sound—form of mechanical energy
   light, radio waves, etc.—all forms of radiant energy
   nuclear energy—energy due to the structure of the nucleus

3. agronomist—field crops and soil
   astronomer—stars, planets, other bodies of the universe
   biologist—living things
   botanist—plant life
   entomologist—insects
   geochemist—chemical properties and changes in the earth's crust
   geologist—history of the earth's crust
   geophysicist—physical properties of the earth's crust
   horticulturalist—fruits, vegetables, decorative plants
   metallurgist—metals
   meteorologist—weather
   physicist—energy-matter relationships
   zoologist—animal life

4. There are many that most students can name: pharmacist, doctor, farmer, foundry chemist, biologist. Accept what you wish.

5. Types of facts that may be mentioned: Should the lake be developed? How will it be developed? Will it harm the ecology of the area? What kind of development should it be: single homes, apartments, condominiums? This should produce much discussion regarding facts and value judgments.

Page 13. One More Step

1. Nearly every student can list some of the more common industries. The list will vary with the community, but would include the chemical producing and consuming industries, institutions of higher education, government agencies, medical and pharmaceutical institutions.

2. Cockcroft and Walton bombarded ^{7}Li nuclei with protons and obtained two alpha particles as products. From the balancing of the mass-energy of the system before and after the change, the Einstein equivalence hypothesis was established.

Suggested Readings for Faculty and Students

Bernardo, James V., "Solid Waste: Resource Recovery and Reuse." *The Science Teacher,* Vol. 40, No. 9 (December 1973), pp. 31-35.

de Nevers, Noel, "Enforcing the Clean Air Act of 1970." *Scientific American,* Vol. 228, No. 6 (June 1973), pp. 14-21.

Goldwater, Leonard J., "Mercury in the Environment." *Scientific American,* Vol. 224, No. 5 (May 1971), pp. 15-21.

Ihde, Aaron J., "Analytical Chemistry and the Effectiveness of Food Laws." *Journal of Chemical Education,* Vol. 51, No. 5 (May 1974), pp. 295-297.

Kermode, G. O., "Food Additives." *Scientific American,* Vol. 226, No. 3 (March 1972), pp. 15-21.

Klein, David H., "Some General and Analytical Aspects of Environmental Mercury Contamination." *Journal of Chemical Education,* Vol. 49, No. 1 (January 1972), pp. 7-10.

Marshall, Nelson, "Oceanography, The New Frontier for the Twenty-First Century." *The Science Teacher,* Vol. 40, No. 8 (November 1973), pp. 16-19.

Medeiros, Robert W., "Smog Formation Simplified." *Chemistry,* Vol. 45, No. 1 (January 1972), pp. 16-18.

Newell, Reginald E., "The Global Circulation of Atmospheric Pollutants." *Scientific American,* Vol. 224, No. 1 (January 1971), pp. 32-42.

Peakall, David B., "Pesticides and the Reproduction of Birds." *Scientific American,* Vol. 222, No. 4 (April 1970), pp. 72-78.

Squires, Arthur M., "Clean Power from Dirty Fuels." *Scientific American,* Vol. 227, No. 4 (October 1972), pp. 26-35.

Wolfendenm, John H., "The Role of Chance in Chemical Investigation." *Journal of Chemical Education,* Vol. 44, No. 5 (May 1967), pp. 299-303.

Youmans, Hubert L., "Career Opportunities in Chemistry." *Chemistry,* Vol. 44, No. 3 (March 1971), pp. 18-20.

Chapter 2

Performance Objectives

GOAL: Students will gain knowledge and understanding of basic measurement and related calculations used by chemists.

Objectives: Upon completion of the reading and activities, and when asked to diagram, demonstrate, or respond orally or on a written test, students will:

2:1	K	state the difference between mass and weight.
2:2-4	K	list the standard measurements in length, time, and temperature.
2:5-8	P,S	perform basic conversions in the metric system.
2:9	P	perform simple calculations related to density.
2:10	P,S	use significant digits in recording measurements.
2:11	K	differentiate between *accuracy* and *precision.*
2:12-14	P,S	perform calculations using scientific notation.
2:15-17	P	use the factor-label method for problem solving.

Upon completion of the reading and activities, students will exhibit an interest in science by:

A	voluntarily completing one or more of the One More Step activities listed at the end of the chapter on their own time.
A	reading unassigned literature related to the ideas presented in the chapter.

Note: All calculations are done with hand calculators. Slide rule answers may differ in third significant digit.

Suggestion: Point out that the factor-label method is only a useful model. Labels are not factors, but they may be treated as such for purpose of mathematical expediency.

Page 32.   Section 2:14

1. a. 5.52×10^5

   b. 3.15×10^{-2}

   c. 7.50

   d. 3.88×10^3

   e. 3.43

Page 37.   Section 2:17

2. a. $\dfrac{346 \cancel{cg}}{} \left| \dfrac{1 \cancel{g}}{100 \cancel{cg}} \right| \dfrac{10^6 \, \mu g}{1 \cancel{g}} = 3.46 \times 10^6 \, (\mu g)$

b. $\dfrac{1 \text{ Mm}}{1 \text{ Mm}} \Big| \dfrac{10^6 \text{ m}}{} \Big| \dfrac{1 \text{ terameter}}{10^{12} \text{ m}} = 10^{-6}$ terameters (Tm)

c. $\dfrac{81.9 \text{ picoseconds}}{} \Big| \dfrac{1 \text{ second}}{10^{12} \text{ picoseconds}} \Big| \dfrac{1 \text{ kilosecond}}{10^3 \text{ seconds}} = 8.19 \times 10^{-14}$ kiloseconds (ksec)

d. $\dfrac{513 \text{ mg}}{} \Big| \dfrac{1 \text{ g}}{10^3 \text{ mg}} \Big| \dfrac{1 \text{ gigagram}}{10^9 \text{ g}} = 5.13 \times 10^{-10}$ gigagrams (Gg)

e. $\dfrac{8.59 \text{ nanometers}}{} \Big| \dfrac{1 \text{ meter}}{10^9 \text{ nanometers}} \Big| \dfrac{10 \text{ decimeters}}{1 \text{ meter}} = 8.59 \times 10^{-8}$ decimeters (dm)

3. a. $\dfrac{80.3 \text{ seconds}}{} \Big| \dfrac{1 \text{ hectosecond}}{10^2 \text{ seconds}} = 8.03 \times 10^{-1}$ hectoseconds (hsec)

b. $\dfrac{402 \text{ dg}}{} \Big| \dfrac{10 \text{ g}}{1 \text{ dg}} \Big| \dfrac{1 \text{ kg}}{1000 \text{ g}} = 4.02$ kilograms (kg)

c. $\dfrac{9.05 \text{ Mm}}{} \Big| \dfrac{10^6 \text{ m}}{1 \text{ Mm}} \Big| \dfrac{10^6 \text{ } \mu\text{m}}{1 \text{ m}} = 9.05 \times 10^{12}$ micrometers (μm)

d. $\dfrac{512 \text{ centiseconds}}{} \Big| \dfrac{1 \text{ second}}{10^2 \text{ centiseconds}} \Big| \dfrac{1 \text{ megasecond}}{10^6 \text{ seconds}} = 5.12 \times 10^{-6}$ megaseconds (Msec)

e. $\dfrac{22.9 \text{ dg}}{} \Big| \dfrac{1 \text{ g}}{10 \text{ dg}} \Big| \dfrac{10^3 \text{ mg}}{1 \text{ g}} = 2.29 \times 10^3$ milligrams (mg)

4. a. $V = lwh$

$= 2.00 \times 2.00 \times 9.00 = 36 \text{ cm}^3$

$D = m/V$

$= \dfrac{108 \text{ g}}{36 \text{ cm}^3} = 3.00 \text{ g/cm}^3$

b. $V = lwh$

$= 5.00 \times 10.0 \times 23.0 = 1150 \text{ cm}^3$

$D = m/V$

$= \dfrac{3.22 \text{ kg}}{1150 \text{ cm}^3} \Big| \dfrac{1000 \text{ g}}{1 \text{ kg}}$

$= 2.80 \text{ g/cm}^3$

c. $D = m/V$

$= \dfrac{6120 \text{ g}}{9 \text{ l}} \Big| \dfrac{1 \text{ l}}{1000 \text{ cm}^3} = 0.680 \text{ g/cm}^3$

d. $D = m/V$

$= \dfrac{2.06 \text{ kg}}{2.00 \text{ l}} \Big| \dfrac{1000 \text{ g}}{1 \text{ kg}} \Big| \dfrac{1 \text{ l}}{1000 \text{ cm}^3}$

$= 1.03 \text{ g/cm}^3$

e. $V = lwh$

$= 23.0 \times 15.0 \times 15.5 = 5350 \text{ cm}^3$

$D = m/V$

$= \dfrac{10.22 \text{ kg}}{5350 \text{ cm}^3} \Big| \dfrac{1000 \text{ g}}{1 \text{ kg}} = 1.91 \text{ g/cm}^3$

5. $D = m/V; \; m = D \times V$

$m = \dfrac{9.80 \text{ g}}{1 \text{ cm}^3} \Big| \dfrac{3.02 \text{ cm}^3}{1}$

$m = 29.6 \text{ g}$

6. $V = m/D$

$$V = \frac{12.5\ \text{g}}{7.87\ \text{g}} \bigg| 1\ \text{cm}^3$$

$$V = 1.59\ \text{cm}^3$$

e. $V = m/D$

$$= \frac{2.13\ \text{kg}}{}\bigg|\frac{1000\ \text{g}}{1\ \text{kg}}\bigg|\frac{1\ \text{cm}^3}{7.28\ \text{g}} = 293\ \text{cm}^3$$

Page 39. End of Chapter

7. a. $m = DV$

$$= \frac{1.84\ \text{g}}{1\ \text{cm}^3}\bigg| 6.96\ \text{cm}^3 = 12.8\ \text{g}$$

b. $m = DV$

$$= \frac{2.74\ \text{g}}{1\ \text{cm}^3}\bigg| 610\ \text{cm}^3 = 1670\ \text{g}$$

c. $m = DV$

$$= \frac{6.32\ \text{g}}{1\ \text{cm}^3}\bigg| 86.0\ \text{cm}^3 = 544\ \text{g}$$

d. $m = DV$

$$= \frac{6.70\ \text{g}}{1\ \text{cm}^3}\bigg| 3.28\ \text{cm}^3 = 22.0\ \text{g}$$

e. $m = DV$

$$= \frac{19.3\ \text{g}}{1\ \text{cm}^3}\bigg| 0.253\ \text{cm}^3 = 4.88\ \text{g}$$

8. a. $V = m/D$

$$= \frac{3.37\ \text{g}}{2.15\ \text{g}}\bigg| 1\ \text{cm}^3 = 1.57\ \text{cm}^3$$

b. $V = m/D$

$$= \frac{706\ \text{g}}{3.17\ \text{g}}\bigg| 1\ \text{cm}^3 = 223\ \text{cm}^3$$

c. $V = m/D$

$$= \frac{40.5\ \text{g}}{5.50\ \text{g}}\bigg| 1\ \text{cm}^3 = 7.36\ \text{cm}^3$$

d. $V = m/D$

$$= \frac{32.9\ \text{g}}{1.74\ \text{g}}\bigg| 1\ \text{cm}^3 = 18.9\ \text{cm}^3$$

e. $V = m/D$

$$= \frac{2.13\ \text{kg}}{}\bigg|\frac{1000\ \text{g}}{1\ \text{kg}}\bigg|\frac{1\ \text{cm}^3}{7.28\ \text{g}} = 293\ \text{cm}^3$$

9. a. 1   d. 1   g. 3   j. 4
   b. 1   e. 2   h. 4
   c. 4   f. 3   i. 3

10. $D = m/V$

$$= \frac{1.2 \times 10^9\ \text{kg}}{1.0\ \text{km}^3}\bigg|\frac{1000\ \text{g}}{1\ \text{kg}}\bigg|\frac{1\ \text{km}^3}{(10^3\ \text{m})^3}\bigg|\frac{1\ \text{m}^3}{(10^2\ \text{cm})^3} =$$

$$= 1.2 \times 10^{-3}\ \text{g/cm}^3$$

11. a. $$\frac{8.00\ \text{hr}}{1\ \text{hr}}\bigg|\frac{60\ \text{min}}{1\ \text{min}}\bigg| 60\ \text{sec} = 28{,}800\ \text{sec}$$

b. $$\frac{0.0200\ \text{Mm}}{1\ \text{Mm}}\bigg|\frac{10^6\ \text{m}}{1\ \text{m}}\bigg| 10\ \text{dm} = \begin{array}{l} 2.00 \times 10^5\ \text{dm} \\ 200{,}000\ \text{dm} \end{array}$$

c. $$\frac{1.00\ \text{dl}}{10\ \text{dl}}\bigg|\frac{1\ \text{l}}{1\ \text{l}}\bigg| 10^6\ \text{ml} = \begin{array}{l} 1.00 \times 10^5\ \mu\text{l} \\ 100{,}000\ \mu\text{l} \end{array}$$

12. a. $$\frac{3\ \text{kg}}{1\ \text{kg}}\bigg| 1000\ \text{g} = 3000\ \text{g}$$

b. $$\frac{9\ \text{cm}}{100\ \text{cm}}\bigg| 1\ \text{m} = 0.09\ \text{m}$$

c. $$\frac{5.00\ \text{hr}}{1\ \text{hr}}\bigg|\frac{60\ \text{min}}{1\ \text{min}}\bigg| 60\ \text{sec} = 1.8 \times 10^4\ \text{sec}$$

d. $$\frac{0.05\ \text{km}}{1\ \text{km}}\bigg|\frac{1000\ \text{m}}{1\ \text{m}}\bigg| 100\ \text{cm} = 5.0 \times 10^3\ \text{cm}$$

e. $$\frac{8\ \text{cm}}{1\ \text{cm}}\bigg| 10\ \text{mm} = 80\ \text{mm}$$

13. a. $45.9 = 4.59 \times 10$
    b. $0.0359 = 3.59 \times 10^{-2}$
    c. $45{,}967{,}800 = 4.59678 \times 10^7$
    d. $0.0005976 = 5.976 \times 10^4$
    e. $345{,}690{,}000{,}000 = 3.4569 \times 10^{11}$

14. a. $3.59 \times 10^2 = 359$
    b. $4.32 \times 10^{-3} = 0.00432$
    c. $3.05 \times 10^{-5} = 0.0000305$
    d. $5.29 \times 10^5 = 529{,}000$
    e. $6.94 \times 10^1 = 69.4$

15. a. $1.29 \times 10^5 + 7.56 \times 10^4$

$$\begin{array}{r} 12.9 \ \times 10^4 \\ 7.56 \times 10^4 \\ \hline 20.5 \ \times 10^4 = 2.05 \times 10^5 \end{array}$$

b. $4.59 \times 10^{-5} - 6.02 \times 10^{-6}$

$$\begin{array}{r} 4.59 \ \times 10^{-5} \\ - \ .602 \times 10^{-5} \\ \hline 3.99 \ \times 10^{-5} \end{array}$$

c. $(5.40 \times 10^2)(3.20 \times 10^{-3})$
$17.3 \times 10^{-1} = 1.73$

d. $(4.84 \times 10^{-5}) \div (2.42 \times 10^{-7})$
$$= 2.00 \times 10^2$$

e. $(48.6 \times 10^2)(0.524 \times 10^{-2}) \div$
$(2.20 \times 10^3) \ 11.6 \times 10^{-3} = 0.0116$

16. a. 1.5600×10^8 5 sig. digits
    b. 6.890000×10^8 7 sig. digits
    c. 4.9300×10^9 5 sig. digits
    d. 8.4200000×10^8 8 sig. digits
    e. 6.000×10^{-6} 4 sig. digits

17. limiting factor underlined
    a. 5 × 0.00559   1 sig. digit

    b. $0.7 \times 9.48 \times 10^1$ 1 sig. digit

    c. 875 × 67   2 sig. digits

    d. 0.3 ÷ 0.0586   1 sig. digit

    e. $0.658 \div (9.59 \times 10^1)$ 3 sig. digits

18. a. $52 + 0.08990 = 52 \left(\begin{array}{c} \text{nearest} \\ \text{whole number} \end{array} \right)$

    b. $4 + 6 = 10 \left(\begin{array}{c} \text{nearest} \\ \text{whole number} \end{array} \right)$

    c. $0.9 - 0.00005 = 0.9 \left(\begin{array}{c} \text{nearest} \\ \text{tenth} \end{array} \right)$

    d. $0.06 + 2 = 2 \left(\begin{array}{c} \text{nearest} \\ \text{whole number} \end{array} \right)$

    e. $63 + 93 = 156 \left(\begin{array}{c} \text{nearest} \\ \text{whole number} \end{array} \right)$

19. a. $\dfrac{24 \ \text{mg}}{} \bigg| \dfrac{1 \ \text{g}}{1000 \ \text{mg}} \bigg| \dfrac{1 \ \text{kg}}{1000 \ \text{g}} = 2.4 \times 10^{-5} \ \text{kg}$

b. $\dfrac{8.6 \ \text{cg}}{} \bigg| \dfrac{1 \ \text{g}}{100 \ \text{cg}} = 8.6 \times 10^{-2} \ \text{g}$

c. $\dfrac{2600 \ \text{dm}^3}{} \bigg| \dfrac{1 \ \text{l}}{1 \ \text{dm}^3} = 2.6 \times 10^2 \ \text{l}$

d. $\dfrac{92 \ \text{cm}^3}{} \bigg| \dfrac{(1 \ \text{m})^3}{(100 \ \text{cm})^3} = 9.2 \times 10^{-5} \ \text{m}^3$

e. $\dfrac{79 \ \text{m}^3}{} \bigg| \dfrac{(10 \ \text{dm})^3}{(1 \ \text{m})^3} \bigg| \dfrac{1 \ \text{l}}{1 \ \text{dm}^3} \bigg| \dfrac{100 \ \text{cl}}{1 \ \text{l}}$
$= 7.9 \times 10^6 \ \text{cl}$

20. $\dfrac{99 \ \text{kg}}{\text{m}^3} \bigg| \dfrac{1000 \ \text{g}}{1 \ \text{kg}} \bigg| \dfrac{\text{m}^3}{(100 \ \text{cm})^3}$
$= 9.9 \times 10^{-2} \ \text{g/cm}^3$
$= 0.099 \ \text{g/cm}^3$

21. $\dfrac{30 \ \text{km}}{1 \ \text{hr}} \bigg| \dfrac{1000 \ \text{m}}{1 \ \text{km}} \bigg| \dfrac{100 \ \text{cm}}{\text{m}} \bigg| \dfrac{1 \ \text{hr}}{60 \ \text{min}} \bigg| \dfrac{1 \ \text{min}}{60 \ \text{sec}}$
$= 830 \ \text{cm/sec}$

22. $D = m/V; \ m = D \times V$

$m = \dfrac{1.25 \ \text{g}}{1 \ \text{l}} \bigg| \dfrac{1 \ \text{l}}{1000 \ \text{cm}^3} \bigg| \dfrac{(100 \ \text{cm})^3}{1 \ \text{m}^3} \bigg| \dfrac{1.00 \ \text{m}^3}{}$
$= 1250 \ \text{g}$

Page 41.   One More Step

1. $\text{viscosity} = \dfrac{\text{mass}}{\text{length} \times \text{time}}$

$\text{power} = \dfrac{\text{mass} \times \text{length}^2}{\text{time}^3}$

$\text{torque} = \dfrac{\text{mass} \times \text{length}^2}{\text{time}^2}$

$\text{rate of heat transfer} = \dfrac{\text{heat}}{\text{time}}$

2. A computer is basically a series of "off-on" switches. Most high speed computers operate on the *binary system* which contains only two symbols, 0 and 1. It is possible to construct all of the integers (1, 2, 3, . . .) using only these two symbols and the off and on positions of a series of switches or lights as follows:

decimal number	computer panel	binary number
0		
1	X	1
2	X	10
3	XX	11
4	X	100
5	X X	101
6	XX	110
7	XXX	111
8	X	1000
9	X X	1001
etc.		

Such a computer performs all mathematical operations by either adding or subtracting over and over in rapid succession in a manner determined by its program. For instance, 4 would be divided by 2 by adding two's until the sum was four and recording the number of times the number was added.

$$\frac{4}{2} = 2 + 2 = 2 \text{ additions}$$

$$\frac{8}{2} = 2 + 2 + 2 + 2 = 4 \text{ additions}$$

For more information, see *Algebra Two With Circular Functions,* by Vannatta, Goodwin, and Crosswhite, Columbus, Ohio, Charles E. Merrill Publishing Co., 1970, Chapter 17.

3. The most modern and most simplified abacus is the Japanese soroban which consists of two series of movable beads arranged in columns.

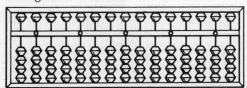

The Chinese abacus, called a suan-pan, contains an extra row of five beads and an extra row of unit beads.

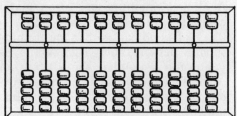

To add 14 + 25:
Set 14 on the abacus.

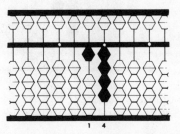

Add 2 beads to the tens column and a five bead to the ones column.

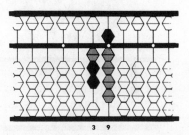

Read the answer as 39.

To multiply 4 × 2:
Set the 2 and 4 as indicated, leave two spaces between:

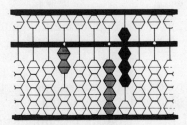

Mentally multiply 2 × 4 and set the product 8 as indicated. Clear the 4.

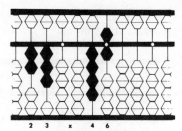

To multiply 46 × 23:
Set the 23 and 46 as indicated.

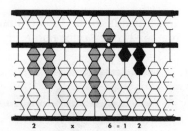

Order of procedure:
Both numbers have two digits.

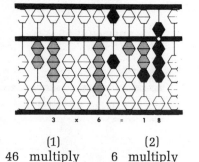

(1)	(2)	
46 multiply	6 multiply	40
×23	×23	×23

a. First multiply:

(1)   6 last digit of multiplicand
    ×2 first digit of multiplier
    ─────
    12

Then:

(2)   6 last digit of multiplicand
    ×3 last digit of multiplier
    ─────
    18

b. Next, do the same thing for the first digit of the multiplicand:

(1)   4 first digit of multiplicand
    ×2 first digit of multiplier
    ─────
    8

Then:

(2)   4 first digit of multiplicand
    ×3 last digit of multiplier
    ─────
    12

Record the operations on the abacus as follows:

23 × 46
2 × 6 = 12
3 × 6 = 18
2 × 4 = 8
3 × 4 = 12

The answer is 1058.

The chief advantage offered by the abacus is its complete mechanization of the four basic mathematical operations. A skilled operator can often match a computer in both accuracy and speed. Its chief handicap is that the training of such a person must begin while he is young and cannot be done in a few hours. Also, the abacus leaves no record of the operations performed or the results obtained.

4. Scientists often wish to compare numbers, on a "rough" basis, to the nearest power of ten. If number A is roughly ten times larger than number B, A is said to be an order of magnitude larger than B. Other examples:

> 147 is 5 orders of magnitude larger than 0.00218.

> 827 and 411 are of the same order of magnitude.

> 46.8 is 7 orders of magnitude smaller than 468,000,000.

Suggested Readings for Faculty and Students

Ambler, Ernest, "Measurement Standards, Physical Constants, and Science Teaching." *The Science Teacher*, Vol. 38, No. 8 (November 1971), pp. 63-71.

Astin, Allen V., "Standards of Measurement." *Scientific American*, Vol. 218, No. 6 (June 1968), pp. 50-62.

Chisholm, L. J., *Units of Weights and Measures*. NBS Misc. Pub. 286. Washington, U.S. Government Printing Office, 1967.

Frasier, E. Lewis, "Improving an Imperfect Metric System." *Bulletin of the Atomic Scientists*, Vol. 30, No. 2 (February 1974), p. 9ff.

Himes, Gary K., *Solving Problems in Chemistry*. Columbus, Charles E. Merrill Publishing Company, 1975.

National Bureau of Standards, "Policy for NBS Usage of SI Units." *Journal of Chemical Education*, Vol. 48, No. 9 (September 1971), pp. 569-572.

Norris, A. C., "SI Units in Physico-Chemical Calculations." *Journal of Chemical Education*, Vol. 48, No. 12 (December 1971), pp. 797-800.

Pinkerton, R. C., and Gleit, C. E., "The Significance of Significant Figures." *Journal of Chemical Education*, Vol. 44, No. 4 (April 1967), pp. 232-234.

Ritchie-Calder, Lord, "Conversion to the Metric System." *Scientific American*, Vol. 223, No. 1 (July 1970), pp. 17-25.

Sienko, M. J., *Chemical Problems*. Menlo Park, California, W. A. Benjamin, Inc., 1972 2nd Ed., Chapter 1.

Taylor, Barry N., Langenberg, Donald N., and Parker, William H., "The Fundamental Physical Constants." *Scientific American*, Vol. 222, No. 4 (October 1970), pp. 62-78.

Chapter 3

Performance Objectives

GOAL: Students will gain an understanding of the ways in which matter is classified and of the changes undergone by matter.

Objectives: Upon completion of the reading and activities, and when asked to diagram, demonstrate, or respond either orally or on a written test, students will:

3:1-2	K	distinguish between homogeneous and heterogeneous materials.
3:1-3	K	differentiate between elements, compounds, and mixtures.
3:4	P	list examples of extensive and intensive properties.
3:5-8	K	differentiate between physical changes and chemical changes.
3:6	P	explain the use of physical changes to separate mixtures.
3:6-8	P	list examples of physical and chemical changes.

Upon completion of the reading and activities, students will exhibit an interest in science by:

A	voluntarily completing one or more of the One More Step activities listed at the end of the chapter on their own time.
A	reading unassigned literature related to the ideas presented in the chapter.

Page 48. Section 3:3

1. a. solution (Gases in gases are homogeneous solutions rather than mixtures.)
   b. heterogeneous mixture

c. heterogeneous mixture
d. compound
e. compound

2. a. heterogeneous mixture
   b. heterogeneous mixture (When homogenized, milk is an emulsion—a colloid.)
   c. element
   d. compound
   e. element

Page 53. Section 3:8

3. a. physical   d. chemical
   b. chemical   e. physical
   c. physical

4. a. chemical
   b. physical — although some reaction must occur in nerves doing detection
   c. chemical
   d. physical—polar interactions only; HCl is reacting, not dissolving
   e. chemical

5. a. chemical   d. physical
   b. chemical   e. physical
   c. chemical

6. a. chemical   d. physical
   b. physical   e. physical
   c. chemical

Page 55. End of Chapter

7. a. heterogeneous mixture
   b. compound
   c. heterogeneous mixture
   d. heterogeneous mixture
   e. solution

8. a. chemical
   b. physical—it is conceivable that in the process you break a molecule
   c. physical
   d. physical
   e. chemical

9. a. inspection
   b. evaporate liquid
   c. examine under a microscope
   d. extract with a solvent
   e. evaporate liquid

   For all of these there is the possibility that the process of examination causes

some chemical change, particularly in b. and d. However, admission of this does not destroy the usefulness of the concept.

10. Suggested list of phases — soda, ice cream, cream, cherry, straw, spoon, glass, CO_2, air.

    Suggested list of interfaces — soda-glass, soda-ice cream, soda-straw, soda-spoon, soda-gas (two: in cream and "fizz"), ice cream-cream, ice cream-glass, ice cream-straw, ice cream-spoon, ice cream-gas (2), cream-gas, cream-cherry, cherry-gas.

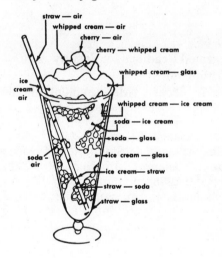

11. Ammonia, soft drink, cleaning fluid, window cleaner, paint thinner, air deodorizer.

12. Most cooking procedures (particularly baking), photography, explosives exploding, gasoline engine burning gasoline, any action of the body, and a dry cell or a battery discharging.

Page 55. One More Step

1. Action of salt water on bacteria is physical. Too high a concentration of salt causes the cells to lose water from their cytoplasm and to dry up. Too low a concentration of salt causes the cells to absorb water and to "explode."

2. Can be extension of problem 12: RNA and DNA production, secretion of pepsin and other digestive enzymes, coagula-

tion of proteins, chlorophyll synthesis, sugar production, water purification, sewage disposal, food metabolism, starch production, protein production, fat production, lactic acid production in muscles, oxidation, respiration, perspiration, glandular secretions, oil on surface of skin, iodine in thyroid, secretion of saliva in the mouth, secretion of insulin by the pancreas, production of CO_2 in the cells, cooking, decomposition, rusting, corroding, fermenting, $3\ O_2 \rightarrow 2\ O_3$, $2\ H_2 + O_2 \rightarrow 2\ H_2O$, $N_2 + 3\ H_2 \rightarrow 2\ NH_3$, fuel combustion, etc.

3. Dissolve salt in water, filter, wash, dry copper in filter paper, evaporate filtrate.

4. There are several ways to convert oil shale to crude oil. One way involves preparation and retorting. Preparation involves breaking the shale into correct size pieces by crushing and screening.

Primary crushing is with jaw crushers and gyratory crushers; secondary crushing is by roll crusher. One kind of retort procedure subjects shale to high-pressure steam which vaporizes the oil. The steam also extracts ammonia and nitrogen gases as well as naphtha. The vapors are scrubbed to separate the crude oil vapor from the ammonia, naphtha, and other gases. Then the crude oil is refined.

Suggested Readings for Faculty and Students

Amoore, John E., Johnston, J. W. Jr., and Rubin, M., "The Sterochemical Theory of Odor." *Scientific American,* Vol. 210, No. 2 (February 1964), pp. 42-49.

*Guild, Walter, Jr., "Theory of Sweet Taste." *Journal of Chemical Education,* Vol. 49, No. 3 (March 1972), pp. 171-173.

(*Faculty only)

Chapter 4

Performance Objectives

GOAL: Students will develop an understanding of the meanings and use of chemical symbols.

Objectives: Upon completion of the reading and activities, and when asked to diagram, demonstrate, or respond either orally or on a written test, students will:

4:1	K	list symbols of common elements.
4:2	K	differentiate between a symbol and a formula.
4:3	P,S	write simple formulas of chemical compounds.
4:4	P	name common compounds for which formulas are given.
4:5	K,P	differentiate between molecular and empirical formulas.
4:6	K	define a formula unit.
4:7-9	P,S	write and balance equations representing four different classifications of reactions.
4:10	P	use symbols to denote the physical state of reactants and products in a reaction.
4:11	K	differentiate between endothermic and exothermic reactions.
4:11	K	define the role of activation energy in chemical reactions.

Upon completion of the reading and activities, students will exhibit an interest in science by:

	A	voluntarily completing one or more of the One More Step activities listed at the end of the chapter on their own time.
	A	reading unassigned literature related to the idea presented in the chapter.

Page 63. Section 4:4

1.
   a. $TlNO_3$
   b. $Rb_2C_4H_4O_6$
   c. $NaCN$
   d. $Pb_3(AsO_4)_2$
   e. NaF
   f. $AlCl_3$
   g. TlI
   h. ZnI_2
   i. $CoCO_3$
   j. KH

2.
   a. barium nitrate
   b. potassium fluoride
   c. thallium(I) iodate
   d. silicon oxide
   e. iron(II) chloride
   f. barium hydride
   g. ammonium selenate

h. cobalt(II) selenide
i. tungsten(VI) boride
j. rubidium nitrate

3. a. BaF_2
   b. Tl_2O
   c. $Al(ClO_4)_3$
   d. $CdBr_2$
   e. FeF_3

4. a. nickel(II) selenide
   b. lithium acetate
   c. thallium(I) hexafluorosilicate
   d. ammonium sulfide
   e. mercury(II) acetate

5. a. $PbSeO_4$
   b. MnC_2O_4
   c. $ZnSO_3$
   d. $(NH_4)_2C_4H_4O_6$
   e. $FeCO_3$

6. a. lead(II) bromide
   b. strontium selenate
   c. mercury(II) fluoride
   d. ammonium carbonate
   e. thallium(I) carbonate

7. a. $FeBr_2$
   b. $Ni_3(AsO_4)_2$
   c. $Zn(C_2H_3O_2)_2$
   d. $Cu(CN)_2$
   e. Na_2SO_4

8. a. copper(II) oxalate
   b. rubidium hexafluorosilicate
   c. bismuth oxalate
   d. ammonium perchlorate
   e. iron(II) hydroxide

9. a. $Mn(NO_3)_2$
   b. $NaOH$
   c. TiC
   d. $CsIO_3$
   e. $ZnSiF_6$

10. a. cobalt(II) acetate
    b. silver perchlorate
    c. beryllium carbide
    d. calcium phosphate
    e. iron(II) sulfate

Page 66. Section 4:6

11. a. 1 formula unit of silver carbonate

b. 3 formula units of thallium(I) bromide
c. 2 formula units of iron(II) nitrate
d. 4 formula units of mercury(II) iodide
e. 6 formula units of mercury(II) chloride

12. a. SrC_2O_4
    b. $Na_2C_2O_4$
    c. K_2SeO_4
    d. Na_2O
    e. Ag_2Se

13. a. mercury(II) cyanide
    b. iron(II) phosphate
    c. copper(II) fluoride
    d. potassium hydroxide
    e. sodium carbonate

14. a. CaC_2O_4
    b. Li_3AsO_4
    c. Ba_3N_2
    d. K_3AsO_4
    e. Cs_2CO_3

15. a. magnesium nitrate
    b. thallium(I) sulfate
    c. mercury(II)oxalate
    d. cerium selenate
    e. ammonium sulfite

Page 70. Section 4:9

16. a. $2\,Ac(OH)_3 \rightarrow Ac_2O_3 + 3\,H_2O$

b. $Ca(AlO_2)_2 + 8\,HCl \rightarrow 2\,AlCl_3$
$+ CaCl_2 + 4\,H_2O$

c. Balanced $Cu + Cl_2 \rightarrow CuCl_2$

d. $3\,Hf + 2\,N_2 \rightarrow Hf_3N_4$

e. $La(NO_3)_3 + 3\,NH_4OH \rightarrow La(OH)_3$
$+ 3\,NH_4NO_3$

f. $5\,O_2 + Sb_2S_3 \rightarrow Sb_2O_4 + 3\,SO_2$

g. $PdCl_2 + 2\,HNO_3 \rightarrow Pd(NO_3)_2 + 2\,HCl$

h. Balanced. $RbBr + AgCl \rightarrow AgBr$
$+ RbCl$

i. Balanced. $RhO_3 \rightarrow RhO + O_2$

j. Balanced. $Te + H_2O \rightarrow TeO + H_2$

17. a. $BaCO_3 + C + H_2O \rightarrow 2\,CO$
$+ Ba(OH)_2$

b. $2\,CeO_2 + 2\,KI + 8\,HCl \rightarrow 2\,KCl$
$+ 2\,CeCl_3 + 4\,H_2O + I_2$

c. $2\,Ga + 3\,H_2SO_4 \rightarrow Ga_2(SO_4)_3 + 3\,H_2$

d. $3\,HfCl_3 + Al \rightarrow 3\,HfCl_2 + AlCl_3$

e. Balanced. $CuO + H_2 \rightarrow Cu + H_2O$

18. a. $2\,PaI_5 \rightarrow 2\,Pa + 5\,I_2$

b. $Ra + 2\,C \rightarrow RaC_2$

c. $2\,Re + 3\,Br_2 \rightarrow 2\,ReBr_3$

d. $2\,Sb + 3\,H_2O \rightarrow Sb_2O_3 + 3\,H_2$

e. $Zn + 2\,CrCl_3 \rightarrow 2\,CrCl_2 + ZnCl_2$

Page 74. End of Chapter

19. a. $AsCl_3(s) + 3\,H_2O(l) \rightarrow 3\,HCl\,(aq)$
$+ As(OH)_3(aq)$

b. $2\,Ho(s) + 6\,H_2O(l) \rightarrow 2\,Ho(OH)_3(aq)$
$+ 3\,H_2(g)$

c. $2\,IrCl_3(aq) + 3\,NaOH(aq) \rightarrow Ir_2O_3(s)$
$+ 3\,HCl(aq) + 3\,NaCl(aq)$

d. $2\,MoO_3(s) + 3\,Zn(s) + 3\,H_2SO_4(l)$
$\rightarrow Mo_2O_3(s) + 3\,ZnSO_4(aq) + 3\,H_2O(l)$

e. $4\,Na(s) + O_2(g) \rightarrow 2\,Na_2O(s)$

20. a. Balanced. $NbI_3(s) + I_2(s) \rightarrow NbI_5(s)$

b. $Pb(C_2H_3O_2)_2(aq) + K_2CrO_4(aq)$
$\rightarrow PbCrO_4(s) + 2\,KC_2H_3O_2(aq)$

c. $RbCl(s) + 2\,O_2(g) \rightarrow RbClO_4(s)$

d. $3\,SiF_4(s) + 3\,H_2O(l) \rightarrow 2\,H_2SiF_6(aq)$
$+ H_2SiO_3(s)$

e. $Sn(s) + 2\,KOH(aq) \rightarrow K_2SnO_2(s)$
$+ H_2(g)$

21. a. $CuCO_3(s) \rightarrow CuO(s) + CO_2(g)$

b. $2\,Na(s) + 2\,H_2O(l) \rightarrow 2\,NaOH(aq)$
$+ H_2(g)$

c. $NH_4NO_2(s) \rightarrow 2\,H_2O(l) + N_2(g)$

d. $2\,Cu(s) + S(s) \rightarrow Cu_2S(s)$

e. $2\,K(s) + 2\,H_2O(l) \rightarrow 2\,KOH(aq)$
$+ H_2(g)$

22. a. $HC_2H_3O_2(aq) + NH_4OH(aq)$
$\rightarrow H_2O(l) + NH_4C_2H_3O_2(aq)$

b. $CaCO_3(s) + 2\,HCl(aq) \rightarrow CaCl_2(aq)$
$+ H_2O(l) + CO_2(g)$

c. $NH_4NO_3(s) \rightarrow 2\,H_2O(l) + N_2O(g)$

d. $Cr(s) + 2\,HCl(aq) \rightarrow H_2(g)$
$+ CrCl_2(aq)$

e. $Ba(OH)_2(aq) + CO_2(g) \rightarrow BaCO_3(s)$
$+ H_2O(l)$

23. a. $Cu(s) + 2\,AgNO_3(aq) \rightarrow Cu(NO_3)_2(aq)$
$+ 2\,Ag(s)$

b. $2\,Mg(s) + O_2(g) \rightarrow 2\,MgO(s)$

c. $HCl(aq) + AgNO_3(aq) \rightarrow HNO_3(aq)$
$+ AgCl(s)$

d. $Mg(s) + 2\,HCl(aq) \rightarrow MgCl_2(aq)$
$+ H_2(g)$

e. $Zn(s) + 2\,HCl(aq) \rightarrow ZnCl_2(aq)$
$+ H_2(g)$

24. a. $4\,Fe(s) + 3\,O_2(g) \rightarrow 2\,Fe_2O_3(s)$

b. $Fe(s) + S(s) \rightarrow FeS(s)$

c. $Ca(OH)_2(aq) + H_2SO_4(aq)$
$\rightarrow CaSO_4(s) + 2\,H_2O(l)$

d. $Zn(s) + S(s) \rightarrow ZnS(s)$

e. $3\,Mg(s) + N_2(g) \rightarrow Mg_3N_2(s)$

Page 75. One More Step

1. a. $FeCl_3(aq) + 3\,NH_4OH(aq)$
$\rightarrow Fe(OH)_3(s) + 3\,NH_4Cl(aq)$

b. $Cu_2S(s) + 12\,HNO_3(aq)$
$\rightarrow Cu(NO_3)_2(aq) + CuSO_4(aq)$
$+ 10\,NO_2(g) + 6\,H_2O(g)$

c. $CH_4(g) + 2\,O_2(g) \rightarrow CO_2(g) + 2\,H_2O(l)$

d. $2\,Ce(IO_3)_4(aq) + 24\,H_2C_2O_4(aq)$
$\rightarrow Ce_2(C_2O_4)_3(aq) + 4\,I_2(aq)$
$+ 42\,CO_2(g) + 24\,H_2O(l)$

e. $MnCl_2(s) + Br_2(l) + 4\,NH_4OH(aq)$
$\rightarrow MnO_2(s) + 2\,NH_4Cl(aq)$
$+ 2\,NH_4Br(aq) + 2\,H_2O(l)$

2. Brown bottles delay the spoiling of foods in which the decomposition reaction is activated by light.

3. Exposing the film involves the light-sensitive reaction

$$AgBr \xrightarrow{\text{light}} AgBr \text{ (exposed)}$$

Developing the exposed film replaces the exposed AgBr with Ag,

AgBr + C₆H₄(OH)₂

$$\text{AgBr} + \text{C}_6\text{H}_4(\text{OH})_2$$
(exposed)

$$\rightarrow 2\,\text{Ag} + \text{C}_6\text{H}_4\text{O}_2 + 2\,\text{HBr.}$$
(image)

Fixing the film involves removal of the unexposed AgBr,

$$\text{AgBr} + 2\,\text{Na}_2\text{S}_2\text{O}_3$$
(unexposed)

$$\rightarrow \text{NaBr} + \text{Na}_3\text{Ag}(\text{S}_2\text{O}_3)_2.$$

4. The temperature at which a heated liquid will flash momentarily when exposed to "flame" is called the flash point.

5. double displacement

6. In the medicine cabinet: These can be used to pique interest.
   aspirin (sodium acetyl salicylate)
   SnF_2
   sodium citrate
   magnesium aluminum hydroxide
   sodium monofluoro phosphate
   hydrogen peroxide
   isopropyl alcohol
   boric acid

(each list should have some in common and some different)

In the kitchen:
ammonia
sodium bicarbonate
sodium chloride
monosodium glutamate
calcium sulfate
calcium propionate
disodium phosphate
sugar
many different vitamins
(any number will suffice)

Suggested Readings for Faculty and Students

Cahn, R. S., *An Introduction to Chemical Nomenclature.* New York, Plenum Press, 1968, Chapters 1-2.

Szokefalvi-Nagy, Zoltan, "How and Why of Chemical Symbols." (Translated by Ralph E. Oesper) *Chemistry,* Vol. 40, No. 2 (February 1967), pp. 21-23.

Strong, Lawrence E., "Balancing Chemical Equations." *Chemistry,* Vol. 47, No. 1 (January 1974), pp. 13-15.

Chapter 5

Performance Objectives

GOAL: Students will gain knowledge and understanding of the mole concept and will apply this concept in solving simple chemical quantitative problems.

Objectives: Upon completion of the reading and activities, and when asked to diagram, demonstrate, or respond orally or on a written test, students will:

5:1 P calculate the formula mass of any given substance.

5:2 K state Avogadro's number.

5:3 K define the mole concept.

5:3 P determine the number of moles in a given mass of a specific substance.

5:4 P calculate the percentage composition of any given compound.

5:5 P determine an empirical formula from percentage composition data.

5:6 P find the molecular formula given the molecular mass and the empirical formula.

5:7 S,P determine the percentage of water in a hydrate.

5:8-9 P solve problems based on mass relationships in chemical reactions.

5:10-11 S,P determine energy changes through use of a calorimeter.

5:12 K differentiate between and describe heats of fusion and vaporization.

5:13 P calculate change in enthalpy in a chemical reaction.

5:14-15 P determine the heats of reaction and formation through enthalpy changes.

Upon completion of the reading and activities, students will exhibit an interest in science by:

A   voluntarily completing one or more of the One More Step activities listed at the end of the chapter on their own time.

A   reading unassigned literature related to the ideas presented in the chapter.

Page 78. Section 5:1

1. a. 689   d. 142   3. a. 310   d. 424
   b. 135   e. 245   b. 484   e. 302
   c. 193   c. 381

2. a. 126   d. 178
   b. 88   e. 108
   c. 136

Page 81. Section 5:3

4. a. $\dfrac{1.00 \times 10^{23} \text{ molecules MgSiF}_6}{} \Bigg| \dfrac{1 \text{ mole}}{6.02 \times 10^{23} \text{ molecules}} \Bigg| \dfrac{166 \text{ g MgSiF}_6}{1 \text{ mole MgSiF}_6} = 27.6 \text{ g MgSiF}_6$

   b. $\dfrac{76.0 \text{ g HNO}_3}{} \Bigg| \dfrac{1 \text{ mole HNO}_3}{63 \text{ g HNO}_3} = 1.21 \text{ moles HNO}_3$

   c. $\dfrac{0.400 \text{ moles H}_2\text{O}}{} \Bigg| \dfrac{6.02 \times 10^{23} \text{ molecules}}{1 \text{ mole}} = 2.41 \times 10^{23} \text{ molecules H}_2\text{O}$

   d. $\dfrac{1.00 \times 10^{26} \text{ molecules NaNH}_2}{} \Bigg| \dfrac{1 \text{ mole}}{6.02 \times 10^{23} \text{ molecules}} = 166 \text{ moles NaNH}_2$

   e. $\dfrac{46.0 \text{ g MnSi}}{83 \text{ g MnSi}} \Bigg| \dfrac{1 \text{ mole MnSi}}{} \Bigg| \dfrac{6.02 \times 10^{23} \text{ molecules}}{1 \text{ mole}} = 3.34 \times 10^{23} \text{ molecules MnSi}$

5. a. $\dfrac{3.00 \text{ moles As}_2\text{S}_3}{} \Bigg| \dfrac{246 \text{ g As}_2\text{S}_3}{1 \text{ mole As}_2\text{S}_3} = 738 \text{ g As}_2\text{S}_3$

   b. $\dfrac{4.70 \times 10^{42} \text{ molecules CaCO}_3}{} \Bigg| \dfrac{1 \text{ mole}}{6.02 \times 10^{23} \text{ molecules}} = 7.81 \text{ moles CaCO}_3$

   c. $\dfrac{18.0 \text{ g HBr}}{80.9 \text{ g HBr}} \Bigg| \dfrac{1 \text{ mole HBr}}{} = 0.222 \text{ moles HBr}$

   d. $\dfrac{9.30 \text{ moles SiH}_4}{} \Bigg| \dfrac{6.02 \times 10^{23} \text{ molecules}}{1 \text{ mole}} = 5.60 \times 10^{24} \text{ molecules SiH}_4$

   e. $\dfrac{8.00 \times 10^{19} \text{ molecules H}_2\text{O}}{} \Bigg| \dfrac{1 \text{ mole}}{6.02 \times 10^{23} \text{ molecules}} \Bigg| \dfrac{18 \text{ g H}_2\text{O}}{1 \text{ mole H}_2\text{O}} = 0.00239 \text{ g H}_2\text{O}$

Page 82. Section 5:4

6. a. $Cs = \dfrac{133}{152} \Bigg| \dfrac{100\%}{1} = 87.5\%$

   $F = \dfrac{19}{152} \Bigg| \dfrac{100\%}{1} = 12.5\%$

          1 Cs @ 133
          1 F   @   19
                    152

   b. $In = \dfrac{115}{242} \Bigg| \dfrac{100\%}{1} = 47.5\%$

   $I = \dfrac{127}{242} \Bigg| \dfrac{100\%}{} = 52.5\%$

          1 In @ 115
          1 I   @ 127
                    242

c. $Hg = \dfrac{401}{542} \left|\dfrac{100\%}{1}\right. = 74.0\%$

$N = \dfrac{14}{542} \left|\dfrac{100\%}{1}\right. = 2.58\%$

$I = \dfrac{127}{542} \left|\dfrac{100\%}{1}\right. = 23.4\%$

$$\begin{array}{l} 2\ Hg\ @\ 200.5 = 401 \\ 1\ N\ \ @\ \ \ 14\ \ = \ \ 14 \\ 1\ I\ \ \ @\ 127\ \ \ = 127 \\ \hline \hspace{3.5cm} 542 \end{array}$$

d. $K = \dfrac{39.1}{322} \left|\dfrac{100\%}{1}\right. = 12.1\%$

$C = \dfrac{216}{322} \left|\dfrac{100\%}{1}\right. = 67.0\%$

$H = \dfrac{35.3}{322} \left|\dfrac{100\%}{1}\right. = 10.9\%$

$O = \dfrac{32.0}{322} \left|\dfrac{100\%}{1}\right. = 9.92\%$

$$\begin{array}{l} \ \ 1\ K\ @\ 39 = \ \ \ 39 \\ 18\ C\ @\ 12 = 216 \\ 35\ H\ @\ \ 1 = \ \ \ 35 \\ \ \ 2\ O\ @\ 16 = \ \ \ 32 \\ \hline \hspace{3cm} 322 \end{array}$$

e. $N = \dfrac{14}{280} \left|\dfrac{100\%}{1}\right. = 5.00\%$

$H = \dfrac{4.03}{280} \left|\dfrac{100\%}{1}\right. = 1.44\%$

$Ga = \dfrac{69.7}{280} \left|\dfrac{100\%}{1}\right. = 24.9\%$

$S = \dfrac{64.1}{280} \left|\dfrac{100\%}{1}\right. = 22.9\%$

$O = \dfrac{128}{280} \left|\dfrac{100\%}{1}\right. = 45.7\%$

$$\begin{array}{l} 1\ N\ \ @\ 14 = \ \ \ 14 \\ 4\ H\ \ @\ \ 1 = \ \ \ \ \ 4 \\ 1\ Ga\ @\ 70 = \ \ \ 70 \\ 2\ S\ \ \ @\ 32 = \ \ \ 64 \\ 8\ O\ \ @\ 16 = 128 \\ \hline \hspace{3cm} 280 \end{array}$$

7. a. $Bi = \dfrac{418}{466} \left|\dfrac{100\%}{1}\right. = 89.7\%$

$O = \dfrac{48}{466} \left|\dfrac{100\%}{1}\right. = 10.3\%$

$$\begin{array}{l} 2\ Bi\ @\ 209 = 418 \\ 3\ O\ @\ \ 16\ = \ \ 48 \\ \hline \hspace{2.5cm} 466 \end{array}$$

b. $Cu = \dfrac{63.5}{151.5} \left|\dfrac{100\%}{1}\right. = 41.9\%$

$C = \dfrac{24}{151.5} \left|\dfrac{100\%}{1}\right. = 15.8\%$

$O = \dfrac{72}{151.5} \left|\dfrac{100\%}{1}\right. = 42.2\%$

$$\begin{array}{l} 1\ Cu\ @\ 63.5 = 63.5 \\ 2\ C\ \ @\ 12\ \ = 24.0 \\ 4\ O\ \ @\ 16\ \ = 64.0 \\ \hline \hspace{3cm} 151.5 \end{array}$$

c. $Li = \dfrac{13.9}{13.4} \left|\dfrac{100\%}{1}\right. = 10.3\%$

$Ge = \dfrac{72.6}{134} \left|\dfrac{100\%}{1}\right. = 54.0\%$

$O = \dfrac{48.0}{134} \left|\dfrac{100\%}{1}\right. = 35.7\%$

$$\begin{array}{l} 2\ Li\ \ @\ \ 7 = 14 \\ 1\ Ge\ @\ 73 = 73 \\ 3\ O\ \ \ @\ 16 = 48 \\ \hline \hspace{2.5cm} 135 \end{array}$$

d. $Pt = \dfrac{195}{449} \left|\dfrac{100\%}{1}\right. = 43.5\%$

$I = \dfrac{254}{449} \left|\dfrac{100\%}{1}\right. = 56.5\%$

e. $Ag = \dfrac{216}{240} \left|\dfrac{100\%}{1}\right. = 90.0\%$

$C = \dfrac{24}{240} \left|\dfrac{100\%}{1}\right. = 10.0\%$

$$2 \text{ Ag } @ 108 = 216$$
$$2 \text{ C } @ \ 12 = \underline{\ 24}$$
$$240$$

Page 84. Section 5:5

8. a. $\text{Ce} = \dfrac{1.67}{140} = 0.0119$

   $\text{I} = \dfrac{4.54}{127} = 0.0357$

   $0.0119/0.0357 \approx 1{:}3$
   $\therefore \text{CeI}_3$

   b. $\text{Mg} = \dfrac{31.9}{24.3} = 1.31$

   $\text{P} = \dfrac{27.1}{31.0} = 0.874$

   $1.31/0.874 \approx 3{:}2$
   $\therefore \text{Mg}_3\text{P}_2$

   c. $\text{Pb} = \dfrac{287}{207} = 1.39$

   $\text{S} = \dfrac{44.4}{32.0} = 1.39$

   $1.39/1.39 \approx 1{:}1$
   $\therefore \text{PbS}$

   d. $\text{Ni} = \dfrac{9.11}{58.7} = 0.155$

   $\text{F} = \dfrac{5.89}{19.0} = 0.310$

   $0.155/0.310 \approx 1{:}2$
   $\therefore \text{NiF}_2$

   e. $\text{Ca} = \dfrac{6.27}{40.1} = 0.156$

   $\text{N} = \dfrac{1.46}{14.00} = 0.104$

   $0.156/0.104 \approx 3{:}2$
   $\therefore \text{Ca}_3\text{N}_2$

9. a. $\text{Fe} = \dfrac{0.0134}{55.8} = 0.000240$

   $\text{S} = \dfrac{0.00769}{32.0} = 0.000240$

   $\text{O} = \dfrac{0.0115}{16.0} = 0.000719$

   $0.000240/0.000240/0.000719 \approx 1{:}1{:}3$
   $\therefore \text{FeSO}_3$

   b. $\text{Al} = \dfrac{1.21}{27.0} = 0.0448$

   $\text{N} = \dfrac{1.88}{14.0} = 0.134$

   $\text{O} = \dfrac{6.44}{16.0} = 0.403$

   $0.0448/0.134/0.403 \approx 113{:}9$
   $\therefore \text{Al (NO}_3)_3$

   c. $\text{Co} = \dfrac{1.39}{58.9} = 0.0235$

   $\text{I} = \dfrac{5.98}{127} = 0.0470$

   $\text{O} = \dfrac{2.26}{16.0} = 0.142$

   $0.023/50.0470/0.142 \approx 1{:}3{:}6$
   $\therefore \text{Co(IO}_3)_2$

   d. $\text{Tl} = \dfrac{0.463}{204} = 0.00226$

   $\text{C} = \dfrac{0.0544}{12.0} = 0.00453$

   $\text{H} = \dfrac{0.00685}{1.01} = 0.00635$

   $\text{O} = \dfrac{0.0725}{16.0} = 0.00453$

   $0.00226/0.00453/0.00635/0.00453 \approx 1{:}2{:}3{:}2$
   $\therefore \text{TlC}_2\text{H}_3\text{O}_2$

   e. $\text{Ca} = \dfrac{12.2}{40.0} = 0.304$

   $\text{H} = \dfrac{1.22}{1.01} = 1.20$

$$P = \frac{18.8}{31.0} = 0.606$$

$$O = \frac{38.9}{16.0} = 2.43$$

$$0.304/1.20/0.606/2.43 \approx 1:4:2:8$$
$$CaH_4P_2O_8 \approx Ca(H_2PO_4)_2$$

10. a. $Cr = \frac{32.8}{52.0} = 0.630$

$$Cl = \frac{67.2}{35.5} = 1.90$$

$$\frac{0.630}{1.90} \approx \frac{1}{3} \quad \therefore \; CrCl_3$$

b. $Ir = \frac{75.1}{192} = 0.391$

$$S = \frac{24.9}{32.1} = 0.775$$

$$\frac{0.391}{0.775} \approx \frac{1}{2} \quad \therefore \; IrS_2$$

c. $Nd = \frac{27.5}{144} = 0.191$

$$I = \frac{72.5}{127} = 0.570$$

$$\frac{0.191}{0.570} \approx \frac{1}{3} \quad \therefore \; NdI_3$$

d. $Ra = \frac{58.5}{226} = 0.259$

$$Br = \frac{41.5}{79.9} = 0.520$$

$$\frac{0.259}{0.520} \approx \frac{1}{2} \quad \therefore \; RaBr_2$$

e. $Sn = \frac{26.8}{119} = 0.225$

$$Cl = \frac{16.0}{35.5} = 0.450$$

$$I = \frac{57.2}{127} = 0.450$$

$$\frac{0.225/0.450/0.450}{\approx 1/2/2} \quad \therefore \; SnCl_2I_2$$

11. a. $H = \frac{1.1}{1.01} = 1.09$

$$B = \frac{12.3}{10.8} = 1.14$$

$$F = \frac{86.6}{19.0} = 4.56$$

$$1.09/1.14/4.54 \approx 1/1/4 \quad \therefore \; HBF_4$$

b. $Mg = \frac{28.8}{24.3} = 1.19$

$$C = \frac{14.2}{12.0} = 1.18$$

$$O = \frac{57.0}{16.0} = 3.56$$

$$1.19/1.18/3.56 \approx 1/1/3 \quad \therefore \; MgCO_3$$

c. $K = \frac{55.3}{39.1} = 1.41$

$$B = \frac{38.3}{10.8} = 3.54$$

$$H = \frac{6.4}{1.01} = 6.33$$

$$1.41/3.54/6.33 \approx 2/5/9 \quad \therefore \; K_2B_5H_9$$

d. $Ag = \frac{46.6}{108} = 0.431$

$$W = \frac{39.7}{184} = 0.215$$

$$O = \frac{13.7}{16} = 0.858$$

$$0.431/0.215/0.858 \approx 2/1/4 \quad \therefore \; Ag_2WO_4$$

e. $Zn = \frac{67.1}{65} = 1.03$

$$O = \frac{32.9}{16} = 2.06$$

$$\frac{1.03}{2.06} = \frac{1}{2} \qquad \therefore \quad ZnO_2$$

Page 85. Section 5:6

12. Empirical formula mass
$$= 12 + 1 + 16 + 35.5 = 64.5$$
$$\frac{129}{64.5} = 2$$
$\therefore C_2H_2O_2Cl_2$ is molecular formula

13. Empirical formula mass
$$= 12 + 35.5 + 14 = 61.5$$
$$\frac{184.5}{61.5} = 3$$
$\therefore C_3Cl_3N_3$ is molecular formula

14. Empirical formula mass
$$= 204 + 24 + 2 + 48 = 278$$
$$\frac{557}{278} \approx 2$$
$\therefore Tl_2C_4H_4O_6$ is molecular formula

Page 86. Section 5:7

15. a.
$$\frac{0.391 \text{ g } Li_2SiF_6}{} \left| \frac{1 \text{ mole}}{156 \text{ g } Li_2SiF_6} \right. = 0.0025 \text{ moles} \qquad \frac{0.0903 \text{ g } H_2O}{} \left| \frac{1 \text{ mole}}{18 \text{ g } H_2O} \right. = 0.0050 \text{ moles}$$

molecular mass $= 2(7) + 28 + 6(19)$ molecular mass $= 2(1) + 16 = 18$
$14 + 28 + 114 = 156$
$0.0025/0.0050 = 1/2 \qquad \therefore Li_2SiF_6 \cdot 2 H_2O$

b.
$$\frac{0.737 \text{ g } MgSO_3}{} \left| \frac{1 \text{ mole}}{104 \text{ g } MgSO_3} \right. = 0.0070 \text{ moles} \qquad \frac{0.763 \text{ g } H_2O}{} \left| \frac{1 \text{ mole}}{18 \text{ g } H_2O} \right. = 0.0423 \text{ moles}$$

$0.007/0.042 \approx 1/6 \qquad \therefore MgSO_3 \cdot 6 H_2O$

c.
$$\frac{95.3 \text{ g } LiNO_3}{} \left| \frac{1 \text{ mole}}{69 \text{ g } LiNO_3} \right. = 1.38 \text{ moles} \qquad \frac{74.7 \text{ g } H_2O}{} \left| \frac{1 \text{ mole}}{18 \text{ g } H_2O} \right. = 4.15 \text{ moles}$$

molecular mass $= 7 + 14 + 3(16) = 69$
$1.38/4.15 \approx 1/3 \qquad LiNO_3 \cdot 3 H_2O$

d. Assume 100 g of material
$\therefore$ 76.9 g $CaSO_3$, 23.1 g H_2O
$$\frac{76.9 \text{ g } CaSO_3}{} \left| \frac{1 \text{ mole}}{120 \text{ g } CaSO_3} \right. = 0.64 \text{ moles}$$
molecular mass $= 40 + 32 + 3(16) =$ $\frac{23.1 \text{ g } H_2O}{} \left| \frac{1 \text{ mole}}{18 \text{ g } H_2O} \right. = 1.28 \text{ moles}$
120
$0.64/1.28 \approx 1/2 \qquad \therefore CaSO_3 \cdot 2 H_2O$

e. Assume 100 g of material
$\therefore$ 89.2 g $BaBr_2$, 10.8 g H_2O
$$\frac{89.2 \text{ g } BaBr_2}{} \left| \frac{1 \text{ mole}}{297 \text{ g } BaBr_2} \right. = 0.30 \text{ moles} \qquad \frac{10.8 \text{ g } H_2O}{} \left| \frac{1 \text{ mole}}{18 \text{ g } H_2O} \right. = 0.60 \text{ moles}$$

molecular mass $= 137 + 2(80) = 297$
$0.30/0.60 \approx 1/2 \qquad \therefore BaBr_2 \cdot 2 H_2O$

16. $2 Na(s) + 2 H_2O(l) \rightarrow 2 NaOH(aq) + H_2(g)$

$$\frac{11.5 \text{ g Na}}{} \left| \frac{1 \text{ mole Na}}{23 \text{ g Na}} \right| \frac{1 \text{ mole } H_2}{2 \text{ moles Na}} = 0.250 \text{ moles } H_2$$

17. $N_2(g) + 3 H_2(g) \rightarrow 2 NH_3(g)$

$$\frac{2.00 \text{ g } H_2}{} \left| \frac{1 \text{ mole } H_2}{2.02 \text{ g } H_2} \right| \frac{2 \text{ moles } NH_3}{3 \text{ moles } H_2} = 0.661 \text{ moles } NH_3$$

18. $C(s) + O_2(g) \rightarrow CO_2(g)$

$$\frac{18 \text{ g C}}{} \left| \frac{1 \text{ mole C}}{12 \text{ g C}} \right| \frac{1 \text{ mole } O_2}{1 \text{ mole C}} \left| \frac{32 \text{ g } O_2}{1 \text{ mole } O_2} \right. = 48.0 \text{ g } O_2$$

19.
$$\frac{18 \text{ g C}}{} \left| \frac{1 \text{ mole C}}{12 \text{ g C}} \right| \frac{1 \text{ mole } CO_2}{1 \text{ mole C}} \left| \frac{44 \text{ g } CO_2}{1 \text{ mole } CO_2} \right. = 66.0 \text{ g } CO_2$$

20. $2 KClO_3(s) \rightarrow 2 KCl(s) + 3 O_2(g)$

$$\frac{16 \text{ g } O_2}{} \left| \frac{1 \text{ mole } O_2}{32 \text{ g } O_2} \right| \frac{2 \text{ moles KCl}}{3 \text{ moles } O_2} \left| \frac{74.6 \text{ g KCl}}{1 \text{ mole KCl}} \right. = 24.9 \text{ g KCl}$$

21.
$$\frac{28 \text{ g Fe}}{} \left| \frac{1 \text{ mole Fe}}{55.8 \text{ g Fe}} \right| \frac{3 \text{ moles CO}}{2 \text{ moles Fe}} \left| \frac{28 \text{ g CO}}{1 \text{ mole CO}} \right. = 21.1 \text{ g CO}$$

22. $2 HCl(aq) + Ca(OH)_2(s) \rightarrow CaCl_2(aq) + 2 H_2O(l)$

$$\frac{10.0 \text{ g Ca(OH)}_2}{} \left| \frac{1 \text{ mole Ca(OH)}_2}{74.1 \text{ g Ca(OH)}_2} \right| \frac{2 \text{ moles HCl}}{1 \text{ mole Ca(OH)}_2} \left| \frac{36.5 \text{ g HCl}}{1 \text{ mole HCl}} \right. = 9.84 \text{ g HCl}$$

23. $2 Al(s) + 6 HCl(aq) \rightarrow 2 AlCl_3(aq) + 3 H_2(g)$

$$\frac{5.00 \text{ g Al}}{} \left| \frac{1 \text{ mole Al}}{27 \text{ g Al}} \right| \frac{3 \text{ moles } H_2}{2 \text{ moles Al}} \left| \frac{2.02 \text{ g } H_2}{1 \text{ mole } H_2} \right. = 0.560 \text{ g } H_2$$

24.
$$\frac{\text{g}}{254 \text{ g}} \left| \frac{1 \text{ mole}}{1 \text{ mole}} \right| \frac{3650 \text{ cal}}{} \left| \frac{1 \text{ kcal}}{1000 \text{ cal}} \right. = 0.365 \text{ kcal}$$

25. $\dfrac{\cancel{g}}{106\,\cancel{g}} \Big| \dfrac{1\,\cancel{mole}}{} \Big| \dfrac{4120\,\cancel{cal}}{1\,\cancel{mole}} \Big| \dfrac{1\,kcal}{1000\,\cancel{cal}}$

$= 0.164\ kcal$

26. heat = mass (ΔT) (specific heat constant)

$\dfrac{45.0\,\cancel{g}}{133\,\cancel{g}/\cancel{mole}} \Big| \dfrac{(28.6-24)\,C°}{} \Big| \dfrac{7.18\,cal}{\cancel{mole}\text{-}\cancel{C°}}$

$= 11.2\ cal$ to heat to m.p.

$\dfrac{0.34\,\cancel{moles}}{} \Big| \dfrac{520\,cal}{1\,\cancel{mole}} = 176\ cal$ to melt

$\dfrac{0.34\,\cancel{moles}}{} \Big| \dfrac{(690-28.5)\,\cancel{C°}}{} \Big| \dfrac{8.0\,cal}{1\,\cancel{mole}\text{-}\cancel{C°}}$

$= 1790\ cal$ to heat to b.p.

$\dfrac{0.34\,\cancel{moles}}{} \Big| \dfrac{21,300\,cal}{1\,\cancel{mole}}$

$= 7210\ cal$ to vaporize

$\dfrac{0.34\,\cancel{mole}}{} \Big| \dfrac{(880-690)\,\cancel{C°}}{} \Big| \dfrac{4.97\,cal}{\cancel{mole}\text{-}\cancel{C°}}$

$= 319\ cal$ to heat to 880°C

total heat = 11.2 cal + 176 cal + 1790 cal
$\qquad\qquad$ + 7210 cal + 319 cal

$\qquad\quad = 9510\ cal = 9.51\ kcal$

27. heat = (mass) (ΔT) (specific heat)

$\dfrac{5580\,\cancel{g}}{} \Big| \dfrac{(1000-20)\,\cancel{C°}}{} \Big| \dfrac{0.107\,cal}{\cancel{g}\text{-}\cancel{C°}}$

$= 5.85 \times 10^5\ cal$

$= 5.85 \times 10^2\ kcal$

or 585 kcal

28. heat = (mass) (ΔT) (specific heat)

$\dfrac{50.0\,\cancel{g}}{} \Big| \dfrac{0-(-32)\,\cancel{C°}}{} \Big| \dfrac{0.500\,cal}{1\,\cancel{g}\text{-}\cancel{C°}}$

$= 800\ cal$ to heat to m.p.

$\dfrac{50.0\,\cancel{g}}{} \Big| \dfrac{76.4\,cal}{\cancel{g}} = 3820\ cal$ to melt

$\dfrac{50.0\,\cancel{g}}{} \Big| \dfrac{(100-0)\,\cancel{C°}}{} \Big| \dfrac{1\,cal}{\cancel{g}\text{-}\cancel{C°}}$

$= 5000\ cal$ to heat to b.p.

$\dfrac{50.0\,\cancel{g}}{} \Big| \dfrac{539\,cal}{\cancel{g}} = 27000\ cal$ to vaporize

$\dfrac{50.0\,\cancel{g}}{} \Big| \dfrac{(400-100)\,\cancel{C°}}{} \Big| \dfrac{0.482\,cal}{\cancel{g}\text{-}\cancel{C°}}$

$= 7500\ cal$ to heat to 400°C

total heat = 800 cal + 3820 cal + 5000 cal
$\qquad$ + 27000 cal + 7230 cal = 43,850 cal
$\qquad = 43.8\ kcal$

Page 102. Section 5:14

29. $NH_3(g) + HBr(g)\ \ NH_4\,Br(s)$

$\Delta H^0 = \Delta H_f^0$ products $- \Delta H_f^0$ reactants

$\Delta H^0 = (-64,730) - [(-11,020) +$
$(-8700)]$

$\Delta H^0 = -45,010\ cal/mole$

$\dfrac{193\,\cancel{g}}{97.9\,\cancel{g}} \Big| \dfrac{1\,\cancel{mole}}{} \Big| \dfrac{-45,010\,cal}{1\,\cancel{mole}}$

$= -88.7\ kcal$

30. $CoCO_3(s) \rightarrow CoO(s) + CO_2(g)$

$\Delta H^0 = [(-57,200) + (-94,051)] -$
$[-172,700]$

$\Delta H^0 = 21,449\ cal/mole$

$\dfrac{0.772\,\cancel{g}}{119\,\cancel{g}} \Big| \dfrac{1\,\cancel{mole}}{} \Big| \dfrac{21,449\,cal}{1\,\cancel{mole}}$

$= 139\ cal$

31. $2\,NaBr(aq) + Cl_2(g) \rightarrow 2\,NaCl(aq) +$
$Br_2(g)$

$\Delta H^0 = [(-98,230) + (0)] - [(-86,030)$
$+ (0)]$

$\Delta H^0 = -12,200$

$\dfrac{0.0663\,\cancel{g}}{160\,\cancel{g}} \Big| \dfrac{1\,\cancel{mole}}{} \Big| \dfrac{-12,200\,cal}{1\,\cancel{mole}}$

$= -5.06\ cal$

Page 104. End of Chapter

32. a. 174 b. 250 c. 190 d. 709 e. 305

33. a. 134 b. 759 c. 143 d. 476 e. 388

34. a. $\dfrac{10.0\,\cancel{g}}{100\,\cancel{g}} \Big| \dfrac{1\,mole}{} = 0.100\ mole\ CaCO_3$

b. $\dfrac{10^{25} \text{ molecules}}{}\ \bigg|\ \dfrac{1 \text{ mole}}{6.02 \times 10^{23} \text{ molecules}}\ \bigg|\ \dfrac{254 \text{ g}}{1 \text{ mole}} = 4.22 \times 10^3 \text{ g } I_2$

c. $\dfrac{0.426 \text{ moles}}{}\ \bigg|\ \dfrac{6.02 \times 10^{23} \text{ molecules}}{1 \text{ mole}} = 2.56 \times 10^{23} \text{ molecules } H_2S_3$

d. $\dfrac{26.8 \text{ moles}}{}\ \bigg|\ \dfrac{6.02 \times 10^{23} \text{ molecules}}{1 \text{ mole}} = 1.61 \times 10^{25} \text{ molecules } PBrCl_4$

e. $\dfrac{681 \text{ formula units}}{}\ \bigg|\ \dfrac{1 \text{ mole}}{6.02 \times 10^{23} \text{ formula units}} = 1.13 \times 10^{-21} \text{ moles } K_2CS_3$

35. a. $K = \dfrac{78.2}{138}\ \bigg|\ \dfrac{100\%}{1} = 56.6\%$

$C = \dfrac{12.0}{138}\ \bigg|\ \dfrac{100\%}{1} = 8.69\%$

$O = \dfrac{48.0}{138}\ \bigg|\ \dfrac{100\%}{1} = 34.7\%$

$\begin{array}{lll} 2\ K & @\ 39 = & 78 \\ 1\ C & @\ 12 = & 12 \\ 3\ O & @\ 16 = & \underline{\ 48} \\ & & 138 \end{array}$

b. $C = \dfrac{24.0}{60}\ \bigg|\ \dfrac{100\%}{1} = 40.0\%$

$H = \dfrac{4.03}{60}\ \bigg|\ \dfrac{100\%}{1} = 6.71\%$

$O = \dfrac{32.0}{60}\ \bigg|\ \dfrac{100\%}{1} = 53.3\%$

$\begin{array}{lll} 2\ C & @\ 12 = & 24 \\ 4\ H & @\ 1 = & 4 \\ 2\ O & @\ 16 = & \underline{32} \\ & & 60 \end{array}$

c. $Al = \dfrac{54.0}{916}\ \bigg|\ \dfrac{100\%}{1} = 5.89\%$

$S = \dfrac{128}{916}\ \bigg|\ \dfrac{100\%}{1} = 14.0\%$

$O = \dfrac{640}{916}\ \bigg|\ \dfrac{100\%}{1} = 69.8\%$

$Na = \dfrac{46.0}{916}\ \bigg|\ \dfrac{100\%}{1} = 5.02\%$

$H = \dfrac{48.4}{916}\ \bigg|\ \dfrac{100\%}{1} = 5.28\%$

$\begin{array}{lll} 2\ Al & @\ 27 = & 54 \\ 4\ S & @\ 32 = & 128 \\ 40\ O & @\ 16 = & 640 \\ 2\ Na & @\ 23 = & 46 \\ 48\ H & @\ 1 = & \underline{\ 48} \\ & & 917 \end{array}$

d. $Tl = \dfrac{409}{625}\ \bigg|\ \dfrac{100\%}{1} = 65.4\%$

$Cr = \dfrac{104}{625}\ \bigg|\ \dfrac{100\%}{1} = 16.6\%$

$O = \dfrac{112}{625}\ \bigg|\ \dfrac{100\%}{1} = 17.9\%$

$\begin{array}{lll} 2\ Tl & @\ 204.5 = & 409 \\ 2\ Cr & @\ 52 = & 104 \\ 7\ O & @\ 16 = & \underline{112} \\ & & 625 \end{array}$

e. $Ba = \dfrac{137}{375}\ \bigg|\ \dfrac{100\%}{1} = 36.6\%$

$Mn = \dfrac{110}{375}\ \bigg|\ \dfrac{100\%}{1} = 29.3\%$

$O = \dfrac{128}{375}\ \bigg|\ \dfrac{100\%}{1} = 34.1\%$

$\begin{array}{lll} 1\ Ba & @\ 137 = & 137 \\ 2\ Mn & @\ 55 = & 110 \\ 8\ O & @\ 16 = & \underline{128} \\ & & 375 \end{array}$

36. $Ca = \dfrac{33.3}{40.1} = 0.83$

$O = \dfrac{40}{16.0} = 2.5$

$S = \dfrac{26.67}{32.1} = 0.83$

$0.83/2.5/0.83 \approx 1/3/1$

$\therefore CaSO_3$

37. $C = \dfrac{92.3}{12.0} = 7.68$

$H = \dfrac{7.7}{1.01} = 7.62$

$7.68/7.62 \approx 1/1$

$(CH)_n = 78$ g

$n = 6 \quad \therefore C_6H_6$

38. $P = \dfrac{26.7}{31.0} = 0.860$

$N = \dfrac{12.1}{14.0} = 0.864$

$Cl = \dfrac{61.2}{35.5} = 1.725$

$0.860/0.864/1.725 \approx 1/1/2$

$(PNCl_2)_n = 695$ g

$n = 6 \quad \therefore P_6N_6Cl_{12}$

39. $\Delta H^0 = (mass)\,(\Delta T)\,(specific\ heat)$

$= \dfrac{198{,}000\ \cancel{g}\ \Big|\ (300-25)\ \cancel{C^0}\ \Big|\ 0.1225\ cal}{\Big|\ \Big|\ \cancel{g}\text{-}\cancel{C^0}}$

$= 6.67 \times 10^6\ cal$

40. $\Delta H^0 = (mass)\,(\Delta T)\,(specific\ heat)$

$= \dfrac{50.0\ \cancel{g}\ \Big|\ (100-24)\ \cancel{C^0}\ \Big|\ 0.0530\ cal}{\Big|\ \Big|\ \cancel{g}\text{-}\cancel{C^0}}$

$= 201\ cal$

41. mass of ice $= \dfrac{10^3\ \cancel{g}\ water\ \Big|\ (100-0)\ \cancel{C^0}\ \Big|\ 1\ \cancel{cal}\ \Big|\ 1\ g}{\Big|\ \cancel{g}\text{-}\cancel{C^0}\ \Big|\ 76.4\ \cancel{cal}} = 1310$ g

42. $\dfrac{1.46\ \cancel{g\ AgCl_3}\ \Big|\ 1\ \cancel{mole\ AgCl_3}\ \Big|\ 1\ \cancel{mole\ NaAlO_2}\ \Big|\ 82\ g\ NaAlO_2}{\Big|\ 133\ \cancel{g\ AgCl_3}\ \Big|\ 1\ \cancel{mole\ AgCl_3}\ \Big|\ 1\ \cancel{mole\ NaAlO_2}} = 0.898$ g $NaAlO_2$

43. $\dfrac{61.5\ \cancel{g\ Ce_2(C_2O_4)_3}\ \Big|\ 1\ mole\ \cancel{Ce_2(C_2O_4)_3}\ \Big|\ 42\ \cancel{moles\ CO_2}\ \Big|\ 44\ g\ CO_2}{\Big|\ 544\ \cancel{g\ Ce_2(C_2O_4)_3}\ \Big|\ 1\ \cancel{mole\ Ce_2(C_2O_4)_3}\ \Big|\ 1\ \cancel{mole\ CO_2}} = 209$ g CO_2

44. $2NO(g) + O_2(g) \rightarrow 2NO_2(g)$

$\Delta H^0 = [2(7930)] - [2(21{,}570) + (0)]$

$\Delta H^0 = -27{,}280$ or -27.3 kcal

45. $4FeO(s) + O_2(g) \rightarrow 2Fe_2O_3(s)$

$\Delta H^0 = [2(-196{,}500)] - [4(-63{,}700) + (0)]$

$\Delta H^0 = -138{,}200$ or -138 kcal

Page 105. One More Step

1. The method of predicting molar heat content involves an application of Kopp's law: The molar heat content of a solid inorganic compound is roughly equal to the sum of the atomic heats of its constituents.

2. The specific heat of water decreases as the temperature increases from 0°C to 34°C, then increases as the temperature goes from 35°C to 100°C. The specific heat of mercury decreases as the temperature rises from its melting point to 300°C, then increases as the temperature

rises to its boiling point. The specific heat of most other liquids increases rather uniformly from the melting point to the boiling point. The decrease in specific heat is due to the breaking up of associated molecules in the liquid state. The increase is due to the work expended in expanding the liquid as well as in raising the temperature of the water.

3. The change in order of the reaction will also determine whether or not the reaction will take place. (Entropy change $= \Delta S$.)

4. Any changes of mass to energy (or vice versa) which are associated with ordinary chemical reactions are too small to be detectable with present instruments. In molecular rearrangements (for example, chemical reactions) it is the change in potential energy of the particles involved (for example, the relative positions of the particles) which manifests itself as ΔE.

5. Hess's law: The heat of reaction for a multi-step process is the sum of the heats of reaction of the individual steps. The law may also be stated: The ΔH of a reaction depends only upon the initial and final energy states, not on the path from the initial energy state to the final energy state.

6. The amount of heat per mole of a fuel is a determinant in the selection of a fuel. Other factors of selection are cost per mole of processing and use. Certainly given equal cost for obtaining and delivering two fuels, the one with greater heat content would provide more heat per dollar.

Suggested Readings for Faculty and Students

*Hawthorne, Robert M., Jr., "The Mole and Avogadro's Number." *Journal of Chemical Education*, Vol. 50, No. 4 (April 1973), pp. 282-284.

Kopperl, Sheldon, and Parascandola, John, "The Development of the Adiabatic Calorimeter." *Journal of Chemical Education*, Vol. 48, No. 4 (April 1971), pp. 237-242.

Sienko, M. J., *Chemistry Problems*. Menlo Park, California, W. A. Benjamin, Inc., 1972, 2nd Ed., Chapters 2-4 and 8.

*Garst, John F., "The Extent of Reaction as a Unifying Basis for Stoichiometry in Elementary Chemistry." *Journal of Chemical Education*, Vol. 51, No. 3 (March 1974), pp. 194-196.

(*Faculty only)

Chapter 6

Performance Objectives

GOAL: Students will gain knowledge and understanding of atomic theory using the Rutherford-Bohr atom as a model.

Objectives: Upon completion of the reading and activities, and when asked to diagram, demonstrate, or respond orally or on a written test, students will:

6:1-5 K state a brief history of atomic theory.

6:2 K state the law of conservation of mass.

6:3 K state the law of definite proportions.

6:4 K list the elements of Dalton's hypothesis.

6:5 K list examples of the law of multiple proportions.

6:6-8 K differentiate among the properties of the electron, proton, and neutron.

6:9-10 K define atomic number and its relationship to isotopes.

6:11 K define the standard for atomic mass units (a.m.u.).

6:12 K list uses for the mass spectrometer.

6:13-18 K specify the size and shape of the atom and its parts.

6:19-20 K state the relationship between quantum theory and the location of an electron.

6:21 K define the photoelectric effect. Upon completion of the reading and activities, students will exhibit an interest in science by:

A   voluntarily completing one or more of the One More Step activities listed at the end of the chapter on their own time.

A   reading unassigned literature related to the ideas presented in the chapter.

Page 129. Section 6:20

The first two problems are not difficult. The solutions consist of dividing velocity by wavelength in the first problem, and velocity by frequency in the second.

1. $\nu = \dfrac{v}{\lambda} = \dfrac{3 \times 10^{10}\ \cancel{cm}}{sec} \left| \dfrac{1}{410\ \cancel{nm}} \right| \dfrac{10^7\ \cancel{nm}}{1\ \cancel{cm}}$
$= 7.32 \times 10^{14}$ Hz

2. $\lambda = \dfrac{v}{\nu} = \dfrac{3 \times 10^{10}\ \cancel{cm}}{\cancel{sec}} \left| \dfrac{\cancel{sec}}{6 \times 10^{14}} \right| \dfrac{10^8\ \overset{\circ}{A}}{1\ \cancel{cm}}$
$= 5000\ \overset{\circ}{A}$ or 500 nm

3. $\dfrac{6.62 \times 10^{-27}\ \text{erg-}\cancel{sec} \left| 7.32 \times 10^{14} \right.}{\cancel{sec}}$
$= 4.85 \times 10^{-12}$ ergs

4. $\dfrac{6.62 \times 10^{-27}\ \text{erg-}\cancel{sec} \left| 6 \times 10^{14} \right.}{\cancel{sec}}$
$= 3.97 \times 10^{-12}$ ergs

Page 132. End of Chapter

5. a. Dalton reintroduced the atomic theory and gathered experimental evidence to support his theory.

b. Thomson, who made the Cavendish Laboratory famous, made several important advances. He discovered the electron and showed that canal rays actually consist of positively charged particles. Thomson also calculated the mass of the proton.

c. Rutherford demonstrated that the nucleus is a small heavy core in an atom which consists mostly of space.

d. Chadwick showed that rays discovered by Walter Bothe in 1930 were really a beam of uncharged particles.

Chadwick is credited with discovery of the neutron.

e. Moseley did research which resulted in a modification of the atomic theory to include atomic number.

f. Bohr originated the idea that electrons travel in a definite energy level around the nucleus. He applied Planck's idea of small packets or quanta of energy to his electron model.

g. Planck introduced the idea that (electromagnetic) energy is radiated in small packets called quanta.

6. Demonstrate conservation of mass by burning a candle in a closed container. Measure the mass of the candle and container before and after burning. There should be no change in mass if mass is conserved.

7. Analyze a compound to determine what elements it is composed of and the percentage of each element present. Synthesize the same compound (such as water) being careful to measure the reactants and products accurately. If the same ratio of elements is always involved, you have demonstrated the law of definite proportions.

8. The atomic number is equal to the number of protons in the nucleus of an atom. The atomic number is 18. The mass number would be $(18 + 22) = 40$.

9. $(0.6)\ (69) + (0.4)\ (71) = 41.4 + 28.4$
$= 69.8$ a.m.u.

or consider 100 atoms in a random sample 60 are 69 and 40 are 71

$\dfrac{60 \times 69 + 40 \times 71}{100} = 69.8$

10. $\dfrac{50(4.31) + 52(83.8) + 53(9.55) + 54(2.38)}{100}$
$= 52.1$ a.m.u.

11. $\dfrac{2.01\ \cancel{cm} \left| 10^8\ \overset{\circ}{A} \right.}{1\ \cancel{cm}} = 2.01 \times 10^8\ \overset{\circ}{A}$

12. Energy of light = energy of photon + release energy:

$(1.20 \times 10^{-12}) + (3.60 \times 10^{-12})$
$= 4.80 \times 10^{-12}$ ergs

then determine the frequency:

$$E = h\nu$$

$$\therefore \nu = \frac{E}{h} = \frac{4.80 \times 10^{-12} \text{ erg}}{6.62 \times 10^{-27} \text{ erg-sec}}$$

$$= 7.25 \times 10^{14}/\text{sec}$$

We conclude:

$$\lambda = \frac{v}{\nu} = \frac{3 \times 10^{10} \text{ cm}}{\text{sec}} \left| \frac{1 \text{ sec}}{7.25 \times 10^{14}} \right| \frac{10^8 \text{ Å}}{1 \text{ cm}}$$

$$= 4140 \text{ Å} = 414 \text{ nm}$$

13. Dalton's Theory:
    (1) All matter is composed of atoms which are indivisible.
    (2) Atoms of the same element are identical, atoms of different elements are dissimilar.

(3) Atoms can unite with other atoms in simple numerical ratios.

Modified Theory:
(1) Atoms are composed of electrons, protons, and neutrons.
(2) All atoms of the same element have the same number of protons in the nucleus but the number of neutrons may vary.
(3) Remains unchanged.

14.

	charge	relative mass	location
proton	+1	1	nucleus
neutron	0	1	nucleus
electron	−1	0	orbitals

Page 133.   One More Step

1. Note: Because research in this area is so current, only a partial list is given.

Particle	Mass	Charge	Lifetime
electron	1	−	∞
electron's neutrino	0	0	∞
muon	207	−	$2.2^0 + 10^{-6}$ sec
muon's neutrino	0	0	∞
pion	273	+	$2.6^0 \times 10^{-8}$ sec
pion	264	0	0.8×10^{-16} sec
kaon	966	+	$1.2^4 \times 10^{-8}$ sec
kaon	974	0	$\begin{cases} 5.17 \times 10^{-8} \text{ sec} \\ 0.86 \times 10^{-10} \text{ sec} \end{cases}$
eta	1074	0	2.53×10^{-19} sec
proton	1836	+	∞
neutron	1839	0	0.93×10^3 sec
lambda	2183	0	2.5×10^{-10} sec
sigma	2328	+	8.0×10^{-11} sec
sigma	2334	0	$<1 \times 10^{-11}$ sec
sigma	2343	−	1.49×10^{-10} sec
xi	2573	0	3.0×10^{-10} sec
xi	2586	−	1.66×10^{-10} sec
omega	3273	−	1.3×10^{-10} sec

2.

Atomic Number	Mass Number	Atomic Number	Mass Number	Atomic Number	Mass Number	Atomic Number	Mass Number
1	1	2	3	3	6	4	⑦
	2		4		7		9
	③*		⑥		⑧		⑩
			⑧		⑨		11
							⑫

*Radioactive isotopes are circled.

Atomic Number / Mass Number tables. Circled mass numbers are shown in parentheses.

Atomic Number	Mass Number
5	(8)
	10
	11
	(12)
	(13)
6	(9)
	(10)
	(11)
	12
	13
	(14)
	(15)
	(16)
7	(12)
	(13)
	14
	15
	16
	(17)
	(18)
8	(13)
	(14)
	(15)
	16
	17
	18
	19
	(20)
9	(17)
	(18)
	19
	(20)
	(21)
	(22)
10	(17)
	(18)
	(19)
	20
	21
	22
	(23)
	(24)
11	(20)
	(21)
	(22)
	23
	(24)
	25
	26
12	(20)
	(21)

Atomic Number	Mass Number
	(22)
	23
	24
	25
	26
	(27)
	(28)
13	24
	(25)
	(26)
	27
	(28)
	(29)
	(30)
14	(25)
	(26)
	(27)
	28
	29
	30
	(31)
	(32)
15	(28)
	(29)
	(30)
	31
	(32)
	(33)
	(34)
16	(29)
	(30)
	(31)
	32
	33
	34
	(35)
	36
	(37)
	38
17	(32)
	(33)
	(34)
	35
	(36)
	37
	(38)
	(39)
	(40)
18	(33)
	(34)
	(35)

Atomic Number	Mass Number
	36
	(37)
	38
	(39)
	40
	(41)
	(42)
	(43)
	(44)
19	(36)
	(37)
	(38)
	39
	(40)
	(41)
	42
	(43)
	(44)

Atomic Number	Mass Number
	(45)
	(46)
	(47)
20	(37)
	(38)
	(39)
	40
	(41)
	42
	43
	44
	(45)
	46
	(47)
	48
	(49)
	(50)

3. Dalton 37
 Thomson 41
 Rutherford 39
 Chadwick 41
 Moseley 26
 Bohr 28
 Planck 42

4. The Japanese physicist Hantaro Nagaoka suggested the planetary model for the atom in 1904.

5. *Encyclopaedia Britannica,* "Proton: Characteristics;" also, Hofstadter's Nobel address, 1962. (The method is essentially electron diffraction.)

6. Fluorometry is the analysis of fluorescent substances, i.e., those substances which absorb light at one wavelength, usually UV, and then emit light at another longer wavelength. It is used for the analysis of steroids, amino acids, and vitamins.
 Nephelometry is the analysis of colloids or suspensions by their light-scattering ability. It is used in analysis of bacteria concentration, particle size in turbid water, concentration of ion producing colloidal precipitates with analytical reagents.

7. EPR (or ESR, Electron Spin Resonance) is completely analagous to NMR (Nuclear Magnetic Resonance). A spinning electron has a magnetic field. If an external field is imposed, the electron will tend to

align with it. The energy required to "flip" the electron over can be measured. The energy required is related to the environment of the electron and helps deduce electronic structures.

Suggested Readings for Faculty and Students

Braun, Robert D., and Sapio, Joseph P., "Atomic Absorption Spectroscopy." *Chemistry,* Vol. 47, No. 6 (June 1974), pp. 9-13.

*Cambell, M. M., and Runquist, O., "Fragmentation Mechanisms in Mass Spectrometry." *Journal of Chemical Education,* Vol. 49, No. 2 (February 1972), pp. 104-108.

*Eiss, Albert F., 'The Electromagnetic Spectrum." *The Science Teacher,* Vol. 34, No. 7 (October 1967), pp. 67-68.

Holliday, Leslie, "Early Views on Forces between Atoms." *Scientific American,* Vol. 222, No. 5 (May 1970), pp. 116-122.

Kendall, Henry W., and Panofsky, Wolfgang, 'The Structure of the Proton and the Neutron." *Scientific American,* Vol. 224, No. 6 (June 1971), pp. 60-77.

Patterson, Elizabeth C., *John Dalton and the Atomic Theory.* Garden City, New York, Doubleday and Company, Inc. 1970.

Pecsok, Robert L., and Shields, L. D., *Modern Methods of Chemical Analysis.* New York, John Wiley and Sons, Inc., 1968, Chapter 13.

Reed, R. I., and Robertson, D. H., "Mass Spectrometry." *Chemistry,* Vol. 42, No. 6 (June 1969), pp. 7-11.

*Rice, Oscar Knefler, *Electronic Structure and Chemical Binding.* New York, Dover Publications, Inc., 1969, Chapters 1-2. (A reprint of a classic older work which contains much valuable material.)

Rioux, Frank, "The Stability of the Hydrogen Atom." *Journal of Chemical Education,* Vol. 50, No. 8 (August 1973), pp. 550-552.

(*Faculty only)

Chapter 7

Performance Objectives

GOAL: Students will gain an understanding of the electronic structure of the atom.

Objectives: Upon completion of the reading and activities, and when asked to diagram, demonstrate, or respond either orally or on a written test, students will:

7:1-3	K,P	explain the wave-particle duality of the electron as well as other particles.
7:3	P	describe momentum of a particle given its mass and velocity.
7:4	K	define Heisenberg's uncertainty principle.
7:5-7	K,P	use Schrödinger's work to develop a mental model of the atom involving charge clouds.
7:8-12	K	define the four quantum numbers, n, m, l, and s, and explain the effect of each on the charge cloud.
7:13-14	K,P	describe the electron configuration for any atom using the diagonal rule.
7:15	K,P	draw an electron dot diagram for any atom.

Upon completion of the reading and activities, students will exhibit an interest in science by:

A	voluntarily completing one or more of the One More Step activities listed at the end of the chapter on their own time.
A	reading unassigned literature related to the ideas presented in the chapter.

Page 140. Section 7:3

1. $p = mv$

$$= \frac{9.11 \times 10^{-28} \text{ g} \mid 1 \times 10^{10} \text{ cm}}{\mid \text{sec}}$$

$$= 9.11 \times 10^{-18} \text{ g-cm/sec}$$

2. $p = mv$

$$= \frac{1.67 \times 10^{-24} \text{ g} \mid 1.40 \times 10^8 \text{ cm}}{\text{sec}}$$

$$= 2.34 \times 10^{-16} \text{ g-cm/sec}$$

Page 146.   Section 7:9

3. The greatest number of electrons in a given energy level can be determined by finding the value of $2n^2$ where n is the energy level involved; for

$$n = 3, \quad 2n^2 = 2(3)^2 = 18$$
$$n = 5, \quad 2n^2 = 2(5)^2 = 50$$
$$n = 6, \quad 2n^2 = 2(6)^2 = 72$$
$$n = 8, \quad 2n^2 = 2(8)^2 = 128$$

Page 149.   Section 7:12

4.

Note: A jack from the children's game of jacks also makes a good axis on which to build the model.

5. A d sublevel contains 5 orbitals.

6. An f sublevel contains 7 orbitals.

Page 153.   Section 7:14

7. See table on pp. 165-166.

1. $1s^1$ H·

2. $1s^2$ He:

3. $1s^22s^1$ Li·

4. $1s^22s^2$ Be:

5. $1s^22s^22p^1$ B:

6. $1s^22s^22p^2$ ·C:

7. $1s^22s^22p^3$ ·N:

8. $1s^22s^22p^4$ ·Ö·

9. $1s^22s^22p^5$:F·

10. $1s^22s^22p^6$:Ne:

11. $1s^22s^22p^63s^1$ Na·

12. $1s^22s^22p^63s^2$ Mg:

13. $1s^22s^22p^63s^23p^1$ Al:

14. $1s^22s^22p^63s^23p^2$:Si

15. $1s^22s^22p^63s^23p^3$:P·

16. $1s^22s^22p^63s^23p^4$ ·S·

17. $1s^22s^22p^63s^23p^5$ ·Cl:

18. $1s^22s^22p^63s^23p^6$:Ar:

19. $1s^22s^22p^63s^23p^64s^1$ K·

20. $1s^22s^22p^63s^23p^64s^2$ Ca:

Page 156.   End of Chapter

8. See problem 7.

9. Electron configuration of:

chromium
$1s^22s^22p^63s^23p^64s^23d^4$

copper
$1s^22s^22p^63s^23p^64s^23d^9$

cadmium
$1s^22s^22p^63s^23p^64s^23d^{10}4p^65s^24d^{10}$

See table on pp. 165-166.

10. $2n^2 = 2(5)^2 = 50$

11. There are 4 paired electrons in a boron atom.
Boron configuration = $1s^22s^22p^1$.
There are 14 paired electrons in a sulfur atom.
There are 8 paired electrons in a fluorine atom.
Fluorine configuration = $1s^22s^22p^5$.

12. Two electrons are not shown in each electron dot diagram.

$Z = 3$ $1s^22s^1$ Li·   2

$Z = 4$ $1s^22s^2$ Be: 2

$Z = 5$ $1s^22s^22p^1$ B: 2

$Z = 6 \quad 1s^2 2s^2 2p^2 \qquad \cdot\overset{\cdot}{\text{C}}: \qquad 2$

$Z = 7 \quad 1s^2 2s^2 2p^3 \qquad \cdot\overset{\cdot}{\text{N}}: \qquad 2$

$Z = 8 \quad 1s^2 2s^2 2p^4 \qquad \cdot\overset{\cdot\cdot}{\text{O}}\cdot \qquad 2$

$Z = 9 \quad 1s^2 2s^2 2p^5 \qquad :\overset{\cdot\cdot}{\text{F}}\cdot \qquad 2$

$Z = 10 \quad 1s^2 2s^2 2p^6 \qquad :\overset{\cdot\cdot}{\text{Ne}}: \qquad 2$

13. Electron configuration for uranium:

Experimental (p. 166)

$1s^2 2s^2 2p^6 3s^2 3p^6 3d^{10} 4s^2 4p^6 4d^{10}$

$4f^{14} 5s^2 5p^6 5d^{10} 5f^3 6s^2 6p^6 6d^1 7s^2$

or

Diagonal rule (p. 153)

$1s^2 2s^2 2p^6 3s^2 3p^6 4s^2 3d^{10} 4p^6 5s^2$

$4d^{10} 5p^6 6s^2 4f^{14} 5d^{10} 6p^6 7s^2 5f^4$

Experimental Levels

1. 2   2
2. 2 + 6   8
3. 2 + 6 + 10   18
4. 2 + 6 + 10 + 14 32
5. 2 + 6 + 10 + 3 21
6. 2 + 6 + 1   9
7. 2   2
               ____
                92

Predicted (diagonal rule) Levels

1. 2   2
2. 2 + 6   8
3. 2 + 6 + 10   18
4. 2 + 6 + 10 + 14 32
5. 2 + 6 + 10 + 4 22
6. 2 + 6   8
7. 2   2
               ____
                92

Levels 5, 6, and 7 are not full.

14. a. Mn   manganese
    b. Mo   molybdenum

15. Transform kg to grams:

$$\frac{1360 \text{ kg} \quad | \quad 1000 \text{ g}}{| \quad 1 \text{ kg}} = 1,360,000$$

$$= 1.36 \times 10^6 \text{ g}$$

Transform km/hr to cm/sec:

$$\frac{90.0 \text{ km} \quad | \quad 1000 \text{ m} \quad | \quad 100 \text{ cm} \quad | \quad 1 \text{ hr}}{1 \text{ hr} \quad | \quad 1 \text{ km} \quad | \quad 1 \text{ m} \quad | \quad 3600 \text{ sec}}$$

$$= 2500 \text{ cm/sec}$$

$$\lambda = \frac{h}{mv}$$

$$= \frac{6.62 \times 10^{-27} \text{ g-cm}^2 \quad | \quad 1 \quad | \quad 1 \text{ sec}}{1 \text{ sec} \quad | \quad 1.36 \times 10^6 \text{ g} \quad | \quad 2500 \text{ cm}}$$

$$= 1.95 \times 10^{-36} \text{ cm}$$

16. First, change Angstroms to centimeters:

$$\frac{0.1 \text{ Å} \quad | \quad 1 \text{ cm}}{| \quad 10^8 \text{ Å}} = 1 \times 10^{-9} \text{ cm}$$

then solve:

$$\Delta p = \frac{h}{\Delta x} = \frac{6.62 \times 10^{-27} \text{ g-cm}^2 \quad | \quad 1}{\text{sec} \quad | \quad 10^{-9} \text{ cm}}$$

$$= 6.62 \times 10^{-18} \text{ g-cm/sec}$$

17. $Z = 7, \quad \cdot\overset{\cdot}{\text{N}}:$

$Z = 15, \quad \cdot\overset{\cdot}{\text{P}}:$

$Z = 33, \quad \cdot\overset{\cdot}{\text{As}}:$ Note that this is column VA of the periodic table.

$Z = 51, \quad \cdot\overset{\cdot}{\text{Sb}}:$

$Z = 83, \quad \cdot\overset{\cdot}{\text{Bi}}:$

18. $\frac{1}{2}, \ -\frac{1}{2}$

Page 156.   One More Step

1. The uncertainty principle has completely changed the physicists' views on causality and reality. If we cannot possibly know both the position and momentum of a particle, does the particle have a *real* existence? See De Broglie, Lewis, *New Perspectives in Physics.* New York, Basic Books, Inc. , 1962, Chapters 7-11. Also: Frisch, Otto R., *Atomic Physics Today.* New York, Basic Books, 1961, pp. 230-241. The entire "anti-quantum mechanics" view is presented in "Quanta and Reality," *American Research Council*, 1962.

2. In relativistic mechanics there is a fourth dimension—time. The experimental evidence indicating the fourth dimension is the splitting of spectral lines (Zeeman effect).

3. First set:

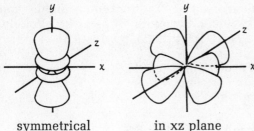

symmetrical
on y axis

in xz plane

in yz plane

in xy plane

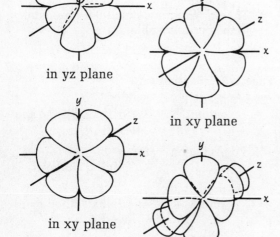

in xy plane

in xz plane

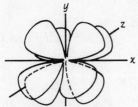

symmetrical about
origin

See: *Journal of Chemical Education*, Volume 41, No. 7 (July 1964), pp. 354 and 358.

4. Wave properties: An electron beam which is passed through a crystal is diffracted and produces a pattern similar to that produced by light and water waves when they are passed through slits of the appropriate size.

Particle properties: The cloud chamber, bubble chamber, cyclotron, synchrotron, and linear accelerator, mass spectrometer, electron gun and Milikan's apparatus all treat the electron successfully as a particle.

5. $\dfrac{\partial^2 \Psi}{\partial x^2} + \dfrac{\partial^2 \Psi}{\partial y^2} + \dfrac{\partial^2 \Psi}{\partial z^2} + \dfrac{8\pi^2 m}{h^2}(E - V)\Psi = 0$

∂ = the mathematical symbol indicating a partial derivative.

Ψ = the Greek letter *psi*. It is the symbol used to indicate the amplitude of a light wave. Ψ is also called the wave function. Ψ^2 determines the probability of finding an electron in a specified region which can be represented on a three dimensional graph by the coordinates:

$$x \text{ and } x + dx,$$
$$y \text{ and } y + dy,$$
$$z \text{ and } z + dz.$$

x, y, z = the coordinates of probable wave location.

m = the mass of an electron = 9.11×10^{-28} g.

h = Planck's constant = 6.63×10^{-27} erg-sec. See p. 126.

E = total energy.

V = potential energy.

Suggested Readings for Faculty and Students

Feld, M. S., and Letokhov, V. S., "Laser Spectroscopy." *Scientific American,* Vol. 229, No. 6 (December 1973), pp. 69-85.

Halliday, David, and Resnick, Robert, *Fundamentals of Physics.* New York, John Wiley and Sons, Inc., 1970, Chapter 40.

*Kittel, Charles, *Thermal Physics.* New York, John Wiley and Sons, Inc., 1969, Chapters 1 and 10. (An advanced work.)

Lambert, Frank L., "Atomic Orbitals from Wave Patterns." *Chemistry,* Part I, Vol.

41, No. 2 (February 1968), pp. 10-15; Part II, Vol. 41, No. 3 (March 1968), pp. 8-11.

Luder, William Fay, *The Electron-Repulsion Theory of the Chemical Bond*. New York, Reinhold Publishing Corporation, 1967, Chapters 1-3.

Luder, William F., "Electron-Repulsion Theory; Atomic Orbitals and Atom Models." *Chemistry*, Vol. 42, No. 6 (June 1969), pp. 16-19.

*Orchin, Milton, and Jaffe, H. H., *Symmetry, Orbitals, and Spectra*. New York, John Wiley and Sons, Inc., 1971, Chapters 1-2. (An advanced work.)

Rice, Oscar Knefler, *Electronic Structure and Chemical Binding*. New York, Dover Publications, Inc., 1969, Chapters 3-6. (A reprint of an older work containing much valuable information.)

Sanderson, R. T., "Ionization Energy and Atomic Structure." *Chemistry*, Vol. 46, No. 5 (May 1973), pp. 12-15.

(*Faculty only)

Chapter 8

Performance Objectives

GOAL: Students will gain an understanding of the periodic table and the relationship between the periodic properties of the elements and their electronic structure.

Objectives: Upon completion of the reading and activities, and when asked to diagram, demonstrate, or respond either orally or on a written test, students will:

8:1-2	K	list early attempts at classification of the elements.
8:3	K	explain the basis for the modern periodic law.
8:4-9	K,P	fill a periodic table based on application of the diagonal rule.
8:10-12	P,S	use the periodic table to predict physical and chemical properties of elements.
8:13	P,S	predict oxidation numbers of elements through use of the periodic table.
8:14-22	K	list various families of elements along with specific similarities and differences of properties within the families.

Upon completion of the reading and activities, students will exhibit an interest in science by:

A	voluntarily completing one or more of the One More Step activities listed at the end of the chapter on their own time.
A	reading unassigned literature related to the ideas presented in the chapter.

Page 173.   Section 8:9

1. a. metal
   b. metal
   c. metal
   d. nonmetal-network element
   e. metal
   f. nonmetal
   g. metal
   h. metalloid

2. There are more metals than nonmetals in the periodic table.

Page 179.   Section 8:13

3. Mo predicted $5s^2 4d^4$
   actual $5s^1 4d^5$ (half-filled d sublevel)

   Pd predicted $5s^2 4d^8$
   actual $4d^{10}$ (full d sublevel)

   Gd predicted $4f^8$
   actual $4f^7 5d^1$ (half-filled f sublevel)

4. Au predicted $6s^2 4f^{14} 5d^9$
   actual $6s^1 4f^{14} 5d^{10}$ (full d sublevel)

   Cm predicted $5f^8$
   actual $5f^7 6d^1$ (half-filled f sublevel)

   Th predicted $5f^2$
   actual $6d^2$ (exception to the rules given in the text)

5. Ar   0   outer level already has 8 electrons

   Eu   2+   loss of the two $6s$ electrons

Al	3+	loss of the two 3s and one 3p electron
Sb	3+	loss of the three 5p electrons
	5+	loss of the two 5s electrons in addition to 5p which are separated by the 4d sublevel
Br	1−	gain of one electron to complete outer level

6.
U	2+	loss of two 7s electrons
	3+	loss of 7s and one 6d electron
	4+	loss of 7s, 6d, and one 5f electron
	5+	loss of 7s, 6d, and two 5f electrons
	6+	loss of 7s, 6d, and three 5f electrons
Na	1+	loss of one 3s electron
Si	4+	loss of two 3p and two 3s electrons
	4−	gain of four electrons to fill outer level
Ce	2+	loss of two 6s electrons
Co	2+	loss of two 4s electrons

7.
Ar	as predicted
Eu	also a 3+ (no apparent explanation)
Al	as predicted
Sb	as predicted (sometimes considered to have a 3− in which the outer level is completed)
Br	as predicted

8.
U	missing 2+ (cannot lose 7s electrons independently of 6d)
Na	as predicted
Si	as predicted
Ce	no 2+; 3+ and 4+ instead (must lose one or both of electrons along with 6s)
Co	also 3+ (no apparent explanation)

Page 190.   Section 8:22

9. a. iron
   b. nickel
   c. fermium
   d. fluorine
   e. gold—This prediction is, of course, not accurate.

10. a. hafnium
    b. sodium
    c. nitrogen
    d. potassium
    e. selenium

Page 192.   End of Chapter

11. a. metal
    b. nonmetal
    c. metal
    d. nonmetal
    e. metal

12. a. metal
    b. nonmetal
    c. metal
    d. nonmetal
    e. metal
    f. nonmetal
    g. nonmetal

13. a. actinium
    b. plutonium
    c. berkelium
    d. carbon
    e. fluorine

14. a. gallium
    b. neptunium
    c. oxygen
    d. cesium
    e. bromine

Page 192.   One More Step

1. Sections 8:1 and 8:2 give a start. Kauffman (see Suggested Readings) also has some information.

2. The noble gases were not listed. In the first 6 rows there were 9 blanks:

scandium	fluorine
gallium	technetium
germanium	rhenium
hafnium	astatine
polonium	

   Nickel and cobalt, iodine and tellurium appeared to be reversed.

3. Mendeleev's predictions about gallium and scandium were about as good as his predictions about germanium. However, his predictions about technetium, rhenium, and neptunium were not as accurate.

4. Lavoisier was beheaded during the French Revolution even though he had worked for tax reforms which would have helped those who killed him.

Moseley was drafted and served as a regular foot soldier during World War I. He was sent to the front line and was killed in the Battle of Gallipoli along with many others in a disastrous defeat.

5. See *Science*, Vol. 138, October 12, 1962, for example of initial reports. XeF_4 is the compound most commonly reported.

6. Element name origins:

Named for Discoverer's Geographic Origin
germanium
lutetium
polonium

Named for Properties

Chemical	Physical
hydrogen	phosphorus
oxygen	iron(?)
sulfur	bromine
argon	tungsten
zinc	osmium
arsenic	lead(?)
antimony	astatine
	radium
	actinium
	protactinium

Named to Honor

A Person	A Place
gadolinium	europium
curium	hafnium
einsteinium	francium
fermium	americium
mendelevium	berkelium
lawrencium	californium
nobelium	

Named for Mythological Character

Due to Property	Due to Other Reason
titanium	vanadium
cobalt	niobium
nickel	tantalum

Named for Color

Of Element	Of Compound	Of Spectra
chlorine	chromium	rubidium
silver	iridium	rhodium
iodine		indium
platinum		cesium
gold		thallium
bismuth		

Named for Discovery

Location	Material	Process
helium	lithium	neon
scandium	carbon	krypton
copper	nitrogen	technetium
gallium	sodium	xenon
ruthenium	potassium	lanthanum
tin	calcium	promethium
holmium	radon	dysprosium
rhenium	samarium	thulium

Named for Mineral

Color	Property	Location
beryllium	fluorine	strontium
boron	aluminum	yttrium
magnesium	silicon	cadmium
zirconium	manganese	terbium
praseodymium	neodymium	erbium
	molybdenum	ytterbium
	barium	thorium

Named for Heavenly Body

Earth	Planet	Asteroid
tellurium	mercury	palladium
Moon	uranium	cerium
selenium	neptunium	
	plutonium	

7. Metalloids are semiconductors. Although Si and Ge have the same crystalline structure as diamond, they will conduct electrons. Heat energy at ordinary temperatures frees electrons from the valence band to the conducting band. The conductivity of semiconductors increases with temperature, and donor and acceptor impurities are easily introduced.

8. Although its ionization energy is higher, the Li^+ ion is so highly hydrated that the entire process:

$$Li\,(s) \rightarrow Li(g) \rightarrow Li^+(g) \rightarrow Li^+(aq)$$

is more exothermic than the process

$$Na(s) \rightarrow Na(g) \rightarrow Na^+(g) \rightarrow Na^+(aq).$$

Suggested Readings for Faculty and Students

*Eighinger, Jack W., Jr., "Anticipating 'Valences' from Electron Configurations." *Journal of Chemical Education*, Vol. 44, No. 11 (November 1967), pp. 689-690.

Frieden, Earl, "The Chemical Elements of Life." *Scientific American*, Vol. 227, No. 1 (July 1972), pp. 52-60.

Kauffman, George B., "American Forerunners of the Periodic Law." *Journal of Chemical Education*, Vol. 46, No. 3 (March 1969), pp. 128-135.

Navratil, James D., "Niobium: Space Age Metal." *Chemistry*, Vol. 43, No. 8 (September 1970), pp. 13-15.

Pratt, Christopher J., "Sulfur." *Scientific American*, Vol. 222, No. 5 (May 1970), pp. 62-72.

Rice, Oscar Knefler, *Electronic Structure and Chemical Bonding*. New York, Dover Publications, Inc., 1969, Chapters 7-8. (A reprint of an older work which contains much valuable material.)

Sanderson, R. T., *Inorganic Chemistry*. New York, Reinhold Publishing Co., 1967, Chapters 1, 5-9, and 22.

Van Spronsen, Johannes W., "The Priority Conflict Between Mendeleev and Meyer." *Journal of Chemical Education*, Vol. 46, No. 3 (March 1969), pp. 136-139.

Zimmerman, Joan, "The Strange World of Helium." *Chemistry*, Vol. 43, No. 2 (February 1970), pp. 14-17.

(*Faculty only)

Chapter 9

Performance Objectives

GOAL: Students will gain an understanding of chemical bonding and factors which affect bonding.

Objectives: Upon completion of the reading and activities, and when asked to diagram, demonstrate, or respond either orally or on a written test, students will:

9:1-2	P	define first ionization energy and compare those of various families of the periodic table.
9:3	K	differentiate among subsequent ionization energies for various atoms.
9:4	K	compare electron affinity to ionization energy.
9:5-6	P	utilize electronegativity to explain bond character.
9:7	K	list general properties of ionic compounds.
9:8-10	P,S	determine bond lengths for ionic compounds and covalent molecules.
9:7-10	P,S	predict oxidation numbers using the periodic table.
9:11	K	define and identify common poly-atomic ions.
9:12	K	define van der Waals radius.
9:13-14	K	explain metallic properties through use of the metallic bond concept.

Upon completion of the reading and activities, students will exhibit an interest in science by:

| A | voluntarily completing one or more of the One More Step activities listed at the end of the chapter on their own time. |
| A | reading unassigned literature related to the ideas presented in the chapter. |

Page 201. Section 9:5

1. Thallium, bismuth, tellurium, chlorine, neon.

2. Radium, gallium, germanium, arsenic, sulfur

3. Peaks for the noble gases are due to the breaking of the complete outer level.
   The first peak *after* each alkali metal is due to the complete s sublevel.
   The second peak after Li and Na is due to the half-filled p sublevel.

   Peak at $Z = 30$, full 3d sublevel.
   Peak at $Z = 33$, half-full 4p sublevel.
   Peak at $Z = 48$, full 4d sublevel.
   Peak at $Z = 80$, full 5d sublevel.

Page 208. Section 9:10

4. Ionic—b, c: cesium and fluorine, fluorine and silicon.

   Covalent—a, d, e: boron and carbon, hydrogen and chlorine, magnesium and nitrogen.

5. Principally ionic—a, b, c, d: beryllium and fluorine, bromine and strontium, chlorine and lithium, chlorine and sodium.

   Principally covalent—e:

   hydrogen and iodine

6. astatine -1 polonium -2
   germanium $+4$ tin $+4$
   mercury $+2$

7. francium $+1$ rubidium $+1$
   hafnium $+2$ tellurium -2
   neodymium $+2$

Page 214. End of Chapter

8. Predictions need only approximate the following experimental values.

   a. 1.98 Å d. 1.42 Å
   b. 1.01 Å e. 1.53 Å
   c. 1.47 Å

9. O_2^- NH^{2-} C_2^{2-} $PH_2O_2^-$
   N_3^- $NHOH^-$ $N_2O_2^{2-}$ SeO_3^{2-}
   NH_2^- $N_2H_3^-$ PHO_3^{2-}

10. 21 Sc 3
    22 Ti 4
    23 V   5
    24 Cr 6
    25 Mn 6
    26 Fe 6
    27 Co 6
    28 Ni 6
    29 Cu 5.5
    30 Zn 4.5

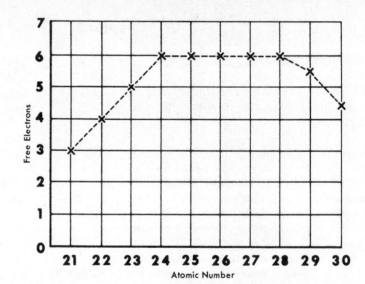

11. N   Se I
    P   Br Ta
    S   Nb W
    Cl Mo Re
    Ti Tc Os
    V   Ru Ir
    Cr Rh Pt
    Mn Te

12. The first four carbon electrons are the hybrids of $2s^2 2p^2$ and are in the outer energy level. Although each requires more energy to remove than the previous due to the factors which affect ionization energies, they are reasonably close in energy. The next two are in the first energy level and are most tightly held. The increased advantage of nuclear positive charge and no shielding electrons makes them most difficult to remove.

13. Fluorine is the most electronegative element. You would expect fluorine to form an ionic compound with xenon.

14. Since 1 kcal/mole $= 4.34 \times 10^{-2} \dfrac{eV}{atom}$

then $\dfrac{1\ eV}{atom} = \dfrac{1\ kcal/mole}{4.34 \times 10^{-2}}$ or $\dfrac{1\ eV}{atom} = 23.0 \dfrac{kcal}{mole}$. Therefore ionization energy can be found in kcal/mole

by dividing the $\dfrac{eV}{atom}$ by 4.34×10^{-2} or multiplying by 23.0.

Thus, from Table 9-3:

H $= 13.60 \times 23.0 = 313$ kcal/mole

He$= 24.59 \times 23.0 = 567$ kcal/mole

Li $= \ \ 5.39 \times 23.0 = 124$ kcal/mole

Re$= \ \ 9.32 \times 23.0 = 215$ kcal/mole

B $= \ \ 8.30 \times 23.0 = 191$ kcal/mole

C $= 11.26 \times 23.0 = 259$ kcal/mole

N $= 14.53 \times 23.0 = 335$ kcal/mole

O $= 13.62 \times 23.0 = 314$ kcal/mole

F $= 17.42 \times 23.0 = 401$ kcal/mole

Ne$= 21.57 \times 23.0 = 497$ kcal/mole

15. Ionic compounds are brittle because any attempts to deform them requires placing like-charged ions next to each other, thus:

```
+ − + −
o o o o
o o o o     before deformation
− + − +

+ − + −
o o o o
→    o o o o     after deformation
force − + − +
```

Further, ionic compounds normally crystallize in sharp, well-defined crystals and cleave (fracture) easily along crystal planes.

16. H—Br, N—H, C—N, Cl—Cl, C—C

17. Al, K, C, K, K

18. Those electrons come from a lower energy level and are held more tightly.

Page 215. **One More Step**

1.

31	Ga	6.00 eV		35	Br	11.81	eV
32	Ge	7.809 eV		36	Kr	14.00	eV
33	As	9.81 eV		37	Rb	4.176	eV
34	Se	9.75 eV		38	Sr	5.69	eV

2. Pauling's equation:

$$Q = 23.06 \sum (X_A - X_B)^2 = 55.1 N_N - 24.2 N_O$$

where $Q = \Delta H_f$ in kcal/mole

X_A = electronegativity of element A

X_B = electronegativity of element B

N_N = number of nitrogen atoms in compound

N_O = number of oxygen atoms in compound

Mulliken's equation:

$$1/2(I_A + E_A) - 1/2(I_B - E_B) = 2.78(X_A - X_B)$$

where I_A and I_B = ionization potentials of A and B

E_A and E_B = electron affinities of A and B

X_A and X_B = electronegativities of A and B

Allred and Rochow's equation:

$$X = 0.359 \frac{Z_{eff}}{r^2} + 0.744$$

where X = electronegativity

Z_{eff} = effective nuclear charge

r = covalent radius

Liu's equation:

$$X = 0.313 \left(\frac{n + 2.6}{r^{2/3}} \right)$$

where X = electronegativity

n = number of valence electrons

r = covalent radius

Gordy's equation:

$$X = 0.31 \left(\frac{n + 1}{r} \right) + 0.50$$

where X = electronegativity

n = number of valence electrons

r = covalent radius

3. X-ray diffraction of crystals; Electron diffraction of gases; Neutron diffraction of crystals; Microwave spectroscopy — From the energy absorbed, the moment of inertia of the molecule can be calculated. Then, using known atomic masses, distances can be calculated.

4. Covalent — one-half length of X — X bond for elements forming diatomic molecules. Others from subtraction of known radius from bond length.

Assumptions: Additivity of radii in bond length
No pi bonding in simple compounds not involving known double or triple bonds
No ionic character
No effect of one atom on electron cloud of another

Ionic — subtract known radius from X-ray diffraction determined internuclear distance.

Assumptions: One set of values (usually lithium halides) has anions in contact
Additivity of radii in bond lengths
No covalent character
No effect of one ion on electron cloud of another
A precisely defined electron cloud

van der Waals — one half non bonded distance in pure element

Assumptions: No effect of one atom on electron of another
A precisely defined electron cloud

5. In complexes — number of ligands bonded to central ion
In crystals — number of ions of opposite sign surrounding a given ion
In metals — number of nearest neighbor atoms

Suggested Readings for Faculty and Students

Baker, Arthur D., Photoelectron Spectroscopy." *Accounts of Chemical Research*, Vol. 3, No. 1 (January 1970), pp. 17-25.

Barrow, Gordon M., "Modern Spectroscopy." *The Science Teacher*, Vol. 37, No. 2 (February 1970), pp. 43-51.

*Christian, Jerry D., "Strength of Chemical Bonds." *Journal of Chemical Education*, Vol. 50, No. 3 (March 1973), pp. 176-177.

Herndon, William C., "Resonance Theory and the Enumeration of Kekule Structures." *Journal of Chemical Education*, Vol. 51, No. 1 (January 1974), pp. 10-15.

*Howald, Reed A., "Bond Energies in the Interpretation of Descriptive Chemistry."*Journal of Chemical Education,* Vol. 45, No. 3 (March 1968), pp. 163-171.

*Johnston, Harold, and Birks, John, "Activation Energies for the Dissociation of Diatomic Molecules are Less than the Bond Dissociation Energies." *Accounts of Chemical Research*, Vol. 5, No. 10 (October 1972), pp. 327-335.

Liebman, Joel F., "Regularities and Relations among Ionization Potentials of Nontransition Elements." *Journal of Chemical Education*, Vol. 50, No. 12 (December 1973), pp. 831-834.

Rice, Oscar Knefler, *Electronic Structure and Chemical Bonding.* New York, Dover Publications, Inc., 1969 (A reprint of an older work which contains much valuable material.) Chapters 9-12 and 15.

Sanderson, R. T., *Inorganic Chemistry.* New York, Reinhold Publishing Corp., 1967, Chapters 2 and 4.

(*Faculty only)

Chapter 10

Performance Objectives

GOAL: Students will gain an understanding of the relationship between chemical bonding and molecular structure.

Objectives: Upon completion of the reading and activities, and when asked to diagram, demonstrate, or respond either orally or on a written test, students will:

10:1-2 K give examples of molecular structures due to electron pair repulsions.

10:3-5 K describe the combination of orbitals to form bonds and the hybridization of carbon bonds.

10:6-8 P utilize the hybridization of bonds to explain single, double, and triple carbon-to-carbon bonds.

10:9 K,P compare combined orbitals in inorganic compounds with those of organic compounds.

10:10 K,P construct electron-dot resonance formulas to explain alternate structures for molecules and polyatomic ions and "average" bond length.

Upon completion of the reading and activities, students will exhibit an interest in science by:

A voluntarily completing one or more of the One More Step activities listed at the end of the chapter on their own time.

A reading unassigned literature related to the ideas presented in the chapter.

Page 234. End of Chapter

1. Predictions need only approximate the following experimental values.
   a. $90°$ d. $98°$
   b. $93°$ e. $109°$
   c. $99°$

2. Hybridization is the formation of equivalent orbitals by electrons from different energy sublevels. For example, one s and two p orbitals might form three equivalent σ_{sp} hybrid orbitals.

3. The resonance structures for the carbonate ion $(CO_3)^{2-}$ are

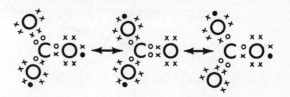

4. Sigma (σ) bonds are end-to-end overlaps of two s orbitals, two p orbitals, or one s and one p orbital. Sigma bonds can also form by end-to-end overlap of s, p, or hybrid orbitals with other hybrid orbitals. Pi (π) bonds result from the sideways overlap of two p orbitals.

5. Benzene has a conjugated ring which in effect results in delocalization of the pi electrons, a very stable form.

6. The double bond $(C{=}C)$ is formed by the σ overlap of two sp^2 orbitals and the π overlap of two p orbitals.

7. a. planar, $\overset{H}{\underset{H}{\diagdown}}C{=}O$, $120°$ bond angles

   b. planar, $O{=}S\diagdown_O \longleftrightarrow O{-}S\diagdown_O$, $120°$ bond angle

   c. planar,

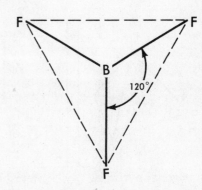

47T

d. octahedral,

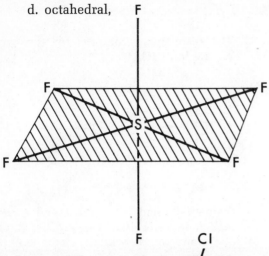

e.

108°

108°

One Cl is 106° from plane of other three atoms.

8.

Benzene

Naphthalene

9. Linear; *sp*; H—C bond is sigma, C≡N is one sigma and two pi bonds.

10. a.

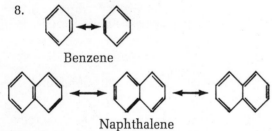

trigonal pyramid,   tetrahedral

c.

d.

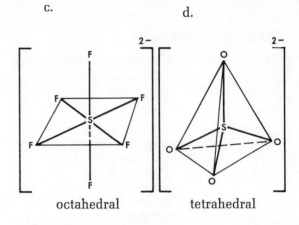

octahedral   tetrahedral

e.

tetrahedral

11. PCl₅ — trigonal bipyramid,

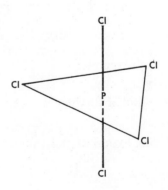

dsp³ hybrid on P

PCl₄⁺ — tetrahedral, *sp³* hybrid on P

PCl₆⁻ — octahedral, *d²sp³* hybrid on P

12. H_2Se

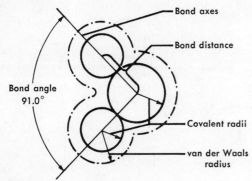

Bond axes

Bond distance

Bond angle
91.0°

Covalent radii

van der Waals
radius

Page 235.   One More Step

1. a. 125°

    b. 108°

    c. 113°

    d. 134°

    e. 115°

2. octahedral; SF_6, $CdCl_6{}^{4-}$, ICl_4^-, BrF_4^-, BrF_5, IF_5, $Co(NH_3)_6{}^{3+}$, $PdCl_6{}^{2-}$, $Fe(CN)_6{}^{3-}$, etc.

3. puckered ring; two shapes of C_6H_{12}:

Chair form   Boat form

The chair form is more stable because of the H—H interference found in boat form:

H — — H

4. a. $H_2C=C=CH_2$ linear, planar on both ends, but one $-CH_2$ is in a plane perpendicular to the other $-CH_2$ group.

    b. $H_2C=C=C=CH_2$ linear; entire molecule planar.

5. Alfred Werner → Langmuir → G. N. Lewis → Sidgwick → Born → Pauling → Ingold

No one theory agrees with all experimental data. No one theory enables one to make sure predictions.

Suggested Readings for Faculty and Students

*Barrett, Edward J., "Models Illustrating d Orbitals Involved in Multiple Bonding." *Journal of Chemical Education*, Vol. 44, No. 3 (March 1967), pp. 146-147.

*Cotton, F. Albert, *Chemical Applications of Group Theory.* New York, John Wiley and Sons, Inc., 1971. 2nd Ed. (An advanced work.)

Dahl, Peter, "The Valence-Shell Electron-Pair Repulsion Theory." *Chemistry*, Vol. 46, No. 3 (March 1973), pp. 17-19.

*Drago, Russell, S., "A Criticism of the Valence Shell Electron Pair Repulsion Model as a Teaching Device." *Journal of Chemical Education*, Vol. 50, No. 4 (April 1973), pp. 244-245.

Gillespie, R. J., "A Defense of the Valence Shell Electron Pair Repulsion (VESPR) Model." *Journal of Chemical Education*, Vol. 51, No. 6 (June 1974), pp. 367-370.

Gillespie, R. J., "The Eectron-Pair Repulsion Model for Molecular Geometry." *Journal of Chemical Education*, Vol. 47, No. 1 (January 1970), pp. 18-23.

Hall, Stephen K., "Symmetry." *Chemistry*, Vol. 46, No. 3 (March 1973), pp. 14-16.

*Herndon, William C., "Resonance Theory and the Enumeration of Kekule Structures." *Journal of Chemical Education*, Vol. 51, No. 1 (January 1974), pp. 10-15.

Holden, Alan, *Shapes, Space, and Symmetry.* New York, Columbia University Press, 1971.

James, B. D., "Structural Studies on Some Complex Species with Bridged Hydrogens." *Journal of Chemical Education*, Vol. 48, No. 3 (March 1971), pp. 176-179.

Lambert, Joseph B., "The Shapes of Organic Molecules." *Scientific American*, Vol. 222, No. 1 (January 1970), pp. 58-70.

*Lederberg, Joshua, "Topology of Molecules." in *The Mathematical Sciences*, Cambridge, The MIT Press, 1969.

Luder, William F., *The Electron-Repulsion Theory of the Chemical Bond.* New York, Reinhold Publishing Corp., 1967, Chapters 4-7.

Luder, William F., "The Electron Repulsion Theory of the Chemical Bond." *Journal of Chemical Education*, Vol. 44,

No. 4 (April 1967), pp. 206-212, and Vol. 44, No. 5 (May 1967), pp. 269-273.

Orchin, Milton, and Jaffe, H. H., *Symmetry, Orbitals, and Spectra.* New York, John Wiley and Sons, Inc., 1971, Chapters 3-12 (An advanced work.)

Ramsay, O. Bertrand, "Molecules in Three Dimensions." *Chemistry*, Vol. 47, No. 1 (January 1974), pp. 6-9.

Tobias, R. Stuart, "Raman Spectroscopy in Inorganic Chemistry." *Journal of Chemical Education*, Vol. 44, No. 2 (February 1967), pp. 70-79.

Wahl, Arnold C., "Chemistry by Computer." *Scientific American*, Vol. 222, No. 4 (April 1970), pp. 54-70.

(*Faculty only)

Chapter 11

Performance Objectives

GOAL: Students will gain an understanding of the properties of molecular compounds and their relationship to molecular shape and structure.

Objectives: Upon completion of the reading and activities, and when asked to diagram, demonstrate, or respond either orally or on a written test, students will:

11:1	K,P	define and give examples of various kinds of isomeric compounds.
11:2	K,P	define and give examples of optical activity of isomers.
11:3	K,P,S	list covalent bonds in order of polarity given a table of electronegativities.
11:4-7	K	list and describe various chromatographic processes for chemical analysis.
11:8-10	K	name and describe formation of different kinds of coordination compounds and complex ions.
11:11	K,P	distinguish among the types of weak bonds and/or attractive forces which hold molecules together.

Upon completion of the reading and activities, students will exhibit an interest in science by:

A   voluntarily completing one or more of the One More Step activities listed at the end of the chapter on their own time.

A   reading unassigned literature related to the ideas presented in the chapter.

Page 242. Section 11:3

1. d, a, e, c, b
   iodine and technetium
   boron and nitrogen
   nitrogen and oxygen
   hydrogen and selenium
   carbon and sulfur

Page 256. End of Chapter

2. a, b, e, d, c
   arsenic and oxygen
   chlorine and silicon
   phosphorus and bromine
   oxygen and fluorine
   nitrogen and chlorine

3. Hexane has five isomers:

(1) C — C — C — C — C — C

(2)
```
C — C — C — C — C
        |
        C
```

(3)
```
C — C — C — C — C
    |
    C
```

(4)
```
        C   C
        |   |
C — C — C — C
```

(5)
```
C — C — C — C
    |
    C
```

4. Both depend upon selective adsorption. In the column, the solvent is run through the adsorbent, while on paper, the solvent moves by capillary action.

5. Octahedral

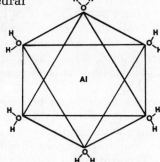

6. central ion-center of complex, coordination number-number of ligands, ligand-coordinated group

7. size and charge

8. The transition metals have empty d orbitals to accept e^- and are relatively small, thus, they have large charge-to-radius ratio.

9. van der Waals forces caused by dipole-dipole, dipole-induced dipole, and dispersion forces

10. Geometric isomerism results from groups being able to take two different positions with respect to double bonds.

Positional isomers are formed when a particle may bond at different points on a chain of carbons.

Functional isomerism results when a particle may be bonded in two or more ways.

Page 257. One More Step

1. a. PCl_5 forms a trigonal bipyramid with P at center.

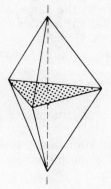

Three of the chlorine atoms are arranged in a plane about P. The other two are arranged above and below P.

b. IF_7 forms a pentagonal bipyramid.

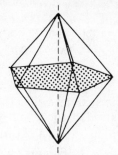

Five of the fluorine atoms are arranged in a plane about P. The other two are arranged above and below P.

c. Nb_2Cl_{10} forms two octahedrons with a common edge.

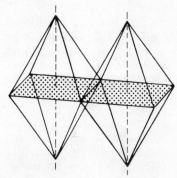

Each of the two niobium atoms is surrounded by four chlorine atoms in a plane and each atom has one chlorine atom above it and one below it. Two of the chlorine atoms are contained in both octahedrons.

d. B_2H_6

$$\begin{array}{ccc} H\diagdown & H & \diagup H \\ & B \hspace{0.3cm} B & \\ H\diagup & H & \diagdown H \end{array}$$

The two boron atoms and the two bridging hydrogen atoms are in the same plane. The four terminal hydrogens are in the same plane which is perpendicular to the boron-containing plane. The bond lengths are 1.33 Å for bridging hydrogens and 1.19 Å for terminal hydrogens. The H—B—H bond angle (both H's terminal) is 122°. The B—H—B bond angle is 82°.

e. Al_2Cl_6

Cl, Cl, Cl
   Al   Al
Cl   Cl   Cl

Same structure as B_2H_6 above with Al substituted for B and Cl for H. Bond lengths: Al—Cl (Terminal) 2.17 Å; Al—Cl (bridging) 2.29 A. Bond angles: Al—Cl—Al is 85°; Cl—Al—Cl is 119°.

2. To separate amino acids from casein:
a. Precipitate casein: Dilute the milk with an equal amount of distilled water and heat the solution to 30-60°C. Add 0.03 ml 1.5M acetic acid for each milliliter of milk solution. Add the acid one drop at a time. The casein precipitates out and can be separated from the materials still in solution by filtering.

b. Hydrolyze casein: Use a reflux condenser to reflux the casein with 35% sulfuric acid for 20 minutes. Use 10 ml of acid for each gram of casein. This operation may require much more than 20 minutes if the casein is precipitated too rapidly. (When no precipitate remains, the digestion can be considered complete, if at least 20 minutes have elapsed.)

Neutralize the remaining sulfuric acid with a *stoichiometrically* equal amount of barium hydroxide (equal to the sulfuric acid added originally). Filter off the $BaSO_4$ precipitate. The hydrolysate is ready for use.

c. Prepare Chromatogram: Cut and fold an ordinary filter paper circle as shown and place it on a small (150 ml) beaker which contains the solvent. Cover the filter paper and small beaker with a large (1000 ml) beaker.

Place a little of the hydrolysate on the filter paper. This is called spotting. Several universal solvents may be used: 40% n-butanol, 10% glacial acetic acid, 50% water. Another possible solvent is composed of 95% methanol and 5% water. Place spots on the filter paper and dry them immediately to avoid diffusion. The filter paper with the tip about 1 cm in the solvent is placed on the beaker and left overnight so the whole system is covered with an inverted beaker. Remove the paper before the solvent reaches the outer circumference of the circle. Dry over a hot plate, spray with ninhydrin (0.1%) and redry.

3. R_f values must be found for a particular system with standards of known concentration. Once that piece of apparatus has been standardized for a substance, an unknown containing that substance can be analyzed. The volume of the chromatographic chamber, for instance, has a large effect on R_f values. Values from one chamber cannot be applied to another chamber of different geometry. Other factors affecting R_f values are the state of subdivision of the adsorbent, temperature, purity of the solvent, separation of a multi-component solvent, and evaporation. Solvents and/or adsorbents from the same manufacturer but from different batches will give different R_f values. However, the *relative* values are quite useful in analysis.

4. Mg, 4, phaeophorbide, planar

5. Fe, 4, porphyrin, planar

6. The formation of a heterocyclic ring with a metal atom in the ring is the process of chelation.

disodium ethylenediaminetetraacetate copper chelate

7. Ni = dimethylglyoxime
   Al = ammonium aurin tricarboxylate
   Zr = sodium alizarin sulfonate

Suggested Readings for Faculty and Students

Cotton, F. Albert, and Wilkinson, Geoffrey, *Advanced Inorganic Chemistry: A Comprehensive Text,* Third Ed. New York, John Wiley and Sons, Inc., 1972.

Dence, Joseph B., "Conformational Analysis or How Some Molecules Wiggle." *Chemistry,* Vol. 43, No. 6 (June 1970), pp. 6-10.

Foust, Richard D., Jr., and Ford, Peter C., "Isomerism in Transition Metal Complexes." *Journal of Chemical Education,* Vol. 47, No. 2 (February 1970), pp. 165-166.

Heck, Louis J., and Haworth, Daniel T., "Disc Paper Chromatography of Inks." *School Science and Mathematics,* Vol. 74, No. 1 (January 1974), pp. 3-4.

House, J. E., Jr., "Substitution Reactions in Metal Complexes." *Chemistry,* Vol. 43, No. 6 (June 1970), pp. 11-14.

House, J. E., Jr., "Weak Intermolecular Interactions." *Chemistry,* Vol. 45, No. 4 (April 1972), pp. 13-15.

Ikan, Raphael, and Rapaport, Eleizer, "Test Tube and Glass Rod TLC." *Journal of Chemical Education,* Vol. 44, No. 5 (May 1967), pp. 297-298.

Kollman, Peter A., and Allen, Leland C., "The Theory of the Hydrogen Bond." *Chemical Reviews,* Vol. 72, No. 3 (June 1972), pp. 283-303.

Magliulo, Anthony, "Medical Chelating Agents." *Chemistry,* Vol. 47, No. 1 (January 1974), pp. 25-26.

Pecsok, Robert L., and Shields, L. D., *Modern Methods of Chemical Analysis.* New York, John Wiley and Sons, Inc., 1968, Chapters 4-7.

Ruchelman, Maryon W., "Gas Chromatography: Medical Diagnostic Aid." *Chemistry,* Vol. 43, No. 11 (December 1970), pp. 14-19.

Sanderson, R. T., "What Is Bond Polarity and What Difference Does It Make?" *Chemistry,* Vol. 46, No. 8 (September 1973), pp. 12-16.

Strain, Harold H., and Sherma, Joseph, "Michael Tswett's Contributions to Sixty Years of Chromatography." *Journal of Chemical Education,* Vol. 44, No. 4 (April 1967), pp. 235-237.

Tswett, M., "Absorption Analysis and Chromatographic Methods: Application to the Chemistry of the Chlorophylls." Trans. by Harold H. Strain and Joseph Sherma. *Journal of Chemical Education,* Vol. 44, No. 4 (April 1967), pp. 238-242.

Walsh, Joseph M., "The Use of Talc as a TLC Adsorbent." *Journal of Chemical Education,* Vol. 44, No. 5 (May 1967), pp. 294-296.

Chapter 12

Performance Objectives

GOAL: Students will gain an understanding of the kinetic theory and its relationship to the states of matter.

Objectives: Upon completion of the reading and activities, and when asked to diagram, demonstrate, or respond either orally or on a written test, students will:

12:1	K	define and describe mean free path of a molecule in motion.
12:2	K	relate pressure to molecular motion.
12:3	P,S	describe the use of a manometer in measuring gas pressure and solve resulting problems.

12:4   K   define kinetic energy as $\frac{1}{2}mv^2$.

12:5-6 P   relate temperature and heat transfer to molecular motion.

12:7   K   describe the three normal states of matter in terms of kinetic theory.

12:8   K   distinguish the plasma state of matter as a special case.

         Upon completion of the reading and activities, students will exhibit an interest in science by:

A   voluntarily completing one or more of the One More Step activities listed at the end of the chapter on their own time.

A   reading unassigned literature related to the ideas presented in the chapter.

Page 263.   Section 12:3

1. $1 \text{ mm Hg} = 1 \text{ torr} = \dfrac{1}{760} \text{ atm}$

$P_{oxygen} = 749 \text{ torr} - 6 \text{ torr} = 743 \text{ torr}$

$P_{oxygen} = \dfrac{743 \text{ torr} \mid 1 \text{ atm}}{\phantom{743 \text{ torr}} \mid 760 \text{ torr}} = 0.978 \text{ atm}$

2. $P_{helium} = \dfrac{86 \text{ torr} \mid 1 \text{ atm}}{\phantom{86 \text{ torr}} \mid 760 \text{ torr}} = 0.11 \text{ atm}$

Page 265.   Section 12:4

3. $\dfrac{V_{hydrogen}}{V_{oxygen}} = \dfrac{\sqrt{m_{oxygen}}}{\sqrt{m_{hydrogen}}} = \dfrac{\sqrt{32g}}{\sqrt{2g}}$

$= \sqrt{\dfrac{32}{2}} = \sqrt{16} = \dfrac{4}{1}$

4. $\dfrac{V_{helium}}{V_{radon}} = \dfrac{\sqrt{m_{radon}}}{\sqrt{m_{helium}}} = \dfrac{\sqrt{222g}}{\sqrt{4g}}$

$= \sqrt{55.5} = \dfrac{7.45}{1}$

Page 271.   End of Chapter

5. $740 + 12 = 752 \text{ torr} = $ pressure of

contained gas

$\dfrac{752 \text{ torr} \mid 1 \text{ atm}}{\phantom{752 \text{ torr}} \mid 760 \text{ torr}} = 0.989 \text{ atm}$

6. 400 torr

7. a. $828°K - 273° = 555°C$

b. $751°C + 273° = 1024°K$

c. $16°C + 273° = 289°K$

d. $3°K - 273° = -270°C$

e. $62°C + 273° = 335°K$

8. $\dfrac{V_{helium}}{V_{oxygen}} = \sqrt{\dfrac{m_{oxygen}}{m_{helium}}}$

$\dfrac{V_{helium}}{0.076 \text{m/sec}} = \sqrt{\dfrac{32g}{4g}} = \sqrt{8} = 2\sqrt{2}$

$V_{helium} = 2(\sqrt{2})\,(0.076 \text{m/sec})$

$= (2.83)\,(0.076 \text{m/sec})$

$= 0.215 \text{m/sec}$

9. The molecular mass of ammonia is: $14 + 3 = 17$. The molecular mass of chlorine gas is: $2(35.5) = 71.0$. Since the velocity of gas molecules varies inversely as the square root of their mass, the *ammonia* which is composed of lighter molecules will be expected to cross the room first.

10. The mean free path of an atom or molecule is the average distance it travels between collisions.

11. Each molecule moves independently of other molecules in a gas. A molecule appears to vibrate about a moving point in a liquid. Molecules appear to vibrate about fixed, unmoving points in a solid.

Page 271.   One More Step

1. Oxygen:

$K.E. = 1/2\,mv^2$

$V_{oxygen} = 4.61 \times 10^4 \text{ cm/sec (see page 259).}$

$K.E. = \dfrac{1}{2} \left| \dfrac{32.0\,g}{6.02 \times 10^{23} \text{ molecules}} \right|$

$$\frac{(4.61 \times 10^4)^2 \ \cancel{cm^2}}{\cancel{sec^2}} \ \left| \ \frac{erg}{\frac{g\text{-}\cancel{cm^2}}{\cancel{sec^2}}} \right.$$

$$= 5.65 \times 10^{-14} \ \text{ergs/molecule}$$

Automobile:

$$K.E. = \tfrac{1}{2} mv^2$$

$$K.E. = \frac{1}{2} \left| \frac{1500 \ \cancel{kg}}{1 \ \cancel{kg}} \ \right| \frac{1000 \ \cancel{g}}{} \ \left| \frac{(50.0 \ \cancel{km})^2}{(1 \ \cancel{hr})^2} \ \right| \frac{(1000 \ \cancel{m})^2}{(1 \ \cancel{km})^2} \right.$$

$$- \ \left| \frac{(100 \ \cancel{cm})^2}{(1 \ \cancel{m})^2} \ \right| \frac{(1 \ \cancel{hr})^2}{(3600 \ \cancel{sec})^2} \ \left| \frac{1 \ erg}{1 \frac{g\text{-}\cancel{cm^2}}{\cancel{sec^2}}} \right.$$

$$= 1.45 \times 10^{12} \ \text{ergs}$$

2. $$\frac{v_{hydrogen}}{v_{oxygen}} = \sqrt{\frac{m_{oxygen}}{m_{hydrogen}}}$$

$$\frac{v_{hydrogen}}{4.61 \times 10^4 \ \text{cm/sec}} = \sqrt{\frac{32 \ \cancel{g}}{2 \ \cancel{g}}}$$

$$v_{hydrogen} = (4.61 \times 10^4 \ \text{cm/sec}) \sqrt{16}$$
$$= 4 \, (4.61 \times 10^4 \ \text{cm/sec})$$
$$= 1.84 \times 10^5 \ \text{cm/sec}$$

3.

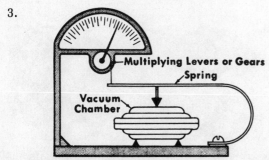

Other instruments used to measure pressure: steam gauge, depth gauge, altimeter.

4. Plasma is the term applied to highly ionized gases in strong magnetic fields. This "state of matter" is used primarily to control thermonuclear reactions. The student may be interested in the "pinch effect." Further information can be found in the *Columbia Encyclopedia; Physics* by Gamow and Cleveland, Prentice-Hall, 1960; *Plasma Physics* by Chandrasekhar, University of Chicago Press, paperback.

Suggested Readings for Faculty and Students

Avco Everett Research Laboratory, Environmental Pollution Control Through MHD Power Generation. Everett, Mass., May, 1971. For further information on magnetohydrodynamics, contact Avco Everett Research Laboratory, 2385 Revere Beach Parkway, Everett, Massachusetts 02149.

*Halliday, David, and Resnick, Robert, *Fundamentals of Physics*. New York, John Wiley and Sons, Inc., 1970, Chapter 20.

*Hicks, John F. G., "Glass Formation and Crystal Structure." *Journal of Chemical Education*, Vol. 51, No. 1 (January 1974), pp. 28-31.

*Johari, Gyan P., "Introduction to the Glassy State in the Undergraduate Curriculum." *Journal of Chemical Education*, Vol. 51, No.1 (January 1974), pp. 23-27.

*Kittel, Charles, *Thermal Physics*. New York, John Wiley and Sons, Inc., 1969, Chapter 13 (An advanced work.)

*Rice, B., and Raw, C. J. G., "The Assumption of Elastic Collisions in Elementary Gas Kinetic Theory." *Journal of Chemical Education*, Vol. 51, No. 2 (February 1974), p. 139.

(*Faculty only)

Chapter 13

Performance Objectives

GOAL: Students will gain an understanding of crystal structure and its relationship to properties of solids.

Objectives: Upon completion of the reading and activities, and when asked to diagram, demonstrate, or respond either orally or on a written test, students will:

13:1	K	list examples of the seven crystal systems.
13:2-5	K,P,S	identify examples of unit cells.
13:2-5	P,S	accept the concept of the space lattice.
13:6-7	P	distinguish between ionic,

covalent, and van der Waals forces as means by which crystals are held together.

13:8   K   identify types and uses of crystal defects.

13:9   K   describe the chemistry of the transistor.

13:10   P   distinguish between polymorphism and isomorphism.

13:11   K,P   define and give examples of hygroscopy, efflorescence, and deliquescence.

Upon completion of the reading and activities, students will exhibit an interest in science by:

A   voluntarily completing one or more of the One More Step activities listed at the end of the chapter on their own time.

A   reading unassigned literature related to the ideas presented in the chapter.

Page 290.   End of Chapter

Suggestion: For problems 1 and 2, obtain 23 styrofoam spheres and construct the BCC and FCC cubes or have a student construct them. Most students will have trouble visualizing these cells.

1. FCC cube—The diagonal of a face has a length of

$$d = 4(2.19) = 8.76 \ \overset{\circ}{A}$$

The maximum distance between adjacent particles is the length of an edge.

$$e^2 + e^2 = d^2 \qquad e = \sqrt{\dfrac{(8.76)^2}{2}}$$

$$2e^2 = d^2 \qquad e = \sqrt{\dfrac{76.73}{2}}$$

$$e^2 = \dfrac{d^2}{2} \qquad e = \sqrt{38.37}$$

$$e = \sqrt{\dfrac{d^2}{2}} \qquad e = 6.19 \ \overset{\circ}{A}$$

The maximum distance between particles is the length of the diagonal of the cube.

$$C^2 = e^2 + d^2$$

$$C^2 = (6.19)^2 + (8.76)^2$$

$$C^2 = 38.37 + 76.73$$

$$C = \sqrt{38.37 + 76.73}$$

$$C = 10.6 \ \overset{\circ}{A}$$

2. BCC cube—Note that the spheres along the edges of the cube do not touch. Each of these spheres, however, touches the central sphere. We can, therefore, find the length of the diagonal of the cube.

$$d = 4(2.19) = 8.76 \ \overset{\circ}{A}$$

In a body centered cubic structure, the particles which are at a maximum distance are those at the ends of a diagonal of the cube. Since, as we have observed, these two particles are tangent to the particle in the center of the cube, the maximum distance is 8.76 $\overset{\circ}{A}$.

3.

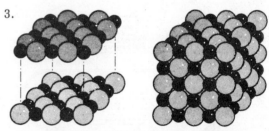

A one-to-one correspondence exists between the chlorine and sodium ions.

4. Na⁺   1.12 $\overset{\circ}{A}$

   Cl⁻   1.70 $\overset{\circ}{A}$

          2.82 $\overset{\circ}{A}$

5. The relationship of the positive ions and negative ions in one pair of compounds is the same as the positive to negative and negative to positive in the other pair.

6. $$\begin{array}{rcl} 1\ Cu\ @\ 63.5 &=& 63.5 \\ 1\ S\ @\ 32.0 &=& 32.0 \\ 4\ O\ @\ 16.0 &=& 64.0 \\ 5\ H_2O\ @\ 18.0 &=& 90.0 \\ \hline & & 249.5 = 250 \end{array}$$

$$\% \ H_2O = \frac{90.0}{250} \times 100 = 36.0\% \ H_2O$$

7. a. nickel sulfate heptahydrate

b. $$\begin{array}{rcl} 1\ Ni\ @\ 58.7 &=& 58.7 \\ 1\ S\ @\ 32.0 &=& 32.0 \\ 4\ O\ @\ 16.0 &=& 64.0 \\ 7\ H_2O\ @\ 18.0 &=& 126.0 \\ \hline & & 280.7 = 281 \end{array}$$

$$\% \ H_2O = \frac{126}{281} \times 100 = 44.8\% \ H_2O$$

c. 11 O in $NiSO_4 \cdot 7\ H_2O$ @ 16.0 = 176

$$\% \ O = \frac{176}{281} \times 100 = 62.6\% \ O$$

8. a. barium hydroxide octahydrate

b. $$\begin{array}{rcl} 1\ Ba\ @\ 137 &=& 137. \\ 2\ O\ @\ 16.0 &=& 32.0 \\ 2\ H\ @\ 1.01 &=& 2.02 \\ 8\ H_2O\ @\ 18.0 &=& 144. \\ \hline & & 315.02 = 315 \end{array}$$

$$\% \ H_2O = \frac{144}{315} \times 100 = 45.7\% \ H_2O$$

c. 10 O in $Ba(OH)_2 \cdot 8\ H_2O$ @ 16.0 = 160

$$\% \ O = \frac{160}{315} \times 100 = 50.8\% \ O$$

9. a. sodium carbonate decahydrate

b. $$\begin{array}{rcl} 2\ Na\ @\ 23.0 &=& 46.0 \\ 1\ C\ @\ 12.0 &=& 12.0 \\ 3\ O\ @\ 16.0 &=& 48.0 \\ 10\ H_2O\ @\ 18.0 &=& 180. \\ \hline & & 286.0 \end{array}$$

$$\% \ H_2O = \frac{180}{286} \times 100 = 62.9\% \ H_2O$$

c. 13 O in $Na_2CO_3 \cdot 10\ H_2O$ @ 16.0 = 208

$$\% \ O = \frac{208}{286} \times 100 = 72.7\% \ O$$

Page 291.   One More Step

1. See p. 280. Also see the *Encyclopaedia Britannica* article on crystallography (Vol. 6). This gives an excellent treatment of the history of X-ray probing.

2. One source is the Bell Telephone Laboratories book, *Conductors and Semiconductors,* by Alan Holden.

3. See p. 276.

4. Each sulfur atom contains 6 electrons in the outer level ($\cdot \ddot{S} \cdot$). When a sulfur atom forms two covalent bonds (one to a sulfur atom on either side), it then has 8 electrons in the outer level. If the ring were planar, the S—S—S bond angle would be $[n - 2(180)/n] = 135°$. However, the four pairs of electrons in the outer level repel so as to assume a tetrahedral arrangement about the sulfur atom. In the puckered ring arrangement, the tetrahedral bond angle of $109°28'$ is attained by all eight sulfur atoms.

Suggested Readings for Faculty and Students

Benfey, Theodor, "Geometry and Chemical Bonding." *Chemistry*, Vol. 40, No. 5 (May 1967), pp. 20-26.

Bertman, Bernard, and Guyer, Robert A., "Solid Helium." *Scientific American*, Vol. 217, No. 2 (August 1967), pp. 84-95.

Bragg, Sir Lawrence, "X-ray Crystallography." *Scientific American*, Vol. 219, No. 1 (July 1968), pp. 58-70.

Companion, Audrey, and Schug, Kenneth, "Ceramics and Glass." *Chemistry*, Vol. 46, No. 9 (October 1973), pp. 27-31.

Gurnee, Edward F., Fundamental Principles of Semiconductors." *Journal of Chemical Education*, Vol. 46, No. 2 (February 1969), pp. 80-85.

*Kapecki, Jon A., "An Introduction to X-ray Structure Determination." *Journal of Chemical Education*, Vol. 49, No. 4 (April 1972), pp. 231-236.

*Kittel, Charles, *Introduction to Solid State Physics*, 4th Ed. New York, John Wiley and Sons, Inc., 1971 (An advanced work.)

Mason, Brian, "The Lunar Rocks." *Scientific American*, Vol. 225, No. 4 (October 1971), pp. 48-58.

*Rice, Oscar Knefler, *Electronic Structure and Chemical Binding*. New York, Dover Publications, Inc., 1969, Chapters 13-14 and 16-18. (A reprint of an older work which contains much valuable material.)

*Sanderson, R. T., "The Nature of 'Ionic' Solids." *Journal of Chemical Education*, Vol. 44, No. 9 (September 1967), pp. 516-523.

*Weller, Paul F., "An Introduction to Principles of the Solid State." *Journal of Chemical Education*, Vol. 47, No. 7 (July 1970), pp. 501-507.

Weller, Paul F., "An Introduction to Principles of the Solid State." *Journal of Chemical Education*, Vol. 48, No. 12 (December 1971), pp. 831-836.

Wood, John A., "The Lunar Soil." *Scientific American*, Vol. 223, No. 2 (August 1970), pp. 14-23.

(*Faculty only)

Chapter 14

Performance Objectives

GOAL: Students will gain an understanding of the properties of liquids and their relationship to molecular structure and the kinetic theory.

Objectives: Upon completion of the reading and activities, and when asked to diagram, demonstrate, or respond either orally or on a written test, students will:

14:1-2	P,K	explain the reasons for vapor pressure of a solid or liquid.
14:3	K,P	define and give examples of Le Chatelier's Principle.
14:4	K,S	identify methods for determining vapor pressures.
14:5-7	K	define melting point and boiling point in terms of vapor pressure.
14:8	K	list the conditions for liquefaction of gases.
14:8	K	define critical temperature and critical pressure.
14:9	S,K	read M.P., B.P., critical temperature and critical pressure.
14:10-11	K	define and give examples of hydrogen bonding.
14:12	K,P	explain surface tension and capillary rise on the basis of unbalanced surface forces.
14:13	K,P	list examples of amorphous substances.

Upon completion of the reading and activities, students will exhibit an interest in science by:

A   voluntarily completing one or more of the One More Step activities listed at the end of the chapter on their own time.

A   reading unassigned literature related to the ideas presented in the chapter.

Page 303.   Section 14:9

Teacher Suggestion:

Obtain a piece of dry ice and a coin. Press the coin against the surface of the dry ice with the eraser end of a pencil and listen to the coin "sing."

Problem: Following is a phase diagram of CO_2.

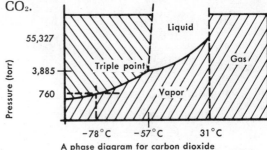

A phase diagram for carbon dioxide

Now answer this: Do you think it would be fun to skate on dry ice? (Yes and No.) Why? (Dangerous.) Would it be easier or harder than skating on ice? (Easier but perhaps fatal if you slipped and fell. A piece of metal placed in contact with a slab of dry ice has practically no friction at the interface between metal and ice because of rapid generation of CO_2 gas.)

Page 313. End of Chapter

1. Above the critical temperature, T_c, no amount of pressure will cause the gas to liquefy.

   The critical pressure, P_c, is the pressure that will cause the gas to liquefy at the critical temperature.

2. The triple point is the temperature and pressure at which the vapor pressures of the three phases of a substance, gas, liquid, and solid, are in equilibrium.

   The triple point for:

$$\text{water} = 4.6 \text{ torr at } +0.01°C,$$
$$\text{carbon dioxide} = 3885 \text{ torr at } -57°C.$$

   Note: Students will probably overestimate the temperature of the triple point for water because the slant of the solid-liquid line in Figure 14-12 has been exaggerated to emphasize that the triple point is not at 0°C.

3. Le Chatelier's principle: If stress is applied to a system at equilibrium, the system readjusts so that the stress is reduced.

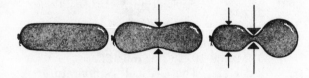

   As pressure is applied to one portion of a balloon surface, another portion bulges and the increased pressure is distributed evenly over the entire balloon surface.

4. Molecules appear to vibrate about points in a solid. By chance, a molecule near the surface may undergo a collision or series of collisions which result in a velocity (direction and speed) or kinetic energy sufficiently large to counterbalance the forces of attraction of surrounding molecules. If these forces are weak enough, the molecule "escapes" from the surface. The loss of molecules from the surface of a liquid in this manner is called evaporation. The loss of molecules from the surface of a solid is called sublimation. Camphor is an excellent example.

5. See number 6 of the summary on page 312. Sublimation is the change of state in which a substance passes directly from the solid to the gaseous state. Three examples: dry ice changes to a gas, naphthalene balls (mothballs) gradually disappear, and in cold weather, snow or ice sublimes. Frozen clothes hanging on a clothesline gradually become soft and flexible.

6. The boiling point is the temperature at which the vapor pressure of the liquid equals the atmospheric pressure. The melting point is the temperature at which the vapor pressure of the solid and liquid are equal.

7. The HBr molecule is not highly polar and does not form hydrogen bonds. HF does form hydrogen bonds and therefore has a higher boiling point.

8. In the ice crystal lattice, each oxygen atom touches four hydrogen atoms and each hydrogen atom touches two oxygen atoms (note that this follows from the formula, H_2O). In the solid, the repulsion of similar atoms results in the formation of an open lattice but as the molecular motion increases and becomes more random, the open crystal collapses, causing the molecules to move closer together and the ordered structure of the ice crystal is destroyed. This results in a decrease in volume as the ice melts and as the temperature rises from 0°C to 4°C.

9. Volatile substances evaporate rapidly at room temperature. Nonvolatile substances evaporate slowly at room temperature. Volatile substances have a higher vapor pressure at a given temperature than nonvolatile substances. Ether is a volatile liquid, iodine a volatile

solid. Mercury is a nonvolatile liquid, iron a nonvolatile solid.

10. The tables on pages 212 and 254 give the bonding types with a brief description of each type: covalent, ionic, metallic, dipole, hydrogen, and dispersion forces.

11. The temperature remains at $0°C$ because the energy added with the warm water or absorbed by the ice simply causes the equilibrium to shift. Some of the ice melts and becomes liquid or the water freezes. The temperature does not change until all of the ice has melted or all of the water has frozen. The equilibrium is then destroyed.

12.

	x	y
B.P.	$243°K$	$430°K$
M.P.	$131°K$	$300°K$
T.P.	$124°K$, 245 torr	$300°K$, 0.6 atm
T_c	$260°K$	$655°K$
P_c	870 torr	8.1 atm

Page 314. One More Step

1. The pressure exerted on the ice by the wire causes an equilibrium shift directly under the wire, the ice melts and the wire moves downward. The water remaining above the wire is at $0°C$ and is no longer under pressure so it refreezes. As the wire passes through the block of ice, the equilibrium shifts first from solid to liquid, then from liquid to solid. See pp. 296-297, Section 14:3.

2. Faraday sealed crystals of a chlorine compound in closed bent glass tube and cooled one leg of the bent tube. He heated the crystals which released chlorine gas. As the gas was evolved, pressure in the tube increased and the chlorine gas condensed to a liquid in the cooled portion of the tube. Under these conditions of pressure and temperature, chlorine is a liquid.

3. The CO_2 is under pressure in the extinguisher. When the pressure is released, the gas expands and as a result is cooled due to the Joule-Thomson effect. Each molecule which escapes causes

the average K.E. to decrease, thus cooling the gas. The CO_2 is at atmospheric pressure and reduced temperature ($-78°C$). Under these conditions, CO_2 is a solid.

4. Freezing points:

H_2O	$0°C$
H_2S	$-85.5°C$
H_2Se	$-60.4°C$
H_2Te	$-49°C$

The hydrogen bonding raises the freezing point to $0°C$. The hydrogen bonding also causes ice at $0°C$ to be less dense than water. This causes ice to float on top of water.

5. Antimony and bismuth expand on freezing. When melting, the metals change from crystalline form to a polyatomic molecular liquid which is a more compact arrangement.

Suggested Readings for Faculty and Students

Apfel, Robert E., "The Tensile Strength of Liquids." Scientific American, Vol. 227, No. 6 (December 1972), pp. 58-71.

Ashcroft, N. W., "Liquid Metals." Scientific American, Vol. 221, No. 1 (July 1969), pp. 72-82.

*Barker, John A., and Henderson, Douglas, "Some Aspects of the Theory of Liquids." Accounts of Chemical Research, Vol. 4, No. 9 (September 1971), pp. 303-307.

Barton, A. F. M., "Internal Pressure." Journal of Chemical Education, Vol. 48, No. 3 (March 1971), pp. 156-162.

*Pilar, F. L., 'The Critical Temperature: A Necessary Consequence of Gas Non-Ideality." Journal of Chemical Education, Vol. 44, No. 5 (May 1967), pp. 284-285.

*Rice, Oscar Knefler, Electronic Structure and Chemical Binding. New York, Dover Publications, Inc., 1969, Chapter 19 (An older work containing much valuable information.)

Rice, Stuart A., "Properties of Simple Liquids." The Science Teacher, Vol. 35, No. 5 (May 1968), pp. 17-19.

Webb, Valerie, J., "Hydrogen Bond: 'Special Agent.'" Chemistry, Vol. 41, No. 6 (June 1968), pp. 16-20.

(*Faculty only)

Chapter 15

Performance Objectives

GOAL: Students will gain an understanding of the ideal gas laws based on the kinetic theory model and the actual behavior of real gases.

Objectives: Upon completion of the reading and activities, and when asked to diagram, demonstrate, or respond either orally or on a written test, students will:

15:1-2 P,S   solve volume-pressure variation problems using Boyle's Law.

15:3   P,S   utilize Dalton's Law of Partial Pressures to find the dry volume of a gas collected over water.

15:4-5 P,S   solve volume-temperature variation problems using Charles' Law.

15:6   P,S   determine the volume of a gas under changing conditions of temperature and pressure.

15:7-8 S,K,P   explain Graham's Law and use it to determine relative rates of diffusion of various gases.

15:9   P,S   determine the density of a dry gas given original volume$_x$ and mass$_x$ and alteration of conditions.

15:10   K   list properties of real gases which lead to deviations from the ideal gas laws.

     Upon completion of the reading and activities, students will exhibit an interest in science by:

A   voluntarily completing one or more of the One More Step activities listed at the end of the chapter on their own time.

A   reading unassigned literature related to the ideas presented in the chapter.

Page 323.   Section 15:2

1. a. $\dfrac{952 \text{ ml} \mid 561 \text{ torr}}{\mid 760 \text{ torr}} = 703 \text{ ml}$

b. $\dfrac{273 \text{ ml} \mid 166 \text{ torr}}{\mid 760 \text{ torr}} = 59.6 \text{ ml}$

c. $\dfrac{338 \text{ l} \mid 6.30 \text{ atm}}{\mid 1 \text{ atm}} = 2130 \text{ l}$

d. $\dfrac{598 \text{ ml} \mid 5.00 \text{ atm}}{\mid 1 \text{ atm}} = 2990 \text{ ml}$

e. $\dfrac{77.0 \text{ l} \mid 180 \text{ torr}}{\mid 760 \text{ torr}} = 18.2 \text{ l}$

2. a. $\dfrac{930 \text{ ml} \mid 697 \text{ torr}}{\mid 760 \text{ torr}} = 853 \text{ ml}$

b. $\dfrac{50.0 \text{ l} \mid 413 \text{ torr}}{\mid 760 \text{ torr}} = 27.2 \text{ l}$

c. $\dfrac{36.0 \text{ l} \mid 0.650 \text{ atm}}{\mid 1 \text{ atm}} = 23.4 \text{ l}$

d. $\dfrac{329 \text{ ml} \mid 1.65 \text{ atm}}{\mid 1 \text{ atm}} = 543 \text{ ml}$

e. $\dfrac{231 \text{ ml} \mid 605 \text{ torr}}{\mid 760 \text{ torr}} = 184 \text{ ml}$

3. a. $\dfrac{0.600 \text{ l} \mid 669 \text{ torr} \mid 1 \text{ atm}}{\mid 0.870 \text{ atm} \mid 760 \text{ torr}}$
$= 0.607 \text{ l}$

b. $\dfrac{380 \text{ ml} \mid 772 \text{ torr}}{\mid 804 \text{ torr}} = 365 \text{ ml}$

c. $\dfrac{0.388 \text{ l} \mid 364 \text{ torr} \mid 1 \text{ atm}}{\mid 0.589 \text{ atm} \mid 760 \text{ torr}} = 0.275 \text{ l}$

d. $\dfrac{459 \text{ ml} \mid 4.32 \text{ atm}}{\mid 9.40 \text{ atm}} = 211 \text{ ml}$

e. $\dfrac{0.123 \text{ l} \mid 0.832 \text{ atm} \mid 760 \text{ torr}}{\mid 865 \text{ torr} \mid 1 \text{ atm}} = 0.0899 \text{ l}$

4. a. $\dfrac{388 \text{ ml} \mid 0.581 \text{ atm} \mid 760 \text{ torr}}{\mid 500 \text{ torr} \mid 1 \text{ atm}}$
$= 343 \text{ ml}$

b. $$\frac{0.951 \text{ l} \mid 0.791 \text{ atm} \mid 760 \text{ torr}}{326 \text{ torr} \mid 1 \text{ atm}}$$
$$= 1.75 \text{ l}$$

c. $$\frac{31.5 \text{ ml} \mid 142 \text{ torr}}{122 \text{ torr}} = 36.7 \text{ ml}$$

d. $$\frac{524 \text{ ml} \mid 166 \text{ torr}}{910 \text{ torr}} = 95.6 \text{ ml}$$

e. $$\frac{171 \text{ ml} \mid 332 \text{ torr} \mid 1 \text{ atm}}{0.877 \text{ atm} \mid 760 \text{ torr}}$$
$$= 85.2 \text{ ml}$$

Page 327.   Section 15:3

Note that the volume temperature relationship has not been discussed. Charles' Law is discussed in the following section, Section 15:4, page 328. The temperature is included to allow students to correct for the vapor pressure of water at different temperatures. Instruct students to use Table 15-1 page 325 to make these corrections.

5. a. corrected gas pressure $= (700 - 12)$
$$= 688 \text{ torr}$$
$$\frac{888 \text{ ml} \mid 688 \text{ torr}}{760 \text{ torr}} = 804 \text{ ml}$$

b. corrected gas pressure $= (581 - 13.6)$
$$= 567 \text{ torr}$$
$$\frac{30.0 \text{ ml} \mid 567 \text{ torr}}{760 \text{ torr}} = 22.4 \text{ ml}$$

c. corrected gas pressure $= (618 - 15.5)$
$$= 602 \text{ torr}$$
$$\frac{34.0 \text{ l} \mid 602 \text{ torr}}{760 \text{ torr}} = 26.9 \text{ l}$$

d. corrected gas pressure $= (587 - 10.5)$
$$= 576 \text{ torr}$$
$$\frac{384 \text{ ml} \mid 576 \text{ torr}}{760 \text{ torr}} = 291 \text{ ml}$$

e. corrected gas pressure $= (655 - 26.7)$
$$= 628 \text{ torr}$$

$$\frac{8.23 \text{ l} \mid 628 \text{ torr}}{760 \text{ torr}} = 6.80 \text{ l}$$

6. a. corrected gas pressure $= (715 - 22.4)$
$$= 693 \text{ torr}$$
$$\frac{903 \text{ ml} \mid 693 \text{ torr}}{760 \text{ torr}} = 823 \text{ ml}$$

b. corrected gas pressure $= (851 - 23.8)$
$$= 827 \text{ torr}$$
$$\frac{317 \text{ ml} \mid 827 \text{ torr}}{760 \text{ torr}} = 345 \text{ ml}$$

c. $$\frac{1.08 \text{ atm} \mid 760 \text{ torr}}{1 \text{ atm}} = 821 \text{ torr}$$
corrected gas pressure $= (821 - 17.5)$
$$= 803 \text{ torr}$$
$$\frac{7.83 \text{ ml} \mid 803 \text{ torr}}{760 \text{ torr}} = 8.27 \text{ l}$$

d. corrected gas pressure $= (836 - 30)$
$$= 806 \text{ torr}$$
$$\frac{964 \text{ ml} \mid 806 \text{ torr}}{760 \text{ torr}} = 1020 \text{ ml}$$

e. corrected gas pressure $= (624 - 32)$
$$= 592 \text{ torr}$$
$$\frac{402 \text{ cm}^3 \mid 592 \text{ torr}}{760 \text{ torr}} = 313 \text{ cm}^3$$

Page 330.   Section 15:5

7. a. $(273 + 9)°\text{K} = 282°$
$$\frac{617 \text{ ml} \mid 273°\text{K}}{282°\text{K}} = 597 \text{ ml}$$

b. $(273 + 83)°\text{K} = 356°\text{K}$
$$\frac{609 \text{ ml} \mid 273°\text{K}}{356°\text{K}} = 467 \text{ ml}$$

c. $22°\text{C} = 295°\text{K}$
$$\frac{942 \text{ ml} \mid 273°\text{K}}{295°\text{K}} = 872 \text{ ml}$$

d. $$\frac{7.16 \text{ l} \mid 273°\text{K}}{280°\text{K}} = 6.98 \text{ l}$$

e. $7°C = 280°K$

$$\frac{4.40 \text{ l} \mid 273°\cancel{K}}{280°\cancel{K}} = 4.29 \text{ l}$$

8. a. $21°C = 294°K$

$$\frac{819 \text{ ml} \mid 273°\cancel{K}}{294°\cancel{K}} = 761 \text{ ml}$$

b. $$\frac{5.80 \text{ l} \mid 273°\cancel{K}}{514°\cancel{K}} = 3.08 \text{ l}$$

c. $79°C = 352°K$

$$\frac{5.94 \text{ l} \mid 273°\cancel{K}}{352°\cancel{K}} = 4.61 \text{ l}$$

d. $$\frac{7.12 \text{ l} \mid 273°\cancel{K}}{988°\cancel{K}} = 1.97 \text{ l}$$

e. $99°C = 372°K$

$$\frac{213 \text{ l} \mid 273°\cancel{K}}{372°\cancel{K}} = 156 \text{ l}$$

9. a. temperature increases − volume increases

$23°C = 296°K$

$$\frac{2.91 \text{ l} \mid 296°\cancel{K}}{226°\cancel{K}} = 3.80 \text{ l}$$

b. temperature increases — volume increases

$73°C = 346°K$

$$\frac{608 \text{ ml} \mid 346°\cancel{K}}{158°\cancel{K}} = 1330 \text{ ml}$$

c. temperature increases — volume increases

$52°C = 325°K$

$$\frac{7.91 \text{ l} \mid 538°\cancel{K}}{325°\cancel{K}} = 13.1 \text{ l}$$

d. temperature increases — volume increases

$72°C = 345°K$

$$\frac{2.97 \text{ l} \mid 502°\cancel{K}}{345°\cancel{K}} = 4.32 \text{ l}$$

e. temperature increases — volume increases

$53°C = 326°K$

$$\frac{19.0 \text{ ml} \mid 326°\cancel{K}}{56.0°\cancel{K}} = 111 \text{ ml}$$

10. a. $°K = °C + 273°$
$= 6° + 273° = 279°K$

$°K = °C + 273°$
$= 76° + 273° = 349°K$

The temperature change is from $349°K$ to $279°K$. The gas will contract.

$$\frac{5.18 \text{ l} \mid 279°\cancel{K}}{349°\cancel{K}} = 4.14 \text{ l}$$

b. $°K = °C + 273°$
$= 27° + 273° = 300°K$

The temperature change is from $300°K$ to $744°K$. The gas will expand.

$$\frac{994 \text{ ml} \mid 744°\cancel{K}}{300°\cancel{K}} = 2470 \text{ ml}$$

c. $°K = °C + 273°$
$= 27° + 273° = 300°K$

$°K = °C + 273°$
$= 84° + 273° = 357°K$

The temperature change is from $300°K$ to $357°K$. The gas will expand.

$$\frac{833 \text{ ml} \mid 357°\cancel{K}}{300°\cancel{K}} = 991 \text{ ml}$$

d. $°K = °C + 273°$
$= 52° + 273° = 325°K$

The temperature change is from $563°K$ to $325°K$. The gas will contract.

$$\frac{880 \text{ ml} \mid 325°\cancel{K}}{563°\cancel{K}} = 508 \text{ ml}$$

e. $°K = °C + 273°$
$= 44° + 273° = 317°K$

$°K = °C + 273°$
$= 17° + 273° = 290°K$

The temperature change is from $317°K$ to $290°K$. The gas will contract.

$$\frac{5.94 \text{ l} \mid 290°\cancel{K}}{317°\cancel{K}} = 5.43 \text{ l}$$

11. a. $\dfrac{7.51\ \text{l} \left|\ \overset{273}{(0 + 273)^{\circ}K}\ \right|\ 449\ \cancel{\text{torr}}}{\left|\ \underset{278}{(5 + 273)^{\circ}K}\ \right|\ 760\ \cancel{\text{torr}}}$

$= 4.36\ \text{l}$

b. $\dfrac{149\ \text{ml} \left|\ \overset{341}{(68 + 273)^{\circ}K}\ \right|\ 710\ \cancel{\text{torr}}}{\left|\ \underset{291}{(18 + 273)^{\circ}K}\ \right|\ 618\ \cancel{\text{torr}}}$

$= 201\ \text{ml}$

c. $\dfrac{7.03\ \text{l} \left|\ \overset{273}{(0 + 273)^{\circ}K}\ \right|\ 2.14\ \cancel{\text{atm}}}{\left|\ \underset{304}{(31 + 273)^{\circ}K}\ \right|\ 1\ \cancel{\text{atm}}}$

$= 13.5\ \text{l}$

d. $\dfrac{955\ \text{ml} \left|\ \overset{349}{(76 + 273)^{\circ}K}\ \right|\ 3.12\ \cancel{\text{atm}} \left|\ 760\ \cancel{\text{torr}} \right.}{\left|\ \underset{331}{(58 + 273)^{\circ}K}\ \right|\ 923\ \cancel{\text{torr}} \left|\ 1\ \cancel{\text{atm}} \right.}$

$= 2590\ \text{ml}$

e. $\dfrac{960\ \text{ml} \left|\ \overset{286}{(13 + 273)^{\circ}K}\ \right|\ 5.80\ \cancel{\text{atm}} \left|\ 760\ \cancel{\text{torr}} \right.}{\left|\ \underset{344}{(71 + 273)^{\circ}K}\ \right|\ 445\ \cancel{\text{torr}} \left|\ 1\ \cancel{\text{atm}} \right.}$

$= 7910\ \text{ml}$

12. a. $\dfrac{654\ \text{ml} \left|\ \overset{277}{(4 + 273)^{\circ}K}\ \right|\ 490\ \cancel{\text{torr}} \left|\ 1\ \cancel{\text{atm}} \right.}{\left|\ \underset{279}{(6 + 273)^{\circ}K}\ \right|\ 2.91\ \cancel{\text{atm}} \left|\ 760\ \cancel{\text{torr}} \right.}$

$= 144\ \text{ml}$

b. $\dfrac{2.13\ \text{l} \left|\ \overset{273}{(0 + 273)^{\circ}K}\ \right|\ 3.79\ \cancel{\text{atm}}}{\left|\ \underset{368}{(95 + 273)^{\circ}K}\ \right|\ 1\ \cancel{\text{atm}}}$

$= 5.99\ \text{l}$

c. $\dfrac{4.76\ \text{l} \left|\ \overset{273}{(0 + 273)^{\circ}K}\ \right|\ 934\ \cancel{\text{torr}}}{\left|\ \underset{279}{(6 + 273)^{\circ}K}\ \right|\ 760\ \cancel{\text{torr}}}$

$= 5.72\ \text{l}$

d. $\dfrac{61.4\ \text{ml} \left|\ \overset{273}{(0 + 273)^{\circ}K}\ \right|\ 726\ \cancel{\text{torr}}}{\left|\ \underset{340}{(67 + 273)^{\circ}K}\ \right|\ 760\ \cancel{\text{torr}}}$

$= 47.1\ \text{ml}$

e. $\dfrac{164\ \text{ml} \left|\ \overset{294}{(21 + 273)^{\circ}K}\ \right|\ 760\ \cancel{\text{torr}}}{\left|\ \underset{273}{(0 + 273)^{\circ}K}\ \right|\ 735\ \cancel{\text{torr}}}$

$= 183\ \text{ml}$

13. $\dfrac{v_{He}}{v_{Ar}} = \sqrt{\dfrac{m_{Ar}}{m_{He}}}$

$= \sqrt{\dfrac{39.9}{4}} = \dfrac{3.17}{1}$

14. $\dfrac{v_{Ar}}{v_{Rn}} = \sqrt{\dfrac{m_{Rn}}{m_{Ar}}} = \sqrt{\dfrac{222}{39.9}}$

$= \sqrt{\dfrac{5.56}{1}} = \dfrac{2.36}{1}$

15. a. $\dfrac{1.64\ \text{g} \left|\ 1000\ \cancel{\text{ml}} \left|\ 337^{\circ}K \right. \left|\ 760\ \cancel{\text{torr}} \right.\right.}{969\ \cancel{\text{ml}} \left|\ 1 \left|\ 273^{\circ}K \right. \left|\ 723\ \cancel{\text{torr}} \right.\right.}$

$= 2.20\ \text{g/l}$

b. $\dfrac{0.530\ \text{g} \left|\ 304^{\circ}K \left|\ 760\ \cancel{\text{torr}} \right.\right.}{4.98\ \text{l} \left|\ 273^{\circ}K \left|\ 776\ \cancel{\text{torr}} \right.\right.}$

$= 0.116\ \text{g/l}$

c. $\dfrac{8.3\ \text{g} \left|\ 1000\ \cancel{\text{ml}} \left|\ 372^{\circ}K \right. \left|\ 1\ \cancel{\text{atm}} \right.\right.}{833\ \cancel{\text{ml}} \left|\ 1\ \text{l} \left|\ 273^{\circ}K \right. \left|\ 2.6\ \cancel{\text{atm}} \right.\right.}$

$= 5.22\ \text{g/l}$

d. $\dfrac{3.69\ \text{g} \left|\ 1000\ \cancel{\text{ml}} \left|\ 310^{\circ}K \right. \left|\ 760\ \cancel{\text{torr}} \right.\right.}{883\ \cancel{\text{ml}} \left|\ 1\ \text{l} \left|\ 273^{\circ}K \right. \left|\ 863\ \cancel{\text{torr}} \right.\right.}$

$= 4.18\ \text{g/l}$

e. $\dfrac{5.03\ \text{g} \left|\ 299^{\circ}K \left|\ 760\ \cancel{\text{torr}} \right.\right.}{475\ \text{l} \left|\ 273^{\circ}K \left|\ 694\ \cancel{\text{torr}} \right.\right.}$

$= 1.27\ \text{g/l}$

16. a. $\dfrac{6.40 \text{ g}}{7.13 \text{ l}} \left| \dfrac{354^\circ K}{273^\circ K} \right| \dfrac{1 \text{ atm}}{3.95 \text{ atm}} = 0.295 \text{ g/l}$

b. $\dfrac{1.64 \text{ g}}{5.61 \text{ l}} \left| \dfrac{327^\circ K}{273^\circ K} \right| \dfrac{1 \text{ atm}}{2.45 \text{ atm}} = 0.143 \text{ g/l}$

c. $\dfrac{6.57 \text{ g}}{5.59 \text{ l}} \left| \dfrac{370^\circ K}{273^\circ K} \right| \dfrac{760 \text{ torr}}{501 \text{ torr}} = 2.42 \text{ g/l}$

d. $\dfrac{0.0365 \text{ g}}{0.513 \text{ l}} \left| \dfrac{345^\circ K}{273^\circ K} \right| \dfrac{760 \text{ torr}}{765 \text{ torr}} = 0.0893 \text{ g/l}$

e. $\dfrac{0.0135 \text{ g}}{0.158 \text{ l}} \left| \dfrac{314^\circ K}{273^\circ K} \right| \dfrac{760 \text{ torr}}{746 \text{ torr}} = 0.100 \text{ g/l}$

Page 338.   End of Chapter

17. $\dfrac{928 \text{ ml}}{\underset{300}{(273 + 27)^\circ K}} \left| \dfrac{273^\circ K}{} \right| \dfrac{800 \text{ torr}}{760 \text{ torr}}$

$\qquad\qquad\qquad = 889 \text{ ml}$

18. $\dfrac{325 \text{ ml}}{273^\circ K} \left| \dfrac{(273 + 20)^\circ K}{} \right| \dfrac{760 \text{ torr}}{700 \text{ torr}}$

$\qquad\qquad\qquad = 379 \text{ ml}$

19. $\dfrac{2.97 \text{ g}}{1 \text{ l}} \left| \dfrac{273^\circ K}{\underset{300}{(273 + 27)^\circ K}} \right| \dfrac{750 \text{ torr}}{760 \text{ torr}}$

$\qquad\qquad\qquad = 2.67 \text{ g/l}$

20. $\dfrac{5.01 \text{ g}}{1 \text{ l}} \left| \dfrac{325^\circ K}{273^\circ K} \right| \dfrac{760 \text{ torr}}{800 \text{ torr}} = 5.67 \text{ g/l}$

21. $\dfrac{96 \text{ ml}}{300^\circ K} \left| \dfrac{343^\circ K}{} \right| \dfrac{\overset{887}{(914 - 27)} \text{ torr}}{952 \text{ torr}}$

$\qquad\qquad\qquad = 102 \text{ ml}$

22. $\dfrac{372 \text{ ml}}{363^\circ K} \left| \dfrac{275^\circ K}{} \right| \dfrac{\overset{306}{(832 - 526)} \text{ torr}}{735 \text{ torr}}$

$\qquad\qquad\qquad = 117 \text{ ml}$

23. $\dfrac{5.08 \text{ l}}{276^\circ K} \left| \dfrac{317^\circ K}{} \right| \dfrac{\overset{721}{(727 - 6)} \text{ torr}}{882 \text{ torr}} = 4.77 \text{ l}$

24. $\dfrac{30 \text{ ml}}{293^\circ K} \left| \dfrac{273^\circ K}{} \right| \dfrac{682 \text{ torr}}{760 \text{ torr}} = 25.1 \text{ ml}$

25. $\dfrac{8 \text{ ml}}{} \left| \dfrac{755 \text{ torr}}{760 \text{ torr}} = 7.95 \text{ ml} \right.$

Page 339.   One More Step

1. Connect the pump to the gauge by a very short section of rubber tubing. Pushing the plunger half-way down should make the gauge read 14.7 lb/in.²

   However, because of heat generated in the process, and the volume of the tubing and gauge, rarely will the reading be perfect.

2. The most common equation is that of van der Waals.

$$\left(P + \dfrac{an^2}{V^2} \right)(V - nb) = nRT$$

For N_2:

$a = 1.39 \text{ l}^2 \text{ atm/mole}^2$, $b = 0.0394 \text{ l/mole}$

Solving for V (assuming 1 mole) gives 0.0736 l. Solving the ideal gas equation gives 0.0560. The % is then,

$$\dfrac{(0.0736 - 0.0560)}{0.0560} \left| \dfrac{100\%}{1} = 31.4\% \right.$$

Other equations are:

Keyes $\left(P = \dfrac{a}{V - l^2} \right)(V - d)$

$\qquad\qquad\qquad = RT$ for 1 mole

Berthelot $\left(P = \dfrac{n^2 A}{TV^2} \right)(V - nB) = nRT$

Suggested Readings for Faculty and Students

Hall, Marie Boas, "Robert Boyle." *Scientific American,* Vol. 217, No. 2 (August 1967), pp. 97-102.

*Horvath, A. L., "Critical Temperature of Elements and the Periodic System." *Journal of Chemical Education,* Vol. 50, No. 5 (May 1973), pp. 335-336.

*Kittel, Charles, *Thermal Physics*. New York, John Wiley and Sons, Inc., 1969, Chapters 11, 12, and 20 [An advanced work.]

*Koons, Lawrence F., "Teaching Kinetic Molecular Theory by the Factor Change Method." *Journal of Chemical Education*, Vol. 44, No. 5 (May 1967), pp. 288-289.

*Mason, E. A., and Kronstadt, Barbara, "Graham's Laws of Diffusion and Effusion." *Journal of Chemical Education*, Vol. 44, No. 12 (December 1967), pp. 740-744.

*Ott, J. Bevan, Goates, J. Rex, and Hall, H. Tracey, Jr., "Comparisons of Equations of State in Effectively Describing PVT Relations." *Journal of Chemical Education*, Vol. 48, No. 8 (August 1971), pp. 515-517.

Sienko, M. J., *Chemical Problems*. Menlo Park, California, W. A. Benjamin, Inc., 1972, 2nd Ed., Chapter 7.

*Wilhelm, Emmerich, and Battino, Rubin, "Thermodynamic Functions of the Solubilities of Gases in Liquids at 25°C." *Chemical Reviews*, Vol. 73, No. 1 (February 1973), pp. 1-9.

(*Faculty only)

Chapter 16

Performance Objectives

GOAL: Students will gain an understanding of the molar volume of a gas and its use in solving gas reaction problems.

Objectives: Upon completion of the reading and activities, and when asked to diagram, demonstrate, or respond either orally or on a written test, students will:

16:1-2	K,P	determine the molar volume of a gas by means of Avogadro's Principle.
16:3	P,S	find the fourth variable given any three of pressure, temperature, volume, and number of particles of a gas by use of the ideal gas equation.
16:4	P,S	determine molecular mass from gas density.
16:5-10	P,S	find the volume or mass of reactants or products in a reaction involving gases given the mass or volume of one or more of the reactants or products under standard or non standard conditions.

Upon completion of the reading and activities, students will exhibit an interest in science by:

A	voluntarily completing one or more of the One More Step activities listed at the end of the chapter on their own time.
A	reading unassigned literature related to the ideas presented in the chapter.

Page 345.   Section 16:3

1. $P = \dfrac{nRT}{V}$

$$\frac{0.300 \text{ mole} \left| 0.082 \text{ l-atm} \right| (18 + 273)°\text{K}}{8.00 \text{ l} \left| 1 \text{ mole-}°\text{K} \right|} = 0.896 \text{ atm}$$

2. $n = \dfrac{PV}{RT}$

$$\frac{1 \text{ mole-}°\text{K} \left| 500 \text{ torr} \right| 1 \text{ atm} \left| 486 \text{ ml} \right| 1 \text{ l}}{0.0821 \text{ l-atm} \left| (10 + 273)°\text{K} \right| 760 \text{ torr} \left| \right| 1000 \text{ ml}} = 0.0138 \text{ mole}$$

283

Page 346.   Section 16:4

3. $M = \dfrac{mRT}{PV}$

$$\frac{0.800\ g}{800\ \cancel{torr}} \left| \frac{760\ \cancel{torr}}{1\ \cancel{atm}} \right| \frac{0.0821\ \cancel{l\text{-}atm}}{1\ mole\text{-}^{\circ}\cancel{K}} \left| \frac{373^{\circ}\cancel{K}}{372\ \cancel{ml}} \right| \frac{1000\ \cancel{ml}}{1\ \cancel{l}} = 62.6\ g/mole$$

4. $\dfrac{32\ g}{22.4\ l} \left| \dfrac{754\ \cancel{torr}}{760\ \cancel{torr}} \right| \dfrac{273^{\circ}K}{296^{\circ}K} = 1.31\ g/l$

Page 349.   Section 16:6

5. $3\ H_2(g) + N_2(g) \rightarrow 2\ NH_3(g)$

$$\frac{14\ \cancel{gN_2}}{28\ \cancel{gN_2}} \left| \frac{1\ \cancel{mole\ N_2}}{1\ \cancel{mole\ N_2}} \right| \frac{2\ \cancel{moles}\ NH_3}{1\ \cancel{mole}} \left| \frac{22.4\ l}{} \right| = 22.4\ l\ NH_3$$

6. $Zn(s) + H_2SO_4(aq) \rightarrow ZnSO_4(aq) + H_2(g)$

$$\frac{28\ \cancel{gZn}}{65.4\ \cancel{gZn}} \left| \frac{1\ \cancel{mole\ Zn}}{1\ \cancel{mole\ Zn}} \right| \frac{1\ \cancel{mole}\ H_2}{1\ \cancel{mole}} \left| \frac{22.4\ l}{} \right| = 9.59\ l\ H_2$$

7. $H_2(g) + Br_2(g) \rightarrow 2\ HBr(g)$

$$\frac{5.6\ \cancel{l\ H_2}}{22.4\ \cancel{l}} \left| \frac{1\ \cancel{mole}}{1\ mole\ \cancel{H_2}} \right| \frac{2\ \cancel{moles}\ HBr}{1\ \cancel{mole\ HBr}} \left| \frac{80.9\ g\ HBr}{} \right| = 40.5\ g\ HBr$$

8. $2\ Sb(s) + 3\ Cl_2(g) \rightarrow 2\ SbCl_3(s)$

$$\frac{6.72\ \cancel{l\ Cl_2}}{22.4\ \cancel{l}} \left| \frac{1\ \cancel{mole}}{3\ \cancel{moles\ Cl_2}} \right| \frac{2\ \cancel{moles\ SbCl_3}}{1\ \cancel{mole\ SbCl_3}} \left| \frac{228\ g\ SbCl_3}{} \right| = 45.6\ g\ SbCl_3$$

Page 356.   Section 16:8

9. $2\ C_4H_{10}(g) + 13\ O_2(g) \rightarrow 8\ CO_2(g) + 10\ H_2O(g)$

$$\frac{401\ \cancel{ml\ C_4H_{10}}}{} \left| \frac{13\ ml\ O_2}{2\ \cancel{ml\ C_4H_{10}}} \right| = 2610\ ml\ O_2 = 2.61\ l\ O_2$$

10. $\dfrac{75.2\ \cancel{ml\ Cl_2}}{} \left| \dfrac{1\ ml\ Br_2}{1\ \cancel{ml\ Cl_2}} \right| = 75.2\ ml\ Br_2$

11. $\dfrac{2.10\ \cancel{g\ NaBr}}{} \left| \dfrac{1\ mole\ NaBr}{103\ \cancel{g\ NaBr}} \right| = 0.0204\ mole\ NaBr\ \text{(limiting reactant)}$

$$\frac{9.42\ \cancel{g\ H_2SO_4}}{} \left| \frac{1\ mole\ H_2SO_4}{98.1\ \cancel{g\ H_2SO_4}} \right| = 0.0960\ mole\ H_2SO_4$$

$$\frac{0.0204\ \cancel{mole\ NaBr}}{} \left| \frac{1\ \cancel{mole\ Br_2}}{2\ \cancel{moles\ NaBr}} \right| \frac{160\ g\ Br_2}{1\ \cancel{mole\ Br_2}} = 1.63\ g\ Br_2$$

12. $\dfrac{4.14\ \cancel{g\ Ca_3(PO_4)_2}}{} \left| \dfrac{1\ mole\ Ca_3(PO_4)_2}{310\ \cancel{g\ Ca_3(PO_4)_2}} \right| = 0.0134\ mole\ Ca_3(PO_4)_2$

$$\frac{1.20 \text{ g } SiO_2 \mid 1 \text{ mole } SiO_2}{\mid 60.1 \text{ g } SiO_2} = 0.0200 \text{ mole } SiO_2 \text{ (limiting reactant)}$$

$$\frac{0.0200 \text{ mole } SiO_2 \mid 10 \text{ moles } CO \mid 22.4 \text{ l}}{\mid 6 \text{ moles } SiO_2 \mid 1 \text{ mole}} = 0.747 \text{ l } CO$$

13. $O_2(g) + 2 NO(g) \rightarrow 2 NO_2(g)$

$$\frac{0.500 \text{ l } NO \mid 1 \text{ l } O_2}{\mid 2 \text{ l } NO} = 0.250 \text{ l } O_2$$

14. $$\frac{941 \text{ ml } C_6H_6 \mid 4 \text{ ml } H_2}{\mid 1 \text{ ml } C_6H_6} = 3760 \text{ ml } H_2$$

15. $$\frac{4.11 \text{ g } I_2 \mid 1 \text{ mole } I_2}{\mid 254 \text{ g } I_2} = 0.0162 \text{ mole } I_2$$

$$\frac{317 \text{ ml } H_2S \mid 1 \text{ mole}}{\mid 22,400 \text{ ml}} = 0.0142 \text{ mole } H_2S \text{ (limiting reactant)}$$

$$\frac{0.0142 \text{ mole } H_2S \mid 1 \text{ mole } S \mid 32.1 \text{ g } S}{\mid 1 \text{ mole } H_2S \mid 1 \text{ mole } S} = 0.456 \text{ g } S$$

16. $$\frac{116 \text{ ml } Cl_2 \mid 1 \text{ mole}}{\mid 22,400 \text{ ml}} = 0.00518 \text{ mole } Cl_2 \text{ (limiting reactant)}$$

$$\frac{7.62 \text{ g } HgO \mid 1 \text{ mole } HgO}{\mid 217 \text{ g } HgO} = 0.0351 \text{ mole } HgO$$

$$\frac{116 \text{ ml } Cl_2 \mid 1 \text{ ml } Cl_2O}{\mid 2 \text{ ml } Cl_2} = 58.0 \text{ ml } Cl_2O$$

Page 359. End of Chapter

17. $$P = \frac{nRT}{V} = \frac{0.4 \text{ mole} \mid 0.0821 \text{ l-atm} \mid 300°K}{10 \text{ l} \mid \text{mole-}°K \mid} = 0.985 \text{ atm}$$

18. $$M = \frac{mRT}{V} = \frac{10.0 \text{ g} \mid 760 \text{ torr} \mid 0.0821 \text{ l-atm} \mid 250°K}{380 \text{ torr} \mid 1 \text{ atm} \mid 1 \text{ mole-}°K \mid 0.500 \text{ l}} = 821 \text{ g/mole}$$

19. $2 C_2H_6(g) + 7 O_2(g) \rightarrow 4 CO_2(g) + 6 H_2O(g)$

$$\frac{10.0 \text{ l } C_2H_6 \mid 4 \text{ l } CO_2}{\mid 2 \text{ l } C_2H_6} = 20.0 \text{ l } CO_2$$

20. $$\dfrac{10.0 \ \cancel{1 \ C_2H_6}}{} \ \bigg| \ \dfrac{7 \ 1 \ O_2}{2 \ \cancel{1 \ C_2H_6}} = 35.0 \ 1 \ O_2$$

21. $CS_2(g) + 3 \ O_2(g) \quad \rightarrow CO_2(g) + 2 \ SO_2(g)$

$$\dfrac{7.00 \ \cancel{1 \ CS_2}}{} \ \bigg| \ \dfrac{2 \ 1 \ SO_2}{1 \ \cancel{1 \ CS_2}} = 14 \ 1 \ SO_2$$

22. $$\dfrac{7.00 \ \cancel{1 \ CS_2}}{} \ \bigg| \ \dfrac{1 \ 1 \ CO_2}{1 \ \cancel{1 \ CS_2}} \ \bigg| \ \dfrac{1 \ mole}{22.4 \ 1}$$
$$= 0.313 \ mole \ CO_2$$

23. $Ni(s) + S(g) \rightarrow NiS(s)$

$$Ni = \dfrac{10.0}{58.7} = 0.170 \ moles$$

$$S = \dfrac{4.00}{32.1} = 0.125 \ moles$$

S is the limiting reactant

$$\dfrac{0.125 \ \cancel{moles \ S}}{} \ \bigg| \ \dfrac{1 \ \cancel{mole \ NiS}}{1 \ \cancel{mole \ S}} \ \bigg| \ \dfrac{90.8 \ g \ NiS}{1 \ \cancel{mole \ NiS}}$$
$$= 11.4 \ g \ NiS$$

24. $CaO(s) + H_2O(l) \rightarrow Ca(OH)_2(aq)$

$$CaO = \dfrac{7.00}{56.1} = 0.125 \ moles$$

$$H_2O = \dfrac{2.00}{18.0} = 0.111 \ moles$$

H_2O is the limiting reactant

$$\dfrac{0.111 \ \cancel{moles \ H_2O}}{} \ \bigg| \ \dfrac{1 \ \cancel{mole \ Ca(OH)_2}}{1 \ \cancel{mole \ H_2O}} \ \bigg| \ \dfrac{74.1 \ g \ Ca(OH)_2}{1 \ \cancel{mole \ Ca(OH)_2}} = 8.23 \ g \ Ca(OH)_2$$

25. $2 \ Na(s) + Cl_2(g) \rightarrow 2 \ NaCl(c)$

$$Na = \dfrac{23.0}{23.0} = 1 \ mole$$

Na is the limiting reactant (2 moles Na required for 1 mole Cl_2)

$$Cl_2 = \dfrac{22.4}{22.4} = 1 \ mole$$

$$\dfrac{1 \ \cancel{mole \ Na}}{} \ \bigg| \ \dfrac{2 \ \cancel{moles \ NaCl}}{2 \ \cancel{moles \ Na}} \ \bigg| \ \dfrac{58.5 \ g \ NaCl}{1 \ \cancel{mole \ NaCl}}$$
$$= 58.5 \ g \ NaCl$$

26. $$Fe_2O_3 = \dfrac{16.0}{160} = 0.100 \ mole$$

Fe_2O_3 is the limiting reactant (0.1 mole Fe_2O_3 required for 0.3 mole CO)

$$CO = \dfrac{10.0}{22.4} = 0.446 \ mole$$

$$\dfrac{0.100 \ \cancel{mole \ Fe_2O_3}}{} \ \bigg| \ \dfrac{3 \ \cancel{moles} \ CO_2}{1 \ \cancel{mole \ Fe_2O_3}} \ \bigg| \ \dfrac{22.4 \ 1}{1 \ \cancel{mole}} = 6.72 \ 1 \ CO_2$$

27.
$$\frac{6.72 \, l \; | \; 300°\cancel{K} \; | \; 760 \, \cancel{torr}}{273°\cancel{K} \; | \; 800 \, \cancel{torr}}$$
$$= 7.02 \, l \, CO_2$$

28.
$$\frac{44 \, g \; | \; 273°\cancel{K} \; | \; 800 \, \cancel{torr}}{22.4 \, l \; | \; 300°\cancel{K} \; | \; 760 \, \cancel{torr}} = 1.88 \, g/l$$

29. Gay-Lussac's Law states that one volume of nitrogen will produce two volumes of ammonia when combined with the appropriate amount of hydrogen. Avogadro's hypothesis, that equal volumes contain the same number of molecules under the same conditions, can be extended to say that twice the volume would contain twice the molecules. From this we can see that a given number of nitrogen molecules will produce twice their number of ammonia molecules, or one nitrogen molecule produces two ammonia molecules. Each ammonia molecule must contain at least one whole nitrogen atom, so the original nitrogen molecule must have contained at least two nitrogen atoms.

Page 359.   One More Step

1. In 1858 Cannizzaro wrote a paper in an Italian scientific journal in which he explained how Avogadro's hypothesis could be used in teaching chemistry. At the Karlsruhe Congress in 1860, Cannizzaro argued persuasively for the adoption of Avogadro's hypothesis and won over a number of prominent chemists. Distribution of reprints of the earlier paper also bore fruit when some of the delegates had a chance to read it at length after the congress.

2. In a time-of-flight spectrometer, a burst or pulse of ionized particles is fired through a series of electrodes or grids. Ions of different mass require varying times to transit the path; by proper interpretation of the electrode currents, the sample may be analyzed for e/m values.

3. The amount of materials to be used in the iron foundry could be calculated. Analysis could be used to determine whether the iron had the correct amount of carbon, manganese, and other additives. Knowledge of reactions to produce a given amount of a product could be used. Mostly these would involve mass-mass rather than mass-volume problems, however. Students may wish to check into the chemistry of iron more closely.

Suggested Readings for Faculty and Students

Bowman, William H., and Lawrence, Richard M., "The Cabin Atmosphere in Manned Space Vehicles." *Journal of Chemical Education,* Vol. 48, No. 3 (March 1971), pp. 152-153.

*Brown, Theodore L., "The Chemistry of Metallic Elements in the Ionosphere and Mesosphere." *Chemical Reviews,* Vol. 73, No. 6 (December 1973), pp. 645-667.

*McEwan, Murray J., and Phillips, Leon F., "Chemistry in the Upper Atmosphere." *Acounts of Chemical Research,* Vol. 3, No. 1 (January 1970), pp. 9-17.

McFarland, John H., and Benton, C. S., "The Oxides of Nitrogen and Their Detection in Automotive Exhaust." *Journal of Chemical Education,* Vol. 49, No. 1 (January 1972), pp. 21-24.

Rakestraw, Norris W., "Controlling Breathing Atmospheres." *Chemistry,* Vol. 43, No. 9 (October 1970), pp. 18-23.

(*Faculty only)

Chapter 17

Performance Objectives

GOAL: Students will gain an understanding of the relationship of enthalpy, entropy, and free energy to chemical reactions.

Objectives: Upon completion of the reading and activities, and when asked to diagram, demonstrate, or respond either orally or on a written test, students will:

17:1-2 K   define entropy and enthalpy and explain their relationship to exothermic and endothermic reactions.

Page 371.   End of Chapter

1. $\Delta G° = \Delta G_f°$ products $- \Delta G_f°$ reactants

   $\Delta G° =$ [1 mole $(-75,080$ cal/mole$)$ $+ 1$ mole $(0$ cal/mole$)] -$ [1 mole $(-62,600$ cal/mole$) +$ 1 mole $(0$ cal/mole$)]$

   $\Delta G° = -12,480$ cal

   $\Delta G° < 0$, reaction spontaneous

2. $\Delta G° = (-54,634) - (-56,687)$

   $\Delta G° = +2053$ cal

   $\Delta G° > 0$, reaction not spontaneous

3. $\Delta G° =$ [8 $(-94,258) + 10$ $(-56,687)] -$ [2 (-3754)]

   $\Delta G° = -1,313,426$ cal

   $\Delta G° < 0$, reaction spontaneous

4. $\Delta G° =$ [2 $(-11,700)$] $-$ [1 $(-20,600) + 1$ (0)]

   $\Delta G° = -2800$ cal

$\Delta G° < 0$, reaction spontaneous

5. $\Delta G° =$ [1 $(-158,200)$] $-$ [1 $(-11,700) + 2$ (0)]

   $\Delta G° = -146,500$ cal

   $\Delta G° < 0$, reaction spontaneous

6. $Hg_2Cl_2 + Cl_2 \rightarrow 2\ HgCl_2$

Value (per mole)	Hg_2Cl_2	Cl_2	$HgCl_2$
$\Delta G_f°$	$-50,377$	0	$-42,200$
$\Delta H_f°$	$-63,390$	0	$-55,000$
$S°$	46.0	53.288	28.5

$\Delta H° = 2\ (-55,000$ cal$) - (-63,390$ cal$)$

$\Delta H° = -46,610$ cal

$\Delta G° = 2\ (-42,200$ cal$) - (-50,377$ cal$)$

$\Delta G° = -34,023$ cal

$\Delta S° = -\dfrac{(\Delta G° - \Delta H°)}{T}$ $T = 25° + 273°$
$= 298°K$

$\Delta S° = -\dfrac{(-34,023\text{ cal}) - (-46,610\text{ cal})}{298°K}$

$\Delta S° = -\dfrac{12,587\text{ cal}}{298°K} = -42.2$ cal/°K

$\Delta S° = S°$ products $- S°$ reactants

-42.2 cal/°K $= S°$ products $-$ $(46.0 + 53.288)$

$S°$ products (2 moles $HgCl_2$) $= 57.09$

$S°\ HgCl_2 = \dfrac{57.09}{2} = 28.5$ cal/°K

7. $3\ Be + N_2 \rightarrow Be_3N_2$

Value (per mole)	Be	N_2	Be_3N_2
$\Delta G_f°$	0	0	$-122,400$
$\Delta H_f°$	0	0	$-135,700$
$S°$	2.28	45.77	(3.45)

$$\Delta G° = (-122{,}400) - 3(0) + (0)$$

$$\Delta G° = -122{,}400 \text{ cal}$$

$$\Delta H° = (-135{,}700) - 3(0) + (0)$$

$$\Delta H° = -135{,}700 \text{ cal}$$

$$\Delta S° = -\frac{\Delta G - \Delta H}{T}$$

$$\Delta S° = -\frac{(-122{,}400) - (-135{,}700)}{298°}$$

$$\Delta S° = -44.6 \text{ cal/°K}$$

$$-44.6 = S° \text{ Be}_3\text{N}_2 - (2.28 + 45.77)$$

$$S° \text{ Be}_3\text{N}_2 = 3.45 \text{ cal/°K}$$

8. $CoCO_3 \rightarrow CoO + CO_2$

Value (per mole)	CoCO₃	CoO	CO₂
ΔG_f^o	−155,360	−51,000	−94,258
ΔH_f^o	−172,700	−57,200	−94,051
$S°$	(23.5)	10.5	51.06

$$\Delta G° = [(-51{,}000) + (-94{,}258)] - (-155{,}360)$$

$$\Delta G° = 10{,}102 \text{ cal}$$

$$\Delta H° = [(-94{,}051) + (-57{,}200)] - (-172{,}700)$$

$$\Delta H° = 21{,}449 \text{ cal}$$

$$\Delta S° = \frac{\Delta G° - \Delta H°}{T} = \frac{\Delta H° - \Delta G°}{T}$$

$$\Delta S° = -\frac{10{,}102 - 21{,}449}{298}$$

$$\Delta S° = 38.1 \text{ cal/°K}$$

$$38.1 = (10.5 + 51.06) - (S°_{\text{CoCO}_3})$$

$$S°_{\text{CoCO}_3} = 23.5 \text{ cal/°K}$$

9. $2\,H_2O_2 \rightarrow 2\,H_2O + O_2$

Value (per mole)	H₂O₂	H₂O(l)	O₂
ΔG_f^o	−28,780	−56,687	0
ΔH_f^o	−44,881	−68,315	0
$S°$	26.2	16.71	49,003

Find $\Delta S°$ first.

$$\Delta S° = [2\,(16.71) + 49.003] - [2\,(26.2)]$$

$$\Delta S° = 30.02 \text{ cal/°K}$$

Then find $\Delta G°$.

$$\Delta G° = [2\,(-56{,}687) + 0] - [2\,(-28{,}780)]$$

$$\Delta G° = -55{,}814 \text{ cal}$$

$$\Delta H° = \Delta G° + T\Delta S°$$

$$\Delta H° = -55{,}814 + 298\,(30.02)$$

$$\Delta H° = -46{,}868 \text{ cal}$$

$$\Delta H° = \Delta H° \text{ products} - \Delta H° \text{ reactants}$$

$$-46{,}868 = [2\,(-68{,}315) + 0] - 2\,\Delta H_{\text{H}_2\text{O}_2}$$

$$\Delta H°_{\text{H}_2\text{O}_2} = -44{,}881 \text{ cal}$$

10. $2NO + O_2 \rightarrow 2NO_2$

Value (per mole)	NO	O₂	NO₂
ΔG_f^o	(20,685)	0	12,260
ΔH_f^o	21,570	0	7930
$S°$	50,347	49,003	57.35

$$\Delta S° = [2\,(57.35)] - [2\,(50.347) + (49.003)]$$

$$\Delta S° = -34.997 \text{ cal/°K}$$

$$\Delta H° = [2\,(7930)] - [2\,(21{,}570) + 0]$$

$$\Delta H° = -27{,}280 \text{ cal}$$

$$\Delta G° = \Delta H° - T\Delta S°$$

$$\Delta G° = (-27{,}280) - 298\,(-34{,}997)$$

$$\Delta G^\circ = -16{,}851 \text{ cal}$$

$$-16{,}851 = [2\,(12{,}260)] - [2\Delta G^\circ{}_{NO} + 0]$$

$$\Delta G^\circ_{f\,NO} = 20{,}685 \text{ cal}$$

Page 371.   One More Step

1. Heat capacity is the heat required to raise the temperature of a certain amount of a substance a specified number of degrees, usually one.

   Heat content is used in two ways by chemists: (a) The total thermal (kinetic) energy of molecules determined by their mass and velocity. (b) The enthalpy, which is the heat lost (or gained) during an isothermal reaction.

2. Work function is usually known as the Helmholtz free energy. It is represented by the letter A and is defined by the equation $A = E - TS$. It is of use principally in constant-volume systems and is not as useful as G for chemists who are usually working at constant pressure. ΔA represents the maximum work obtainable from a constant-volume, isothermal process. If $\Delta A > 0$, then work must be done on the system. In a similar manner, ΔG is the maximum work at constant pressure and temperature.

Suggested Readings for Faculty and Students

*Bent, Henry A., "The First Law." *Journal of Chemical Education*, Vol. 50, No. 5 (May 1973), pp. 323-328.

Dasent, W. E., *Inorganic Energetics.* Baltimore, Penguin Books, 1970.

Keller, Eugenia, "Photography." *Chemistry*, Part I, Vol. 43, No. 9 (October 1970), pp. 6-12; Part II, Vol. 43, No. 11 (December 1970), pp. 8-11.

Kitaigorodskiy, A. I., *Order and Disorder in the World of Atoms.* New York, Springer-Verlag Inc., 1967.

*Kittel, Charles, *Thermal Physics.* New York, John Wiley and Sons, Inc., 1969, Chapters 4, 5, 7, 18, 19, and 21 (An advanced work.)

Sanderson, R. T., *Inorganic Chemistry.* New York, Reinhold Publishing Corp., 1967, Chapter 10.

Schneider, H. W., "A New, Long-Lasting Luminol Chemiluminescent Cold Light." *Journal of Chemical Education*, Vol. 47, No. 7 (July 1970), pp. 519-522.

Schubert, Leo, "The How and Why of Chemical Reactions." *The Science Teacher*, Vol. 37, No. 1 (January 1970), pp. 45-52.

*White, Emil H., and Roswell, David F., "The Chemiluminescence of Organic Hydrazides." *Accounts of Chemical Research*, Vol. 3, No. 2 (February 1970), pp. 54-62.

Wildeman, Thomas R., "The Automobile and Air Pollution." *Journal of Chemical Education*, Vol. 51, No. 5 (May 1974), pp. 290-294.

(*Faculty only)

Chapter 18

Performance Objectives

GOAL: Students will gain an understanding of the various types of solutions and their properties as well as the properties of colloids.

Objectives: Upon completion of the reading and activities, and when asked to diagram, demonstrate, or respond either orally or in a written test, students will:

18:1	K	describe the solvation mechanism.
18:2-5	K	list the types, kinds, and concentration descriptions of solutions.
18:6-8	K	describe the factors which affect solution rate.
18:9-11	K,P,S	solve problems involving molar concentration, molal concentration, and mole fraction of solutions.
18:12-16	K,P	utilize Raoult's Law to develop, explain, or solve problems related to: a. fractional distillation b. boiling point elevation c. freezing point depression d. molecular mass
18:17	K	explain solution deviations due to ion activity.

18:18-21 K describe the properties of colloids and their uses in the everyday world.

Upon completion of the reading and activities, students will exhibit an interest in science by:

A voluntarily completing one or more of the One More Step activities listed at the end of the chapter on their own time.

A reading unassigned literature related to the ideas presented in the chapter.

Page 382. Section 18:11

1. a. $\dfrac{316\ \cancel{g\ MgBr_2}}{859\ \cancel{ml\ sol'n}} \bigg| \dfrac{1\ \text{mole}\ MgBr_2}{184\ \cancel{g\ MgBr_2}} \bigg| \dfrac{1000\ \cancel{ml\ sol'n}}{1\ l} = 2.00\ \text{M}\ MgBr_2\ (\text{mole}/l = \text{M})$

b. $\dfrac{8.28\ \cancel{g\ Ca(C_5H_9O_2)_2}}{414\ \cancel{ml\ sol'n}} \bigg| \dfrac{1\ \text{mole}\ Ca(C_5H_9O_2)_2}{242\ \cancel{g\ Ca(C_5H_9O_2)_2}} \bigg| \dfrac{1000\ \cancel{ml\ sol'n}}{1\ l} = 0.0826\text{M}\ Ca(C_5H_9O_2)_2$

c. $\dfrac{31.1\ \cancel{g\ Al_2(SO_4)_3}}{756\ \cancel{ml\ sol'n}} \bigg| \dfrac{1\ \text{mole}\ Al_2\,(SO_4)_3}{342\ \cancel{g\ Al_2(SO_4)_3}} \bigg| \dfrac{1000\ \cancel{ml\ sol'n}}{1\ l} = 0.120\text{M}\ Al_2(SO_4)_3$

d. $\dfrac{59.5\ \cancel{g\ CaCl_2}}{100\ \cancel{ml\ sol'n}} \bigg| \dfrac{1\ \text{mole}\ CaCl_2}{111\ \cancel{g\ CaCl_2}} \bigg| \dfrac{1000\ \cancel{ml\ sol'n}}{1\ l} = 5.36\text{M}\ CaCl_2$

e. $\dfrac{313.5\ \cancel{g\ LiClO_3}}{250\ \cancel{ml\ sol'n}} \bigg| \dfrac{1\ \text{mole}\ LiClO_3}{90.4\ \cancel{g\ LiClO_3}} \bigg| \dfrac{1000\ \cancel{ml\ sol'n}}{1\ l} = 13.9\text{M}\ LiClO_3$

2. a. $\dfrac{199\ \cancel{g\ NiBr_2}}{500\ \cancel{g\ H_2O}} \bigg| \dfrac{1\ \text{mole}\ NiBr_2}{219\ \cancel{g\ NiBr_2}} \bigg| \dfrac{1000\ \cancel{g\ H_2O}}{1\ kg\ H_2O} = 1.82\text{m}\ NiBr_2\ (\text{mole}/kg = \text{m})$

b. $\dfrac{92.3\ \cancel{g\ KF}}{1000\ \cancel{g\ H_2O}} \bigg| \dfrac{1\ \text{mole}\ KF}{58.1\ \cancel{g\ KF}} \bigg| \dfrac{1000\ \cancel{g\ H_2O}}{1\ kg\ H_2O} = 1.59\text{m}\ KF$

c. $\dfrac{98.0\ \cancel{g\ RbBr}}{824\ \cancel{g\ H_2O}} \bigg| \dfrac{1\ \text{mole}\ RbBr}{165\ \cancel{g\ RbBr}} \bigg| \dfrac{1000\ \cancel{g\ H_2O}}{1\ kg\ H_2O} = 0.721\text{m}\ RbBr$

d. $\dfrac{85.2\ \cancel{g\ SnBr_2}}{140\ \cancel{g\ H_2O}} \bigg| \dfrac{1\ \text{mole}\ SnBr_2}{279\ \cancel{g\ SnBr_2}} \bigg| \dfrac{1000\ \cancel{g\ H_2O}}{1\ kg\ H_2O} = 2.18\text{m}\ SnBr_2$

e. $\dfrac{10.0\ \cancel{g\ AgClO_3}}{201\ \cancel{g\ H_2O}} \bigg| \dfrac{1\ \text{mole}\ AgClO_3}{191\ \cancel{g\ AgClO_3}} \bigg| \dfrac{1000\ \cancel{g\ H_2O}}{1\ kg\ H_2O} = 0.260\text{m}\ AgClO_3$

3. a. $\dfrac{12.3\ \cancel{g}}{} \bigg| \dfrac{1\ \text{mole}}{68.0\ \cancel{g}} = 0.181\ \text{moles}\ C_4H_4O \qquad \dfrac{0.181\ \cancel{\text{mole}}}{2.35\ \cancel{\text{mole}}} = 0.0770\ \text{mole fraction}\ C_4H_4O$

$\dfrac{100\ \cancel{g}}{} \bigg| \dfrac{1\ \text{mole}}{46\ \cancel{g}} = 2.17\ \text{moles}\ C_2H_6O \qquad \dfrac{2.17\ \cancel{\text{mole}}}{2.35\ \cancel{\text{mole}}} = 0.923\ \text{mole fraction}\ C_2H_6O$

total number of moles $= 2.35$

b.

$$\frac{56.3 \text{ g}}{} \left| \frac{1 \text{ mole}}{342 \text{ g}} \right.$$

$$= 0.165 \text{ moles } C_{12}H_{22}O_{11}$$

$$\frac{300 \text{ g}}{} \left| \frac{1 \text{ mole}}{18 \text{ g}} \right. = 16.7 \text{ moles } H_2O$$

total moles $= 16.865 = 16.9$

$$\frac{0.165 \text{ mole}}{16.9 \text{ mole}}$$

$$= 0.00976 \text{ mole fraction } C_{12}H_{22}O_{11}$$

$$\frac{16.7 \text{ moles}}{16.9 \text{ moles}} = 0.988 \text{ mole fraction } H_2O$$

c.

$$\frac{54.3 \text{ g}}{} \left| \frac{1 \text{ mole}}{128 \text{ g}} \right. = 0.424 \text{ moles } C_{10}H_8$$

$$\frac{600 \text{ g}}{} \left| \frac{1 \text{ mole}}{74 \text{ g}} \right. = 8.11 \text{ moles } C_4H_{10}O$$

total moles $= 8.53$

$$\frac{0.424 \text{ moles}}{8.53 \text{ moles}}$$

$$= 0.0497 \text{ mole fraction } C_{10}H_8$$

$$\frac{8.11 \text{ moles}}{8.53 \text{ moles}}$$

$$= 0.951 \text{ mole fraction } C_4H_{10}O$$

d.

$$\frac{67.4 \text{ g}}{} \left| \frac{1 \text{ mole}}{129 \text{ g}} \right. = 0.522 \text{ moles } C_9H_7N$$

$$\frac{200 \text{ g}}{} \left| \frac{1 \text{ mole}}{46 \text{ g}} \right. = 4.35 \text{ moles } C_2H_6O$$

total moles $= 4.87$

$$\frac{0.522 \text{ moles}}{4.87 \text{ moles}}$$

$$= 0.107 \text{ mole fraction } C_9H_7N$$

$$\frac{4.35 \text{ moles}}{4.87 \text{ moles}}$$

$$= 0.893 \text{ mole fraction } C_2H_6O$$

e.

$$\frac{5.48 \text{ g}}{} \left| \frac{1 \text{ mole}}{150 \text{ g}} \right.$$

$$= 0.0365 \text{ moles } C_5H_{10}O_5$$

$$\frac{3.15 \text{ g}}{} \left| \frac{1 \text{ mole}}{90 \text{ g}} \right.$$

$$= 0.0350 \text{ moles } CH_6ON_4$$

$$\frac{21.2 \text{ g}}{} \left| \frac{1 \text{ mole}}{18 \text{ g}} \right. = 1.18 \text{ moles } H_2O$$

total moles $= 1.25$

$$\frac{0.0365 \text{ mole}}{1.25 \text{ mole}}$$

$$= 0.0292 \text{ mole fraction } C_5H_{10}O_5$$

$$\frac{0.0350 \text{ mole}}{1.25 \text{ mole}}$$

$$= 0.0280 \text{ mole fraction } CH_6ON_4$$

$$\frac{1.18 \text{ mole}}{1.25 \text{ mole}} = 0.944 \text{ mole fraction } H_2O$$

Page 391. Section 18:16

4. a.

$$\frac{0.430 \text{ C}°}{1.86 \text{ C}°} \left| \frac{1 \text{ mole solute}}{1 \text{ kg } H_2O} \right.$$

$$= 0.231 \text{ moles solute/kg } H_2O$$

$$\frac{6.70 \text{ g solute}}{983 \text{ g } H_2O} \left| \frac{1000 \text{ g } H_2O}{1 \text{ kg } H_2O} \right.$$

$$= 6.82 \text{ g solute/kg } H_2O,$$

$$\frac{6.82 \text{ g}}{0.231 \text{ moles}} = 29.5 \text{ g/mole}$$

b.

$$\frac{0.680 \text{ C}°}{0.512 \text{ C}°} \left| \frac{1 \text{ mole solute}}{1 \text{ kg } H_2O} \right.$$

$$= 1.33 \text{ moles solute/kg } H_2O$$

$$\frac{42.6 \text{ g solute}}{189 \text{ g } H_2O} \left| \frac{1000 \text{ g } H_2O}{1.33 \text{ mole solute}} \right.$$

$$= 169 \text{ g/mole}$$

c.

$$\frac{3.1 \text{ C}°}{3.9 \text{ C}°} \left| \frac{1 \text{ mole solute}}{1 \text{ kg } CH_3COOH} \right.$$

$$= 0.795 \text{ mole solute/kg } CH_3COOH$$

$$\frac{17.2 \text{ g}}{128 \text{ g } CH_3COOH} \left| \frac{1000 \text{ g } CH_3COOH}{1 \text{ kg } CH_3COOH} \right.$$

$$= 134 \text{ g/kg } CH_3COOH$$

$$\frac{134 \text{ g}}{0.795 \text{ mole}} = 169 \text{ g/mole}$$

d. $\dfrac{4.7 \; \cancel{C} \;}{7.4 \; \cancel{C} \;} \begin{array}{|l} 1 \text{ mole solute} \\ \hline 1 \text{ kg phenol} \end{array}$

$$= 0.635 \text{ mole solute/kg phenol}$$

$$\frac{15.9 \text{ g solute}}{164 \text{ g phenol}} \begin{array}{|l} 1000 \text{ g phenol} \\ \hline 1 \text{ kg phenol} \end{array}$$

$$= 97.0 \text{ g solute/kg phenol}$$

$$\frac{97.0 \text{ g}}{0.635 \text{ mole}} = 153 \text{ g/mole}$$

e. $\dfrac{2.3 \; \cancel{C} \;}{7.0 \; \cancel{C} \;} \begin{array}{|l} 1 \text{ mole solute} \\ \hline 1 \text{ kg nitrobenzene} \end{array}$

$$= 0.329 \text{ mole solute/kg nitrobenzene}$$

$$\frac{3.54 \text{ g}}{63.5 \text{ g nitrobenzene}} \begin{array}{|l} 1000 \text{ g nitrobenzene} \\ \hline 1 \text{ kg nitrobenzene} \end{array}$$

$$= 55.7 \text{ g/kg nitrobenzene}$$

$$\frac{55.7 \text{ g}}{0.329 \text{ mole}} = 169 \text{ g/mole}$$

Page 394.   Section 18:20

The following apparatus is simple, easy to construct, and is quite suitable for demonstrations.

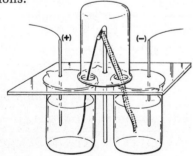

Cover two-250 ml beakers with a lucite plate. In the center of the plate, drill a hole just large enough to allow a glass rod to pass through. The glass rod should be L-shaped. It is used to support the paper. Drill two more holes in the plate large enough to allow the paper strip to dip into the buffer solutions. Invert a tall 250 ml beaker or a ten or twelve ounce water glass over the paper strip. Place a small amount of the solution to be tested, enough to make a spot, at the apex of the paper strip and apply approximately 300 volts across the electrodes.

Use filter paper saturated with buffer solution for this separation. Place a large amount of buffer solution (approx. pH of 7) in the two beakers. If hydrolyzed egg albumin is used, the pH of the buffer should be about 7.2. A 5 to 10 volt DC voltage should be applied for each centimeter of paper. Add one drop of a $\frac{1}{2}\%$ solution of albumin or less of a more cencentrated solution.

Remove the strip after approximately 30 minutes or an hour, dry, spray with a 0.1% ninhydrin solution and dry again in an oven or on a hot plate.

Page 400.   End of Chapter

5. a. not soluble (polar-nonpolar)

b. not soluble — Students may predict solubility since the solvent and solute are similar. This is an example of a general rule which does not hold in every case.

c. miscible (infinite solubility)

d. not soluble (polar-nonpolar)

e. not soluble (polar-nonpolar)

6. a. slightly soluble (4.7 g/100 g H_2O)

b. soluble

c. soluble

d. not soluble

e. soluble

7. a. $\dfrac{1000 \text{ ml sol'n}}{} \begin{array}{|l|} 0.780 \text{ moles Sc(NO}_3)_3 \\ \hline 1000 \text{ ml sol'n} \end{array} \begin{array}{l|} 231 \text{ g Sc(NO}_3)_3 \\ \hline 1 \text{ mole Sc(NO}_3)_3 \end{array} = 180 \text{ g Sc(NO}_3)_3$

b. $\dfrac{200 \text{ ml sol'n}}{} \begin{array}{|l|} 0.301 \text{ moles Er}_2(SO_4)_3 \\ \hline 1000 \text{ ml sol'n} \end{array} \begin{array}{l|} 622 \text{ g Er}_2(SO_4)_3 \\ \hline 1 \text{ mole Er}_2(SO_4)_3 \end{array} = 37.4 \text{ g Er}_2(SO_4)_3$

c. $\dfrac{100 \text{ ml sol'n}}{} \left| \dfrac{0.626 \text{ mole VBr}_3}{1000 \text{ ml sol'n}} \right| \dfrac{291 \text{ g VBr}_3}{1 \text{ mole VBr}_3} = 18.2 \text{ g VBr}_3$

d. $\dfrac{250 \text{ ml sol'n}}{} \left| \dfrac{0.0965 \text{ mole DyCl}_3}{1000 \text{ ml sol'n}} \right| \dfrac{269 \text{ g DyCl}_3}{1 \text{ mole DyCl}_3} = 6.49 \text{ g DyCl}_3$

e. $\dfrac{500 \text{ ml sol'n}}{} \left| \dfrac{0.0978 \text{ mole IrCl}_4}{1000 \text{ ml sol'n}} \right| \dfrac{330 \text{ g IrCl}_4}{1 \text{ mole IrCl}_4} = 16.1 \text{ g IrCl}_4$

8. a. $\dfrac{1000 \text{ g H}_2\text{O}}{} \left| \dfrac{0.851 \text{ moles Fe}_2(\text{C}_2\text{O}_4)_3}{1000 \text{ g H}_2\text{O}} \right| \dfrac{376 \text{ g Fe}_2(\text{C}_2\text{O}_4)_3}{1 \text{ mole Fe}_2(\text{C}_2\text{O}_4)_3} = 320 \text{ g Fe}_2(\text{C}_2\text{O}_4)_3$

b. $\dfrac{1000 \text{ g H}_2\text{O}}{} \left| \dfrac{0.534 \text{ moles VOBr}_3}{1000 \text{ g H}_2\text{O}} \right| \dfrac{307 \text{ g VOBr}_3}{1 \text{ mole VOBr}_3} = 164 \text{ g VOBr}_3$

c. $\dfrac{200 \text{ g C}_2\text{H}_6\text{O}}{} \left| \dfrac{1 \text{ mole C}_2\text{H}_6\text{O}}{46.1 \text{ g C}_2\text{H}_6\text{O}} \right. = 4.34 \text{ moles C}_2\text{H}_6\text{O} \text{ (solvent)}$

$\dfrac{4.34}{0.510} = 8.51 \text{ moles solution}$

$8.51 - 4.34 = 4.17 \text{ moles solute}$

$\dfrac{4.16 \text{ moles C}_7\text{H}_4\text{O}_2\text{Br}_2}{} \left| \dfrac{280 \text{ g C}_7\text{H}_4\text{O}_2\text{Br}_2}{1 \text{ mole C}_7\text{H}_4\text{O}_2\text{Br}_2} \right. = 1170 \text{ g C}_7\text{H}_4\text{O}_2\text{Br}_2$

d. $\dfrac{1000 \text{ g C}_4\text{H}_{10}\text{O}}{} \left| \dfrac{1 \text{ mole C}_4\text{H}_{10}\text{O}}{74.1 \text{ g C}_4\text{H}_{10}\text{O}} \right. = 13.5 \text{ mole C}_4\text{H}_{10}\text{O} \qquad \dfrac{13.5}{1 - 0.363} = 21.2 \text{ moles solution}$

$21.2 - 13.5 = 7.7 \text{ moles solute}$

$\dfrac{7.7 \text{ moles C}_{14}\text{H}_{16}\text{N}_2}{} \left| \dfrac{212 \text{ g C}_{14}\text{H}_{16}\text{N}_2}{1 \text{ mole C}_{14}\text{H}_{16}\text{N}_2} \right. = 1630 \text{ g C}_{14}\text{H}_{16}\text{N}_2$

e. $\dfrac{0.614 \text{ moles LiMnO}_4}{} \left| \dfrac{126 \text{ g LiMnO}_4}{1 \text{ mole LiMnO}_4} \right. = 77.4 \text{ g LiMnO}_4$

9. a. $\dfrac{1000 \text{ ml sol'n}}{} \left| \dfrac{0.0130 \text{ mole YBr}_3}{1000 \text{ ml sol'n}} \right| \dfrac{329 \text{ g YBr}_3}{1 \text{ mole YBr}_3} = 4.28 \text{ g YBr}_3$

b. $\dfrac{100 \text{ ml sol'n}}{} \left| \dfrac{0.528 \text{ mole Li}_2\text{SO}_4}{1000 \text{ ml sol'n}} \right| \dfrac{110 \text{ g Li}_2\text{SO}_4}{1 \text{ mole Li}_2\text{SO}_4} = 5.81 \text{ g Li}_2\text{SO}_4$

c. $\dfrac{200 \text{ ml sol'n}}{} \left| \dfrac{0.0469 \text{ moles KHC}_2\text{O}_4}{1000 \text{ ml sol'n}} \right| \dfrac{128 \text{ g KHC}_2\text{O}_4}{1 \text{ mole KHC}_2\text{O}_4} = 1.20 \text{ g KHC}_2\text{O}_4$

d. $\dfrac{250 \text{ ml sol'n}}{} \left| \dfrac{0.274 \text{ moles UO}_2(\text{NO}_3)_2 \cdot 6 \text{ H}_2\text{O}}{1000 \text{ ml sol'n}} \right| \dfrac{502 \text{ g UO}_2(\text{NO}_3)_2 \cdot 6 \text{ H}_2\text{O}}{1 \text{ mole UO}_2(\text{NO}_3)_2 \cdot 6 \text{ H}_2\text{O}}$

$= 34.4 \text{ g UO}_2(\text{NO}_3)_2 \cdot 6 \text{ H}_2\text{O}$

e. $$\frac{500 \text{ ml sol'n}}{} \left| \frac{0.512 \text{ mole HSO}_3\text{F}}{1000 \text{ ml sol'n}} \right| \frac{100 \text{ g HSO}_3\text{F}}{1 \text{ mole HSO}_3\text{F}} = 25.6 \text{ g HSO}_3\text{F}$$

10. a. $$\frac{97.5 \text{ g C}_{12}\text{H}_{22}\text{O}_{11}}{185 \text{ g H}_2\text{O}} \left| \frac{1 \text{ mole C}_{12}\text{H}_{22}\text{O}_{11}}{342 \text{ g C}_{12}\text{H}_{22}\text{O}_{11}} \right| \frac{1000 \text{ g H}_2\text{O}}{1 \text{ kg H}_2\text{O}} = 1.54m$$

B.P. $= 100° + 1.54° \times 0.512° = 100.788°C$

F.P. $= 0° - 1.54° \times 1.86° = -2.86°C$

b. $$\frac{14.0 \text{ g C}_{10}\text{H}_8}{25.0 \text{ g C}_6\text{H}_6} \left| \frac{1 \text{ mole C}_{10}\text{H}_8}{128 \text{ g C}_{10}\text{H}_8} \right| \frac{1000 \text{ g C}_6\text{H}_6}{1 \text{ kg C}_6\text{H}_6} = 4.38m$$

B.P. $= 80.1° + 4.38° \times 2.53° = 91.2°C$

F.P. $= 5.48° - 4.38° \times 4.90° = -16.0°C$

c. $$\frac{500 \text{ g X}}{500 \text{ g H}_2\text{O}} \left| \frac{1 \text{ mole X}}{511 \text{ g X}} \right| \frac{1000 \text{ g H}_2\text{O}}{1 \text{ kg H}_2\text{O}} = 1.96m$$

B.P. $= 100°C + (1.96 \times 0.512) = 101.00°C$

F.P. $= 0°C - (1.96 \times 1.86) = -3.65°C$

d. $$\frac{250 \text{ g Y}}{500 \text{ g C}_6\text{H}_6} \left| \frac{1 \text{ mole Y}}{246 \text{ g Y}} \right| \frac{1000 \text{ g C}_6\text{H}_6}{1 \text{ kg}} = 2.03m$$

B.P. $= 80.1°C + (2.03 \times 2.53) = 85.2°C$

F.P. $= 5.48°C - (2.03 \times 4.90) = -4.47°C$

e. $$\frac{60.0 \text{ g C}_9\text{H}_{18}}{1 \text{ kg HAc}} \left| \frac{1 \text{ mole C}_9\text{H}_{18}}{126 \text{ g C}_9\text{H}_{18}} \right. = 0.476m$$

B.P. $= 118°C + (0.476 \times 3.07) = 119.0°C$

F.P. $= 16.6°C - (0.476 \times 3.90) = 14.7°C$

11. Motor oil carries away dirt and carbon by dispersion.

12. The Tyndall effect is the scattering of light by colloidal particles.

Page 401.   One More Step

1. See page 31, Figure 3-10, for solubility curves. Any of the compounds listed on the curve can be used. The student may use 50 g of water and the corresponding amount of solute. The temperature should be measured and then increased slowly as more solute is added. By plotting his own solubility curve, the student should be able to determine the substance by comparison with Figure 3-10.

2. In a 400 ml beaker, place about 80-90 ml of distilled water. Heat to near boiling. Add about 200 g of $Na_2S_2O_3 \cdot 5\ H_2O$ (hypo) of reagent grade. Filter while hot into a very clean 250 ml boiling flask. Allow the system to cool without disturbance.

3. See any elementary organic chemistry laboratory manual. Possible mixtures are:

CCl_4 and toluene
1-butanol and 1-octanol
benzene and toluene

benzene and acetic acid
methanol and water

Caution: the mixtures are flammable. Collect five fractions and analyze by refractive index or density.

4. The heat of solution increases with concentration. The curve is asymptotic to 13 kcal/mole for the anhydrous salt. The dodecahydrate is formed. If the $Na_3PO_4 \cdot 12 H_2O$ is dissolved, the curve becomes asymptotic to -15 kcal/mole.

5. The ultracentrifuge was developed by the Swedish scientist The Svedberg. It can, through centrifugal force, produce an effective gravitational field about 500,000 times the earth's. Dissolved particles of large molecular weight settle out quickly and weight values can be determined by this rate. For further information consult *Encyclopaedia Britannica*.

6. Cyclone separators — stack gas forced into a spiral path. Centrifugal force throws dust against sides when it settles out.
Cotrell precipitators — electrostatic precipitation of charged, colloidal dust particles.
Scrubbing towers — gas is bubbled through water, or other wash liquid, which strips out dust as well as noxious gases.

7. According to Pauling, Jean Perrin was able to measure the motion of microscopic particles of a resin suspended in water and to interpret his observations in such a way as to evaluate Avogadro's number. He gives as a reference:

G. P. Harnell and J. J. Livingood, *Experimental Atomic Physics* (McGraw-Hill, New York, 1933), Sec. 1-3 to 3-11.

8. Gelatin forms most useful protective colloids. It is used with silver bromide emulsion in photography, to prevent ice crystals in ice cream, and as an emulsifying agent in many solutions. Egg is an emulsifyer in foods such as salad dressings or mayonnaise. Detergents are special protective colloids.

9. There are many effects at work here. The gold leaf is nearly colloidal in one dimension. Some light is absorbed. Some is dispersed and diffracted. The light which is transmitted is greenish.

10. A living cell is filled principally with water (75-85%). The inorganic salts and some of the smaller organic molecules (if hydrophilic) are in solution. However, the larger molecules in the colloidal range of size and hydrophobic materials are dispersed. The larger molecules would include proteins and nucleic acids; while the hydrophobic materials would include lipids.

Suggested Readings for Faculty and Students

Chave, Keith E., "Chemical Reactions and the Composition of Seawater." *Journal of Chemical Education*, Vol. 48, No. 3 (March 1971), pp. 148-151.

Degens, Egan T., and Ross, David A., "The Red Sea Hot Brines." *Scientific American*, Vol. 222, No. 4 (April 1970), pp. 32-42.

Dye, James L., "The Solvated Electron." *Scientific American*, Vol. 216, No. 2 (February 1967), pp. 76-83.

*Garst, John F., "The Extent of Reaction as a Unifying Basis for Stoichiometry in Elementary Chemistry." *Journal of Chemical Education*, Vol. 51, No. 3 (March 1974), pp. 194-196.

*Hiemenz, Paul C., "The Role of van der Waals Forces in Surface and Colloid Chemistry." *Journal of Chemical Education*, Vol. 49, No. 3 (March 1972), pp. 164-170.

Kester, Dona R., "Chemical Processes in the Ocean." *Journal of Chemical Education*, Vol. 49, No. 1 (January 1972), pp. 11-14.

Leja, J., "Surface Chemistry in Industrial Processes." *Journal of Chemical Education*, Vol. 49, No. 3 (March 1972), pp. 157-161.

*Nilles, George P., and Schuetz, Robert D., "Selected Properties of Selected Solvents." *Journal of Chemical Education*, Vol. 50, No. 4 (April 1973), pp. 267-268.

Rice, Oscar Knefler, *Electronic Structure and Chemical Binding*. New York, Dover Publications, Inc., 1969, Chapter 19 (An older work which contains much valuable material.)

*Rioux, Frank, "Colligative Properties." *Journal of Chemical Education*, Vol. 50, No. 7 (July 1973), pp. 490-492.

Sanderson, R. T., *Inorganic Chemistry*. New York, Reinhold Publishing Corp., 1967, Chapter 11.

Sienko, M. J., *Chemistry Problems*. Menlo Park, California, W. A. Benjamin, Inc., 1972, 2nd Ed., Chapter 10.

(*Faculty only)

Chapter 19

Performance Objectives

GOAL: Students will gain an understanding of the factors which affect reaction rate and the reationship of these factors to quantitative chemical equilibrium.

Objectives: Upon completion of the reading and activities, and when asked to diagram, demonstrate, or respond either orally or on a written test, the students will:

19:1	K	define a reversible reaction.
19:2	K	define reaction rate.
19:3-8	K	list and describe the effect of the factors which affect reaction rate.
19:9	K	explain reaction mechanism.
19:10	P	develop an equilibrium constant for a simple reaction.
19:11	P	explain the relationship of Le-Chatelier's Principle and chemical equilibrium.
19:12	P	describe the relationship of free energy to the equilibrium constant for a reaction.

Upon completion of the reading and activities, students will exhibit an interest in science by:

A   voluntarily completing one or more of the One More Step activities listed at the end of the chapter on their own time.

A   reading unassigned literature related to the ideas presented in the chapter.

Page 415.   Section 19:9

1. a. doubled ($[2H_2] = 2[H_2]$)

b. eight times faster

   ($[2NO]^2 [2H_2] = 8 [NO]^2 [H_2]$)

c. slows down

2. a. Rate $= k[H_2][I_2]$

$$0.2 = k(1)(1)$$
$$k = 0.2 \; l^2/\text{mole-sec}$$
$$0.4 = k(1)(2)$$
$$k = 0.2 \; l^2/\text{mole-sec}$$
$$0.8 = k(2)(2)$$
$$k = 0.2 \; l^2/\text{mole-sec}$$

b. Rate $= 0.2(0.5) (0.5)$

   Rate $= 0.05$ moles/sec

Page 417.   Section 19:10

3. $[HI]^2 = \dfrac{[H_2][I_2]}{K_{eq}}$

$[HI]^2 = \dfrac{(2 \times 10^{-4}) (2 \times 10^{-4})}{1.4 \times 10^{-2}}$

$= 2.86 \times 10^{-6}$

$[HI] = 1.69 \times 10^{-3} M$

4. $K_{eq} = \dfrac{[H_2][CO_2]}{[CO][H_2O]} = \dfrac{(0.32) (0.42)}{(0.2) (0.5)} = 1.3$

5. $[CO] = \dfrac{[H_2][CO_2]}{K_{eq}[H_2O]}$

$[CO] = \dfrac{(0.32) (0.42)}{(2.4) (0.5)}$

[CO] = 0.11M

6. $K_{eq} = \dfrac{[H_2]^2\,[S_2]}{[H_2S]^2}$

$= \dfrac{[2.22 \times 10^{-3}]^2\,[1.11 \times 10^{3-}]}{[7.06 \times 10^{-3}]^2}$

$= 1.10 \times 10^{-4}$

7. $K_{eq} = \dfrac{[NO_2]^2}{[N_2O_4]}$

$[NO_2]^2 = K_{eq}\,[N_2O_4]$

$= (8.75 \times 10^{-2})(1.72 \times 10^{-2})$

$= 15.1 \times 10^{-4}$

$[NO_2] = 3.88 \times 10^{-2}\,M$

Page 423.   End of Chapter

8. a. $K_{eq} = \dfrac{[(NH_4)_2SO_4]}{[NH_3]^2[H_2SO_4]}$

b. $K_{eq} = \dfrac{4}{(2)^2(3)} = 0.3$

c. increases d. shifts right e. changes

9. $H_2(g) + Cl_2(g) \rightarrow 2\,HCl(g)$
Cl_2 is more active than Br_2
HBr is less stable than HCl

10. The reaction rate would increase.

11. The surface area of the log is less than the surface area of the paper. The match cannot raise the temperature of the log to its kindling point but can heat the paper.

12. See Figure 19-4, page 410.

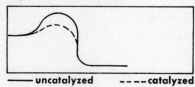
——— uncatalyzed   - - - - catalyzed

13. If [NO] is constant, rate $\propto$ [H]; thus the reaction rate doubles.

14. The reaction rate would increase in the direction which would relieve the pressure. The products would be favored.

Page 423.   One More Step

1. $K_{eq} = \dfrac{[C]^2}{[A]^2[B]} = 8$

initial concentration of A $= \dfrac{0.5}{10} = 0.05M$

initial concentration of B $= \dfrac{0.5}{10} = 0.05M$

If x moles of B react per liter, then 2x moles of A must react per liter and 2x moles of C will be produced per liter. Therefore,

final concentration of A $= 0.05 - 2x$

final concentration of B $= 0.05 - x$

final concentration of C $= 2x$

Note: The final solution to this problem involves a "sticky" third-degree equation:

$$\dfrac{(2x)^2}{(0.05 - 2x)^2(0.05 - x)} = 8$$

$$\dfrac{4x^2}{(0.000125 - 0.0125x + 0.4x^2 - 4x^3)} = 8$$

$4x^2 = 0.001 - 0.1x + 3.2x^2 - 32x^3$

Using Newton's method of approximation:

$f(x) = 32x^3 + 7.2x^2 + 0.1x - 0.001 = 0$

$f'(x) = 96x^2 + 14.4 + 0.1$

$f(0) = -0.001$

$f'(0) = 96 + 14.4 + 0.1 = 110.5$

$x_1 = x_0 \dfrac{f(x_0)}{f'(x_0)}$

$x_1 = 0 - \dfrac{-.001}{110.5} = 0.009$

Since [C] = 2x, [C] = 0.018M,

Then [A] = 0.03M and [B] = 0.041M

2. $E_a = \Delta H^{\circ *} + RT$ for solid and liquid systems

$E_a = \Delta H^{\circ *} - (\Delta n^* - 1)\, RT$ for gaseous systems

$\Delta G^{\circ *} = H^{0*} - T\Delta S^{0*}$

$\Delta G^{\circ *} = -RT \ln K^*$

where E_a = activation energy
$\Delta H^{\circ *}$ = enthalpy of activation
R = gas constant
T = Kelvin temperature
Δn^* = moles of complex minus number of moles of reactants
$\Delta G^{\circ *}$ = free energy of activation
$\Delta S^{\circ *}$ = entropy of activation
$\ln$ = natural logarithm
K^* = equilibrium constant for reactants $\leftrightarrows$ complex in units of concentration

3. There are many multi-step reactions listed in texts on kinetics and physical chemistry. For example:

$$2O_3 \rightarrow 3O_2$$

$$2H_2O_2 \xrightarrow{I^-} 2H_2O + O_2$$

(The I^- is a catalyst for decomposing H_2O_2.)

$$H_2 + Cl_2 \rightarrow 2HCl$$

$$O_3 \rightleftharpoons O_2 + O \quad \text{fast}$$

$$O + O_3 \rightarrow 2O_2 \quad \text{slow}$$

$$H_2O_2 + H_3O^+ \rightleftharpoons H_3O_2^+ \quad \text{fast}$$

$$H_3O_2^+ + I^- \rightarrow H_2O + HOI^+ \quad \text{slow}$$

$$HOI^+ + H_2O_2 \rightarrow H_3O^+ + I^- + I^- + O_2 \quad \text{fast}$$

$$Cl_2 + h\nu \rightarrow 2Cl \qquad \text{slow}$$

chain reaction $\begin{cases} Cl + H_2 \rightarrow HCl + H \quad \text{fast} \\ H + Cl_2 \rightarrow HCl + Cl \quad \text{fast} \end{cases}$

$\left. \begin{array}{l} H + HCl \rightarrow H_2 + Cl \\ Cl + HCl \rightarrow Cl_2 + H \end{array} \right)$ inhibiting reactions

$\left. \begin{array}{l} 2Br \rightarrow Br_2 \\ 2H \rightarrow H_2 \end{array} \right\}$ chain-breaking reactions

Suggested Readings for Faculty and Students

*Arnot, C. L., "Activated Complex Theory of Bimolecular Gas Reactions." *Journal of Chemical Education*, Vol. 49, No. 7 (July 1972), pp. 480-482.

*Faller, Larry, "Relaxation Methods in Chemistry." *Scientific American*, Vol. 220, No. 5 (May 1969), pp. 30-41.

Haensel, Vladimir, and Burwell, Robert L., Jr., "Catalysis." *Scientific American*, Vol. 225, No. 6 (December 1971), pp. 46-58.

*Hartley, F. R., "Homogeneous Catalysis in Industrial Synthesis." *Journal of Chemical Education*, Vol. 50, No. 4 (April 1973), pp. 263-267.

*Oster, Gerald, "The Chemical Effects of Light." *Scientific American*, Vol. 219, No. 3 (September 1968), pp. 158-170.

Slabaugh, Wendell H., "Chemical Equilibrium." *The Science Teacher*, Vol. 34, No. 8 (November 1967), pp. 61-66.

(*Faculty only)

Chapter 20

Performance Objectives

GOAL: Students will gain an understanding of the acid-base theories; the general properties of acids, bases, and salts; and the procedures for naming them.

Objectives: Upon completion of the reading activities, and when asked to diagram, demonstrate, or respond either orally or on a written test, the students will:

20:1-2   K   list the differences and similarities in the Arrhenius, Brönsted-Lowry, and Lewis acid-base theories.

20:4-5   K,P   identify from formulas the names of common acids and bases.

20:4-5   K,P   provide formulas given the names of common acids and bases.

20:6   K   describe acid and basic anhydrides.

20:7   P,S   determine acid-base behavior for given elements.

20:8	K	define and give examples of common salts.
20:9-17	P	use acid-base equilibrium constants to develop and explain: a. ionization constant b. percent of ionization c. common ion effect d. solubility product e. pH scale
20:18-19	P	predict the acidity or basicity of hydrolysis products.
20:20	K,P	describe and give examples of buffered solutions.
20:21	K,P,S	explain titration as a laboratory tool.

Upon completion of the reading and activities, students will exhibit an interest in science by:

A   voluntarily completing one or more of the One More Step activities listed at the end of the chapter on their own time.

A   reading unassigned literature related to the ideas presented in the chapter.

Page 437.   Section 20:11

1. $K_a = \dfrac{[CH_3COO^-]\,[H_3O^+]}{[CH_3COOH]}$

$1.76 \times 10^{-5} = \dfrac{x^2}{0.1 \;\; \cancel{-x}} \leftarrow$ neglect

$x^2 = 1.76 \times 10^{-6}$

$x = 1.33 \times 10^{-3}$

$\% = \dfrac{1.33 \times 10^{-3}}{0.1} \Big| \dfrac{100\%}{1}$

$= 1.33\%$

2. $K_a = \dfrac{[A^-]\,[H_3O^+]}{[HA]} = \dfrac{(0.0200)^2}{0.98}$

$= 4.1 \times 10^{-4}$

Page 441.   Section 20:14

3. $AgI \rightleftharpoons Ag^+ + I^-$

$K_{sp} = [Ag^+]\,[I^-]$

$[Ag^+] = [I^-] = x$

$x^2 = 1.5 \times 10^{-16}$

$x = 1.2 \times 10^{-8} M = [Ag^+]$

4. $D_2A \rightleftharpoons 2D^+ + A^{2-}$

$K_{sp} = [D^+]^2[A^{2-}]$

$2[A^{2-}] = [D^+] = 2.00 \times 10^{-5}$

$[A^{2-}] = 1 \times 10^{-5}$

$K_{sp} = (2.00 \times 10^{-5})^2(1 \times 10^{-5})$

$K_{sp} = 4.00 \times 10^{-15}$

5. $K_{eq} = \dfrac{[H^+]\,[CHCl_2COO^-]}{[CHCl_2COOH]}$

$K_{eq} = \dfrac{(0.200)\,(0.200)}{1.20}$

$= 0.0333 \text{ or } 3.33 \times 10^{-2}$

6. $\dfrac{0.200 \times 100}{1.20 + 0.200} = \dfrac{0.200}{1.40} \Big| \dfrac{100\%}{1} = 14.3\%$

7. $0.0333 = \dfrac{x\,(0.400)}{1.40 - x}$

$0.0466 = 0.0333x = 0.400x$

$0.433x = 0.0466$

$x = 0.108$

$1.40 - x = 1.29M$

Page 458.   End of Chapter

8.

	Conjugate acid	Conjugate base
a.	NH_4^+	H_2O
b.	NH_3	CH_3O^-
c.	H_2O	H_2O
d.	NH_3	OH^-
e.	H_3O^+	ClO_4^-

9. a. $\overset{\displaystyle ..}{\underset{\displaystyle ..}{Al}} \!:\! \overset{\displaystyle ..}{\underset{\displaystyle ..}{Cl}} \!:$ acid (electron pair-acceptor)

b. $:\ddot{O}:S::\ddot{O} \longleftrightarrow \ddot{O}::S:\ddot{O}: \longleftrightarrow :\ddot{O}:S:\ddot{O}:$
　　$:\ddot{O}:$　　　　$:\ddot{O}:$　　　　　　$:\ddot{O}:$
　　　　　　acid (electron-pair acceptor)

c. $:\overset{\text{H}}{\underset{\text{H}}{\text{P}}}:\text{H}$　　base (electron-pair donor)

d. $:\ddot{X}e:$　　base (donor)

e. Zn^{2+}
　　　　acid (electron pair-acceptor)

10. a. hydrobromic　　d. selenious
　　b. hydroselenic　　e. hyponitrous
　　c. iodic

11. a. sodium phosphate Na_3PO_4
　　b. potassium borate K_3BO_3
　　c. chromium perchlorate $Cr(ClO_4)_3$
　　d. cadmium bromide $CdBr_2$
　　e. lithium silicate Li_4SiO_4

12. One mole of NaOH neutralizes one mole HCl.

$$\text{moles NaOH} = 86.2 \text{ ml} \times \frac{0.765 \text{ moles}}{1000 \text{ ml}}$$

$$= 0.0659 \text{ mole NaOH}$$
$$= 0.0659 \text{ mole HCl}$$

$$\frac{1000 \text{ ml}}{1 \text{ l}} \left| \frac{0.0659 \text{ moles}}{30.0 \text{ ml}} \right. = 2.20M$$

13. One mole H_2SO_4 neutralizes two moles KOH.

$$\text{moles } H_2SO_4 = 40.8 \text{ ml} \times \frac{0.106 \text{ moles}}{1000 \text{ ml}}$$

$$= 0.00432 \text{ mole } H_2SO_4$$
$$= 0.00864 \text{ mole KOH.}$$

$$\frac{1000 \text{ ml}}{1 \text{ l}} \left| \frac{0.00864 \text{ mole}}{61.8 \text{ ml}} \right. = 0.140M$$

14. $Mg(OH)_2 \rightarrow Mg^{2+} + 2\ OH^-$
$$K_{sp} = [Mg^{2+}][OH^-]^2$$
$$2[Mg^{2+}] = [OH^-]$$
$$[Mg^{2+}] = x$$
$$1.2 \times 10^{-11} = x(2x)^2$$
$$1.2 \times 10^{-11} = 4x^3$$

$$x^3 = 3.00 \times 10^{-12}$$
$$x = 1.44 \times 10^{-4}$$
$$[OH^-] = 2.88 \times 10^{-4}$$

$$[H^+] = \frac{10 \times 10^{-15}}{2.88 \times 10^{-4}} = 3.47 \times 10^{-11}$$

$$pH = 11 - \log 3.47 = 11 - 0.54$$
$$pH = 10.459$$

or

$$pOH = 4 - \log 2.88 = 4 - 0.459$$
$$pOH = 3.541$$
$$pH = 14 - 3.541 = 10.459$$

15. $[OH^-] = 10^{-4}$　$[H^+] = 10^{-10}$
　　$pH = 10$

16. $[H^+] = 2 \times 5 \times 10^{-3} = 10^{-2}$
　　$pH = 2$

17. a. neutral

　　b. basic
　　　$CO_3^{2-} + H_2O \rightarrow HCO_3^- + OH^-$

　　c. acid $Al(H_2O)_6^{3+} + 2H_2O$
　　　　　　　　$\rightarrow Al(H_2O)_5OH^{2+} + H_3O^+$

　　d. acid $Hg^{2+} + H_2O \rightarrow HgOH^+ + H^+$

　　e. neutral

18. $NH_4OH \rightleftharpoons NH_4^+ + OH^-$

$$K_{eq} = \frac{[NH_4^+][OH^-]}{[NH_4OH]}$$

$$[NH_4^+] = 0.1 + x\ \ [OH^-] = x$$
$$[NH_4OH] = 0.1 - x$$

$$1.77 \times 10^{-5} = \frac{(0.1 + x)x}{(0.1 - x)}$$

neglect $+x$ and $-x$ as small with respect to 0.1

$$1.77 \times 10^{-5} = x = [OH^-]$$

$$[H^+] = \frac{10 \times 10^{-15}}{1.77 + 10^{-5}}$$

$$[H^+] = 5.65 \times 10^{-10}$$

$$pH = 10 - \log 5.65$$
$$pH = 10 - 0.754$$
$$pH = 9.246$$

19. $MnS \rightleftharpoons Mn^{2+} + S^{2-}$

$$K_{sp} = [Mn^{2+}] [S^{2-}]$$
$$1.4 \times 10^{-15} = 0.1 [S^{2-}]$$
$$1.4 \times 10^{-14} = [S^{2-}]$$

20. a. hydrofluoric acid   d. arsenic acid
    b. hydriodic acid   e. periodic acid
    c. hydrotelluric acid

21. a. strontium hydroxide   d. samarium
    b. magnesium hydroxide   hydroxide
    c. chromium (II)   e. cadmium
      hydroxide   hydroxide

22. $KHSO_4 \rightarrow K^+ + HSO_4^- \quad 100\%$

$$H_2O + HSO_4^- \rightarrow H_3O^+ + SO_4^{2-}$$
$$[SO_4^{2-}] = [H_3O^+] = x$$

$$K_a = \frac{[H_3O^+] [SO_4^{2-}]}{[HSO_4^-]} = 1.2 \times 10^{-2}$$

$$= \frac{[H_3O^+]^2}{0.1 - [H_3O^+]} = \frac{x^2}{0.1 - x}$$

The x in $0.1 - x$ is *not* negligible since the concentration (0.1) is so close to the K_a (1.2×10^{-2}).

Solving for x by the quadratic formula:

$$1.2 \times 10^{-3} - 1.2 \times 10^{-2}x = x^2$$
$$x^2 + 1.2 \times 10^{-2}x - 1.2 \times 10^{-3} = 0$$

$$x = \frac{-1.2 \times 10^{-2}}{2}$$

$$\frac{\pm \sqrt{1.44 \times 10^{-4} + 4.8 \times 10^{-3}}}{2}$$

$$x = \frac{-1.2 \times 10^{-2} \pm \sqrt{49.4 \times 10^{-4}}}{2}$$

$$x = \frac{5.83 \times 10^{-2}}{2}$$

$$x = 2.91 \times 10^{-2} = [H^+] = [H_3O^+]$$

23. $\%$ ionization $= \dfrac{[H_3O^+]}{[HSO_4^-]} \bigg| \dfrac{100\%}{1}$

$$= \frac{2.92 \times 10^{-2}}{0.1} \bigg| \frac{100\%}{1} = 29.1\%$$

24. $H_2NOH + H_2O \rightleftharpoons H_3NOH^+ + OH^-$

$$K_b = \frac{[H_3NOH^+][OH^-]}{[H_2NOH]}$$

$$[H_3NOH^+] = [OH^-] = x$$

$$1.1 \times 10^{-8} = \frac{x^2}{0.1 - \boxed{x}} \leftarrow \text{neglect}$$

$$x^2 = 1.1 \times 10^{-9} = 11 \times 10^{-10}$$

$$x = 3.32 \times 10^{-5} = [OH^-]$$

$$[H_3O^+] = \frac{10^{-14}}{[OH^-]} = \frac{10 \times 10^{-15}}{3.32 \times 10^{-5}}$$

$$[H_3O^+] = 3.02 \times 10^{-10}$$

$$pH = -\log (3.02 \times 10^{-10})$$

$$pH = 9.52$$

25. $\%$ ionization $= \dfrac{[H_3NOH^+]}{[H_2NOH]} \bigg| \dfrac{100\%}{1}$

$$= \frac{3.32 \times 10^{-5}}{0.1} \bigg| \frac{100\%}{1}$$

$$= 0.0332\%$$

26. $K_a = \dfrac{[H_3O^+] [C_6H_5COO^-]}{[C_6H_5COOH]}$

$$[H_3O^+] = [C_6H_5COO^-] = x$$

$$K_a = 6.46 \times 10^{-5} = \frac{x^2}{0.05 - \boxed{x}} \leftarrow \text{neglect}$$

$$x^2 = 3.23 \times 10^{-6}$$

$$x = 1.80 \times 10^{-3} = [C_6H_5COO^-]$$

27. $K_a = \dfrac{[H_3O^+][CN^-]}{[HCN]}$

$$K_a = 4.93 \times 10^{-10}$$

$$= \frac{[H_3O^+](0.01)}{0.300} = \boxed{x} \leftarrow \text{neglect}$$

$$[H_3O^+] = \frac{1.48 \times 10^{-10}}{0.01} = 1.48 \times 10^{-8}$$

$$pH = -\log [H_3O^+]$$

$$pH = -\log [1.48 \times 10^{-8}]$$

$$pH = 7.83$$

28. $K_{sp} = [Fe^{2+}][S^{2-}]$

$$3.7 \times 10^{-19} = 0.167 [S^{2-}]$$

$$[S^{2-}] = 2.22 \times 10^{-18}$$

$$H_2S \rightarrow H^+ + HS^-$$

$$HS^- \rightarrow H^+ + S^{2-}$$

$$\left. \begin{array}{l} K_{a1} = \dfrac{[H^+][HS^-]}{[H_2S]} \\[1.5em] K_{a2} = \dfrac{[H^+][S^{2-}]}{[HS^-]} \end{array} \right\} \begin{array}{l} \text{Solve both} \\ \text{equations} \\ \text{for } [HS^-] \end{array}$$

$$[HS^-] = \frac{K_{a1}[H_2S]}{[H^+]}$$

$$[HS^-] = \frac{[H^+][S^{2-}]}{K_{a2}}$$

$$\therefore \frac{K_{a1}[H_2S]}{[H^+]} = \frac{[H^+][S^{2-}]}{K_{a2}}$$

Solve for $[H^+]$

$$[H^+]^2 = \frac{K_{a1}K_{a2}[H_2S]}{S^{2-}}$$

$$[H^+] = \sqrt{\frac{K_{a1}K_{a2}[H_2S]}{[S^{2-}]}}$$

$$[H^+] = \sqrt{\frac{(10^{-7})(1.2 \times 10^{-13})(0.1)}{2.22 \times 10^{-18}}}$$

$$[H^+] = \sqrt{5.41 \times 10^{-4}}$$

$$[H^+] = 2.32 \times 10^{-2}$$

$$pH = -\log 2.32 \times 10^{-2}$$

$$pH = 1.63$$

29. $NaOH \rightarrow Na^+ + OH^-$ 100% ionization

$$NH_4OH \rightleftharpoons NH_4^+ + OH^-$$

$$K_b = \frac{[NH_4^+][OH^-]}{[NH_4OH]}$$

$$NH_4^+ = x$$

$$OH^- = x + 0.1 \quad \overset{\text{from NaOH}}{\underset{\text{from } NH_4OH}{}}$$

$$K_b = 1.77 \times 10^{-5}$$

$$= \frac{x(\boxed{x} + 0.1)}{1 - \boxed{x}} \quad \text{neglect}$$

$x = 1.77 \times 10^{-4}$ (negligible compared to the amount from NaOH)

$$[OH^-] = 0.1 = 10^{-1}$$

$$[H_3O^+] = \frac{10^{-14}}{10^{-1}} = 10^{-13}M$$

30. $HOOC-COOH + H_2O \rightleftharpoons HOOC-COO^- + H_3O^+$ neglect second ionization (3 orders of magnitude less)

$$K_a = \frac{[HOOC-COO^-][H_3O^+]}{[HOOC-COOH]}$$

$$[HOOC-COO^-] = [H_3O^+] = x$$

$$K_a = 5.90 \times 10^{-2} = \frac{x^2}{0.2 - x}$$

$$1.18 \times 10^{-2} - 5.90 \times 10^{-2}x = x^2$$

$$x^2 + 5.90 \times 10^{-2}x - 1.18 \times 10^{-2} = 0$$

$$= \frac{-5.90 \times 10^{-2} \pm \sqrt{3.48 \times 10^{-3} + 4.72 \times 10^{-2}}}{2}$$

$$= \frac{-5.90 \times 10^{-2} \pm \sqrt{5.07 \times 10^{-2}}}{2}$$

$$= \frac{-5.90 \times 10^{-2} \pm 2.25 \times 10^{-1}}{2}$$

$$= \frac{1.66 \times 10^{-1}}{2} = 8.31 \times 10^{-2}M = [H_3O^+]$$

31. oxalic acid $= \dfrac{5.90 \times 10^{-2}}{6.40 \times 10^{-5}} = 9.22 \times 10^2$

carbonic acid $= \dfrac{4.30 \times 10^{-7}}{5.61 \times 10^{-11}}$
$= 7.66 \times 10^3$

phosphoric acid $= \dfrac{7.52 \times 10^{-3}}{6.23 \times 10^{-8}}$
$= 1.21 \times 10^5$

sulfurous acid $= \dfrac{1.5 \times 10^{-2}}{1.0 \times 10^{-7}}$
$= 1.5 \times 10^5$

chromic acid $= \dfrac{1.8 \times 10^{-1}}{3.20 \times 10^{-7}}$
$= 5.6 \times 10^{-5}$

selenious acid $= \dfrac{3.5 \times 10^{-3}}{5 \times 10^{-8}}$
$= 7 \times 10^4$

tellurous acid $= \dfrac{3 \times 10^{-3}}{2 \times 10^{-8}}$
$= 1.5 \times 10^5$

Page 460. One More Step

1. (1) Lavoisier proposed the name oxygen (acid former) for the gaseous element discovered by Priestley. Lavoisier believed that oxygen was a constituent of all acids.
(2) Claude Louis Berthollet in 1798 showed that all acids do not contain oxygen. He proposed that all acids contain hydrogen.
(3) Arrhenius proposed a theory involving the formation of ions (wanderers).
(4) Brönsted-Lowry theory.
(5) Lewis theory.

2. All strong acids ionize completely in water because water is a strong enough base to remove all protons from an acid. However, in less basic solvents, these acids (for example, $HClO_4$, HCl, HNO_3) would not be completely ionized, and an order of relative strength can be set up.

Because water is basic, it "levels" the effect of these acids to equality.

3. H_2SO_5 peroxysulfuric acid (contains —O—O— peroxy group)

$H_2S_2O_7$ disulfuric acid (contains 2 sulfuric acid molecules condensed)

$H_2S_2O_8$ peroxydisulfuric acid (both of above reasons)

HNCO isocyanic acid (HOCN is normal cyanic acid)

HSCN thiocyanic acid (S substituted for O in normal cyanic acid)

4.

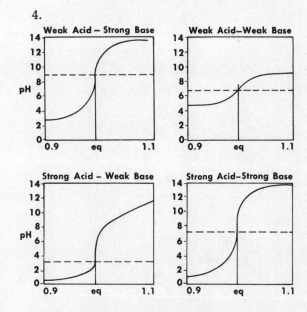

5. a. bromothymol blue, litmus, or phenol red
   b. thymol blue, phenolphthalein
   c. 2,5-dinitrophenol, methyl red
   d. same as 5.a. above
   e. methyl red, 2,5-dinitrophenol (1st proton); bromothymol blue, litmus, phenol red (2nd proton); thymolphthalein (3rd proton)

6. $Ac^- + H_2O \rightarrow HAc + OH^-$

$$K_{eq} = \frac{[H_3O^+][Ac^-]}{[HAc]} = \frac{\left(\dfrac{10^{-14}}{[OH^-]}\right)[Ac^-]}{[HAc]}$$

$$1.76 \times 10^{-5} = \frac{\left(\dfrac{10^{-14}}{x}\right)(0.1 - \boxed{x})}{x}$$

neglect

$$1.76 \times 10^{-5}x = \frac{10^{-15}}{x}$$

$$1.76 \times 10^{-5}x^2 = 10^{-15}$$

$$x^2 = \frac{10 \times 10^{-16}}{1.76 \times 10^{-5}} = 5.68 \times 10^{-11} = 56.8 \times 10^{-12}$$

$$x = 7.54 \times 10^{-6}$$

$$[H^+] = \frac{10 \times 10^{-15}}{7.45 \times 10^{-6}}$$

$$[H^+] = 1.33 \times 10^{-9}$$

$$pH = 9 - \log 1.35 = 9 - 0.123$$

$$pH = 8.877$$

7. $NH_4OH \rightleftharpoons NH_4^+ + OH^-$

$$K_{eq} = \frac{[NH_4^+]\,[OH^-]}{[NH_4OH]}$$

10. phenolphthalein

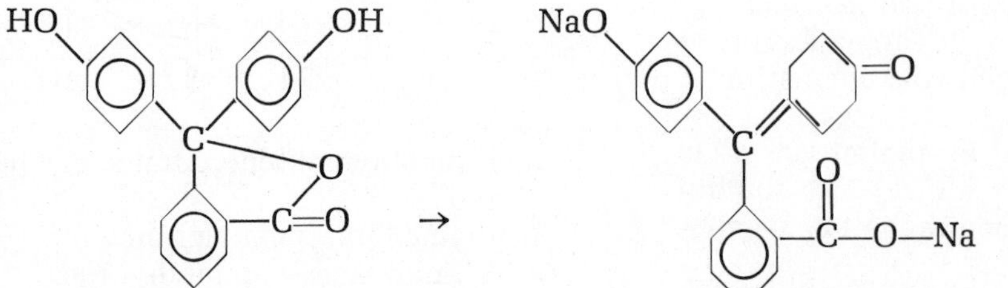

acid → base

alizarin yellow

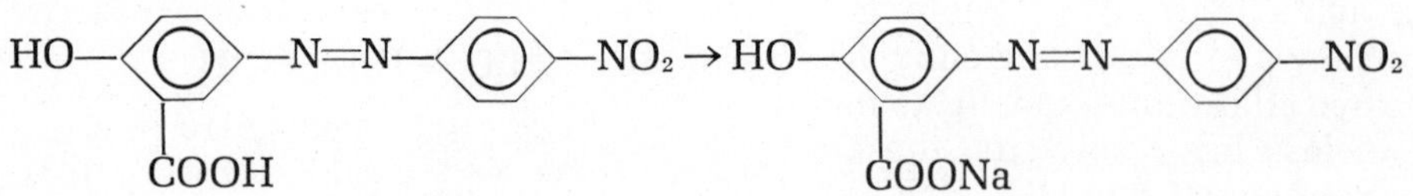

acid → base

$$1.77 \times 10^{-5} = \frac{(1 + \boxed{x})\,(x)}{(0.1 - \boxed{x})}$$

neglect

$$1.77 \times 10^{-6} = x$$

8. $AgCl \rightleftharpoons Ag^+ + Cl^-$

$K_{sp} = [Ag^+]\,[Cl^-]$

$1.56 \times 10^{-10} = (1)\,[Cl^-]$

$[Cl^-] = 1.56 \times 10^{-10}$

$PbCl_2 \rightleftharpoons Pb^{2+} + 2Cl^-$

$K_{sp} = [Pb^{2+}]\,[Cl^-]^2$

$1.7 \times 10^{-5} = (1)\,[Cl^-]^2$

$[Cl^-]^2 = 1.7 \times 10^{-5} = 17 \times 10^{-6}$

$[Cl^-] = 4.1 \times 10^{-3}$

$PbCl_2$ will require a higher concentration of Cl^-, so $AgCl$ will ppt first.

9. From problem 8, we know that $4.1 \times 10^{-3} = [Cl^-]$ when $PbCl_2$ ppts.
$\therefore 1.56 \times 10^{-10} = [Ag^+]\,(4.1 \times 10^{-3})$

$$[Ag^+] = \frac{1.56 \times 10^{-10}}{4.1 \times 10^{-3}} = \frac{15.6 \times 10^{-11}}{4.1 \times 10^{-3}}$$

$[Ag^+] = 3.8 \times 10^{-3}$

thymol blue

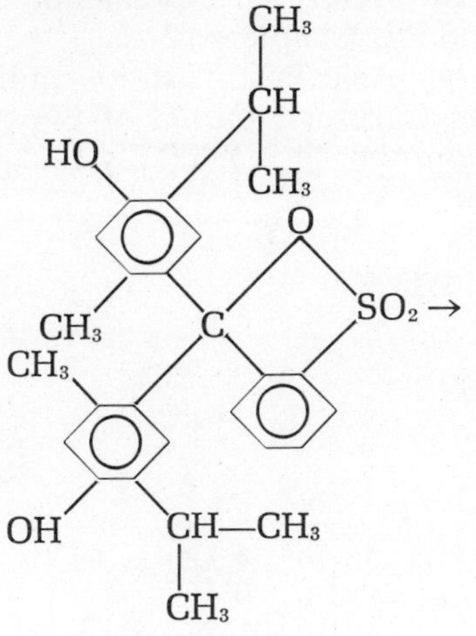

→ base is the same except that OH becomes ONa

acid

methyl orange

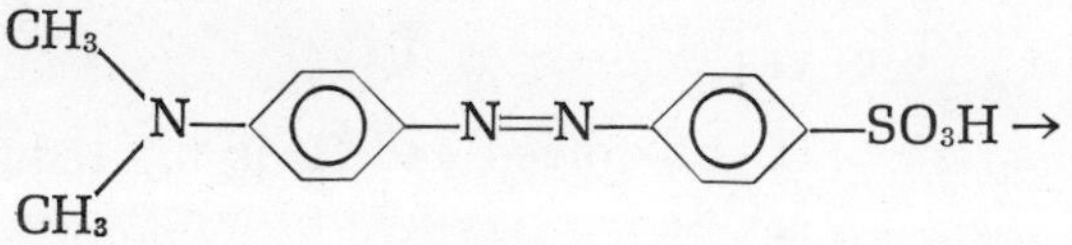

→ base is the same except that SO₃H becomes SO₃Na

acid

methyl red

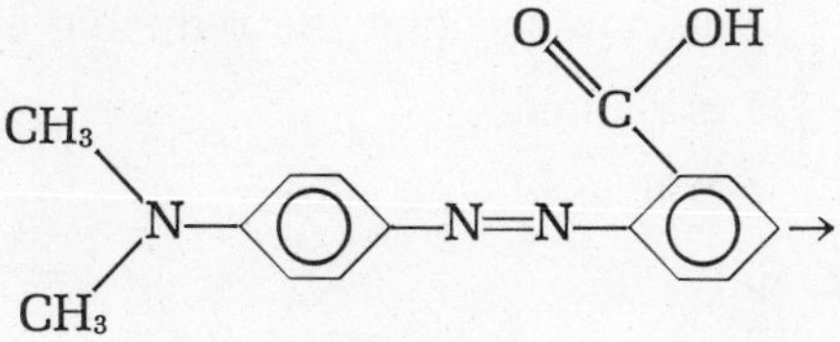

→ base is the same except that COOH becomes COONa

acid

Many other indicators may be found in handbooks and in organic chemistry texts.

Suggested Readings for Faculty and Students

Bixby, Louis W., "Demonstration Quiz on Brönsted-Lowry Acid-Base Theory: Analysis." *Chemistry*, Vol. 47, No. 3 (March 1974), pp. 26-28.

Fischer, Robert B., "Ion-Selective Electrodes." *Journal of Chemical Education*, Vol. 51, No. 6 (June 1974), pp. 387-390.

Jensen, William B., "Lewis Acid-Base Theory." *Chemistry*, Part I, Vol. 47, No. 3 (March 1974), pp. 11-14; Part II, Vol. 47, No. 4 (April 1974), pp. 13-18; Part III, Vol. 47, No. 5 (May 1974), pp. 14-18.

Morris, Daniel Luzon, "Stress Collisions and Constants." *Chemistry*, Part I, Vol. 44, No. 4 (April 1971), pp. 10-12; Part II, Vol. 44, No. 5 (May 1971), pp. 15-19.

Nakayama, F. S., "Hydrolysis of Sodium Carbonate." *Journal of Chemical Education,* Vol. 47, No. 1 (January 1970), pp. 67-68.

*Pearson, Ralph G., "Hard and Soft Acids and Bases." *Journal of Chemical Education,* Part I, Vol. 45, No. 9 (September 1968), pp. 581-587; Part II, Vol. 45, No. 10 (October 1968), pp. 643-648.

Sienko, M. J., *Chemistry Problems.* Menlo Park, California, W.A. Benjamin, Inc., 1972, 2nd Ed., Chapters 12-16.

Waser, Jurg, "Acid-Base Titration and Distribution Curves." *Journal of Chemical Education,* Vol. 44, No. 5 (May 1967), pp. 274-276.

(*Faculty only)

Chapter 21

Performance Objectives

GOAL: Students will gain an understanding of oxidation-reduction reactions and the electron rearrangement that takes place during these reactions.

Objectives: Upon completion of the reading and activities, and when asked to diagram, demonstrate, or respond either orally or on a written test, the students will:

21:1-3	K,P	define and give examples of oxidation, reduction, and oxidizing and reducing agents.
21:4-6	P	assign oxidation numbers to elements in common compounds.
21:7	K,P	identify reactions as redox or nonredox.
21:8-13	P,S	balance the equation for any given oxidation-reduction reaction.

Upon completion of the reading and activities, students will exhibit an interest in science by:

A voluntarily completing one or more of the One More Step activities listed at the end of the chapter on their own time.

A reading unassigned literature related to the ideas presented in the chapter.

Page 470.   Section 21:6

1. a. $4+$
   b. $7+$
   c. $5+$
   d. $4+$

e. $4+$
f. $6+$
g. $6+$
h. $2-$
i. $2+$
j. 0

Page 471.   Section 21:7

2. a. no

   b. yes

   H is oxidized and H_2 is the reducing agent.

   N is reduced and N_2 is the oxidizing agent.

   c. yes

   C is oxidized and the reducing agent

   H is reduced

   H_2O is oxidizing agent

   d. no

   e. no

3. a. no

   b. yes
   O is reduced
   S is oxidized
   H_2O_2 is oxidizing agent
   PbS is reducing agent

   c. no

   d. yes
   N is reduced
   P is oxidized
   HNO_3 is oxidizing agent
   H_3PO_3 is reducing agent

e. yes
   N is reduced
   I is oxidized
   HNO_3 is oxidizing agent
   I_2 is the reducing agent

f. no

g. yes
   N is reduced
   Fe^{2+} is oxidized and the reducing agent
   NO_3^- is oxidizing agent

h. yes
   Br_2 is reduced and the oxidizing agent

Fe^{2+} is oxidized
$FeBr_2$ is reducing agent

i. yes
   I_2 is reduced and the oxidizing agent
   S is oxidized
   $S_2O_3^{2-}$ is reducing agent

j. yes
   Mn is reduced
   O is oxidized
   MnO_4^- is oxidizing agent
   H_2O_2 is reducing agent

Page 480.   Section 21:12

4. a. $(8 H^+ + 5e^- + MnO_4^- \rightarrow Mn^{2+} + 4 H_2O) \times 2$
   $(H_2O + H_2SO_3 \rightarrow HSO_4^- + 2e^- + 3 H^+) \times 5$
   $16 H^+ + 10e^- + 2 MnO_4^- \rightarrow 2 Mn^{2+} + 8 H_2O$
   $5 H_2O + 5 H_2SO_3 \rightarrow HSO_4^- + 10e^- + 15 H^+$

   $H^+ + 2 MnO_4^- + 5 H_2SO_3 \rightarrow 2 Mn^{2+} + 5 HSO_4^- + 3 H_2O$

   b. $(14 H^+ + 6e^- + Cr_2O_7^{2-} \rightarrow 2 Cr^{3+} + 7 H_2O)$
   $(2 I^- \rightarrow I_2 + 2e^-) \times 3$
   $14 H^+ + 6e^- + Cr_2O_7^{2-} \rightarrow 2 Cr^{3+} + 7 H_2O$
   $6 I^- \rightarrow 3 I_2 + 6e^-$

   $Cr_2O_7^{2-} + 14 H^+ + 6 I^- \rightarrow 2 Cr^{3+} + 3 I_2 + 7 H_2O$

   c. $(5 OH^- + NH_3 \rightarrow NO + 5e^- + 4 H_2O) \times 4$
   $4 H_2O + 4e^- + O_2 \rightarrow 2 H_2O + 4 OH^-$
   Simplifying the 2nd equation gives:
   $2 H_2O + 4e^- + O_2 \rightarrow OH^-$
   $(2 H_2O + 4e^- + O_2 \rightarrow 4 OH^-) \times 5$
   $20 OH^- + 4 NH_3 \rightarrow 4 NO + 20e^- + 16 H_2O$
   $10 H_2O + 20e^- + 5 O_2 \rightarrow 20 OH^-$

   $4 NH_3 + 5 O_2 \rightarrow 4 NO + 6 H_2O$

   d. $(5 H_2O + As_2O_3 \rightarrow 2 H_3AsO_4 + 4e^- + 4 H^+) \times 3$
   $(4 H^+ + 3e^- + NO_3^- \rightarrow NO + 2 H_2O) \times 4$
   $15 H_2O + 3 As_2O_3 \rightarrow 6 H_3AsO_4 + 12e^- + 12 H^+$
   $16 H^+ + 12e^- + 4 NO_3^- \rightarrow 4 NO + 8 H_2O$

   $3 As_2O_3 + 4 H^+ + 4 NO_3^- + 7 H_2O \rightarrow 6 H_3AsO_4 + 4 NO$

   e. $(2e^- + I_2 \rightarrow 2 I^-) \times 1$
   $(H_2O + H_2SO_3 \rightarrow HSO_4^- + 2e^- + 3 H^+) \times 1$

   $I_2 + H_2SO_3 + H_2O \rightarrow 2 I^- + HSO_4^- + 3 H^+$

f. $(8\ H^+ + 8e^- + H_3AsO_4 \rightarrow AsH_3 + 4\ H_2O) \times 1$

$(Zn \rightarrow Zn^{2+} + 2e^-) \times 4$

$\quad 8\ H^+ + 8e^- + H_3AsO_4 \rightarrow AsH_3 + 4\ H_2O$

$\quad\quad\quad\quad 4\ Zn \rightarrow 4\ Zn^{2+} + 8e^-$

$\overline{\quad\quad\quad\quad\quad\quad\quad\quad\quad\quad\quad\quad\quad\quad\quad\quad\quad}$

$H_3AsO_4 + 8\ H^+ + 4\ Zn \rightarrow AsH_3 + 4\ H_2O + 4\ Zn^{2+}$

g. $(MnO_4^{2-} \rightarrow MnO_4^- + e^-) \times 2$

$(4\ H^+ + 2e^- + MnO_4^{2-} \rightarrow MnO_2 + 2\ H_2O) \times 1$

$\quad\quad\quad 2\ MnO_4^{2-} \rightarrow 2\ MnO_4^- + 2e^-$

$\overline{\quad\quad\quad\quad\quad\quad\quad\quad\quad\quad\quad\quad\quad\quad\quad\quad}$

$3\ MnO_4^{2-} + 4\ H^+ \rightarrow 2\ MnO_4^- + MnO_2 + 2\ H_2O$

h. $(8\ H^+ + 5e^- + MnO_4^- \rightarrow Mn^{2+} + 4\ H_2O) \times 2$

$\quad\quad (2\ H_2O + SO_2 \rightarrow SO_4^{2-} + 2e^- + 4\ H^+) \times 5$

$\quad 16\ H^+ + 10e^- + 2\ MnO_4^- \rightarrow 2\ Mn^{2+} + 8\ H_2O$

$\quad 10\ H_2O + 5\ SO_2 \rightarrow 5\ SO_4^{2-} + 10e^- + 20\ H^+$

$\overline{\quad\quad\quad\quad\quad\quad\quad\quad\quad\quad\quad\quad\quad\quad\quad\quad\quad\quad\quad}$

$2\ MnO_4^- + 5\ SO_2 + 2\ H_2O \rightarrow 2\ Mn^{2+} + 5\ SO_4^{2-} + 4\ H^+$

i. $e^- + NO_2 \rightarrow NO_2^-$

$2\ OH^- + NO_2 \rightarrow NO_3^- + e^- + H_2O$

$\overline{\quad\quad\quad\quad\quad\quad\quad\quad\quad\quad\quad\quad\quad\quad\quad}$

$2\ NO_2 + 2\ OH^- \rightarrow NO_2^- + NO_3^- + H_2O$

j. $(4\ Cl^- + HgS \rightarrow S + 2e^- + HgCl_4^{2-}) \times 3$

$(4\ H^+ + 3e^- + NO_3^- \rightarrow NO + 2\ H_2O) \times 2$

$\quad\quad\quad\quad 12\ Cl^- + 3\ HgS \rightarrow 3\ S + 6e^- + 3\ HgCl_4^{2-}$

$\quad\quad\quad\quad 8\ H^+ + 6e^- + 2\ NO_3^- \rightarrow 2\ NO + 4\ H_2O$

$\overline{\quad\quad\quad\quad\quad\quad\quad\quad\quad\quad\quad\quad\quad\quad\quad\quad\quad\quad\quad\quad\quad}$

$8\ H^+ + 3\ HgS + 12\ Cl^- + 2\ NO_3^- \rightarrow 3\ HgCl_4^{2-} + 3\ S + 2\ NO + 4\ H_2O$

Page 482. End of Chapter

5. a. $(Cu \rightarrow Cu^{2+} + 2e^-) \times 3$

$(4\ H^+ + 3e^- + NO_3^- \rightarrow NO + 2\ H_2O) \times 2$

$\quad\quad\quad\quad 3\ Cu \rightarrow 3\ Cu^{2+} + 6e^-$

$\quad 8\ H^+ + 6e^- + 2\ NO_3^- \rightarrow 2\ NO + 4\ H_2O$

$\overline{\quad\quad\quad\quad\quad\quad\quad\quad\quad\quad\quad\quad\quad\quad\quad\quad}$

$3\ Cu + 8\ H^+ + 2\ NO_3^- \rightarrow 3\ Cu^{2+} + 2\ NO + 4\ H_2O$

b. $3\ Fe^{2+} \rightarrow 3\ Fe^{3+} + 3e^-$

$\quad\quad 4\ H^+ + 3e^- + NO_3^- \rightarrow NO + 2\ H_2O$

$\overline{\quad\quad\quad\quad\quad\quad\quad\quad\quad\quad\quad\quad\quad\quad\quad}$

$3\ Fe^{2+} + 4\ H^+ + NO_3^- \rightarrow 3\ Fe^{3+} + NO + 2\ H_2O$

c. $(Zn \rightarrow Zn^{2+} + 2e^-) \times 1$

$(2\ H^+ + e^- + NO_3^- \rightarrow NO_2 + H_2O) \times 2$

$\quad\quad\quad\quad Zn \rightarrow Zn^{2+} + 2e^-$

$\quad 4\ H^+ + 2e^- + 2\ NO_3^- \rightarrow 2\ NO_2 + 2\ H_2O$

$\overline{\quad\quad\quad\quad\quad\quad\quad\quad\quad\quad\quad\quad\quad\quad\quad}$

$Zn + 4\ H^+ + 2\ NO_3^- \rightarrow Zn^{2+} + 2\ NO_2 + 2\ H_2O$

d. $(Sb \rightarrow Sb^{3+} + 3e^-) \times 2$

$(3\ H^+ + 2e^- + HSO_4^- \rightarrow SO_2 + 2\ H_2O) \times 3$

$$2 \text{ Sb} \rightarrow 2 \text{ Sb}^{3+} + 6e^-$$
$$\underline{9 \text{ H}^+ + 6e^- + 3 \text{ HSO}_4^- \rightarrow 3 \text{ SO}_2 + 6 \text{ H}_2\text{O}}$$
$$2 \text{ Sb} + 9 \text{ H}^+ + 3 \text{ HSO}_4^- \rightarrow 2 \text{ Sb}^{3+} + 3 \text{ SO}_2 + 6 \text{ H}_2\text{O}$$

e. $(\text{H}_2\text{S} \rightarrow \text{S} + 2e^- + 2 \text{ H}^+) \times 2$

$$4 \text{ H}^+ + 4e^- + \text{H}_2\text{SO}_3 \rightarrow \text{S} + 3 \text{ H}_2\text{O}$$
$$\underline{2 \text{ H}_2\text{S} \rightarrow 2 \text{ S} + 4e^- + 4 \text{ H}^+}$$
$$\text{H}_2\text{SO}_3 + 2 \text{ H}_2\text{S} \rightarrow 3 \text{ S} + 3 \text{ H}_2\text{O}$$

6. a. $(\text{H}_2\text{O} + \text{Cl}^- \rightarrow \text{ClO}^- + 2e^- + 2 \text{ H}^+) \times 3$

$(4 \text{ H}^+ + 3e^- + \text{NO}_3^- \rightarrow \text{NO} + 2 \text{ H}_2\text{O}) \times 2$

$$3 \text{ H}_2\text{O} + 3 \text{ Cl}^- \rightarrow 3 \text{ ClO}^- + 6e^- + 6 \text{ H}^+$$
$$\underline{8 \text{ H}^+ + 6e^- + 2 \text{ NO}_3^- \rightarrow 2 \text{ NO} + 4 \text{ H}_2\text{O}}$$
$$3 \text{ Cl}^- + 2 \text{ H}^+ + 2 \text{ NO}_3^- \rightarrow 3 \text{ ClO}^- + 2 \text{ NO} + \text{H}_2\text{O}$$

b. $(\text{Cl}^- + \text{Ag} \rightarrow \text{AgCl} + e^-) \times 6$

$$6 \text{ H}^+ + 6e^- + \text{ClO}_3^- \rightarrow \text{Cl}^- + 3 \text{ H}_2\text{O}$$
$$\underline{6 \text{ Cl}^- + 6 \text{ Ag} \rightarrow 6 \text{ AgCl} + 6e^-}$$
$$6 \text{ H}^+ + \text{ClO}_3^- + 5 \text{ Cl}^- + 6 \text{ Ag} \rightarrow 3 \text{ H}_2\text{O} + 6 \text{ AgCl}$$

c. $(3 \text{ I}^- \rightarrow \text{I}_3^- + 2e^-) \times 2$

$$6 \text{ I}^- \rightarrow 2 \text{ I}_3^- + 4e^-$$
$$\underline{4 \text{ H}^+ + 4e^- + \text{O}_2 \rightarrow 2 \text{ H}_2\text{O}}$$
$$6 \text{ I}^- + 4 \text{ H}^+ + \text{O}_2 \rightarrow 2 \text{ I}_3^- + 2 \text{ H}_2\text{O}$$

d. $(4 \text{ H}^+ + 3e^- + \text{NO}_3^- \rightarrow \text{NO} + 2 \text{ H}_2\text{O}) \times 2$

$(2 \text{ Hg} \rightarrow \text{Hg}_2^{2+} + 2e^-) \times 3$

$$8 \text{ H}^+ + 6e^- + 2 \text{ NO}_3^- \rightarrow 2 \text{ NO} + 4 \text{ H}_2\text{O}$$
$$\underline{6 \text{ Hg} \rightarrow 3 \text{ Hg}_2^{2+} + 6e^-}$$
$$8 \text{ H}^+ + 2 \text{ NO}_3^- + 6 \text{ Hg} \rightarrow 2 \text{ NO} + 4 \text{ H}_2\text{O} + 3 \text{ Hg}_2^{2+}$$

e. $(\text{H}_2\text{O} + \text{CO} \rightarrow \text{CO}_2 + 2e^- + 2 \text{ H}^+) \times 5$

$$10 \text{ H}^+ + 10e^- + \text{I}_2\text{O}_5 \rightarrow \text{I}_2 + 5 \text{ H}_2\text{O}$$
$$\underline{5 \text{ H}_2\text{O} + 5 \text{ CO} \rightarrow 5 \text{ CO}_2 + 10e^- + 10 \text{ H}^+}$$
$$\text{I}_2\text{O}_5 + 5 \text{ CO} \rightarrow \text{I}_2 + 5 \text{ CO}_2$$

7. Oxidation is a loss of electrons;
reduction is a gain of electrons.

8. $\text{K}_2\text{S}^{4+}\text{O}_3$ $\quad$ $\text{K}_2\text{S}^{6+}\text{O}_4$ $\quad$ lose $2e^-$ per atom S

$\text{KMn}^{7+}\text{O}_4$ $\quad$ Mn^{4+}O_2 $\quad$ gain $3e^-$ per atom Mn

Therefore, need 3 moles K_2SO_3 for 2 moles KMnO_4

$$\frac{7.9 \text{ g } \cancel{\text{KMnO}_4}}{} \left| \frac{1 \text{ mole } \cancel{\text{KMnO}_4}}{158 \text{ g } \cancel{\text{KMnO}_4}} \right| \frac{3 \text{ moles } \cancel{\text{K}_2\text{SO}_3}}{2 \text{ moles } \cancel{\text{KMnO}_4}} \left| \frac{158 \text{ g } \text{K}_2\text{SO}_3}{1 \text{ mole } \cancel{\text{K}_2\text{SO}_3}} \right. = 11.9 \text{ g } \text{K}_2\text{SO}_3$$

9. $KCl^{5+}O_3$ Cl^{1-} gain $6e^-$ per atom Cl

$Cr_2^{3+}O_3$ $K_2Cr^{6+}O_4$ lose $3e^-$ per atom Cr; Cr_2O_3 gives up $6e^-$

Therefore, need one mole Cr_2O_3 for each mole $KClO_3$

$$\frac{20 \text{ ml } Cr_2O_3}{} \left| \frac{0.1 \text{ moles } Cr_2O_3}{1000 \text{ ml } Cr_2O_3} \right| \frac{1 \text{ mole } KClO_3}{1 \text{ mole } Cr_2O_3} \left| \frac{1000 \text{ ml } KClO_3}{0.2 \text{ moles } KClO_3} \right. = 10 \text{ ml } KClO_3$$

Page 483.   One More Step

1. In reference texts, students may wish to start with the Haber process, the Ostwald process, the Solvay process, the contact and chamber processes for H_2SO_4, the action in a Hooker cell, the Hall process for preparation of aluminum. There are many others, but these can provide an easy start.

2. a. PrO
   b. Ba_3N_2
   c. CrO_3
   d. Ca_3P_2
   e. SrH_2
   f. Fr_4C
   g. Li_2O
   h. Fe_2S_3
   i. ScF_3
   j. $TiCl_4$

3. Nature: Bacteria change nitrate to ammonia $(NO_3^- \rightarrow NH_3)$; oxygenation of blood $(O_2 \rightarrow O^{2-})$; energy production in cells.

   Kitchen: Burn meat (fatty substance to carbon); baking powder, burning gas.

4.

   all the O atoms are -2 the central S is $+5$ the peripheral S is -1
   The ion contains 2 atoms of the same element (S) in different oxidation states.

5. -3 NH_4OH ammonium hydroxide
    -2 N_2H_5OH hydrazine hydrate
    -1 NH_2OH hydroxylamine
     0   none $(N_2$, the free element)
    $+1$ N_2O nitrogen(I) oxide
    $+2$ NO   nitrogen(II) oxide
    $+3$ N_2O_3 nitrogen(III) oxide
    $+4$ NO_2 nitrogen(IV) oxide
    $+5$ N_2O_5 nitrogen(V) oxide

Suggested Readings for Faculty and Students

Bishop, John A., "Redox Reactions and the Acid-Base Properties of Solvents." *Chemistry*, Vol. 43, No. 1 (January 1970), p. 18.

*Pacer, Richard A., "Conjugate Acid-Base and Redox Theory." *Journal of Chemical Education*, Vol. 50, No. 3 (March 1973), pp. 178-180.

Sienko, M. J., *Chemistry Problems*. Menlo Park, California, W. A. Benjamin, Inc., 1972, 2nd Ed., Chapter 5.

*Taube, Henry, "Mechanisms of Oxidation-Reduction Reactions." *Journal of Chemical Education*, Vol. 45, No. 7 (July 1968), pp. 452-461.

(*Faculty only)

Chapter 22

Performance Objectives

GOAL: Students will gain an understanding of the relationship of electrolytes, controlled redox reactions, and energy and electron changes in electrochemical reactions.

Objectives: Upon completion of the reading and the activities, and when asked to diagram, demonstrate, or respond either orally or on a written test, the students will:

22:1-2   K   explain similarities and differences in electronic and electrolytic conduction.

22:3-4   P,K   write equations for reactions occurring at the anode and cathode in electrolytic conduction.

Upon completion of the reading and activities, students will exhibit an interest in science by:

A   voluntarily completing one or more of the One More Step activities listed at the end of the chapter on their own time.

A   reading unassigned literature related to the ideas presented in the chapter.

Page 507.   Section 22:14

1. $2\,Cl^- (aq) \rightarrow Cl_2 (g) + 2e^-$

$$\frac{1\ \text{mole-Cl}_2}{5.00\ \text{amp}} \left| \frac{1\ \text{mole}\ e^-}{1\ \text{mole-Cl}_2} \right| \frac{96{,}500\ \text{amp-sec}}{1\ \text{mole}\ e^-} = 3.86 \times 10^4\ \text{sec} = 663\ \text{min} = 10.7\ \text{hr}$$

2. $Cu^{2+} (aq) + 2e^- \rightarrow Cu^0$

$$\frac{2.00\ \text{moles-Cu}}{3\ \text{min}} \left| \frac{2\ \text{moles}\ e^-}{1\ \text{mole-Cu}} \right| \frac{96{,}500\ \text{amp-sec}}{1\ \text{mole}\ e^-} \left| \frac{1\ \text{min}}{60\ \text{sec}} \right. = 2140\ \text{amp}$$

or

$$\frac{4\ \text{moles}\ e^-}{3\ \text{min}} \left| \frac{96{,}500\ \text{amp-sec}}{1\ \text{mole}\ e^=} \right| \frac{1\ \text{min}}{60\ \text{sec}} = 2140\ \text{amp}$$

3. $Ag^+ (aq) + e^- \rightarrow Ag (c)$

$$\frac{1\ \text{amp}}{} \left| \frac{9650\ \text{sec}}{} \right| \frac{1\ \text{mole}\ e^-}{96{,}500\ \text{amp-sec}} \left| \frac{1\ \text{mole}\ Ag}{1\ \text{mole}\ e^-} \right| \frac{108\ \text{g}\ Ag}{1\ \text{mole}\ Ag} = 10.8\ \text{g}\ Ag$$

or

$$9650\ \text{sec} \times 1\ \text{amp} = 9650\ \text{coulombs}$$

$$\frac{9650}{96500} = \frac{1}{10}\ \text{mole}\ e^- \quad \frac{1}{10} \times 108 = 10.8\ \text{g}\ Ag$$

4. $Ag^+ (aq) + e^- \rightarrow Ag (c)$

$$\frac{5\ \text{amp}}{} \left| \frac{10\ \text{min}}{} \right| \frac{60\ \text{sec}}{1\ \text{min}} \left| \frac{1\ \text{mole}\ e^-}{96{,}500\ \text{amp-sec}} \right| \frac{1\ \text{mole}\ Ag}{1\ \text{mole}\ e^-} \left| \frac{108\ \text{g}\ Ag}{1\ \text{mole}\ Ag} \right. = 3.36\ \text{g}\ Ag$$

5. $Ca^{2+} (aq) + 2e^- \rightarrow Ca (c)$

$$\frac{0.40\ \text{g-Ca}}{10\ \text{amp}} \left| \frac{1\ \text{mole-Ca}}{40\ \text{g-Ca}} \right| \frac{2\ \text{moles}\ e^-}{1\ \text{mole-Ca}} \left| \frac{96{,}500\ \text{amp-sec}}{1\ \text{mole}\ e^-} \right| \frac{1\ \text{min}}{60\ \text{sec}} = 3.22\ \text{min}$$

6.   new mass 28.273 g

   original mass 26.203 g

   mass copper   2.070 g

$$\% \text{ copper} = \frac{2.07}{2.36} \times 100 = 87.7\%$$

9. $2 \text{ NaCl (aq)} + 2 \text{ H}_2\text{O} \rightarrow 2 \text{ NaOH (aq)} + \text{H}_2 \text{ (g)} + \text{Cl}_2 \text{ (g)}$
   See page 492.

$$\frac{40 \text{ g NaOH}}{20 \text{ amp}} \left| \frac{1 \text{ mole NaOH}}{40 \text{ g NaOH}} \right| \frac{1 \text{ mole } e^-}{1 \text{ mole NaOH}} \left| \frac{96,500 \text{ amp-sec}}{1 \text{ mole } e^-} \right. = 4825 \text{ sec} = 1.34 \text{ hr}$$

or

$40 \text{ g NaOH} = 1 \text{ mole NaOH}$

1 mole needs 96,500 coulombs

$$\frac{96,500 \text{ amp-sec}}{20 \text{ amp}} = 4825 \text{ sec} \approx 1.34 \text{ hr}$$

10. a. $\text{Ag}^+ \text{ (aq)} + e^- \rightarrow \text{Ag (c)}$

   b. $\dfrac{5 \text{ amp}}{} \left| \dfrac{2 \text{ hr}}{1 \text{ hr}} \right| \dfrac{60 \text{ min}}{1 \text{ min}} \left| \dfrac{60 \text{ sec}}{96,500 \text{ amp-sec}} \right| \dfrac{1 \text{ mole } e^-}{1 \text{ mole } e^-} \left| \dfrac{1 \text{ mole Ag}}{1 \text{ mole Ag}} \right| \dfrac{108 \text{ g Ag}}{}$

   $$= 40.3 \text{ g Ag}$$

   or

   5 amp for 7200 sec = 36,000 coulombs

   $$\frac{36,000}{96,500} = \text{eq of Ag} = 0.373 \text{ eq}$$

   mass Ag = $0.373 \times 108 \text{ g} = 40.3 \text{ g}$

11. Electronic conduction consists of the movement of electrons through a conductor, electrolytic conduction consists of the migration of ions through a solution or an ionic melt.

12. $\text{Ca (c)} \rightarrow \text{Ca}^{2+} + 2e^-$

   $2 \text{ Ag}^+ + 2e^- \rightarrow 2 \text{ Ag (c)}$

   $\text{Ca} + 2 \text{ Ag}^+ \rightarrow \text{Ca}^{2+} + 2 \text{ Ag (c)}$

   $$\begin{array}{r} 2.87 \text{ V} \\ - (-0.80)\text{V O}_2 \\ \hline 3.67 \text{ V} \end{array}$$

7. (a and e) will proceed spontaneously. (b, c, d) do not proceed spontaneously.

8. The anode is the oxidation point and the cathode is the reduction point. Therefore: run a known electrolysis to determine which (oxidation or reduction) occurs at each electrode.

13. $2 \text{ NaCl (c)} + 2 \text{ H}_2\text{O (l)} \rightarrow 2 \text{ NaOH (aq)} + \text{H}_2 \text{ (g)} + \text{Cl}_2 \text{ (g)}$

14. $(2e^- + 2 \text{ H}_2\text{O} \rightarrow \text{H}_2 + 2 \text{ OH}^-) \times 2$

   $2 \text{ H}_2\text{O} \rightarrow \text{O}_2 + 4 \text{ H}^+ + 4e^-$

   $\underline{4e^- + 4 \text{ H}_2\text{O} \rightarrow 2 \text{ H}_2 + 4 \text{ OH}^-}$

   $6 \text{ H}_2\text{O} \rightarrow \text{O}_2 + 2 \text{ H}_2 + 4 \text{ H}_2\text{O}$

   $2 \text{ H}_2\text{O} \rightarrow \text{O}_2 + 2 \text{ H}_2$

$$\frac{10 \text{ g H}_2\text{O}}{} \left| \frac{1 \text{ mole H}_2\text{O}}{18 \text{ g H}_2\text{O}} \right| \frac{1 \text{ mole O}_2}{2 \text{ mole H}_2\text{O}} \left| \frac{22.4 \text{ l O}_2}{1 \text{ mole O}_2} \right.$$

$$= 6.22 \text{ l O}_2 \text{ STP}$$

Page 511.   One More Step

1. *Encyclopaedia Brittanica* is a good source. Start with Thales → Franklin → nuclear reactors. Another good source is the Bell Telephone Laboratories book, *Conductors and Semiconductors*.

2.
$$E = 0 - \frac{0.0592}{0} \log \frac{10^{-1}}{10^0}$$

$$= - \frac{0.0592}{2} \log 10^{-1}$$

$$= \frac{0.0592}{2} = 0.0296 \text{ volts}$$

3.
$$E = E^0 - \frac{RT}{nF} \ln \frac{[C][D]}{[A][B]}$$

$$E = 0.762 - \frac{0.0592}{2} \log 2$$

$$= 0.762 - (0.0296)(0.301)$$

$$= 0.762 - 0.00888 = 0.753 \text{ volts}$$

Suggested Readings for Faculty and Students

*Biegler, T., and Woods, R., "The Standard Hydrogen Electrode." *Journal of Chemical Education,* Vol. 50, No. 9 (September 1973), pp. 604-605.

*Burrows, Brian, "Principles of Electrochemical Energy Conversion." *Journal of Chemical Education,* Vol. 48, No. 11 (November 1971), pp. 732-736.

Kozawa, Akiya, and Powers, R. A., "Electrochemical Reactions in Batteries." *Journal of Chemical Education,* Vol. 49, No. 9 (September 1972), pp. 587-591.

Sapio, Joseph P., and Braun, Robert D., "Ion-Selective Electrodes." *Chemistry,* Vol. 46, No. 6 (June 1973), pp. 14-17.

Sienko, M. J., *Chemistry Problems.* Menlo Park, California, W. A. Benjamin, Inc., 1972, 2nd Ed., Chapter 9.

Slabaugh, W. H., "Corrosion." *Journal of Chemical Education,* Vol. 51, No. 4 (April 1974), pp. 218-220.

Weissman, Eugene Y., "Batteries: The Workhorses of Chemical Energy Conversion." *Chemistry,* Vol. 45, No. 10 (November 1972), pp. 6-11.

(*Faculty only)

Chapter 23

Performance Objectives

GOAL: Students will gain an understanding of natural and artificial nuclear reactions and the instruments used by chemists to study, control, and utilize radioactive materials and nuclear processes.

Objectives: Upon completion of the reading and activities, and when asked to diagram, demonstrate, or respond either orally or on a written test, the students will:

23:1-2	K	describe properties of the nucleus of radioactive atoms.
23:3-4	K,P	list and classify elementary particles.
23:5-7	K	describe some simple radiation detectors.
23:8-9	K	describe radioactive nuclides and give examples of their use as tracers.
23:10	K	define half-life and give examples of its use.
23:11	K	list and describe three factors which compare stability of nuclides.
23:12	K	trace the history of accelerators.
23:13-16	K	describe and give examples of fission, fusion, and other natural and manmade reactions.

Upon completion of the reading and activities, students will exhibit an interest in science by:

A	voluntarily completing one or more of the One More Step activities listed at the end of the chapter on their own time.

A   reading unassigned literature related to the ideas presented in the chapter.

Page 538. End of Chapter

1. Alpha particles are helium nuclei; beta particles are electrons; gamma rays are electromagnetic radiation.

   α and β radiation consist of particles while γ radiation consists of electromagnetic waves. α particles are positively charged and several thousand times as heavy as the negatively charged β particles.

   increasing penetration

   α β γ

   increasing ionizing power

2. Stability tests:

   a. Binding energy. A greater binding energy per particle indicates greater stability.

   b. Neutron-proton ratio. The more closely the ratio approximates 1, the more stable the atom.

   c. In general, the atoms having an even number of neutrons and protons are more stable than those having an odd number of neutrons and protons.

3. Radiation passes through the gas of detection chamber and causes the gas to ionize. The ionized gas then conducts a current across the chamber or tube and activates the counter mechanism.

4.

Protium $_1^1$H

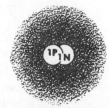

Deuterium $_1^2$H

Tritium $_1^3$H

5. Radioactive isotopes are used to:

   a. gauge wear of pistons in automobile engines.

   b. determine location of certain substances in the human body.

   c. produce γ-rays.

   d. trace the progress of radioactive chemicals in plants.

6. Fusion is the joining of several small nuclei to form one large nucleus. Fission is the splitting of a large nucleus into several smaller nuclei.

7. a. $_1^3\text{H} \rightarrow {}_2^3\text{He} + {}_{-1}^{0}e$

   b. $_{30}^{61}\text{Zn} \rightarrow {}_{29}^{61}\text{Cu} + {}_{+1}^{0}e$

   c. $_3^9\text{Li} \rightarrow {}_4^9\text{Be} + {}_{-1}^{0}e$

   d. $_{96}^{240}\text{Cm} \rightarrow {}_{94}^{236}\text{Pu} + {}_2^4\text{He}$

   e. $_{84}^{199}\text{Po} + {}_{-1}^{0}e \rightarrow {}_{83}^{199}\text{Bi}$

Page 538. One More Step

1. a. Intensity is inversely proportional to the square of the distance between source and detector.

   b. Relative effectiveness for equal thicknesses of: paper 1, masonry 16, iron 50, lead 100. (Figures will vary with type of paper and type of masonry.)

2. This cannot be answered, because two plants of the same species will not always give the same type of radiogram. Tomato plants, for instance, distribute radioactive phosphorus principally in the cell walls and radioactive sulfur in protoplasm.

3. There are many answers to this question. Below are some illustrative examples.

^3H medical studies of body fluids and lubrication studies

^{131}I medical studies of metabolic rate

^{60}Co treatment of tumors and industrial radiographs of castings

^{14}C almost every phase of organic and biochemistry research

^{35}S metabolic studies

^{85}Kr thickness gauge in some paper mills

^{45}Ca durability of masonry

^{90}Sr food preservation

4. Strong interactions involve the forces between nucleons and heavier particles, while weak interactions generally involve neutrinos.

weak interactions

muon decay
neutron decay
antineutrino capture
pion decay
kaon decay
neutrino capture

strong interactions

internuclear forces
hyperon-nuclear reactions
nucleon-nucleon reactions
production of nucleons, pions, hyperons, and kaons

(Strong interactions are 10^{14} times as strong as weak interactions.)

5. Cyclotron — see page 528 of text. Betatron accelerates electrons by means of magnetic fields alone.

Synchroton — synchronizes an electric field and a magnetic field in order to accelerate the particles.

See: Wilson, Robert R., and Littauer, Raphael, *Accelerators: Machines of Nuclear Physics.* Garden City; Doubleday and Co., 1960.

6. For about 20 years physicists have been working toward the goal of harnessing the nuclear fusion process to obtain power. One of the systems studied is the magnetohydrodynamic (MHD) generator in which the fusion reaction is confined by magnetic means. Another system involves laser fusion which is based on ignition of a pellet of fuel by focused laser beams.

Suggested Readings for Faculty and Students

Alfven, Hannes, "Antimatter and Cosmology." *Scientific American,* Vol. 216, No. 4 (April 1967), pp. 106-114.

Auer, P. L., and Sudan, R. N., "Progress in Controlled Fusion Research." *The Science Teacher,* Vol. 39, No. 3 (March 1972), pp. 44-50.

*Ayrey, G., Barnard, D., and Houseman, T.H., "The Use of Radioisotopically Labeled Analytical Reagents in Organic Chemistry." *Chemical Reviews,* Vol. 71, No. 4 (April 1971), pp. 371-393.

Baranger, Michel, and Sorensen, Raymond A., "The Size and Shape of Atomic Nuclei." *Scientific American,* Vol. 221, No. 2 (August 1969), pp. 58-73.

Bump, T. R., "A Third Generation of Breeder Reactors." *Scientific American,* Vol. 216, No. 5 (May 1967), pp. 25-33.

Choppin, Gregory R., "Nuclear Fission." *Chemistry,* Vol. 40, No. 7 (July-August 1967), pp. 25-30.

Clark, Herbert M., "The Origin of Nuclear Science." *Chemistry,* Vol. 40, No. 7 (July-August 1967), pp. 8-11.

Coppi, Bruno, and Rem, Jan, "The TOKAMAK Approach in Fusion Research." *Scientific American,* Vol. 227, No. 1 (July 1972), pp. 65-75.

Gough, William C., and Eastlund, Bernard J., "The Prospects of Fusion Power." *Scientific American,* Vol. 224, No. 2 (February 1971), pp. 50-64.

Herber, R. H., "Mossbauer Spectroscopy." *Scientific American,* Vol. 225, No. 4 (October 1971), pp. 86-95.

Hudis, J., "Nuclear Reaction." *Chemistry,* Vol. 40, No. 7 (July-August 1967), pp. 20-24.

Hyde, Earl K., "Nuclear Models." *Chemistry,* Vol. 40, No. 7 (July-August 1967), pp. 8-19.

Iben, Icko, "Stellar Evolution: Comparison of Theory with Observation." *Science,* Vol. 155, No. 3764 (February 17, 1967), pp. 785-796.

Johnson, Russell H., "Radiation Chemistry." *Chemistry,* Vol. 40, No. 7 (July-August 1967), pp. 31-36.

Landis, John W., "Fusion Power." *Journal of Chemical Education,* Vol. 50, No. 10 (October 1970), pp. 658-662.

Libby, Willard F., "Dating by Radiocarbon." *Accounts of Chemical Research,* Vol. 5, No. 9 (September 1972), pp. 289-295.

Lubin, Moshe J., and Fraas, Arthur P., "Fusion by Laser." *Scientific American,* Vol. 224, No. 6 (June 1971), pp. 21-23.

*Lukens, H. R., "Neutron Activation Analysis." *Journal of Chemical Education,* Vol. 44, No. 11 (November 1967), pp. 668-672.

Pecsok, Robert L., and Shields, L. D., *Modern Methods of Chemical Analysis.* New York, John Wiley and Sons, Inc., 1968, Chapter 12.

Rancitelli, L., and others, "Potassium:Argon Dating of Iron Meteorites." *Science,* Vol. 155, No. 3765 (February 24, 1967), pp. 999-1000.

Rose, Peter H., and Wittkower, Andrew B., "Tandem Van de Graaff Accelerators." *Scientific American,* Vol. 223, No. 2 (August 1970), pp. 24-34.

Seaborg, Glenn T., and Bloom, Justin L., "Fast Breeder Reactors." *Scientific American,* Vol. 223, No. 5 (November 1970), pp. 13-21.

Seaborg, Glenn T., and Bloom, Justin L., "The Synthetic Elements: IV." *Scientific American,* Vol. 220, No. 4 (April 1969), pp. 56-67.

Wagner, John J., "Nuclear Magnetic Resonance Spectroscopy — An Outline." *Chemistry,* Vol. 43, No. 3 (March 1970), pp. 13-15.

Wahl, W. H., and Kramer, H. H., "Neutron-Activation Analysis." *Scientific American,* Vol. 216, No. 4 (April 1967), pp. 68-82.

Zafirates, Chris D., "The Texture of the Nuclear Surface." *Scientific American,* Vol. 227, No. 4 (October 1972), pp. 100-108.

(*Faculty only)

Chapter 24

Performance Objectives

GOAL: Students will gain an understanding of organic chemistry through an introductory discussion of structure, nomenclature, substituents (functional groups), and simple reactions.

Objectives: Upon completion of the reading and activities, and when asked to diagram, demonstrate, or respond either orally or on a written test, the students will:

24:1	K	list the major classifications of hydrocarbons.
24:2-9	P,K	name and draw structural formulas for saturated and unsaturated hydrocarbons.
24:10-12	K	identify and name substituted hydrocarbons.
24:13-16	K	identify and describe various organic reactions.
24:17-21	K	list and describe the manufacture of products derived from organic compounds including gasoline, plastics, and fibers.

Upon completion of the reading and activities, students will exhibit an interest in science by:

A   voluntarily completing one or more of the One More Step activities listed at the end of the chapter on their own time.

A   reading unassigned literature related to the ideas presented in the chapter.

Page 547.   Section 24:4

1. a. 2,3-dimethylpentane

   b. octane

   c. 2,2,3-trimethylheptane

d. 2,3,4-trimethylhexane

e. 2,2-dimethylbutane

2. a.
$$CH_3-\overset{\overset{\displaystyle CH_3}{|}}{CH}-CH_2-CH_2-CH_2-$$
$$CH_2-CH_3$$

b.
$$CH_3-\overset{\overset{\displaystyle CH_3}{|}}{\underset{\underset{\displaystyle CH_3}{|}}{C}}-\overset{\overset{\displaystyle CH_3}{|}}{\underset{\underset{\displaystyle CH_3}{|}}{C}}-CH_3$$

c.
$$CH_3-\overset{\overset{\displaystyle CH_3}{|}}{\underset{\underset{\displaystyle CH_3}{|}}{C}}-CH_2-\overset{\overset{\displaystyle CH_3}{|}}{CH}-CH_3$$

d.
$$CH_3-\overset{\overset{\displaystyle CH_3}{|}}{CH}-\overset{\overset{\displaystyle \overset{\displaystyle CH_3}{|}}{\underset{\displaystyle CH_2}{|}}}{CH}-CH_2-CH_3$$

e.
$$CH_3-CH_2-\overset{\overset{\displaystyle CH_2}{|}}{\underset{\underset{\underset{\displaystyle CH_3}{|}}{\underset{\displaystyle CH_2}{|}}}{CH}}-CH_2-CH_2-CH_3$$

3. a. C—C—C—C—C—C

b.
$$\overset{\overset{\displaystyle C}{|}}{C}-\overset{\overset{\displaystyle C}{|}}{C}-C-C-C$$

c.
$$C-C-\overset{\overset{\displaystyle C}{|}}{C}-C-C$$

d.
$$C-\overset{\overset{\displaystyle C}{|}}{\underset{\underset{\displaystyle C}{|}}{C}}-C-C$$

e.
$$C-\overset{\overset{\displaystyle C}{|}}{C}-\overset{\overset{\displaystyle C}{|}}{C}-C$$

4. a. hexane

b. 2-methylpentane

c. 3-methylpentane

d. 2,2-dimethylbutane

e. 2,3-dimethylbutane

Page 568.   End of Chapter

5. $CH_2\!\!=\!\!CH_2(g) + HI(g) \rightarrow CH_3-CH_2I(l)$

6. $CH_2\!\!=\!\!CH_2(g) + $ ⬡—CH$=$CH$_2$ (l) $\rightarrow$ —CH—CH$_2$—CH$_2$—CH$_2$—(amor)

7. a. $Cl_2(g) + CH_2\!\!=\!\!CH-CH_3(g) \rightarrow CH_2-\overset{\overset{\displaystyle Cl}{|}}{\underset{\underset{\displaystyle Cl}{|}}{CH}}-CH_3(l)$

b. $CH_3-CH_2-CH_2-CH_2-CH_2-OH(l) + CH_3-\overset{\overset{\displaystyle O}{\|}}{C}-OH(l) \rightarrow$

$CH_3-\overset{\overset{\displaystyle O}{\|}}{C}-O-CH_2-CH_2-CH_2-CH_2-CH_3$ (l) $+ H_2O(l)$

c. $2 C_6H_6(l) + 15 O_2(g) \rightarrow 12 CO_2(g) + 6 H_2O(g)$

d.
$$CH_2\!-\!CH_2\!-\!CH_2\!-\!CH_3(l) \xrightarrow{\ H_2SO_4\ } CH_2\!=\!CH\!-\!CH_2\!-\!CH_3(g) + H_2O(l)$$
$|$
OH

e.
$$
\begin{array}{c}
\quad\quad\quad\quad O \\
\quad\quad\quad\quad \| \\
CH_2\!-\!O\!-\!C\!-\!(CH_2)_{17}\!-\!CH_3 \\
| \\
\quad\quad\quad\quad O \\
\quad\quad\quad\quad \| \\
CH\!-\!O\!-\!C\!-\!(CH_2)_{17}\!-\!CH_3 \quad\quad + 3 NaOH(aq) \\
| \\
\quad\quad\quad\quad O \\
\quad\quad\quad\quad \| \\
CH_2\!-\!O\!-\!C\!-\!(CH_2)_{17}\!-\!CH_3 (amor) \rightarrow
\end{array}
$$

$$
\begin{array}{c}
\quad\quad\quad\quad\quad\quad\quad\quad\quad\quad\quad\quad\quad\quad O \\
\quad\quad\quad\quad\quad\quad\quad\quad\quad\quad\quad\quad\quad\quad \| \\
CH_2\!-\!CH\!-\!CH_2 + 3[CH_3\!-\!(CH_2)_{17}\!-\!C\!-\!O^-Na^+](aq) \\
|\quad\quad\ |\quad\quad\ | \\
OH\quad OH\quad OH(l)
\end{array}
$$

8.
methane	undecane	heneicosane
ethane	dodecane	docosane
propane	tridecane	tricosane
butane	tetradecane	tetracosane
pentane	pentadecane	pentacosane
hexane	hexadecane	hexacosane
heptane	heptadecane	heptacosane
octane	octadecane	octacosane
nonane	nonadecane	nonacosane
decane	eicosane	triacontane

9. a. C—C—C—C—C—C—C

   b.
   $$
   \begin{array}{c}
   \quad C \\
   \quad | \\
   C\!-\!C\!-\!C\!-\!C\!-\!C\!-\!C
   \end{array}
   $$

   c.
   $$
   \begin{array}{c}
   \quad\quad\quad C \\
   \quad\quad\quad | \\
   C\!-\!C\!-\!C\!-\!C\!-\!C\!-\!C
   \end{array}
   $$

   d.
   $$
   \begin{array}{c}
   \quad\quad C \\
   \quad\quad | \\
   C\!-\!C\!-\!C\!-\!C\!-\!C \\
   \quad\quad | \\
   \quad\quad C
   \end{array}
   $$

   e.
   $$
   \begin{array}{c}
   \quad\quad C\quad C \\
   \quad\quad |\quad\ | \\
   C\!-\!C\!-\!C\!-\!C\!-\!C
   \end{array}
   $$

f.
$$
\begin{array}{c}
\quad\quad\quad\quad C \\
\quad\quad\quad\quad | \\
\quad\quad\quad\quad C \\
\quad\quad\quad\quad | \\
C\!-\!C\!-\!C\!-\!C\!-\!C \\
\quad\quad\quad\quad C
\end{array}
$$

g.
$$
\begin{array}{c}
\quad\quad\quad\quad C \\
\quad\quad\quad\quad | \\
C\!-\!C\!-\!C\!-\!C\!-\!C \\
\quad\quad\quad\quad | \\
\quad\quad\quad\quad C \\
\quad\quad\quad\quad | \\
\quad\quad\quad\quad C
\end{array}
$$

h.
$$
\begin{array}{c}
C\!-\!C\!-\!C\!-\!C \\
\quad\ |\quad | \\
\quad\ C\quad C
\end{array}
$$

i.
$$
\begin{array}{c}
\quad C\quad\quad\ C \\
\quad |\quad\quad\ | \\
C\!-\!C\!-\!C\!-\!C\!-\!C
\end{array}
$$

10. nonane = 35 isomers

    decane = 75 isomers

11. a. 4-ethyl-2,6-dimethyloctane

    b. 1,1,4-trimethylcyclohexane

    c. 1,3-pentadiene

d. 3,3-dimethyl-1-butyne

e. 1,2-diethylbenzene

$$CH_2-CH_3$$
$$|$$
12. a. $CH_3-CH_2-CH-CH_2-CH_2-CH_3$

b.

c. $CH_2=C-CH_3$
$\quad\quad\quad |$
$\quad\quad\quad CH_3$

d. $CH\equiv C-CH_2-CH_2-CH_2-CH_3$

e.

13. $C_{40}H_{82}$

$40(12) + 82(1) = 562$

14. a. 1-propanol

b. 2-butanol

c. 2-methyl-2-propanol

d. 1-pentoxyhexane

e. butanal

f. 2-hexanone

g. butanoic acid

h. hexyl propanoate

i. 1-propanomine
(1-amino propane)

j. butanamide

15. a. $CH_3-CH_2-CH_2-CH_2-OH$

$\quad\quad\quad CH_3\;\; OH$
$\quad\quad\quad |\quad\quad |$
b. $CH_3-CH-CH_2$

c. $CH_3-CH_2-CH_2-O-CH_2-CH_2-CH_2-CH_3$

$\quad\quad\quad\quad O$
$\quad\quad\quad\quad \|$
d. CH_3-CH

$\quad\quad\quad\quad\quad\quad O$
$\quad\quad\quad\quad\quad\quad \|$
e. $CH_3-CH_2-C-CH_2-CH_3$

$\quad\quad\quad\quad\quad\quad\quad\quad O$
$\quad\quad\quad\quad\quad\quad\quad\quad \|$
f. $CH_3-CH_2-CH_2-O-C-H$

$\quad\quad\quad CH_3$
$\quad\quad\quad |$
g. CH_3-N-CH_3

$\quad\quad\quad\quad\quad\quad O$
$\quad\quad\quad\quad\quad\quad \|$
h. CH_3-CH_2-C-OH

$\quad\quad\quad\quad\quad\quad O$
$\quad\quad\quad\quad\quad\quad \|$
i. $CH_3-CH_2-C-NH_2$

j. CH_3-NO_2

Page 570.   One More Step

1. There is a fairly regular change in the melting points and boiling points from one member of the alkanes to the next. (See also graph on page 104T.)

Name	Formula	M.P.(°C)	B.P.(°C)	Name	Formula	M.P.(°C)	B.P.(°C)
methane	CH_4	-182	-164	undecane	$C_{11}H_{24}$	-25.6	196
ethane	C_2H_6	-183	-88.6	dodecane	$C_{12}H_{26}$	-9.6	216
propane	C_3H_8	-190	-42.1	tridecane	$C_{13}H_{28}$	-5.5	235
butane	C_4H_{10}	-138	-0.5	tetradecane	$C_{14}H_{30}$	5.86	254
pentane	C_5H_{12}	-130	36.1	pentadecane	$C_{15}H_{32}$	10	271
hexane	C_6H_{14}	-95	69.0	hexadecane	$C_{16}H_{34}$	18.2	287
heptane	C_7H_{16}	-90.6	98.4	heptadecane	$C_{17}H_{36}$	22	302
octane	C_8H_{18}	-56.8	126	octadecane	$C_{18}H_{38}$	28.2	316
nonane	C_9H_{20}	-51	151	nonadecane	$C_{19}H_{40}$	32.1	330
decane	$C_{10}H_{22}$	-29.7	174	eicosane	$C_{20}H_{42}$	36.8	343

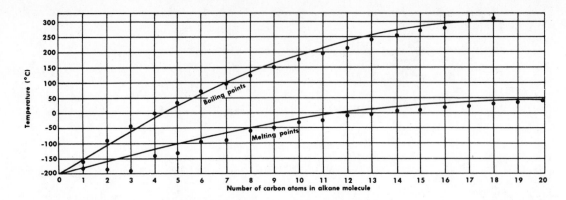

2. Grignard Reagents. In 1901, the French chemist Victor Grignard made the important observation that alkyl halides dissolved in diethyl ether

$$(C_2H_5-O-C_2H_5)$$

will react with metallic magnesium to form ether-soluble alkylmagnesium halides. These latter halides are now called Grignard reagents. The reaction producing them will be illustrated here by the formation of methylmagnesium iodide from methyl iodide. The diethyl ether solvent must be very pure, and the apparatus and reagents must be moisture free.

$$CH_3I + Mg \rightarrow CH_3MgI$$

methylmagnesium iodide

Grignard reagents react with water to produce alkanes. Since the step leading to the formation of the Grignard reagent and the hydrolysis process both produce a good yield, this reaction sequence is an attractive one for the conversion of alkyl halides to the corresponding alkanes. The hydrolysis of methylmagnesium iodide produces methane in the following manner:

$$CH_3-Mg-I + H-O-H$$
$$\rightarrow CH_4 + MgI(OH)$$

This type of reaction sequence may be generalized as:

$$R-X + Mg \rightarrow RMgX$$
$$R\boxed{MgX + H-O}H \rightarrow R-H + MgX(OH)$$

The following equations summarize the preparation and reactions of some Grignard reagents. The symbol R is used here both for alkyl and aryl groups.

(1) $RX + Mg \xrightarrow{ether} RMgX$

(2) $RMgX + H_2O \rightarrow RH + Mg(OH)X$

(3) $RMgX + CO_2 \rightarrow RCO_2MgX$

$$\xrightarrow{H_2O} RCO_2H + Mg(OH)X$$

(4) $RMgX + CH_2\underset{\diagdown O \diagup}{-}CH_2 \rightarrow RCH_2CH_2OMgX$

$$\xrightarrow{H_2O} RCH_2CH_2OH + Mg(OH)X$$

(5) $RMgX + CH_2O \rightarrow RCH_2OMgX$

$$\xrightarrow{H_2O} RCH_2OH + Mg(OH)X$$

(6) $RMgX + R'CHO \rightarrow R-\underset{OMgX}{CH}-R'$

$$\xrightarrow{H_2O} R-\underset{OH}{CH}-R' + Mg(OH)X$$

(7) $RMgX + R'CR' \rightarrow RC(R')R'$
   (with $\underset{O}{\overset{\|}{}}$ and $\underset{OMgX}{}$)

$$\xrightarrow{H_2O} RC(R')R' + Mg(OH)X$$
   (with $\underset{OH}{}$)

104T

(8) $2 RMgX + R'CO_2R' \rightarrow R'CR_2$
$$\underset{\underset{OMgX}{|}}{}$$

$$\xrightarrow{H_2O} R'CR_2 + Mg(OH)X$$
$$\underset{\underset{OH}{|}}{}$$

The Wurtz Synthesis. Some years prior to the work of Grignard, another famous French chemist, Charles Wurtz, became interested in the reactions of alkyl halides with metals. In 1855, he reported that the treatment of two moles of alkyl halide with an equivalent amount of sodium produced an alkane containing twice the number of carbons as the halide. The reaction is illustrated here by the preparation of n-butane from ethyl bromide.

$$2 CH_3—CH_2—Br + 2 Na \rightarrow$$

$$CH_3—CH_2—CH_2—CH_3 + 2 NaBr$$

The Wurtz synthesis has greater limitations than the Grignard reaction, and not all alkyl halides produce useful yields of alkanes. The general equation for the reaction is:

$$R—X + 2 Na + X \quad R \rightarrow R—R + 2 NaX$$

The reaction between two different alkyl halides and sodium leads to a mixture of alkanes which limits the usefulness of this synthesis to the preparation of symmetrical alkanes.

3. Nucleic acids are complex structures which hydrolyze to yield various nitrogen compounds, sugars, and phosphoric acid. They are found in the nuclei of cells of living organisms and are presently being studied because they are basic constituents in genetic material. For current information, see the *Scientific American* magazine for article or series of articles involving genetics, heredity, or evolution.

4. Heterocyclic compounds are organic ring compounds containing other atoms in addition to carbon atoms (for example oxygen, nitrogen, sulfur) in the ring.

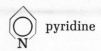 pyridine

See a text on organic synthesis for laboratory procedures for preparing some of these compounds.

$$\text{glycine} + \text{urea} \xrightarrow[\underset{\text{1 hour}}{110°C}]{\text{NaOH}} \text{hydantoic acid}$$

$$\text{Hydantoic acid} \xrightarrow[\underset{\text{15 minutes}}{110°C}]{\text{conc. HCl}} \text{hydantoin}$$

5. Saran = copolymer of vinyl chloride and vinylidene chloride

Kodel = copolymer of ethylene glycol and terephthalic acid

Acrilan = acrylonitrile

Dynel = copolymer of acrylonitrile and vinyl chloride

Mylar = copolymer of ethylene glycol and terephthalic acid

vinyl chloride $\quad CH_2=CH—Cl$

vinylidene chloride $\quad CH_2=CCl_2$

ethylene glycol

$$HO—CH_2—CH_2—OH$$

terephthalic acid

$$H—O—\underset{\underset{O}{\|}}{C}—\bigcirc—\underset{\underset{O}{\|}}{C}—O—H$$

acrylonitrile $\quad CH_2=CH—C\equiv N$

Suggested Readings for Faculty and Students

Billmeyer, Fred W., Jr., *Synthetic Polymers.* Garden City, Doubleday, 1972.
Breslow, Ronald, "The Nature of Aromatic Molecules." *Scientific American,* Vol. 227, No. 2 (August 1972), pp. 32-40.

Cahn, R. S., *An Introduction to Chemical Nomenclature*. New York, Plenum Press, 1968, Chapters 3-9.

Dence, Joseph B., "Covalent Carbon — Metal(loid) Compounds." *Chemistry*, Vol. 46, No. 1 (January 1973), pp. 6-13.

Edelman, Gerald M., "The Structure and Function of Antibodies." *Scientific American*, Vol. 223, No. 2 (August 1970), pp. 34-42.

Fletcher, John H., Dermer, Otis C., and Fox, Robert B., *Nomenclature of Organic Compounds*. Wash. D.C., American Chemical Society, 1974 (Advances in Chemistry Series 126).

Geohegan, J. T., and Bambrick, W. E., "Turpentine and Its Derivatives." *Chemistry*, Vol. 45, No. 3 (March 1972), pp. 6-9.

Grant, Nancy, and Naves, Renee G., "Perfumes and the Art of Perfumery." *Journal of Chemical Education*, Vol. 49, No. 8 (August 1972), pp. 526-528.

Hall, Dana, and Allen, Earle, "The Many Faces of Rubber." *Chemistry*, Vol. 45, No. 6 (June 1972), pp. 6-12.

*Harrison, Ian T., *Compendium of Organic Synthetic Methods*. New York, John Wiley and Sons, Inc., 1971.

MacKenzie, Charles A., *Experimental Organic Chemistry*, 4th Ed., Englewood Cliffs, Prentice-Hall Inc., 1971.

Miller, Larry L., "Organic Ion Radical Chemistry." *Journal of Chemical Education*, Vol. 48, No. 3 (March 1971), pp. 168-173.

Mills, G. Alex, "Ubiquitous Hydrocarbons." *Chemistry*, Part I, Vol. 44, No. 2 (February 1971), pp. 8-13; Part II, Vol. 44, No. 3 (March 1971), pp. 12-17.

Pryor, William A., "Free Radicals in Biological Systems." *Scientific American*, Vol. 223, No. 2 (August 1970), pp. 70-83.

Snyder, Lloyd R., "Petroleum Nitrogen Compounds and Oxygen Compounds." *Accounts of Chemical Research*, Vol. 3, No. 9 (September 1970), pp. 290-299.

(*Faculty only)

CHEMISTRY
A Modern Course

ROBERT C. SMOOT
Chairman, Science Department
McDonogh School
McDonogh, Maryland

JACK PRICE
San Diego City Schools
San Diego, California

CHARLES E. MERRILL PUBLISHING CO.
A Bell & Howell Company   Columbus, Ohio

A Merrill Science Program

Chemistry: A Modern Course

Chemistry: A Modern Course—Teacher's Annotated
Edition and Solutions Manual

Chemistry: A Modern Course
Spirit Duplicating Evaluation Program

Laboratory Chemistry

Laboratory Chemistry—
Teacher's Annotated Edition

Solving Problems in Chemistry

Project Editor: Marie P. Duffy

Book Design: Lester L. Shumaker

Biographical Art: Lloyd Ostendorf

Cover Photo

The burning of a candle, a familiar chemical reaction, symbolizes many of the concerns of the modern chemist. The wax in the candle changes state as it melts and vaporizes. The vaporized wax reacts with the oxygen of the air. In this reaction, new products quite different from the original reactants are formed and energy is released in the form of heat and light. Under normal conditions, this process will continue until the candle has disappeared.

Through a study of chemistry, you will gain an understanding of matter, its properties, its chemical composition, and the physical and chemical changes which it undergoes as well as the energy changes involved in these processes. Thus, you will also become more aware of problems of environment, of the responsible use of natural resources, of finding new sources of energy, and of the potential role which you may play in finding answers to some of these problems.

ISBN-0-675-07528-9

Published by

CHARLES E. MERRILL PUBLISHING CO.
A Bell & Howell Company

Columbus, Ohio 43216

Printed in the United States of America

Preface

The new 1975 edition of CHEMISTRY: A MODERN COURSE offers you an integrated chemistry program which is both vital and basic. In combining the theories and concepts of chemistry with practical applications, this program both meets the needs of and challenges today's chemistry student.

Throughout this text, the student is encouraged to think independently. Examples have been selected that are closely related to the average student's past experience and everyday life. The basic learning principle of proceeding from the known to the unknown has been observed. The approach of the text recognizes that a certain amount of repetition is helpful to the learning process. Principles of structure, matter-energy relationships, the mole concept, thermodynamics, and chemical equilibrium appear several times in the text in varying degrees of emphasis. A sense of confidence is thus established as the student recognizes already familiar concepts presented in greater depth. Questions are frequently presented which can be answered by performing a simple experiment, by applying knowledge based on experience, or by further reading. A minimum of emphasis has been placed on memorization of fact.

The content is presented in a logical manner which is flexible enough so that later chapters may be studied in a variety of sequences and in a variety of groupings. The initial chapters present some descriptive chemistry as well as the "mechanics" of chemistry. This approach facilitates the early introduction of laboratory work. Several chapters are then devoted to the structure of matter and the periodicity of the elements. The principles developed in these chapters provide the vehicle for the remainder of the text. Introduction of the mole concept early in the text enables students to perform quantitative studies as well as qualitative experiments within the first few weeks of the course. The text then deals with the behavior of matter in terms of acidity, oxidation-reduction, and electrical potential. It concludes with descriptive material in nuclear and organic chemistry.

Each chapter is introduced with a photograph and a thought-provoking paragraph which relate the theme of the chapter to the world of the student. It tells why the chapter is important or useful to the student in today's world. Moreover, many of these introductory paragraphs pose questions the student can answer by studying the chapter.

A *Goal* statement appears at the beginning of each chapter. This statement gives an overall purpose for the study of the chapter. A system of margin notes appears throughout the text to highlight important ideas and to assist students in organizing study and review.

Reading level has been carefully controlled. New words are defined, spelled phonetically, and printed in italic type when introduced.

Photographs and artwork, much of it in full color, are used extensively to illustrate chemistry principles and their applications to situations encountered in everyday living and research.

Problems, many with answers included, appear throughout the chapters to enable the student to check independently his understanding of the material just studied. Many sample problems with step-by-step solutions are also provided to guide the student in mastery of problem-solving.

At the conclusion of each chapter is an extensive *Summary*, a comprehensive list of problems as well as questions to test the student's understanding. Another feature is a series of problems entitled *One More Step* which may be used to lead the student into projects, papers, talks, or collections which can benefit the entire class.

The tabular material in the appendices includes supplementary data. This enables the teacher to compose his own problems without resorting to the preparation of extra tables for the students.

Throughout, this text reflects the consensus of recent recommendations made by committees studying the chemistry curriculum. In harmony with the best current thinking of scientists and educators, it takes into account a realistic appraisal of the capability and maturity of the typical student.

The authors wish to express their sincere thanks to the many chemistry students, teachers, and science educators who have made suggestions for changes based on their use of CHEMISTRY: A MODERN COURSE.

Contents

4   *Chemical Shorthand* _____ 56

Chapter 4 introduces symbols and the use of these symbols as a means of chemical shorthand formulas and equations.

5   *The Mole* _____ 76

Chapter 5 introduces gram-molecular mass and the use of this concept in manipulating formulas and equations. The first three sections explain the mole; the other sections develop applications of the mole concept to quantitative chemistry.
This chapter might also be entitled, "How much?" It introduces students to the setting up and solving of chemical quantitative problems.

8   *The Periodic Table*   158

Chapter 8 introduces and develops the periodic table and reveals some of the periodic characteristics of the elements based upon their electronic structures.

9   *Chemical Bonding* _____ 194

Chapter 9 introduces chemical bonding and examines the factors which help determine the nature of the bond.

10   *Molecular Shape* _____ 216

Chapter 10 introduces atomic and molecular orbitals and describes the relationship between chemical bonding and molecular structure.

11   *Structure and Properties of Molecules* 236

Chapter 11 introduces molecular structure and its relationship to molecular properties. It also includes a description of some of the procedures used by chemists in analytical research.

12   Kinetic Theory —————— 258

Chapter 12 introduces the Kinetic Theory. It also leads to an understanding of the ideal gas, the ideal gas equation, the relationship between the four physical states of matter, and relates them to the mole concept studied in Chapter 5.

13   Solids ————————— 272

Chapter 13 introduces crystal theory through a study of unit cells. Three of these unit cells are discussed and their relationship to the space lattice and to the seven crystal systems is developed. The chapter ends with a study of variation and crystal defects.

17   Energy and Order _____ 360

Chapter 17 introduces the student to thermodynamics through a study of state functions.

18   Solutions _____ 372

Chapter 18 classifies mixtures of homogeneous aggregates into nine groups of solutions. The properties of the nine groups are predicted and these properties are discussed along with a study of colloids.

19 Reaction Rate and Chemical Equilibrium _____ 402

Chapter 19 introduces the quantitative study of equilibrium.

20 Acids, Bases, and Salts _____ 424

Chapter 20 begins with a definition of acids, bases, and salts, and an introduction to three acid-base theories. It also includes a discussion of the general properties of acids, bases, and salts.

21 Oxidation-Reduction _____ 462

Chapter 21 presents the idea that redox reactions involve the transfer of electrons from one atom to another. Two ways to balance redox reactions are demonstrated and chemical equivalence is introduced.

24 Organic Chemistry —————————— 540

Chapter 24 introduces the student to organic chemistry through a systematic study of hydrocarbons and their derivatives.

Chapter Opening Photo Descriptions and Credits

1*	Discovery of Phosphorus	*Fisher Collection, Fisher Scientific Co.*
2*	Chronometer	*Smithsonian Institution*
3*	Gas Storage Tanks	*Marathon Oil Company*
4*	Acrilan Fibers	*Monsanto Textiles Company*
5	Glass Rods	*National Bureau of Standards*
6	Tungsten Atoms	*Dr. Erwin W. Mueller, Pennsylvania State University, Department of Physics*
7	Telephone	*Reprinted with permission of General Electric*
8	Glass Bottles	*Glass Containers Manufacturers Institute, Inc.*
9	Pool Table	*Charles Phillips, Smithsonian Institution, 1972.*
10	Molecular Model	*F. Bernard Daniel*
11	Drain Pipes	*AEC: Wescott*
12*	Golden Gate Bridge	*San Francisco Convention & Visitors Bureau*
13	Crystals in Silica Gel	*Photo taken by Victor Neumier, Air Force Cambridge Research Laboratories*
14*	Winter Scene	*Orville Andrews*
15	Hot Air Balloon	*Photo by James M. Jackson, Courtesy of Chauncy M. Dunn*
16	Priestly's Laboratory	*Smithsonian Institution*
17	Gibbs' Surface Model	*Smithsonian Institution*
18*	Solutions	*Calgon Corporation*
19	Motorcycle	*Rick Kocks*
20	Building Column	*W. Keith Turpie*
21*	Corrosion Testing Chamber	*BASF Wyandotte Corporation*
22	Electric Light Bulbs	*Dow Corning Corporation*
23	Nuclear Fuel Pellet	*AEC*
24*	Coal Gasification Plant	*Institute of Gas Technology*

---

*H and I Services, Inc., Chicago, employs an Identicolor© process to transform black and white photos into color. By utilizing the percent differences in the gray scale of a black and white photo, this chemical technique can produce unique color prints.

Phosphorus, a substance which glows in the dark under special conditions, was first prepared and studied by a German alchemist in 1669. It is only one of many interesting and unusual substances you will learn about in your study of chemistry. What role does chemistry play in your everyday life? What role do you expect research in chemistry to play in your future?

Man, Nature, and Chemistry _____ 1

Chapter 1 introduces the student to the development and
procedures of science, and to the matter-energy relationship.

Throughout recorded history (and even before), man has tried to
improve his way of life and modify his environment. Such "tinkering" has had unexpected applications and long range effects.

Some of the earliest examples we have of man modifying his
surroundings involve agriculture. More than 4000 years ago, the
Sumerians of the lower Tigris-Euphrates valley built a system of
canals and dikes to control yearly floodwaters and to irrigate dry
areas. This irrigation system collected water and carried it to the
crops. As the water flowed down from the mountains, however, it
picked up salts in the hills. The water was used at once, either by
the plants or by evaporation. The salts remained in the soil and
they collected over the centuries. Eventually, the salt content of the
soil became so high that crops could not grow. The Babylonians, who
succeeded the Sumerians, paid the price for such "tinkering."

When the early Egyptian pharoahs built their massive pyramids
about 4500 years ago, they had to quarry huge quantities of stone.
For example, the Great Pyramid alone needed over five million
metric tons (5,750,000 tons) of rock! In the process of quarrying, the
landscape was badly scarred.

In India, about the fifth century B.C., a method for making rust-
resistant iron was discovered. The method spread to the Persians
and then to the Arabs. The fine "Damascus" steel in the swords used
in so many "holy wars" was an eventual application of Indian
metallurgy.

About 600 A.D., the Chinese discovered an explosive mixture containing potassium nitrate. They used it to make fireworks for enter-
tainment. Five centuries later, this same mixture was being used
as gunpowder.

There is nothing good or bad about water, salt, stone, steel or
potassium nitrate. Man determines whether these things benefit
or injure himself. The Sumerians and the Indians could not have

GOAL: You will gain an understanding of the nature of
chemistry through relationships ranging from science-
mankind to matter-energy.

In an attempt to improve the
quality of life, man has
changed his environment.

You may find other examples of
man despoiling his planet acci-
dentally.

Progress may have undesirable side effects.

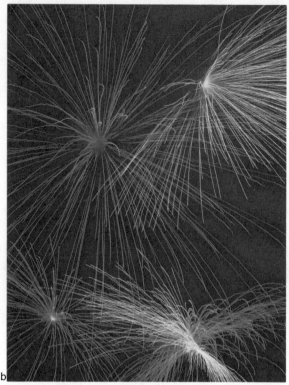

FIGURE 1-1. Man has modified his environment both directly by reshaping the land (a) and indirectly by uses of discoveries (b).

foreseen the damage their developments would bring. Their aim was simply to improve the quality of life for their fellow man. Unintentionally, their work led to undesirable results.

MANKIND AND PROGRESS

1:1 Limitations and Opportunities

Today, the human race faces a number of problems resulting from past attempts to "tinker" with nature. We have learned that we must plan future modifications with care. However, planning for the future requires making choices.

Livable space on our planet is limited and travel to other planets difficult. It seems unlikely that in the near future man will colonize other worlds. Therefore, we must use our resources wisely. World population is increasing and people need housing, food, and water. Housing and food production both require space. How is the available space to be divided? How is the available water supply to be divided?

Perhaps students can think of other "trade-offs" that must be made.

Today's resources must be used wisely.

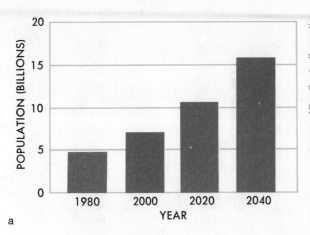

a

b

FIGURE 1-2. An increasing population (a) places additional demands on livable space (b).

Machines make our lives easier and more fun, but machines need energy to run. Our energy resources are limited. Yet, the demand for energy is growing at a tremendous rate. How are known energy resources to be used? These are difficult and controversial questions.

1:2 Finding Out and Making Choices

Citizens and their leaders make daily decisions which affect the environment and natural resources. To make an intelligent choice, one must know the facts on each side of a question. The decision a citizen makes involves a value judgment. That is, the person must apply his own values and beliefs to the facts at hand.

Values vary from country to country and from person to person. Moral and ethical standards also differ. You may judge a person as "good" or "bad" on the basis of how that person behaves. This is a value judgment.

The facts of nature, however, are amoral (neither good nor bad). Established facts are the same for everyone. For example, table salt

Facts are needed for intelligent choices.

Facts are neither "good" nor "bad".

FIGURE 1-3. An increasing demand for energy (a) has resulted in development of new sources of energy such as nuclear power plants (b).

a

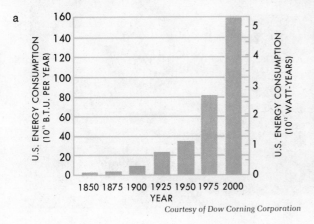

b

a

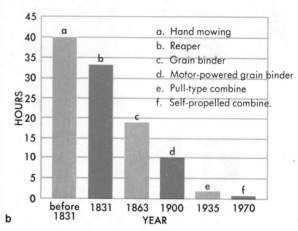

b

USDA Photo

FIGURE 1-4. Development of new machinery (a) has increased food production and reduced the farmer's work (b).

FIGURE 1-5. Citizens and leaders meet to discuss facts and make intelligent decisions.

(sodium chloride) will dissolve in water and a diamond is hard. Both of these statements of facts are amoral. The process of determining the facts is also amoral.

It is the way facts are used which may be moral or immoral. For example, scientists have learned that sudden movements of the earth's crust cause earthquakes. But would you hold scientists responsible when an earthquake destroys life and property? The discovery that huge quantities of energy may be released by causing changes in certain atomic nuclei was a great scientific breakthrough. The use of this knowledge to construct a nuclear bomb involves a value judgment.

Ben Chandler

a   b   c

FIGURE 1-6. Scientists obtain facts in a variety of situations including underwater observations (a), field studies (b), and laboratory research (c).

Science deals with determining facts about the physical universe. The scientist strives to obtain facts untainted by human bias and prejudice. However, methods of finding out facts and applications of facts cannot be divorced from human values.

Scientists attempt to determine facts.

Science is always changing. It is not a set of procedures, a specific group of people, or a collection of facts which never changes. Science should not be viewed as a mysterious realm forever closed to you. Perhaps someday you will become a scientist and seek facts about our world. You would observe natural phenomena, hypothesize (make estimates based on your observations), and experiment to test your hypotheses. You would add to the collection of facts that past scientists have already recorded. This collection of facts is the *product of science*. The information it provides may help us make wiser choices about our future environment.

Some processes of science: observation, prediction, experimentation.

Distinguish between processes and products of science.

Product of science: collection of facts and their relationships.

1:3 Chemistry

Chemistry is the science of materials. A *chemist* investigates the properties of and the changes in materials. For example, in the laboratory, a chemist may study things as varied as the structure of matter in the human brain, or the bonding between rubber and nylon in an automobile tire. These investigations require that a chemist be familiar with all of the sciences, especially physics and mathematics. A chemist expresses the results of these studies as characteristics of the materials being investigated.

Chemists study the properties and changes of materials.

Fortunately, it is not necessary to study the properties and changes of all known materials to be a good chemist. There are certain unifying principles and basic facts. These principles make it possible to

You may wish to point out that many disciplinary boundaries, such as biochemistry, physical chemistry, and biophysics, overlap.

7

study the characteristics of a few materials and then predict with reasonable accuracy the characteristics of many other materials. These basic facts and principles are the foundations of chemistry.

MATTER AND ENERGY

1:4 Matter

All matter exhibits inertia.

Inertia is resistance to change in direction or rate of motion.

All material is called *matter* by scientists. Matter may be as difficult to observe as the particles which produce the odor of perfume. It may be as easy to observe as a block of lead. Matter is defined by scientists as anything which exhibits the property of *inertia*. What is inertia? Consider a moving automobile. Your body tends to continue forward when the brakes are applied suddenly and the car comes to a sudden stop. If the automobile makes a sharp turn at high speed, your body tends to continue in the original direction throwing you against the side of the car opposite from the direction of the turn. In both cases, your body is exhibiting the property of inertia. Inertia is the resistance of matter to a change in either the direction or rate of its motion. All matter exhibits this property.

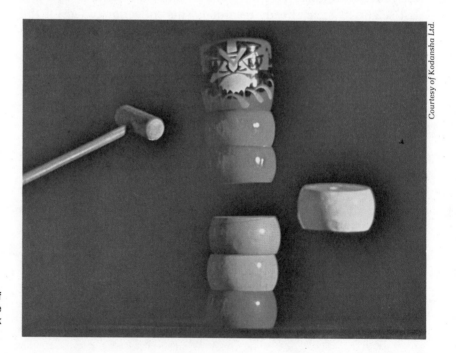

Courtesy of Kodansha Ltd.

FIGURE 1-7. The property of inertia is shown by the white disc which has been struck with a hammer.

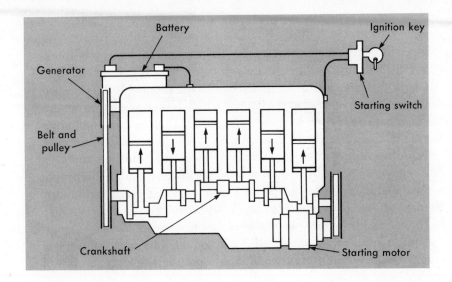

FIGURE 1-8. In the automobile, chemical energy is converted to electrical, mechanical, and heat energy.

1:5 Energy

In the study of science, one of the most difficult concepts to understand is *energy*. For many years, energy has been defined as work, or as the capacity to do work. Unfortunately, this definition is not entirely satisfactory since energy takes so many forms. For instance, consider the battery-generator system of an automobile. As the starter switch is turned on, the chemical energy in the battery is converted to electrical energy. The automobile starts and chemical energy in the gasoline is converted into the energy of the moving

Energy exists in many forms.

Take as long as necessary to develop energy concepts.

FIGURE 1-9. In the solar house, energy from the sun is converted to other useful forms of energy.

Solar House, Institute of Energy Conversion, University of Delaware, Newark, Delaware

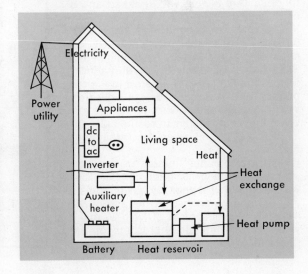

car. As the crankshaft gains speed, its mechanical energy is transferred by belt and pulley to the generator. The generator, in turn, converts the mechanical energy into electrical energy. This electrical energy is transferred to the battery where it is converted to chemical energy. The battery is thus "recharged." During this time, other kinds of energy such as heat are also produced as by-products.

All matter possesses energy.

Defining energy is a difficult task. As a starting point, we shall define energy as a quality possessed by all matter. Under the proper conditions, energy can be changed into work. As we noted before, energy can be converted from one kind to another. Energy can also be transferred from one particle of matter to another. With one major exception (nuclear change), all such conversions and transfers of energy occur without observable loss or gain in the total amount of energy.

Potential energy (P.E.) is energy of position.

The two general forms of energy are potential energy and kinetic energy. *Potential energy* depends upon the position of one portion of matter with respect to another portion. *Kinetic energy* refers to

Antoine Laurent Lavoisier

(1743–1794)

Often referred to as the father of modern chemistry, Lavoisier was certainly one of the outstanding scientists of the eighteenth century. He was the first to grasp the true explanation of combustion. His theories were the basis for great advances in chemistry.

As a young man, he studied astronomy, botany, and mathematics, as well as chemistry, at the Collège Mazarin near his Paris home. His study of law and admission to the bar led to an interest in French politics and a position as tax collector. While in government work he helped develop the metric system to secure uniformity of weights and measures throughout France.

His governmental interests, however, eventually proved his undoing. Lavoisier was branded a traitor by revolutionists in 1794 and guillotined at the age of 51. Ironically, Lavoisier had striven for many years to alleviate the hardships of the peasants.

the motion of one portion of matter with respect to another portion. When you refer to matter in position, you are referring to potential energy. When you refer to matter in motion, you are referring to kinetic energy.

Kinetic energy (K.E.) is energy of motion.

1:6   Matter and Energy

For years, scientists assumed that the total amount of matter and energy in the universe is constant. They have traditionally stated this belief in the form of two laws. These laws are *the law of conservation of matter* and *the law of conservation of energy.*

The law of conservation of matter states that matter is always conserved. This statement means that the total amount of matter in the universe remains constant. Matter is never created and never destroyed. It is only changed in form.

The law of conservation of energy states that energy is always conserved. This statement means that the total amount of energy in the universe must remain constant. Energy is never created and never destroyed. It is only changed in form.

The brilliant work of Albert Einstein, however, has shown that matter can be changed to energy, and energy can be changed to matter. Einstein expressed this relationship in the form of his now-famous equation:

Matter can be changed to energy; energy can be changed to matter.

$$E = mc^2$$

(E is energy, m is mass, and c is the speed of light.)

According to Einstein's equation, mass and energy are equivalent. The two laws, then, are really one and the same: the law of conservation of mass-energy. This new law of conservation is sometimes called *the law of conservation of matter and energy.* It can be stated: Matter and energy are always conserved. Their total cannot be increased or decreased. They can, however, be interconverted (changed from one to the other).

The law of conservation of matter and energy: Matter and energy are always conserved.

The amount of mass changed into energy or energy changed into mass that occurs in ordinary chemical reactions is very small. It cannot be measured on any existing chemical balance. In our laboratory work and in our discussions, therefore, we will always assume the original laws of matter and energy conservation are entirely correct.

In ordinary chemical reactions, mass-energy interchange is not easily observed.

Matter may be considered as another form of energy.

SUMMARY

1. For thousands of years, man has modified his physical environment. Often, this has led to harmful results.
2. Man, today, faces many decisions involving management of the environment and natural resources.
3. In order to make intelligent decisions, people must be provided with the facts pertaining to the decision to be made.
4. It is the function of science to provide these facts.
5. Chemistry is the science of materials.
6. A chemist investigates the properties of and the changes in materials.
7. Matter is anything with the property of inertia. Inertia is the resistance of a body or particle to a change in either its direction or rate of motion.
8. Energy is a property of matter. Under the proper conditions, energy can be transferred, made to do work, or converted to matter. Energy can also be created from matter.

PROBLEMS

1. Make a list of at least five different forms of energy. Use reference materials in your school library, particularly physics texts, to help you. Potential, kinetic, electrical, mechanical, thermal, radiant

2. Define each of the forms of energy that you listed in your answer to Problem 1.
3. Using a dictionary, find out what phases of nature are investigated by each of the following scientists: agronomist, astronomer, biologist, botanist, entomologist, geochemist, geologist, geophysicist, horticulturist, metallurgist, meteorologist, physicist, and zoologist.
4. Find out what kinds of careers require a knowledge of chemistry. Use career education materials that your counselor may have, including the Dictionary of Occupational Titles.
5. Assume that there is a remote mountain lake that can be developed as a vacation spot for city dwellers. What facts must be determined before development starts? What value judgments must be made?

ONE MORE STEP
See Teacher's Guide at the front of this book.

1. Make a list of the industries and institutions in your community which make use of the services of a chemist.
2. Investigate the Cockcroft-Walton experiment which confirmed Einstein's matter-energy hypothesis. Use reference materials from your library.

The One More Step Section is intended to provide impetus for further research into topics related to the chapter.

Suggested Readings for this chapter may be found in the Teacher's Guide at the front of this book.

What time is it? How long is the piece of glass tubing? What is the mass of the test tube? In order to give meaningful answers to these questions, you must have a system of standard units and standard measuring devices. The marine chronometer shown here is a standard time-measuring device designed to tell location at sea on the basis of time. What are some other measuring devices and standard units? How do you use them in daily living?

Measuring and Calculating ————— 2

Chapter 2 introduces the student to scientific measurement and to mathematical concepts which will be used in this text. These concepts include: scientific notation, the metric system, ratio, and the factor-label method of problem solving.

Thus far, we have discussed two properties of matter: inertia and energy. Since we often refer to properties as we consider particular materials, it is helpful to learn how to measure properties of matter.

Any kind of measurement has three basic requirements. (1) We must know exactly what we are trying to measure. (2) We must have some standard with which to compare the thing we are measuring. (3) We must have some method of making this comparison.

GOAL: You will gain knowledge and understanding of basic measurements and related calculations used by chemists.

MEASUREMENT

2:1 Mass

In chemistry, finding the quantity of matter is very important. For instance, we may wish to measure the amount of wood in a small block. One way of doing this is to weigh the block. Suppose we weigh such a block on a spring scale and find that its weight is 1 newton (N). Now suppose we take the scale and the block to the top of a high mountain. There we weigh the block again. The weight now will be slightly less than 1 N. The weight has changed because the weight of an object depends on its distance from the center of the earth. Weight is a measure of the gravitational force between two bodies. For our purposes, these two bodies are the object being weighed and the earth. This gravitational force changes when the distance from the center of the earth changes.

Weight depends on distance from the center of the earth.

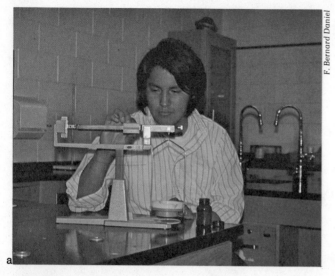

FIGURE 2-1. Mass can be measured on a student balance (a) or on an analytical balance (b)

Mass measures the quantity of matter.

Standard for mass is one kilogram (kg).
A balance is used to determine mass.

FIGURE 2-2. Weight is measured with a spring scale.

We have seen that the weight of an object can vary from place to place. Scientific work, however, requires a measurement which does not change with location. The term *mass* is applied to this measurement. Mass is a measure of the quantity of matter.

The standard for mass is a piece of metal kept at the International Bureau of Weights and Measures in Sèvres, France. This object is called the International Prototype Kilogram. Its mass is defined as 1 *kilogram* (kg).

Assume that we have completed the first two requirements for making a measurement. We know what property we are going to measure and what our standard of comparison will be. Now we must compare the object with our standard. To do this we use a *balance*. Look at the balance shown in Figure 2–1. A balance is an instrument used to compare unknown mass to known mass. To make our comparison we first place the object with unknown mass on the left side of the balance. Then we add our standard masses to the right side until the two masses are equal. This comparison is possible because the known masses and the unknown mass (the object) are the same distance from the center of the earth. They are, therefore, subject to the same attraction by the earth. If the balance is moved to the top of a mountain, the unknown mass and known masses will still be equally distant from the center of the earth. Their attraction by the earth will still be equal, and the balance will indicate no change in mass. The mass of the standard kilogram you use in the laboratory may not be exactly the same as the mass of the standard kilogram at Sèvres. However, your standard has been manufactured with a degree of precision that is acceptable.

Matter may be altered in many ways. As noted in Section 1:6, under special conditions matter can be converted to energy. When this happens, the mass changes. Under usual conditions, the mass of a given quantity of matter cannot be increased or decreased. This principle is called the *law of conservation of mass*. It is another way of stating the law of conservation of matter.

Unfortunately, many terms which apply to the measurement of weight are also applied to the measurement of mass. Standard masses used on the balance are incorrectly called "weights." The process of comparing masses by means of a balance is known as "weighing." Keep in mind, however, that when you use the balance you are measuring mass. Develop the habit of referring to "standard masses" rather than "weights."

Battelle Memorial Institute, Columbus, Ohio

FIGURE 2-3. In a nuclear reactor, matter can be converted to energy.

2:2   Length

A second important measurement is that of length. *Length* is the distance covered by a line segment connecting two points. The standard for measuring length was for many years another piece of metal kept at Sèvres, France. This metal bar has two scratches on it. The distance between these two scratches was defined as 1 *meter* (m). In 1960, however, the standard meter was redefined. It is now given in terms of the wavelength of a particular color in the electromagnetic spectrum (Appendix B).

Length can usually be measured with a ruler or similar device. Rulers manufactured for everyday use are not as accurate as the standard. They are made as close to the standard as is necessary for

Conservation of mass = conservation of matter.

Standard for length is one meter (m).

FIGURE 2-4. Early historic units of length included the "thumb-knuckle" inch (a), the "36 barleycorn" foot (b), and the "Viking's arm-span" fathom (c).

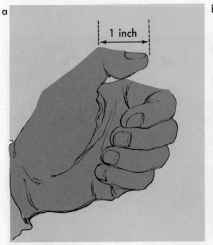

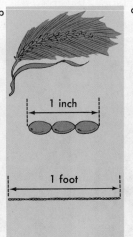

FIGURE 2-5. A common system of measurement with standardized units has led to greater variety and convenience for consumers.

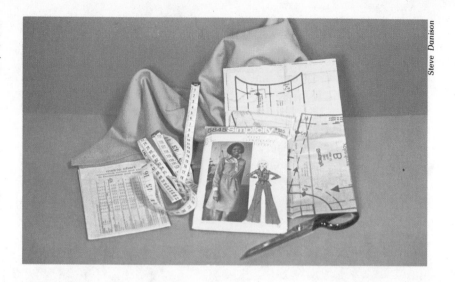

their particular use. The rulers used in a fourth-grade arithmetic class, for example, are not as accurate as the rulers used in scientific laboratories. You may wish to use different manufactured rulers to compare fine measurements.

2:3 Time Some student may wish to report on atomic clocks.

A third basic measurement is that of time. *Time* is the interval between two occurrences. Our present standard of time, like our standard of length, is based on an electronic transition in an atom. The older standard, however, is still adequate for most measurement. It is 1/86,400 of an average day. This division of time is called 1 second (sec). The most common device for measuring time is a watch or clock. More precise timepieces include the chronometer and atomic clock. The second is now defined as the duration of 9,192,631,770 periods of the radiation corresponding to the transition between two hyperfine levels of the fundamental state of the atom of cesium 133.

Standard for time is one second (sec).

FIGURE 2-6. Time can be measured with a simple sundial (a) or the precise cesium clock (b).

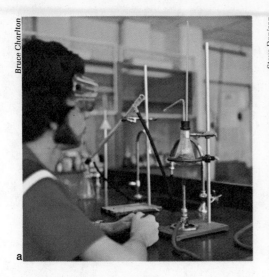

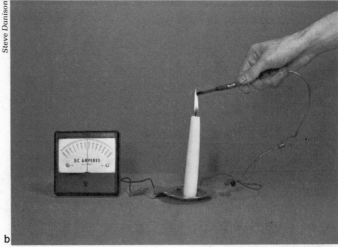

a

b

FIGURE 2-7. Two types of temperature-measuring devices are the thermometer (a) and the thermocouple (b).

2:4 Temperature

"Man, what a hot day it is!" What does that expression mean? It means that there is a greater heat content per unit volume of air that day. What is heat? Heat is a form of energy. Heat always flows from a region of higher intensity to one of lower intensity. Temperature is a measure of heat intensity. Heat flows until the heat intensity (temperature) is the same everywhere. If one end of a metal rod is heated, the other end eventually becomes warm.

Imagine a bucket of water and a glass of water at the same temperature. Now, pour a thimbleful of hotter water into each container. Heat will flow from the hot water into the cold water in both instances. However, when heat flow stops, the glass of water will be at a higher temperature than the bucket of water. Both containers had the same amount of heat energy added. In the glass of water, however, this amount of heat was distributed over much less matter than in the bucket of water. The ratio of heat energy to mass of water is greater in the glass of water. Thus, the final heat intensity (temperature) is greater in the glass of water.

A thermometer is the most common instrument used to measure heat intensity (temperature). In a thermometer, a bulb containing mercury is connected to a capillary (fine bore) tube. When the bulb is heated, the mercury expands and moves up the tube. If the temperature decreases, the mercury contracts and the height of the mercury column decreases. The height of the mercury column can thus be used to measure temperature if a scale is engraved on the glass tube. Many scales are used, but the Celsius scale is now accepted as the standard. It is based on the knowledge that the freezing and boiling temperatures of pure water under normal atmospheric pressure are constant. We will use the Celsius scale in our study of chemistry.

Temperature is a measure of heat intensity.

Heat flows from areas of high intensity to areas of low intensity.

You may wish to carry this out using sensitive thermometers.

Fahrenheit will not be used in this text.

Standard for temperature is one Celsius degree (C°)

19

To construct the Celsius temperature scale, a blank thermometer with uniform bore is placed in freezing water or melting ice. A mark is placed at the top of the mercury column. The same thermometer is then placed in boiling water. Another mark is placed at the top of the expanded mercury column. The distance between these two marks is then divided into 100 equal intervals. Each interval is called a *degree*. The mark for freezing water is zero degrees Celsius (0°C). The mark for boiling water is labeled 100°C.

One Celsius degree $= \dfrac{1}{100}$ of the temperature difference between the normal freezing and boiling points of pure water.

Thermometers are not the only instruments used to measure temperature. For an example of another temperature measuring device, see Figure 2–7b. The thermocouple is used to measure high temperatures which could cause mercury to boil.

THE METRIC SYSTEM

2:5   Origin of the Metric System

Except for time units, the standard units mentioned previously are just now coming into common use in this country. These units

FIGURE 2-8. The metric system has been adopted by most countries.

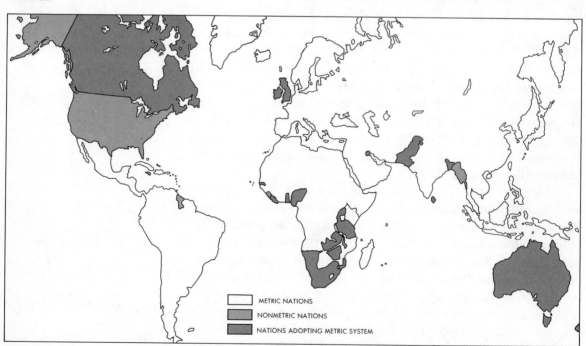

METRIC NATIONS

NONMETRIC NATIONS

NATIONS ADOPTING METRIC SYSTEM

FIGURE 2-9. Many product labels indicate quantity in both metric and English units.

are part of a system of weights and measures called the *metric system*. This system is in common use in most countries and is used by scientists throughout the world.

The metric system originated in the late eighteenth century. The unit of length, the meter, was designed to be 1/10,000,000 of the distance from the equator to one of the poles of the earth. The earth, however, is not a perfect sphere. Also, measurements made at that time are not very precise by today's standards. Because of this difference, the standard bar at Sèvres is only a close approximation to the original definitions.

2:6 Prefixes

In the metric system, a number of prefixes are used to obtain different units for measuring the same property.

Metric system prefixes and their equivalents: Students should memorize the metric prefixes.

Greater than 1

tera (T) = trillion	$1,000,000,000,000 = 10^{12}$	
giga (G) = billion	$1,000,000,000 = 10^{9}$	Order of magnitude is indicated by a prefix.
mega (M) = million	$1,000,000 = 10^{6}$	
kilo (k) = thousand	$1,000 = 10^{3}$	
hecto (h) = hundred	$100 = 10^{2}$	
deka (da) = ten	$10 = 10^{1}$	

21

Less than 1

deci (d) = tenth $\qquad\qquad$ $\dfrac{1}{10} = 10^{-1}$

centi (c) = hundredth $\qquad$ $\dfrac{1}{100} = 10^{-2}$

milli (m) = thousandth $\qquad$ $\dfrac{1}{1,000} = 10^{-3}$

micro (μ) = millionth $\qquad$ $\dfrac{1}{1,000,000} = 10^{-6}$

nano (n) = billionth $\qquad$ $\dfrac{1}{1,000,000,000} = 10^{-9}$

pico (p) = trillionth $\qquad$ $\dfrac{1}{1,000,000,000,000} = 10^{-12}$

femto (f) = quadrillionth $\qquad$ $\dfrac{1}{1,000,000,000,000,000} = 10^{-15}$

atto (a) = quintillionth $\qquad$ $\dfrac{1}{1,000,000,000,000,000,000} = 10^{-18}$

A decimeter (dm) is, therefore, one-tenth of a meter. What is a milli-volt? $\frac{1}{1000}$ volt   What is a kilocycle? 1000 cycles   What is a megaton? 1,000,000 tons

2:7   Other Metric Units

The metric unit of mass is the *gram* (g). Originally, a gram was de-fined to be the mass of a quantity of pure water in the form of a cube 1 centimeter (cm) on a side, at 3.98°C. A kilogram was thus the mass of 1000 cm³ of water at 3.98°C. Because of inaccurate measurement, the standard kilogram at Sèvres is only an approximation of the origi-nal intent. Modern precise measurements show that a cube of water 1 cm on an edge has a mass of 0.999973 g at 3.98°C. (3.98°C is speci-fied because at this temperature water has its greatest density.)

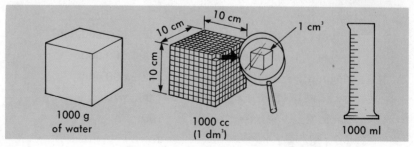

FIGURE 2-10. Metric units of mass, length, and volume are related by definition.

1000 g of water

1000 cc (1 dm³)

1000 ml

Bruce Charlton

FIGURE 2-11. The small yellow cube held by this student measures one centimeter on each edge.

The metric unit of volume is the *liter* (l). A liter was originally defined as exactly 1 cubic decimeter (dm³). It is now defined as the volume occupied by 1 kg of water at 3.98°C. On this basis, modern precise measurements show that a liter is equal to 1.000027 dm³. In the original plan, 1 milliliter (ml) was to exactly equal 1 cubic centimeter (cm³). Since today's measurements so closely approximate this relation, it is common in all but the most exacting experimental work to use the original definition. For calculations in this book, remember that 1 ml = 1 cm³.

The standard for volume is one liter (l).

2:8 Complex Measurements

From the elementary measurements we have now defined, almost all of the measurements necessary in science can be made. Other measurements are simply combinations of these elementary measurements. We are all familiar with the measurement of speed. *Speed* is the distance covered in a single unit of time. It is length per unit time. In automobiles, speed is measured in miles (length) per hour (time). Most scientific measurements of speed are made in centimeters or meters per second. These units are in keeping with the international use of the metric system for scientific work.

Complex measurements can be made by combining elementary measurements.

If students are familiar with vectors, speed and velocity can be compared.

2:9 Density

A less familiar, although common, scientific measurement is mass per unit volume. This measurement is called *density*. To measure density, we must be able to measure mass and volume. Mass can be measured by using a balance. The volume of a solid can be measured by using units of length. For instance, the volume of a cube is the length of an edge cubed (that is, multiplied by itself three times). The volume of a rectangular solid is the length times the width times the height. The volume of a liquid can be measured in a clear container graduated to indicate units of volume. In density measurements of

Density = mass/unit volume. Density of solids and liquids is generally measured in g/cm³.

Demonstration: Pour 10 ml of
mercury into a 25 ml graduate.
Place a small steel ball bearing
or other metal object on the
surface. Carefully add 10 ml
of water. Float a cork on
the water. Discuss.

solids and liquids, volume is usually measured in cubic centimeters
(cm³) and density is expressed in grams per cubic centimeter (g/cm³).
Densities of common substances are listed in tables. Such a table
offers a convenient and accurate means of comparing the masses of

Table 2-1

Densities of Some Common Materials

Material	Density
Blood	1.06 g/cm³
Copper	8.92 g/cm³
Sodium Chloride (table salt)	2.17 g/cm³
Stainless Steel	7.97 g/cm³
Sucrose (table sugar)	1.58 g/cm³

equal volumes of different materials. People sometimes say that
lead is heavier than feathers. However, a truckload of feathers is
heavier than a single lead buckshot. To be exact, we should say that
the density of lead is greater than the density of feathers.

FIGURE 2-12. The density of
materials is not determined by
size alone (a) nor by volume
alone (b).

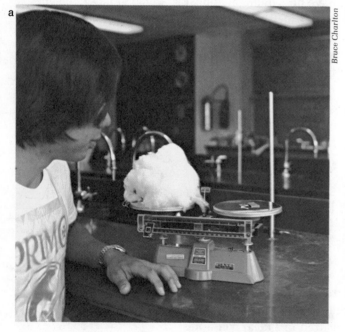

a

b

Bruce Charlton

Lee M. Wilhelm

2:10   Significant Digits

Suppose we want to measure the length of a test tube. We have two rulers. One is graduated in centimeters. The other is graduated in millimeters. With which ruler can we obtain a better measurement of length? The length of the tube in millimeters is the more significant measurement since it is closer to the actual length of the tube. We say that a measurement in millimeters has more *significant digits* than a measurement in centimeters.

Significant digits are determined by actual measurement.

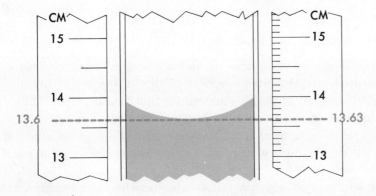

FIGURE 2-13. The precision of the ruler used describes the number of significant digits that can be given.

Suggestion: Have students actually measure the length of several objects using both a centimeter and a millimeter scale. Have them compare the figures obtained and draw conclusions.

Look at Figure 2–13. The measurement on the centimeter scale lies approximately 6/10 of the way from the 13-cm mark to the 14-cm mark. This length is recorded as 13.6 cm. On the millimeter ruler, the length lies approximately 3/10 of the way from the 13.6-cm mark to the 13.7-cm mark. This length is recorded as 13.63 cm. The measurement 13.6 cm has three significant digits. The measurement 13.63 cm has four significant digits.

The last digit of a measurement is considered an approximation.

The exactness of measurements is an important part of experimentation. The observer, as well as anyone reading the results of an experiment, wants to know the number of significant digits in any observation or calculation. Digits other than zero are always significant. Zero may or may not be significant. Zeros used solely for spacing the decimal point are usually not significant. However, any zero used after a number to the right of the decimal point is significant.

Experimental measurements should be precise.

Zeros between two other significant digits are always significant. The following examples illustrate these rules:

Additional examples

30.4	3 sig. dig.
2700	2
5.10	3
0.023	2
7.0200	5
0.04010	4
3.00	3
2.700	4
0.0304	3
51.0	3

967	3 significant digits	
967,000	3 significant digits	(zeros are spacers only)
96.7	3 significant digits	
9.67	3 significant digits	
0.00967	3 significant digits	(zeros are spacers only)
9.6700	5 significant digits	
9.067	4 significant digits	

2:11 Accuracy and Precision

Accuracy is a quality of the measuring instrument.

The terms accuracy and precision are often used in discussing measurements. *Accuracy* refers to quality of the measuring instrument compared with the standard for that measurement. Thus, the centimeter markings on a student's plastic ruler may not be very exact reproductions of 1/100 of the standard meter. In manufacturing the rulers, a number of chances for error occur. On the other hand, a micrometer used to measure engine parts may approximate the standard very closely. The micrometer has a high degree of accuracy. The plastic ruler has a low degree of accuracy.

FIGURE 2-14. Two instruments used for measuring length are the ruler (a) and the micrometer (b).

Precision refers to uncertainty in measurement. If we use a ruler marked off in divisions of 0.1 centimeter to measure a textbook, we might obtain the following data:

Dimension	Measurement	Uncertainty
Length	24.3 cm	±0.1 cm
Width	18.7 cm	±0.1 cm
Depth	4.4 cm	±0.1 cm

The absolute uncertainty in each case is ±0.1 centimeter. But that uncertainty is a different proportion of each dimension. A better reflection of uncertainty is the *relative error*. Relative error is often expressed as the percentage uncertainty in the measurement.

Measurement	Relative Error	Percentage Uncertainty (Precision)
24.3 cm	$\dfrac{0.1}{24.3} = 0.004$	0.4%
18.7 cm	$\dfrac{0.1}{18.7} = 0.005$	0.5%
4.4 cm	$\dfrac{0.1}{4.4} = 0.02$	2%

Thus, we see that, in this case, length and width are far more precise measurements than depth.

NOTATION

2:12 Scientific Notation

In this course we will sometimes use very large numbers. For example, Avogadro's number (Section 5:2) is 602,217,000,000,000,-000,000,000. We will also use extremely small numbers. The distance between particles in a salt crystal, for instance, is 0.000000002814 cm. Working with such numbers can be confusing. It is easy to drop a zero or to lose a decimal place.

Scientific notation makes numbers such as these less confusing. With this method, all numbers are expressed as the product of a number between 1 and 10 and a whole-number power of 10. In scientific notation, numbers are expressed in the form $M \times 10^n$. In this

FIGURE 2-15. This photo is an electron micrograph of a bacterium. The living bacterium is 0.00015 (or 1.5×10^{-4}) of a centimeter long.

In scientific notation, numbers are written in the form $M \times 10^n$.

expression, $1 \leq M < 10$ and n is an integer. This number is read as: M times ten to the nth.

2:13 Expressing Numbers in Scientific Notation

Any number can be expressed in scientific (standard) notation. For example, write 25,900 in scientific notation. Let us go through the process slowly. We divide 25,900 by 10 and then multiply by 10 (to keep the value the same). This equals 2590×10. If we repeat this same operation three more times, we get $2.59 \times 10 \times 10 \times 10 \times 10$. This is the same as 2.59×10^4. The number is now expressed as a number between 1 and 10 and a power of 10. We read this number as: two point five nine times ten to the fourth.

Standard position for the decimal point is after the first significant digit.

In the number 2.59×10^4, the decimal point is in *standard position*. This statement means that one digit precedes the decimal

FIGURE 2-16. Andromeda is a spiral galaxy of a size and shape similar to our own galaxy, the Milky Way. It is 2,200,000 (2.2 $\times 10^6$) light years away.

point. Usually, only three digits will be given, since most of our measurements will be accurate to only three significant digits. Thus, you will be able to do most computations on a slide rule.

Consider the number 0.00159. In scientific notation, it is 1.59×10^{-3}. To get the decimal point in standard position, we must multiply by 1000 or 10^3. Since we do not wish to change the value, we must also divide the number by 10^3. Therefore,

$$\frac{0.00159 \times 10^3}{10^3} = \frac{1.59}{10^3} = 1.59 \times 10^{-3}, \text{ where } 10^{-n} = 1/10^n$$

FIGURE 2-17. A slide rule can be used in solving numerical problems.

It is not really necessary to go through the motions of multiplying and dividing every time a change to scientific notation is desired. As soon as you understand how and why you can make the change to scientific notation, you can make it as simply as you make a decimal point change. For example, to change 4579.2 to standard notation, put the decimal point in standard position (4.5792) and multiply by 10^3 to get 4.5792×10^3. To change 0.004579 to standard notation, put the decimal point in standard position (4.579) and multiply by 10^{-3} to get 4.579×10^{-3}.

One advantage of scientific notation is that it removes any doubt about the number of significant digits. For instance, if the volume of a gas is expressed as 2000 ml, we do not know whether the measurement of the volume was made to only one significant digit or to four significant digits. Suppose the measurement was actually made to the nearest milliliter. Then the volume would be 2000 ml to four significant digits. In scientific notation, we can indicate these additional significant digits by placing zeros to the right of the decimal point. Thus, 2×10^3 ml has only one significant digit, while 2.000×10^3 ml has four significant digits.

To determine the number of significant digits that should appear in the answer to a calculation, we will use two rules. (1) In addition and subtraction, the answer may contain only as many decimal places as the least accurate value used in computing the answer. For example, if 345 is added to 27.6, the answer must be given to the nearest whole number. In adding a column of figures such as:

Some students will need much more practice than others. Make certain all understand before proceeding.

In addition and subtraction, retain no column that is to the right of a column containing an estimated figure.

677
39.2
6.23

Emphasize that an answer can be as precise as the least precise digit in the problem.

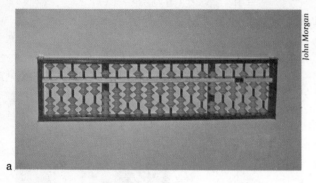 

a   b

FIGURE 2-18. Two examples of calculators are the abacus (a) and the modern desk calculator (b).

In multiplication and division, the answer should have no more significant digits than the term having the least number of significant digits in the problem.

the answer should be rounded off to the nearest whole number. (2) In multiplication and division, the answer may contain only as many significant digits as the least accurate value used to arrive at the answer. For example, in the problem:

$$1.1330 \times 5.12600000$$

the answer will have five significant digits.

In the problem:

$$49.6000 \div 47.40$$

the answer will have four significant digits.

2:14   Using Scientific Notation

Scientific notation is used in solving multiplication and division problems.

There is little advantage to using scientific notation in addition or subtraction. The powers of 10 must be alike for numbers to be added or subtracted so using scientific notation does not make the problem any easier. In multiplication and division, though, scientific notation does make arithmetic easier. Consider the following problem:

$$(0.0427)(593.75) = 25.353125$$

FIGURE 2-19. The answer to the above problem can be calculated to three significant digits (25.4) on a slide rule.

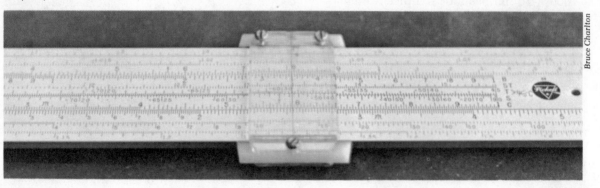

The first number (0.0427) is accurate only to three significant digits. We cannot then expect the answer to be accurate to more than three significant digits (25.4). Scientific notation makes this easier to see. Express all to three significant digits:

Students using slide rules will need much practice in placing the decimal point.

$$(4.27 \times 10^{-2})(5.94 \times 10^2)$$
$$(4.27 \times 5.94)(10^{-2} \times 10^2)$$
$$(25.4)(10^0)$$
$$25.4 \times 1 = 25.4$$

The answer has three significant digits.

We can use the same procedure for problems that combine both multiplication and division. For example, in the following problem the least precise measurement contains three significant digits. Thus,

$$\frac{(12.43)(0.0250)(4257)}{(0.0620)(375)(85.179)} = \frac{(1.24 \times 10^1)(2.50 \times 10^{-2})(4.26 \times 10^3)}{(6.20 \times 10^{-2})(3.75 \times 10^2)(8.52 \times 10^1)}$$

$$= \frac{\overset{1}{1.24} \times \overset{2}{2.50} \times \overset{1}{4.26}}{\underset{5}{6.20} \times \underset{3}{3.75} \times \underset{2}{8.52}} \times \frac{10^1 \times 10^{-2} \times 10^3}{10^{-2} \times 10^2 \times 10^1}$$

$$= \frac{1}{15} \times 10^1 = 0.0667 \times 10^1 = 0.667$$

The answer has three significant digits.

Bruce Charlton

FIGURE 2-20. To be correct, the answer to a multiplication or division problem should not contain more significant digits than the least precise measurement contains.

PROBLEM

1. Perform the following operations:

   a. $(6.09 \times 10^{-1})(9.08 \times 10^5)$ *ans.* 5.53×10^5

   b. $(1.65 \times 10^1) \div (5.24 \times 10^2)$ *ans.* 3.15×10^{-2}

   c. $\dfrac{(3.73 \times 10^6)(1.63 \times 10^1)}{8.11 \times 10^6}$ *ans.* 7.50

   d. $\dfrac{(4.71 \times 10^4)(4.34 \times 10^4)}{(2.16 \times 10^6)(2.44 \times 10^{-1})}$ *ans.* 3.88×10^3

   e. $\dfrac{(8.33 \times 10^2)(4.06 \times 10^6)}{(6.41 \times 10^4)(1.54 \times 10^4)}$ *ans.* 3.43

PROBLEM SOLVING

2:15   The Ratio Method

One way to solve problems is the *ratio method*. We use ratios of the quantities given. These ratios result from changes in the conditions given in the problem. For example, consider the following problem: Nine typists require five days to type 1000 letters. How long will fifteen typists take to type 2000 letters? First, decide what information you are seeking. In this case it is time in work days. Then establish the ratios. Decide how each change will affect the time. More typists should decrease the days work. Thus, multiplying 5

A ratio is a comparison of two quantities by division.

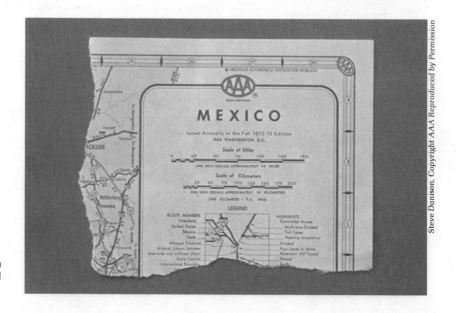

FIGURE 2-21. A ratio is used in relating map distances to road distances.

days by the ratio $\dfrac{9 \text{ typists}}{15 \text{ typists}}$ will give fewer days. However, 2000 let-

ters will take more time than 1000 letters. The ratio $\dfrac{2000 \text{ letters}}{1000 \text{ letters}}$ will

increase the work days required. After determining the ratios, the problem can be set up as:

$$\text{Time} = 5 \text{ days} \times \frac{9 \text{ typists}}{15 \text{ typists}} \times \frac{2000 \text{ letters}}{1000 \text{ letters}}$$

$$= 6 \text{ days}$$

We will use this method extensively in calculations concerning gas volumes (Chapters 15 and 16).

2:16 Conversion Factors

In Section 2:6 the relationships between the various prefixed metric units were described. For example, we saw the relationship between the centimeter and the meter (1 m = 100 cm) and between the kilogram and the gram (1 kg = 1000 g). Using these and similar relationships, we can convert from one unit to any other corresponding unit. Another common relationship is between the liter and the milliliter (1 liter = 1000 ml).

Conversion factors are ratios with a value equal to one.

EXAMPLE – CONVERSION

Let us consider a very simple algebraic relationship which illustrates the use of conversion factors. We know that one liter is equal to 1000 ml. If we want to know how many milliliters there are in five liters, we multiply the number of liters (5) by the number of milliliters in a liter (1000). Using the relationship between liters and milliliters:

$$1 \text{ liter} = 1000 \text{ milliliters}$$

both sides of the equation can be divided by the quantity 1 liter. Now the equation appears as:

$$1 = \frac{1000 \text{ milliliters}}{1 \text{ liter}}$$

Using the known quantity of 5 liters, we can write the equation:

$$5 \text{ liters} = 5 \text{ liters}$$

We can now multiply the right side by the fraction:

$$\frac{1000 \text{ milliliters}}{1 \text{ liter}}$$

Since this fraction is equal to one, the value of the right side of the equation is not changed. (The value of any quantity multiplied by 1 is unchanged.) The equation then becomes:

$$5 \text{ liters} = \frac{5 \text{ liters} \times 1000 \text{ milliliters}}{1 \text{ liter}}$$

Liter appears in both the numerator and the denominator of the right side of the equation. When units appear in both the numerator

Marie Curie

(1867–1934)

A Nobel Prize usually caps the career of a scientist. Marie Curie won two! In 1903, it was awarded in physics for her joint research with her husband Pierre on the radiation phenomenon discovered by Becquerel. In 1911, she won the chemistry prize for the discovery of radium and polonium, and for the study of the nature and compounds of radium. The first woman professor at the Sorbonne in Paris, Madame Curie was devoted not only to scientific research but also to the applications of the research. The use of radium rays in the treatment of cancer is but one example of this concern. In spite of the honors and her fame in the scientific community and the world, she remained modest and unassuming until her death at age 67. In 1935, one year after her death, her daughter, Irene Joliot-Curie (1897–1956) was awarded a Nobel Prize with her husband for the discovery of artificial radioactivity—the torch was passed to a second generation.

and the denominator of a fraction, they may be divided out just as numbers (liter/liter = 1). The equation then reduces to:

$$5 \text{ liters} = 5 \times 1000 \text{ milliliters}$$
$$5 \text{ liters} = 5000 \text{ milliliters}$$

Such a procedure is far too involved for finding the number of milliliters in 5 liters. However, these principles can be used to solve many kinds of problems.

EXAMPLE—CONVERSION

We want to convert 72 cm to meters. We know that:

$$1 \text{ m} = 100 \text{ cm}$$

By dividing both sides of the equation by 100 cm, the equation becomes:

$$\frac{1 \text{ m}}{100 \text{ cm}} = 1, \quad \text{or} \quad 1 = \frac{1 \text{ m}}{100 \text{ cm}}$$

Multiplying both sides of the equation by 72 cm, we get:

$$72 \text{ cm} \times 1 = \frac{72 \text{ cm} \times 1 \text{ m}}{100 \text{ cm}}$$

$$= \frac{72 \text{ m}}{100}$$

$$= 0.72 \text{ m}$$

2:17 Factor-Label Method

The problem-solving method discussed in Section 2:16 is called the *factor-label method*. In effect, unit labels are treated as factors. As common factors, these labels may be divided out. The solution to a problem often depends upon having the correct unit label. Thus, this method aids in solving a problem and provides a check on mathematical operations. The individual conversion factors (ratios whose value is equivalent to one) may usually be written by inspection.

The factor label method is used throughout the text for conversions.

Labels may be regarded as factors, and "divided" out.

Students need much practice on these.

EXAMPLE — CONVERSION OF UNITS

We wish to express 60 kilometers per hour in terms of centimeters per second. First, we write 60 kilometers per hour as a ratio:

$$\frac{60 \text{ km}}{1 \text{ hr}}$$

Since 1000 m = 1 km, we can use the ratio:

$$\frac{1000 \text{ m}}{1 \text{ km}}$$

In the same manner, we use:

$$1 \text{ m} = 100 \text{ cm or } \frac{100 \text{ cm}}{1 \text{ m}}$$

$$1 \text{ hr} = 60 \text{ min or } \frac{1 \text{ hr}}{60 \text{ min}}$$

$$1 \text{ min} = 60 \text{ sec or } \frac{1 \text{ min}}{60 \text{ sec}}$$

All these ratios equal 1. Since any number may be multiplied by 1, or its equivalent, without changing its value:

$$\frac{60 \text{ km}}{1 \text{ hr}} = \frac{60 \text{ km}}{1 \text{ hr}} \times \frac{1000 \text{ m}}{1 \text{ km}} \times \frac{100 \text{ cm}}{1 \text{ m}} \times \frac{1 \text{ hr}}{60 \text{ min}} \times \frac{1 \text{ min}}{60 \text{ sec}} = \frac{1700 \text{ cm}}{\text{sec}}$$

Notice that ratios are arranged so that units can be divided out as factors. This procedure leaves the correct units in the answer and provides a check on the method used.

It is often convenient to represent metric conversion factors in scientific notation.

EXAMPLE — CONVERSION OF UNITS

Express 0.20 kg/m³ as g/cm³:

$$\frac{0.20 \text{ kg}}{1 \text{ m}^3} \times \frac{10^3 \text{ g}}{1 \text{ kg}} \times \frac{1 \text{ m}^3}{(10^2 \text{ cm})^3} = \frac{0.20 \times 10^3 \text{ g} \times 1}{1 \times 1 \times 10^6 \text{ cm}^3}$$

$$= \frac{0.20 \text{ g}}{10^3 \text{ cm}^3}$$

$$= 0.00020 \text{ g/cm}^3$$

We could also express this calculation as

$$\left[\frac{0.20 \text{ kg}}{1 \text{ m}^3}\right] \left[\frac{10^3 \text{ g}}{1 \text{ kg}}\right] \left[\frac{\text{m}^3}{(10^2 \text{ cm})^3}\right] = 0.00020 \text{ g/cm}^3$$

Simplifying further the use of brackets and the fraction bar, we obtain the form used throughout this book for factor-label solutions to conversion problems:

$$\frac{0.20 \text{ kg}}{1 \text{ m}^3} \left| \frac{10^3 \text{ g}}{1 \text{ kg}} \right| \frac{1 \text{ m}^3}{(10^2 \text{ cm})^3} = 0.00020 \text{ g/cm}^3$$

EXAMPLE – FACTOR LABEL

Calcium has a density of 1.54 g/cm³. What mass would 3.00 cm³ of calcium have?

Density is mass per unit volume, or $D = m/V$. Therefore, $m = D \times V$.

$$\text{mass} = \frac{1.54 \text{ g}}{1 \text{ cm}^3} \times \frac{3.00 \text{ cm}^3}{1} = 4.62 \text{ g}$$

EXAMPLE – FACTOR LABEL

Cobalt has a density of 8.90 g/cm³. What volume would 17.8 g of cobalt have? Since $D = m/V$, and $V = m/D$:

$$\text{Volume} = 17.8 \text{ g} \times \frac{1 \text{ cm}^3}{8.90 \text{ g}} = 2.00 \text{ cm}^3$$

PROBLEMS

2. Convert:
   a. 346 centigrams to micrograms   *ans.* $3.46 \times 10^6 \text{ } \mu\text{g}$
   b. 1.00 megameter to terameters   *ans.* $1.00 \times 10^{-6} \text{ Tm}$
   c. 81.9 picoseconds to kiloseconds   *ans.* 8.19×10^{-14} ksec
   d. 513 milligrams to gigagrams   *ans.* $5.13 \times 10^{-10} \text{ Gg}$
   e. 8.59 nanometers to decimeters   *ans.* $8.59 \times 10^{-8} \text{ dm}$

3. Convert:
   a. 80.3 seconds to hectoseconds 8.03×10^{-1} hsec
   b. 402 decagrams to kilograms 4.02 kg
   c. 9.05 megameters to micrometers 9.05×10^2 μm
   d. 512 centiseconds to megaseconds 5.16×10^{-6} Msec
   e. 22.9 decigrams to milligrams 2.29×10^3 mg
4. Find the density in g/cm³ of:
   a. cement, if a rectangular piece 2.00 cm × 2.00 cm × 9.00 cm has mass 108 g   ans.   3.00 g/cm³
   b. granite, if a rectangular piece 5.00 cm × 10.0 cm × 23.0 cm has mass 3.22 kg   ans.   2.80 g/cm³
   c. gasoline, if 9.00 liters has mass 6120 g   ans.   0.680 g/cm³
   d. milk, if 2.00 liters has mass 2.06 kg   ans.   1.03 g/cm³
   e. ivory, if a rectangular piece 23.0 cm × 15.0 cm × 15.5 cm has mass 10.22 kg   ans.   1.91 g/cm³
5. Bismuth has a density of 9.80 g/cm³. What is the mass of 3.02 cm³ of bismuth?   ans.   29.6 g
6. Iron has a density of 7.87 g/cm³. What volume would 12.5 g of iron occupy?   ans. 1.59 cm³

Point out the importance of
reviewing the summary.   **SUMMARY**

1. Much scientific work requires a quantitative approach. In other words, to investigate a phenomenon, certain characteristics must be measured.
2. Mass is a measure of the quantity of matter present. Weight is the net force of gravitational attraction between two bodies.
3. Mass is measured on a balance. The standard of mass is the kilogram.
4. Length is the distance between two points. One common unit of length is the centimeter.
5. Time is measured in terms of the interval between two events. The basic unit of time is the second.
6. Temperature is the measure of heat intensity: how hot something is. It is measured with a thermometer. The unit of temperature is the C°.
7. Scientists are interested in both the accuracy and the precision of their measurements.
8. Metric units are used in science. Metric units are particularly convenient because they are based on multiples of 10.

9. The metric unit of volume is the liter.
10. Speed is length per unit time.
11. Density is the mass of a substance in a unit volume of that substance.
12. Scientific notation is a convenient method for writing extremely large or small numbers.
13. Any number can be expressed in scientific notation as $M \times 10^n$. Where M is some number ≥ 1 and < 10 and n is an integer.
14. Scientific notation indicates clearly the number of significant digits. This notation is particularly helpful in multiplication and division.
15. The ratio method of problem solving is useful in chemistry.
16. In the factor-label method of problem solving, unit labels are treated as factors. This method makes conversion of units easier.

PROBLEMS

7. Solve the following problems for mass:
   a. Ammonium magnesium chromate has a density of 1.84 g/cm³. What is the mass of 6.96 cm³ of this substance? 12.8 g
   b. Barium perchlorate has a density of 2.74 g/cm³. What is the mass of 610 cm³ of this substance? 1670 g
   c. Bismuth phosphate has a density of 6.32 g/cm³. What is the mass of 86.0 cm³ of this substance? 544 g
   d. Antimony has a density of 6.70 g/cm³. What is the mass of 3.28 cm³ of antimony? 22.0 g
   e. Gold has a density of 19.3 g/cm³. What is the mass of 0.253 cm³ of gold? 4.88 g
8. Solve the following problems for volume:
   a. Calcium chloride has a density of 2.15 g/cm³. What is the volume of 3.37 g of this substance? 1.57 cm³
   b. Cerium sulfate has a density of 3.17 g/cm³. What is the volume of 706 g of this substance? 223 cm³
   c. Chromium silicide has a density of 5.50 g/cm³. What is the volume of 40.5 g of this substance? 7.36 cm³
   d. Magnesium has a density of 1.74 g/cm³. What is the volume of 32.9 g of magnesium? 18.9 cm³
   e. Tin has a density of 7.28 g/cm³. What is the volume of 2.13 kg of tin? 293 cm³

9. How many significant digits are there in each of the following?

    a. 9 1   **e.** 0.090 2   **h.** 0.04900 4

    b. 90 1   **f.** 909 3   **i.** 0.0224 3

    c. 900.0 4   **g.** 0.00881 3   **j.** 74.24 4

    d. 0.009 1

10. If 1.0 km³ of air has mass 1,200,000,000 kg, what is the density of air in g/cm³? 1.2×10^{-3} g/cm³

11. Convert:

    a. 8.00 hours (hr) to seconds   *ans.*   28,800 sec

    b. 0.0200 megameter (Mm) to decimeters   *ans.*   200,000 dm

    c. 1.00 deciliter (dl) to microliters (μl)   *ans.*   100,000 μl

12. Convert:

    a. 3 kg to grams 3000 g

    b. 9 cm to meters 0.09 m

    c. 5.00 hr to seconds 1.8×10^4 sec

    d. 0.05 kilometer (km) to centimeters 5.0×10^3 cm

    e. 8 cm to millimeters (mm) 80 mm

13. Express in scientific notation:

    a. 45.9 4.59×10 **d.** 0.0005976 5.976×10^{-4}

    b. 0.0359 3.59×10^{-2} **e.** 345,690,000,000 3.4569×10^{11}

    c. 45,967,800 4.59678×10^7

14. Express as one numeral:

    a. 3.59×10^2 359   **d.** 5.29×10^5 529,000

    b. 4.32×10^{-3} 0.00432   **e.** 6.94×10^1 69.4

    c. 3.05×10^{-5} 0.0000305

15. Perform the following operations:

    a. $1.29 \times 10^5 + 7.56 \times 10^4$ 2.05×10^5

    b. $4.59 \times 10^{-5} - 6.02 \times 10^{-6}$ 3.99×10^{-5}

    c. $(5.4 \times 10^2)(3.2 \times 10^{-3})$ 1.73

    d. $(4.84 \times 10^{-5}) \div (2.42 \times 10^{-7})$ 2.00×10^2

    e. $(48.6 \times 10^2)(0.524 \times 10^{-2}) \div (2.2 \times 10^3)$ 1.16×10^{-2}

16. How many significant digits are there in each of the following?

    a. 1.5600×10^8 *ans.* 5   **d.** 8.4200000×10^8 *ans.*   8

    b. 6.890000×10^8 *ans.* 7   **e.** 6.000×10^{-6} *ans.*   4

    c. 4.9300×10^9 *ans.* 5

17. How many significant digits should appear in the answers to the following problems?

    a. 5×0.00559 *ans.*   1

    b. $0.7 \times 9.48 \times 10^1$ *ans.*   1

    c. 875×67 *ans.*   2

    d. 0.3 divided by 0.0586   *ans.*   1

    e. 0.658 divided by 9.59×10^1 *ans.*   3

18. Perform the following additions and subtractions. Round off the answers to the proper number of decimal places.

a. 0.08990
  $+ 52$ 52

c.   0.9
  $- 0.00005$ 0.9

e.   63 156
  $+ 93$

b.   4
  $+ 6$ 10

d. 0.06
  $+ 2$ 2

19. Make the following conversions:

a. 24 milligrams (mg) to kilograms 2.4×10^{-5} kg
b. 8.6 centigrams (cg) to grams 8.6×10^{-2} g
c. 2600 dm³ to liters 2.6×10^{2} l
d. 92 cm³ to cubic meters (m³) 9.2×10^{-5} m³
e. 79 m³ to centiliters (cl) 7.9×10^{6} cl

20. What is the density of sugar in g/cm³ if its density is 1590 kg/m³? 9.9×10^{-2} g/cm³

21. An automobile is traveling at the rate of 30 kilometers per hour. What is its rate in centimeters per second (cm/sec)? 830 cm/sec

22. The density of a sample of nitrogen gas is 1.25 g/liter. What is the mass of 1.00 m³ of the gas? 1250 g

ONE MORE STEP

See Teacher's Guide at the front of this book.

1. A procedure used by many scientists and engineers is dimensional analysis. Look up this term in an unabridged dictionary in the school library. After you have familiarized yourself with the meaning of the term, predict the units associated with the measurement of the following phenomena: viscosity, power, torque, and rate of heat transfer.

2. Determine how a computer makes computations with large numbers.

3. Determine how an abacus can be used to make computations with large numbers.

4. How does the concept of "magnitude" relate to powers of 10?

Suggested Readings for this chapter may be found in the Teacher's Guide at the front of this book.

What is the nature of the substances stored in these tanks? What materials were used to make the tanks? Why were these materials selected? Gases are stored in these tanks. Because gases are easily compressed, they are often stored under pressure. A construction material is used which can withstand the pressure and which will not react with the gases. What properties determine how some materials are used in your classroom and in your home?

Matter

Chapter 3 introduces atoms, molecules, elements, compounds, and mixtures and describes the general properties of matter and the changes it undergoes.

The world around us is filled with objects of many kinds. There are people, chairs, books, trees, quartz crystals, lumps of sugar, ice cubes, drinking glasses, doorknobs, and an endless number of other familiar objects. Each of these objects may be characterized by its size, shape, use, color, and texture. Many unlike objects have certain important things in common. For example, a tree and a chair are both made of wood. Millions of other objects with different shapes and different purposes may also be made of wood. The word *material* is used in referring to a specific kind of matter (such as wood). Familiar materials include wood, steel, copper, sugar, salt, nickel, marble, concrete, and milk.

GOAL: You will gain an understanding of the ways in which matter is classified and of the changes undergone by matter.

CLASSIFICATION

3:1 Homogeneous Materials

A *homogeneous* (ho mo JEE ne us) material is one which is the same throughout. If you break it up into smaller pieces, each small piece will have the same properties as every other small piece. If you examine one of the pieces under a microscope, it is impossible to distinguish one part as being a different material from any other part. Examples of homogeneous materials are sugar, salt, seawater, quartz, window glass, etc. Any physically distinct sample of homogeneous material is called a phase. A *phase* is any region with a uniform set of properties. Sometimes we can distinguish between different phases of the same homogeneous material. Ice and water, for example, are different phases of the same homogeneous material. All the material in the water region has the same set of properties. Likewise, all the material in the ice region has the same set of properties.

Some homogeneous materials such as pure salt, pure sugar, or pure sulfur always have the same composition. Such materials are called *substances*. Chemistry is sometimes defined as the science of

Homogeneous materials have the same composition throughout.

The same homogeneous material can exist in different phases.

Materials which always have the same composition are substances.

Elements and compounds are substances.

An element is composed of only one kind of atom.

A compound is made up of different kinds of atoms which are always combined in the same ratio.

substances and of the processes by which substances may be transformed into still other substances. The particles in a substance may be identified by a process called chemical analysis.

According to the atomic theory, matter is composed of very tiny particles called atoms. Substances may be divided into two classes. Substances composed of only one kind of atom are called *elements.* Examples are sulfur, oxygen, hydrogen, nitrogen, copper, gold, and chlorine. Substances composed of more than one kind of atom are called *compounds.* The atoms in the particles of compounds are always in definite ratios.

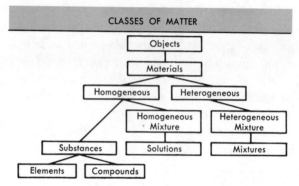

FIGURE 3-1.   Matter can be classified as homogeneous or heterogeneous.

FIGURE 3-2. Elements are examples of homogeneous materials. Clockwise, some metallic elements are (a) mercury, copper, sodium, iron, and magnesium; some nonmetallic elements are (b) bromine, iodine, and sulfur.

Substances are homogeneous materials which always have the same composition. There are other homogeneous materials, such as seawater, window glass, and gold-silver alloys, which vary in composition from sample to sample. If we put a small quantity of pure salt into pure water and let it stand, we get a homogeneous material.

If we add a larger quantity of pure salt to the same amount of pure water, we again get a homogeneous material. The composition of the second sample would differ from the first. The second sample contains more salt in an equal volume of water. Homogeneous materials that have variable compositions are called *solutions*. For example, we may add 5, 10, or 15 grams of salt to 100 grams of water. In each case, the resulting material is homogeneous. A solution may also be defined as a single phase which can vary in composition. Solutions are not necessarily liquid. Air is a homogeneous material composed of nitrogen, oxygen, and smaller quantities of other gases. Its composition varies from place to place. However, each sample of air is a homogeneous mixture. Different types of window glass have different compositions, yet each type is homogeneous. Both air and glass are solutions.

A solution consists of a *solute* (dissolved material) in a *solvent* (dissolving material). The solute is scattered in the solvent in very small particles (molecular or smaller). Because of this scattering, the solution appears uniform, even under the most powerful optical microscope. Since the scattering of particles appears to be completely uniform, solutions are classified as homogeneous materials.

A solution is homogeneous. However, it is not a substance.

Show various kinds of solutions with various concentrations.

A solution has a solute dispersed uniformly in a solvent.

3:2 Heterogeneous Materials

Most of the things we see around us contain two or more distinctly different materials. Sometimes it is necessary to use a microscope to distinguish between two phases. Such nonuniform materials are called *heterogeneous* (het roh JEE ne us). Wood, granite, concrete,

FIGURE 3-3. Examples of heterogeneous materials are granite (a) and milk (b).

and milk are examples. If we look closely at granite, we can see at least three minerals: quartz, biotite, and feldspar. If a piece of granite is crushed into sand-size particles, it is possible to pick out the quartz, biotite, or feldspar. Milk normally appears to be homogeneous. Under a microscope, however, we can see various kinds of particles suspended in water. Milk is not a solution; it is a heterogeneous mixture. One type of particle can be separated from the other particles in milk. Fat globules, for example, are removed by a cream separator.

We may define a heterogeneous material as one that is composed of more than one phase. The different phases in a heterogeneous material are separated from each other by definite boundaries.

It is possible to have a heterogeneous material which contains only one substance. A familiar example is ice water. There is only one substance present, water. But since there are three phases which are not uniformly distributed (solid, liquid, and gas), the sample is heterogeneous. The boundaries between phases in this example are the surfaces of the pieces of ice and water. Surfaces where phases are in contact are called *interfaces*.

The word *mixture* is also used in chemistry. Any material which is composed of more than one substance is called a mixture. A mixture may be homogeneous or heterogeneous. A homogeneous material composed of more than one substance is called a solution. Therefore, a solution is a homogeneous mixture. A heterogeneous material is always composed of more than one phase and is always a mixture.

To summarize, all materials can be classified as one of the following:

substance (element or compound)

solution (homogeneous mixture)

mixture (heterogeneous material or solution)

3:3   Elements and Compounds

The development of this system of classification played a significant role in the early development of chemistry. Early chemists spent much time and energy sorting the pure substances, elements and compounds, from the mixtures. Chemists now know of 88 elementary naturally occurring substances called elements. They can

Courtesy of Kodansha Ltd.

a

Oak Ridge National Laboratory

b

F. Bernard Daniel

c

also make a number of additional elements which do not appear in the natural state on earth. The main interests of chemists today are the interaction of elements and compounds, the analysis of compounds into their component elements, and the synthesis of compounds from elements or other compounds.

FIGURE 3-4. Potassium (a) is a naturally occurring element. Curium (b) is a man-made element. Potassium ferricyanide (c) is a compound.

Tc and Pm do not occur naturally. At and Fr are present in such negligible amounts that they can be ignored as contributors to the earth's mass.

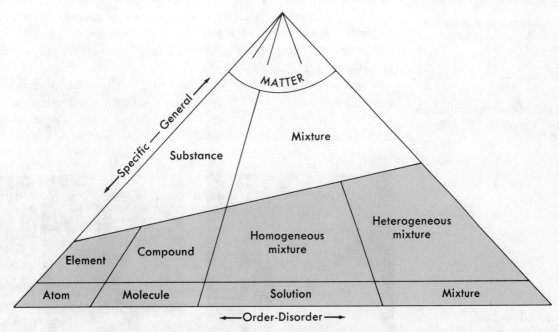

FIGURE 3-5. This pyramid classifies matter in two ways: from general terms to specific terms, and from pure ordered substances to increasingly disordered mixtures.

PROBLEMS

1. a. solution
   b. heterogeneous mixture
   c. heterogeneous mixture
   d. compound
   e. compound

2. a. heterogeneous mixture
   b. heterogeneous mixture
   c. element
   d. compound
   e. element

1. Classify the following materials as heterogeneous mixtures, solutions, compounds, or elements:

   a. air   **c.** paper   **e.** wood alcohol

   b. India ink   **d.** table salt

2. Classify the following materials as heterogeneous mixtures, solutions, compounds, or elements:

   a. apple   **c.** plutonium   **e.** zinc

   b. milk   **d.** water

PROPERTIES AND CHANGES

Properties: 1. physical
          a. extensive
          b. intensive
      2. chemical

3:4 Physical Properties

The properties of a particular substance can be divided into two classes. One class depends primarily on the substance itself. The other depends for the most part on the action of the substance in the presence of other substances. The first class of properties is called *physical properties*. Physical properties may be divided into two groups: extensive properties and intensive properties. *Extensive properties* depend upon the amount of matter present. Among these properties are mass, length, and volume. These terms are already familiar to you.

Extensive properties depend only on the amount of material.

Intensive properties do not depend upon the amount of matter present. For example, each sample of a substance, regardless of its size, has the same density throughout. Other intensive properties include malleability (mal ee uh BIHL uht ee), ductility (duhk TIHL

Intensive properties depend upon the nature of material itself.

a

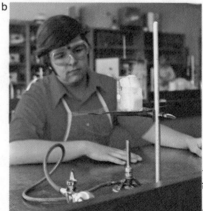

b

FIGURE 3-6. Extensive properties such as volume (a) and time required for a substance to melt (b) depend on the amount of matter present.

F. Bernard Daniel

Bruce Charlton

Courtesy of Kodansha Ltd.

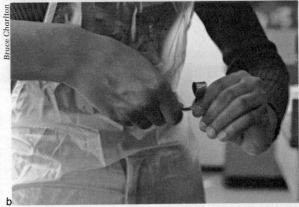

Bruce Charlton

a   b

FIGURE 3-7. Intensive properties such as softness (a) and malleability (b) are independent of amount of matter present.

uht ee), and conductivity (kahn duhk TIHV uht ee). For example, copper can be hammered quite easily into thin sheets. It is more *malleable* than iron, which resists this pounding. Copper can also be drawn out into a fine wire. *Ductility* is a measure of the ease with which this can be done. Both copper and silver have high heat and electrical *conductivity*. High heat conductivity means that a substance offers little resistance to the flow of heat. This high heat conductivity is the reason why a silver spoon left in a hot pan of soup will also become hot.

St. Elmo Brady

(1884–1966)

St. Elmo Brady was the first black student to receive a doctorate in chemistry. He spent the rest of his life making certain that other black students would have the same opportunity. After finishing his degree at the University of Illinois in 1916, he went to Tuskegee Institute to develop what became the first chemistry department there. He moved in 1920 to Howard University and accomplished the same task. In 1927 he moved to Fisk University and served 25 years building both undergraduate and graduate programs. After retirement, when he was nearly 70 years old, Brady was again asked to build a chemistry department, this time at Tougaloo, Mississippi. For the fourth time he responded and produced. As a result of his efforts, thousands of students have had the opportunity for an education in chemistry. He studied and wrote until his death at 82.

a

b

c

FIGURE 3-8. Only a physical change occurs when substances are subdivided (a), poured (b), or stirred (c).

Physical changes affec only physical properties.

3:5 Physical Changes

Changes like pounding, pulling, or heating do not alter the chemical character of the substance. Pounded copper is still copper. Only its physical appearance is changed. Thus, these changes are called *physical changes*. Other examples of physical changes are the dividing of a piece of material into smaller pieces (breaking a window), the dissolving of sugar in water, and the pouring of a liquid from one container to another.

3:6 Changes of State

Some physical changes occur at the melting point and boiling point of the substance. At the melting point, a solid changes to a liquid, or vice versa. At the boiling point, a liquid changes to a gas,

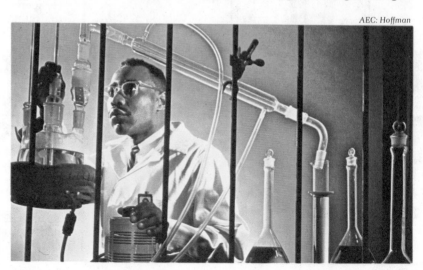

FIGURE 3-9. This chemist is using distillation, a physical change, in a corrosion study.

or vice versa. Such physical changes are called *changes of state*, since the substance is not altered except for its physical state.

One use of physical change that you encounter in chemistry is distillation. Distillation is a change of state operation. It is used to separate substances with different boiling points. For instance, you can separate a solution of salt in water by heating the solution to a temperature equal to the boiling point of the solution. The water will then be turned to steam and escape from the container. The salt, whose boiling point has not yet been reached, will be left behind.

Another separation based on phase difference depends upon the solubility of one substance in another. An insoluble substance which forms from a solution is called a *precipitate*. This process may be called *crystallization* since most substances form crystals when they precipitate. Most substances have a unique solubility in water at a given temperature. Therefore, it is usually possible to separate two substances in the same solution by a process called *fractional crystallization*.

Notice in Figure 3–10 that, at 70°C, potassium bromide is less soluble than potassium nitrate. If the water in a solution containing equal amounts of both substances is allowed to evaporate at 70°C, the potassium bromide will crystallize first. This process is used extensively by chemists to purify laboratory chemicals. It is also used in industry in the production of many crystalline items, such as sugar, salt, and pharmaceuticals.

Both distillation and crystallization are useful in separating mixtures. As a rule, any mixture, whether homogeneous or heterogeneous, can be separated by physical changes. In some cases, however, such separations are not practical.

Changes of state are physical changes.

Distillation is a means of separating substances by boiling point differences.

You may wish to use $AgNO_3$+HCl as a demonstration of a precipitate.

Substances may be separated by crystallization or solubility difference.

You may wish to do this as a demonstration.

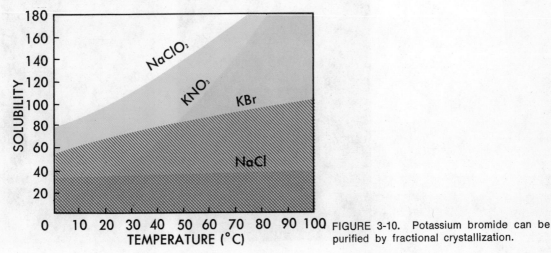

FIGURE 3-10. Potassium bromide can be purified by fractional crystallization.

3:7　Chemical Properties

Some properties of matter depend upon the action of substances
in the presence of other substances. These properties are called
chemical properties. We cannot define the chemical properties of a
substance until we know the kinds of chemical changes that the
substance can undergo. Does it burn? Does it help other substances
to burn? Does it react with water? With what kinds of substances
does it react? Such questions help to determine the chemical properties of a substance.

3:8　Chemical Changes

Suppose you are given two closed tubes. One is partially filled
with water. The other contains reddish-brown nitrogen dioxide gas.
If you dip both tubes into a dry ice-acetone slush (about −50°C),
a strange thing will happen. The water will freeze. This is a physical
change. The other tube, however, will now contain a colorless solid.
The nitrogen dioxide has changed to a new substance with different
properties. This is an example of a chemical change. Let us take another example. Sodium is a silvery, soft metal which reacts violently

FIGURE 3-11. Examples of
chemical changes are the burning of red hot steel in oxygen
(a) and the reaction of copper
with nitric acid (b).

a

Courtesy of Kodansha Ltd.

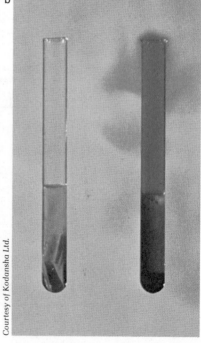

b

Courtesy of Kodansha Ltd.

with water. Chlorine is a greenish-yellow gas, which is highly corrosive and poisonous. However, if these two dangerous elements
are allowed to combine, they produce a white crystalline solid which
neither reacts with water nor is poisonous. It is common table salt—
sodium chloride. In this case, the properties of the reactants have
disappeared. The new substance formed has new properties.

Whenever a substance undergoes a change so that one or more new
substances with different properties are formed, a chemical change
(reaction) has taken place. Burning, digesting, and fermenting are
examples of chemical changes.

Chemical changes produce new substances with new properties.

The separation of compounds into their constituent elements always requires a chemical change. Such a separation is one type of
analysis. Mixtures are always separable by physical means. However, it is sometimes more convenient to separate mixtures by a
chemical change.

*Compounds may be ana-
lyzed by chemical change.*

PROBLEMS

3. Classify the following properties as chemical or physical:
    a. color   *ans.* physical
    b. reactivity   *ans.* chemical
    c. porosity   *ans.* physical
    d. stability   *ans.* chemical
    e. expansion   *ans.* physical

4. Classify the following properties as chemical or physical:
    a. fiammability chemical   **d.** solubility physical
    b. odor physical   **e.** rusting chemical
    c. ductility chemical

5. Classify the following changes as chemical or physical:
    a. digestion of food   *ans.* chemical
    b. fading of dye in cloth   *ans.* chemical
    c. growth of a plant   *ans.* chemical
    d. melting of ice   *ans.* physical
    e. production of sound by the vocal cords   *ans.* physical

6. Classify the following changes as chemical or physical:
    a. explosion of gasoline in an automobile engine chemical
    b. formation of clouds in the air physical
    c. healing of a wound chemical
    d. making of rock candy by evaporating water from a sugar solu-
        tion physical
    e. production of light by an electric lamp physical

SUMMARY

1. Classification of matter requires the use of exact terms.

2. A phase of matter consists of similar parts. One phase is separated from other phases by boundaries called interfaces.

3. Heterogeneous matter is made up of more than one phase. The phases usually can be separated by physical processes.

4. A mixture is a combination of two or more substances which have different properties. Most common kinds of matter are mixtures.

5. Homogeneous matter is made up of only one phase.

6. A substance is homogeneous matter that has a definite chemical composition. Compounds and elements are substances.

7. Three classes of homogeneous matter are solutions, compounds, and elements.

8. A solution is a homogeneous mixture consisting of a solute dissolved in a solvent. The component parts need not be present in any specific ratios.

9. Compounds are substances that can be broken down into simpler substances by ordinary chemical means. The component parts are present in definite ratios.

10. Elements are the basic substances of the universe. They cannot be broken down into simpler substances by ordinary chemical means.

11. Physical properties depend upon the substance itself.

12. Extensive physical properties, such as mass and length, depend upon the amount of matter present. Intensive properties, such as ductility and melting point, do not.

13. A physical change in a substance does not alter its chemical character.

14. A change of state is a physical change from one state—solid, liquid, or gas—to another.

15. Physical changes can be used to separate the substances composing a mixture.

16. The chemical properties of a substance depend upon the action of the substance in the presence of other substances.

17. A chemical change in a substance involves the formation of new substances with different properties. Both physical and chemical changes are accompanied by energy changes.

18. Chemical changes must be used to separate the elements composing a compound.

PROBLEMS

7. By the use of reference materials, classify the following materials as heterogeneous mixtures, solutions, compounds, or elements:
   a. paint heterogeneous mixture   d. leather heterogeneous mixture
   b. orthoclase compound   e. corn syrup solution
   c. granite heterogeneous mixture

8. Classify the following changes as chemical or physical:
   a. burning of coal chemical   d. excavating of earth physical
   b. tearing of a piece of paper— e. exploding of TNT chemical
   c. kicking of a football physical └───physical

9. Indicate how you would demonstrate that each of the following is a heterogeneous mixture or a homogeneous mixture:
   a. a piece of lumber inspection
   b. a glass of soda pop evaporate liquid
   c. a piece of cloth advertised as 50% wool and 50% man-made fiber examine by microscope
   d. a piece of calf's liver extract with a solvent
   e. shaving cream evaporate liquid

10. Estimate the number of phases ⌐ 9 phases present in an ice-cream soda complete with whipped cream and candied cherry. How many interfaces would there be in this system? approximately 13 interfaces   See Teacher's Guide at the front of this book.

11. Make a list of five solutions commonly found in the home.── ammonia, soft drink, cleaning fluid, window cleaner, paint thinner, air deodorizer

12. List five chemical changes familiar to you in which the accompanying energy change is important.── explosion, battery discharging, muscular contraction, cooking (particularly baking), gasoline burning in a gasoline engine

ONE MORE STEP

1. The doctor sometimes recommends gargling with salt water to relieve a sore throat. Determine whether the action of the salt water on bacteria is chemical or physical.

2. List 30 chemical changes which occur every day and are important to the maintenance of your life.

3. Devise an experiment which will allow you to separate a mixture of copper filings and salt.

4. Find out how crude oil may be obtained from shale through physical and chemical means.

See Teacher's Guide at the front of this book.

Suggested Readings for this chapter may be found in the Teacher's Guide at the front of this book.

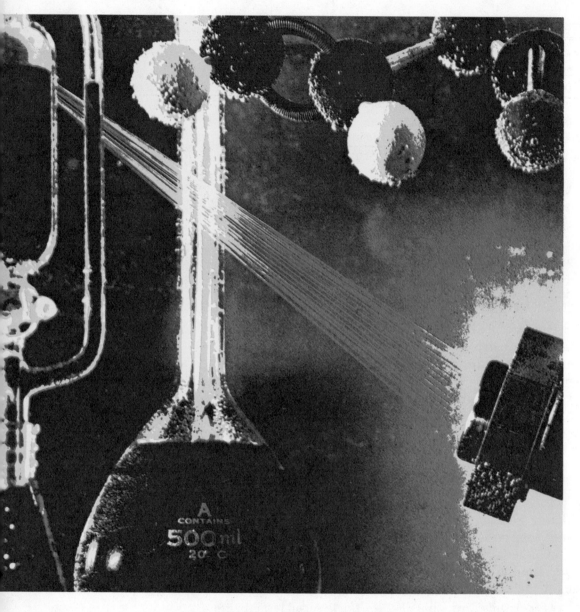

How can you describe the bursting of fireworks, the rusting of objects, or the changes which take place in the manufacture of synthetic fibers? Each of these is an example of a chemical reaction. You might describe them with words or pictures. A chemist would probably use special chemical symbols and combinations of these symbols to describe these reactions. What is a chemical symbol? How are these symbols used? Where did they originate?

Chapter 4 introduces symbols and the use of these symbols as a means of chemical shorthand in writing formulas and equations.

Chemists have a kind of shorthand for describing substances and the changes which they undergo. Consider the following statement: "Two molecules of a gas containing two atoms of carbon and two atoms of hydrogen in each molecule will react with five molecules of a gas containing two atoms of oxygen in each molecule to produce four molecules of a gas containing one carbon atom and two oxygen atoms in each molecule plus two molecules of a liquid containing two atoms of hydrogen and one atom of oxygen in each molecule." How much easier to write

$$2C_2H_2 + 5O_2 \rightarrow 4CO_2 + 2H_2O$$

to express the burning of acetylene! But what do all these symbols and numerals mean?

GOAL: You will develop an understanding of the meanings and use of chemical symbols.

A justification for the use of chemical symbols.

All compounds here are gases. The gas symbol (g) has not yet been introduced.

ELEMENTS

4:1 Symbols

The chemical *symbols* of the elements are a form of shorthand. They take the place of the complete names of the elements. A symbol may represent one atom of an element. For example, Al may represent one atom of aluminum. This usage is acceptable because scientists throughout the world have agreed to represent one atom of aluminum by the symbol Al.

J. J. Berzelius is generally given credit for inventing the modern symbol. Prior to his invention, symbols such as those shown in Figure 4–0 were used. Berzelius proposed that all elements be given a symbol corresponding to the first letter of their names. Any repetitions would be taken care of by adding the second letter or a letter outstanding in the name. In some cases, the Latin name of the element was used. Thus, sulfur is S; selenium, Se; strontium, Sr; and sodium, Na for *natrium,* its Latin name.

The symbols that have been agreed upon for 103 elements are listed in Table 4–1. Notice that they are made up of capital and lowercase letters. Names for elements 104 and 105 have not yet been accepted by the International Union of Pure and Applied Chemistry (IUPAC).

A symbol may be used in place of the name of an element.

Symbols consist of either one or two letters, usually two.

The first letter of a symbol is always capitalized.

Table 4–1

Elements and Their Symbols

Actinium	**Ac**	Hafnium	**Hf**	Praseodymium	**Pr**
Aluminum	**Al***	Helium	**He**	Promethium	**Pm**
Americium	**Am**	Holmium	**Ho**	Protactinium	**Pa**
Antimony	**Sb**	Hydrogen*	**H**	Radium	**Ra**
Argon	**Ar**	Indium	**In**	Radon	**Rn**
Arsenic*	**As**	Iodine*	**I**	Rhenium	**Re**
Astatine	**At**	Iridium	**Ir**	Rhodium	**Rh**
Barium*	**Ba**	Iron*	**Fe**	Rubidium*	**Rb**
Berkelium	**Bk**	Krypton	**Kr**	Ruthenium	**Ru**
Beryllium	**Be**	Lanthanum	**La**	Samarium	**Sm**
Bismuth	**Bi**	Lawrencium	**Lr**	Scandium	**Sc**
Boron*	**B**	Lead*	**Pb**	Selenium*	**Se**
Bromine*	**Br**	Lithium*	**Li**	Silicon*	**Si**
Cadmium*	**Cd**	Lutetium	**Lu**	Silver*	**Ag**
Calcium*	**Ca**	Magnesium*	**Mg**	Sodium*	**Na**
Californium	**Cf**	Manganese*	**Mn**	Strontium*	**Sr**
Carbon*	**C**	Mendelevium	**Md**	Sulfur*	**S**
Cerium	**Ce**	Mercury*	**Hg**	Tantalum	**Ta**
Cesium*	**Cs**	Molybdenum*	**Mo**	Technetium	**Tc**
Chlorine*	**Cl**	Neodymium	**Nd**	Tellurium	**Te**
Chromium*	**Cr**	Neon	**Ne**	Terbium	**Tb**
Cobalt*	**Co**	Neptunium	**Np**	Thallium*	**Tl**
Copper*	**Cu**	Nickel*	**Ni**	Thorium	**Th**
Curium	**Cm**	Niobium	**Nb**	Thulium	**Tm**
Dysprosium	**Dy**	Nitrogen*	**N**	Tin	**Sn**
Einsteinium	**Es**	Nobelium	**No**	Titanium	**Ti**
Erbium	**Er**	Osmium	**Os**	Tungsten	**W**
Europium	**Eu**	Oxygen*	**O**	Uranium	**U**
Fermium	**Fm**	Palladium	**Pd**	Vanadium	**V**
Fluorine*	**F**	Phosphorus*	**P**	Xenon	**Xe**
Francium	**Fr**	Platinum	**Pt**	Ytterbium	**Yb**
Gadolinium	**Gd**	Plutonium	**Pu**	Yttrium	**Y**
Gallium	**Ga**	Polonium	**Po**	Zinc*	**Zn**
Germanium	**Ge**	Potassium*	**K**	Zirconium	**Zr**
Gold	**Au**				

* Symbols for these elements will appear most frequently throughout this text.

COMPOUNDS

4:2 Chemical Formulas

Chemists also use combinations of symbols to represent compounds. *Compounds* are substances in which two or more elements
are chemically combined. Compounds are represented by formulas.

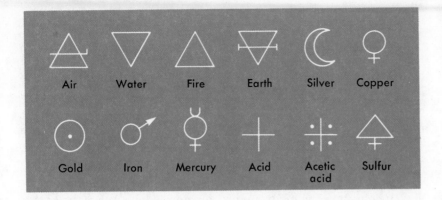

FIGURE 4-1. Many different symbols have been used to represent well known elements. Some of these symbols are shown here.

A *chemical formula* is a combination of symbols which represents the composition of a compound. Formulas often contain numerals to indicate the proportions in which the elements occur within a compound. For example, we have learned from experiments that water is composed of the elements hydrogen and oxygen. We also know that two atoms of hydrogen will react (combine chemically) with one atom of oxygen to form one molecule of water. As a formula for water, we write "H_2O." The small subscript, $_2$, after the H indicates that there are two atoms of hydrogen in a molecule of water. Note that there is no subscript after the oxygen. Whenever a symbol for an element has no subscript, it is understood that only one atom of that element is present. From a formula, then, we can determine two things: the elements present in the compound and the relative number of atoms of each element in the compound. How many atoms of each element are present in each compound in Table 4–2?

Courtesy of Kodansha Ltd.

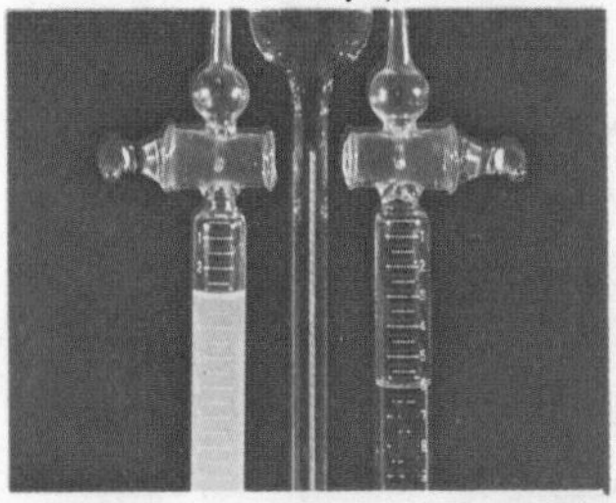

FIGURE 4-2. When water is decomposed by electrolysis, hydrogen and oxygen are formed. The volume of hydrogen collected (right tube) is twice the volume of the oxygen collected (left tube).

Chemical formulas indicate the relative number of atoms of each element present in a compound.

Table 4–2

Some Common Compounds and Their Formulas

Compound	Formula	Elements Present
Ammonia	NH_3	nitrogen, hydrogen
Rust	Fe_2O_3	iron, oxygen
Sucrose	$C_{12}H_{22}O_{11}$	carbon, hydrogen, oxygen
Table salt	$NaCl$	sodium, chlorine
Water	H_2O	hydrogen, oxygen

4:3 Oxidation Number

Through experimentation, chemists have determined the ratios in which most elements combine. They have also learned that these combining ratios depend upon the structure of their atoms. This relationship will be explored fully in a later chapter. In the meantime, you should know that the atoms can acquire an electrical charge. They may also attach themselves to other atoms so that the entire group acquires an electric charge. Such charged atoms are called *ions*. An ion containing more than one atom is called a *polyatomic ion*. When an individual atom acquires a charge, that charge is known as its *oxidation number*. The term, oxidation number, will be more fully discussed (Chapter 21).

An ion is a charged atom or charged group of atoms.

Table 4-3 lists the oxidation numbers of some common elements and the charges of some common polyatomic ions. We may use this information to write correct chemical formulas and describe chemical reactions. Atoms and ions always combine chemically in definite ratios. Oxidation numbers of elements and the charges on polyatomic ions tell us these combining ratios. An easy way to determine the proportion of elements in a compound is to add the charges algebraically. If the charges add up to zero the formula for the compound is correct.

Oxidation numbers represent apparent charge on an atom.

Table 4-3

Charges

Oxidation Numbers (Charges) of Monatomic Ions

1+	3+
Cesium, Cs^+	Aluminum, Al^{3+}
Hydrogen, H^+	Bismuth(III), Bi^{3+}
Lithium, Li^+	Cerium(III), Ce^{3+}
Potassium, K^+	Iron(III), Fe^{3+}
Rubidium, Rb^+	**4+**
Silver, Ag^+	
Sodium, Na^+	Silicon, Si^{4+}
Thallium(I), Tl^+	**1−**
2+	Bromine, Br^-
Barium, Ba^{2+}	Chlorine, Cl^-
Cadmium, Cd^{2+}	Fluorine, F^-
Calcium, Ca^{2+}	Hydrogen, H^-
Cobalt(II), Co^{2+}	Iodine, I^-
Copper(II), Cu^{2+}	**2−**
Iron(II), Fe^{2+}	
Lead(II), Pb^{2+}	Oxygen, O^{2-}
Magnesium, Mg^{2+}	Selenium, Se^{2-}
Manganese(II), Mn^{2+}	Sulfur, S^{2-}
Mercury(II), Hg^{2+}	**3−**
Nickel(II), Ni^{2+}	
Strontium, Sr^{2+}	Boron, B^{3-}
Zinc, Zn^{2+}	Nitrogen, N^{3-}
	Phosphorus, P^{3-}

The algebraic sum of the oxidation numbers of the elements of a compound is zero.

Charges on Polyatomic Ions

1+

Ammonium, NH_4^+

1−

Acetate, $C_2H_3O_2^-$
Cyanide, CN^-
Hydroxide, OH^-
Iodate, IO_3^-
Nitrate, NO_3^-
Perchlorate, ClO_4^-

2−

Carbonate, CO_3^{2-}
Hexafluorosilicate, SiF_6^{2-}
Oxalate, $C_2O_4^{2-}$
Selenate, SeO_4^{2-}
Sulfate, SO_4^{2-}
Sulfite, SO_3^{2-}
Tartrate, $C_4H_4O_6^{2-}$

3−

Arsenate, AsO_4^{3-}
Phosphate, PO_4^{3-}

Courtesy of Kodansha Ltd.

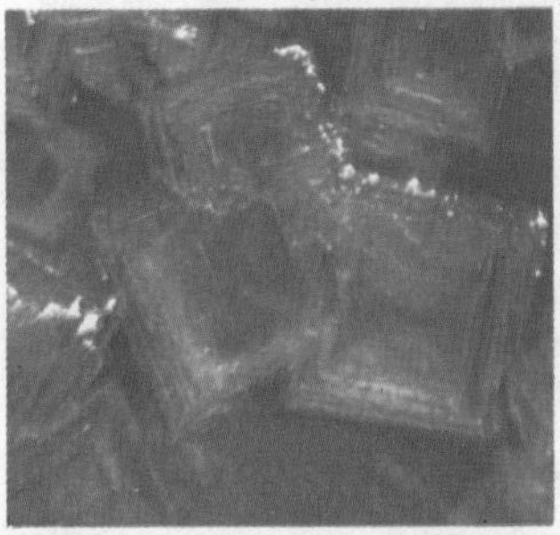

Common table salt (NaCl) is made from sodium (Na) and chlorine (Cl). Table 4–3 gives a 1+ charge for sodium ions and a 1− charge for chloride ions. $1 + (1-) = 0$. Therefore, the formula for salt is NaCl. This formula indicates that a one-to-one ratio exists between sodium ions and chloride ions in a crystal of salt.

Oxygen gas is composed of molecules which are *diatomic* (two atoms). This statement means that one oxygen molecule contains two atoms of oxygen. Oxygen gas is represented by the formula O_2. Six other common elements also occur in diatomic molecules. Nitrogen (N_2), hydrogen (H_2), fluorine (F_2), and chlorine (Cl_2) are diatomic gases under normal conditions. Bromine (Br_2) is a gas above 58.7°C. Iodine (I_2) is a gas above 108°C.

How would you write a formula for a compound of calcium and bromine? Calcium is Ca^{2+} and bromine is Br^-. Since the sum of the charges must be zero, two Br^- are needed to balance one Ca^{2+}. The correct formula is $CaBr_2$. What would be the formula for a compound containing aluminum and sulfur atoms? Aluminum is Al^{3+} and sulfur is S^{2-}. Two Al^{3+} and three S^{2-} must combine for the charges to add up to zero. The formula is Al_2S_3. Write a formula for the compound formed from sodium and sulfur. Na_2S

The formula of a substance represents a specific amount of a compound. In the case of a substance composed of molecules, the formula represents one molecule.

FIGURE 4-3. In a crystal of sodium chloride (NaCl), there is one sodium ion for each chloride ion.

Diatomic gases have two atoms per molecule.

A formula may represent one molecule of a molecular substance.

4:4 Naming Compounds

Unfortunately, there are many names, both common and chemical, for some compounds. However, there is a systematic method of naming practically all the compounds which we will use. The names

N_2O, dinitrogen oxide, nitrogen(I) oxide; NO, nitrogen oxide, nitrogen(II) oxide; N_2O_3, dinitrogen trioxide, nitrogen(III) oxide; NO_2, nitrogen dioxide, nitrogen(IV) oxide; N_2O_5, dinitrogen pentoxide, nitrogen(V) oxide

62   CHEMICAL SHORTHAND   4:4

of only a few compounds, particularly acids, will not be included in this system.

Compounds containing only two elements are called *binary compounds*. To name a binary compound, first write the name of the element having a positive charge. Then add the name of the negative element. The name of the negative element must also be modified to end in *-ide*. For example, the compound formed by aluminum (Al^{3+}) and nitrogen (N^{3-}) with the formula AlN is named aluminum nitride.

The compound of hydrogen (H^+) and selenium (Se^{2-}) with the formula H_2Se is named hydrogen selenide. Another name for water is hydrogen oxide (H_2O). Common table salt is sodium chloride (NaCl).

Some elements have more than one possible charge. Therefore, they may form more than one compound with another element. For instance, nitrogen and oxygen form five different binary compounds with each other! We must have a way of distinguishing the names of these compounds. There are two ways of expressing the names of such compounds:

(1) Add a prefix to the name of each element. The prefix will indicate the number of atoms of that element in a molecule of the substance being named. Examples are dinitrogen oxide for N_2O, dinitrogen trioxide for N_2O_3, and dinitrogen pentoxide for N_2O_5.

The prefixes to be used for one through eight are mono-, di-, tri-, tetra-, penta-, hexa-, hepta-, and octa-.

(2) Write the oxidation number of the element having positive charge after the name of that element. Roman numerals in parentheses are used. Examples are nitrogen(I) oxide for N_2O, nitrogen(III) oxide for N_2O_3, and nitrogen(V) oxide for N_2O_5.

The second system is generally preferred, but there are many compounds that have long been named by the first system. These more common names are usually used. Notable examples are sulfur dioxide (SO_2), sulfur trioxide (SO_3), and carbon disulfide (CS_2).

A few negative ions with names ending in *-ide* do not form binary compounds. Examples are OH^- (hydrox*ide*), NH_2^- (am*ide*), $N_2H_3^-$ (hydraz*ide*), and CN^- (cyan*ide*).

For naming compounds containing more than two elements, several rules apply. The simplest of these compounds are formed from one element and a polyatomic ion. These compounds are named in the same way as binary compounds. However, the ending of the polyatomic ion is not changed. Examples are NH_4Cl, ammonium chloride; $AlPO_4$, aluminum phosphate; and $CuSO_4$, copper(II) sulfate.

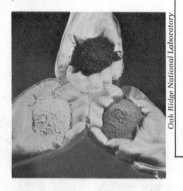

Oak Ridge National Laboratory

FIGURE 4-4. Some elements such as uranium have more than one charge and can form more than one compound with another element.

Prefixes indicating number are used in naming some types of compounds.

Oxidation number of an element having more than one possible oxidation number may be indicated with a Roman numeral.

A few compounds whose names end in -ide are not binary.

In naming compounds containing polyatomic ions, the ending of the name of the polyatomic ion is not changed.

Consider a compound such as aluminum sulfate. The charge of aluminum is 3+ and the charge of the sulfate polyatomic ion is 2−. It is necessary to have two aluminum particles and three sulfate particles in the compound to maintain neutrality. The indication of two aluminum particles in the formula is simple: Al_2. For the sulfate, the entire polyatomic ion must be placed in parentheses to indicate that three particles are required: $(SO_4)_3$. Aluminum sulfate has the formula $Al_2(SO_4)_3$. Another example is ammonium sulfate: $(NH_4)_2SO_4$.

Other rules for naming compounds and writing formulas will be discussed when the need arises. The names of the common acids, for example, do not normally follow these rules. Table 4–4 lists names and formulas for acids which you should memorize.

FIGURE 4-5. Copper (II) sulfate ($CuSO_4$) is composed of copper, sulfur, and oxygen.

Polyatomic ions which contain oxygen (other than OH⁻) have the ending "-ite" or "-ate." Thus, H_2SO_4 is hydrogen sulfate not hydrogen sulfide which is H_2S, a binary compound.

Table 4–4

Acids

Formula	Name	Formula	Name
$HC_2H_3O_2$	Acetic	HNO_2	Nitrous
H_3BO_3	Boric	$H_2C_2O_4$	Oxalic
H_2CO_3	Carbonic	$HClO_4$	Perchloric
HCl	Hydrochloric	H_3PO_4	Phosphoric
HCN	Hydrocyanic	H_2SO_4	Sulfuric
HNO_3	Nitric	H_2SO_3	Sulfurous

Names of common acids should be memorized.

The -ic and -ous endings may have to be introduced if the student will meet them in the laboratory.

PROBLEMS Problems: Assign as many as necessary for mastery.

1. Write the formula for each of the following compounds (use Table 4–3 and Table A–2 in the Appendix):
   a. thallium(I) nitrate   ans. $TlNO_3$
   b. rubidium tartrate   ans. $Rb_2C_4H_4O_6$
   c. sodium cyanide   ans.   NaCN
   d. lead(II) arsenate   ans. $Pb_3(AsO_4)_2$
   e. sodium fluoride   ans.   NaF
   f. aluminum chloride   ans. $AlCl_3$
   g. thallium(I) iodide   ans.   TlI
   h. zinc iodide   ans. ZnI_2
   i. cobalt(II) carbonate   ans. $CoCO_3$
   j. potassium hydride   ans.   KH

2. Write the name for each of the following compounds:
   a. $Ba(NO_3)_2$ *ans.*   barium nitrate
   b. KF   *ans.*   potassium fluoride
   c. $TlIO_3$ *ans.*   thallium(I) iodate
   d. SiO_2 *ans.*   silicon oxide
   e. $FeCl_2$ *ans.*   iron(II) chloride
   f. BaH_2 *ans.*   barium hydride
   g. $(NH_4)_2SeO_4$ *ans.*   ammonium selenate
   h. CoSe   *ans.*   cobalt(II) selenide
   i. WB_2 *ans.*   tungsten(VI) boride
   j. $RbNO_3$ *ans.*   rubidium nitrate

3. Write the formula for each of the following compounds:
   a. barium fluoride BaF_2 d. cadmium bromide $CdBr_2$
   b. thallium(I) oxide Tl_2O e. iron(III) fluoride FeF_3
   c. aluminum perchlorate $Al(ClO_4)_3$

4. Write the name for each of the following compounds:
   a. NiSe nickel(II) selenide   d. $(NH_4)_2S$ ammonium sulfide
   b. $LiC_2H_3O_2$ lithium acetate   e. $Hg(C_2H_3O_2)_2$ mercury(II) acetate
   c. Tl_2SiF_6 thallium(I)hexafluorosilicate

5. Write the formula for each of the following compounds:
   a. lead(II) selenate $PbSeO_4$ d. ammonium tartrate $(NH_4)_2C_4H_4O_6$
   b. manganese(II) oxalate —   e. iron(II) carbonate $FeCO_3$
   c. zinc sulfite $ZnSO_3$ └— MnC_2O_4

6. a. lead(II) bromide
   b. strontium selenate
   c. mercury(II) fluoride
   d. ammonium carbonate
   e. thallium(I) carbonate

6. Write the name for each of the following compounds:
   a. $PbBr_2$ b. $SrSeO_4$ c. HgF_2 d. $(NH_4)_2CO_3$ e. Tl_2CO_3

7. Write the formula for each of the following compounds:
   a. iron(II) bromide $FeBr_2$ d. copper(II) cyanide $Cu(CN)_2$
   b. nickel(II) arsenate _____   e. sodium sulfate Na_2SO_4
   c. zinc acetate $Zn(C_2H_3O_2)_2$ └— $Ni_3(AsO_4)_2$

8. a. copper(II) oxalate
   b. rubidium
      hexafluorosilicate
   c. bismuth oxalate
   d. ammonium perchlorate
   e. iron(II) hydroxide

8. Write the name for each of the following compounds:
   a. CuC_2O_4 c. $Bi_2(C_2O_4)_3$ e. $Fe(OH)_2$
   b. Rb_2SiF_6 d. NH_4ClO_4

9. a. $Mn(NO_3)_2$
   b. NaOH
   c. TiC
   d. $CsIO_3$
   e. $ZnSiF_6$

9. Write the formula for each of the following compounds:
   a. manganese(II) nitrate   d. cesium iodate
   b. sodium hydroxide   e. zinc hexafluorosilicate
   c. titanium(IV) carbide

10. a. cobalt(II) acetate
    b. silver perchlorate
    c. beryllium carbide
    d. calcium phosphate
    e. iron(II) sulfate

10. Write the name for each of the following compounds:
    a. $Co(C_2H_3O_2)_2$ c. Be_2C e. $FeSO_4$
    b. $AgClO_4$ d. $Ca_3(PO_4)_2$

4:5   Molecular and Empirical Formulas

The formulas for compounds that occur in molecules are called the *molecular formulas*. For instance, one compound of hydrogen and oxygen is hydrogen peroxide (H_2O_2). H_2O_2 is a molecular formula because one molecule of hydrogen peroxide contains two atoms of hydrogen and two atoms of oxygen. However, there is another kind of formula chemists also use. The atomic ratio of hydrogen to oxygen in hydrogen peroxide is one to one. Therefore, the simplest formula that would indicate the ratio between hydrogen and oxygen is HO. Such a formula is called an *empirical formula*. As another example, both benzene (C_6H_6) and acetylene (C_2H_2) have the same empirical formula (CH).

For many substances, the empirical formula is the only formula possible. We will discuss these substances later. Note that the molecular formula of the compound is always some whole-number multiple of the empirical formula.

A molecular formula describes a molecule.

An empirical formula indicates the simplest whole-number ratio of atoms in a formula unit.

A molecular formula is a whole number multiple of an empirical formula.

Type of formula	Hexene	Ethene
Empirical formula	CH_2	CH_2
Molecular formula	$6(CH_2) = C_6H_{12}$	$2(CH_2) = C_2H_4$

FIGURE 4-6. These two compounds have different molecular formulas even though their empirical formulas are the same.

4:6   Coefficients

Chemists use the formula of a compound to represent a definite amount of that compound. This may be called a *formula unit*. It may be one molecule or the smallest number of particles giving the true proportions of the elements in the compound. One molecule of water is represented by H_2O. How do we represent two molecules of water? We use the same system as we would use in mathematics: coefficients. When we wish to represent two x, we write 2x. When we wish to represent two molecules of water we write $2H_2O$. Three sodium particles combined with three chloride particles yields $3NaCl$. We will discuss the need for such representations and others in Section 4:7.

Coefficients are used to represent the number of formula units.

11. a. 1 formula unit of
       silver carbonate
    b. 3 formula units of
       thallium(I) bromide
    c. 2 formula units of
       iron(II) nitrate
    d. 4 formula units of
       mercury(II) iodide
    e. 6 formula units of
       mercury(II) chloride

13. a. mercury(II) cyanide
    b. iron(II) phosphate
    c. copper(II) fluoride
    d. potassium hydroxide
    e. sodium carbonate

15. a. magnesium nitrate
    b. thallium(I) sulfate
    c. mercury(II) oxalate
    d. cerium selenate
    e. ammonium sulfite

PROBLEMS

11. What does each of the following represent in terms of formula units?

    a. Ag_2CO_3 **c.** $2Fe(NO_3)_2$ **e.** $6HgCl_2$

    b. $3TlBr$ **d.** $4HgI_2$

12. Write the formula for each of the following compounds:

    a. strontium oxalate SrC_2O_4 **d.** sodium oxide Na_2O

    b. sodium oxalate $Na_2C_2O_4$ **e.** silver selenide Ag_2Se

    c. potassium selenate K_2SeO_4

13. Write the name for each of the following compounds:

    a. $Hg(CN)_2$ **c.** CuF_2 **e.** Na_2CO_3

    b. $Fe_3(PO_4)_2$ **d.** KOH

14. Write the formula for each of the following compounds:

    a. calcium oxalate CaC_2O_4 **d.** potassium arsenate K_3AsO_4

    b. lithium arsenate Li_3AsO_4 **e.** cesium carbonate Cs_2CO_3

    c. barium nitride Ba_3N_2

15. Write the name for each of the following compounds:

    a. $Mg(NO_3)_2$ **c.** HgC_2O_4 **e.** $(NH_4)_2SO_3$

    b. Tl_2SO_4 **d.** $Ce_2(SeO_4)_3$

Jons Jakob Berzelius

(1779–1848)

Jons Jakob Berzelius was one of many medical doctors who became interested in chemistry and contributed greatly to its progress. His early studies rarely took him very far from his native Swedish village near Stockholm.

One of his endeavors included a 10-year analysis of some 2,000 simple and compound materials to determine the proportions of their various elements.

He developed a system of nomenclature —our present system of symbols and formulas. He was also the discoverer of several new elements, including selenium, silicon, and thorium. Throughout his life Berzelius served on national committees and commissions dealing with science, agriculture, and education in an effort to better the life of his fellow Swedes.

REACTIONS

4:7 Representing Chemical Changes

The formulas of compounds can be used to represent the chemical changes that take place in a chemical reaction. A *chemical reaction* is the process by which one or more substances are changed into one or more new substances. A chemical reaction may be represented by an equation. A correct chemical *equation* indicates what changes take place. It also shows the relative amounts of the various elements and compounds that take part in these changes.

Chemical equations are used to represent chemical changes.

4:8 Balancing Equations

To represent a chemical reaction by means of an equation, we must perform correctly three principal steps:

(1) Determine exactly what the starting substances *(reactants)* and the resulting substances *(products)* are. For instance, hydrogen can be prepared by passing steam over red hot iron. The reactants are steam (H_2O) and iron (Fe). The products are iron oxide (Fe_3O_4) and hydrogen gas (H_2).

Reactants are the starting substances and products are the resulting substances in chemical equations.

(2) Write the reactants on one side of the equation, usually on the left, and connect them with plus signs. Then write the products on the other side of the equation. The two sides are connected by an arrow which indicates the direction of the change. Thus,

Reactants are written on the left side of chemical equations; products are indicated on the right.

$$H_2O + Fe \rightarrow Fe_3O_4 + H_2$$

steam plus iron   yield   iron oxide plus hydrogen

reactants   yield   products

The symbols and formulas must be correct. If not, step three will be useless.

(3) Balance the equation. *Balancing* means making the two sides equal. The law of conservation of mass states that the same amount of matter must be present both before and after all ordinary (non-nuclear) chemical reactions. The same number and kinds of atoms must be present on both sides of the equation. Check the preceding equation. It is not balanced. There are four oxygen atoms on the right, but only one on the left. To put the oxygen in balance, we place a

Balanced equations have the same kind and number of atoms on each side.

Coefficients, not subscripts, may be changed to balance an equation.

coefficient of four before the water on the left. In balancing an equation, we can change only the coefficients. Never change the subscripts. To do so would change the substance represented. Our equation now reads

$$4H_2O + Fe \rightarrow Fe_3O_4 + H_2$$

The oxygens are balanced, but the hydrogens are not. By placing a coefficient of four in front of the hydrogen, both hydrogen and oxygen will be in balance. The equation is now

$$4H_2O + Fe \rightarrow Fe_3O_4 + 4H_2$$

Only the iron remains to be balanced. To do this, place a coefficient of three in front of the iron. The entire equation is now balanced:

$$4H_2O + 3Fe \rightarrow Fe_3O_4 + 4H_2$$

In the commercial production of hydrogen, steam (H_2O) is reacted with coke (C) to produce hydrogen (H_2) and carbon monoxide (CO). The equation is

$$H_2O + C \rightarrow H_2 + CO$$

2 hydrogen atoms
1 oxygen atom   yield   2 hydrogen atoms
1 carbon atom   1 carbon atom
                                  1 oxygen atom

The equation is balanced. Be careful not to confuse subscripts and coefficients in balancing equations. Never change the subscript in a formula in an attempt to balance an equation. Changing a subscript changes the substance that is taking part in the reaction. The resulting equation will not represent the chemical change which actually takes place.

4:9 Classifying Chemical Changes

Four simple chemical reactions are: single displacement, double displacement, decomposition, synthesis.

There are hundreds of different "kinds" of chemical reactions. For now, we will consider only four general types. Of these four, three are often used to make, or synthesize, new compounds.

(1) Single Displacement

In this type of reaction, one element displaces another in a compound. For example, in the reaction

$$3Li + CmF_3 \rightarrow 3LiF + Cm$$

lithium displaces curium from curium(III) fluoride. In the reaction

$$Cl_2 + 2KBr \rightarrow 2KCl + Br_2$$

chlorine displaces bromine from potassium bromide. This type of reaction is recognized and predicted because of its general form:

element plus compound yields element plus compound

$A + BC \rightarrow B + AC$

(2) Double Displacement

There are hundreds of reactions in which the positive and negative portions of two compounds are interchanged:

$$PbCl_2 + Li_2SO_4 \rightarrow 2LiCl + PbSO_4$$
$$ZnBr_2 + 2AgNO_3 \rightarrow Zn(NO_3)_2 + 2AgBr$$
$$BaCl_2 + 2KIO_3 \rightarrow Ba(IO_3)_2 + 2KCl$$

The form of these reactions is easy to recognize:

compound plus compound yields compound plus compound

$AB + CD \rightarrow AD + BC$

(3) Decomposition

Many substances will break up into simpler substances when energy is supplied:

$$CdCO_3 \rightarrow CdO + CO_2$$
$$Pb(OH)_2 \rightarrow PbO + H_2O$$

Products of a decomposition are not necessarily elements.

Energy may be supplied in the form of heat, light, mechanical shock, or electricity. The general form for this type of reaction is:

compound yields two or more substances

$AB \rightarrow A + B$

(4) Synthesis

In synthesis reactions, two or more substances combine to form one new substance:

$$NH_3 + HCl \rightarrow NH_4Cl$$
$$CaO + SiO_2 \rightarrow CaSiO_3$$
$$2H_2 + O_2 \rightarrow 2H_2O$$

Reactants of a synthesis are not necessarily elements.

From the name, one might expect that synthesis reactions would be the most common method of preparing new compounds. However, these reactions are rarely as practical as one of the three preceding methods. Here the general form is:

element (or compound) plus element (or compound) yields compound

$A + B \rightarrow AB$

You may wish to use some of the indicated reactions as demonstrations.

a

b

FIGURE 4-7. Two common examples of synthesis reactions are rusting of iron (a) and combustion of carbon in the form of charred wood (b).

Not all reactions take one of the general forms we have described. Other classes of reactions will be taken up later. Until then, we will deal chiefly with displacement (single or double), decomposition, or synthesis reactions.

PROBLEMS

16. Balance each of the following equations:

    a. $Ac(OH)_3 \rightarrow Ac_2O_3 + H_2O$

    b. $Ca(AlO_2)_2 + HCl \rightarrow AlCl_3 + CaCl_2 + H_2O$

    c. $Cu + Cl_2 \rightarrow CuCl_2$

    d. $Hf + N_2 \rightarrow Hf_3N_4$

    e. $La(NO_3)_3 + NH_4OH \rightarrow La(OH)_3 + NH_4NO_3$

    f. $O_2 + Sb_2S_3 \rightarrow Sb_2O_4 + SO_2$

    g. $PdCl_2 + HNO_3 \rightarrow Pd(NO_3)_2 + HCl$

    h. $RbBr + AgCl \rightarrow AgBr + RbCl$

    i. $RhO_3 \rightarrow RhO + O_2$

    j. $Te + H_2O \rightarrow TeO + H_2$

ans.   **c, h, i, j** are balanced

ans.   **a.** $2Ac(OH)_3 \rightarrow Ac_2O_3 + 3H_2O$

ans.   **b.** $Ca(AlO_2)_2 + 8HCl \rightarrow 2AlCl_3 + CaCl_2 + 4H_2O$

ans.   **d.** $3Hf + 2N_2 \rightarrow Hf_3N_4$

ans.   **e.** $La(NO_3)_3 + 3NH_4OH \rightarrow La(OH)_3 + 3NH_4NO_3$

ans.   **f.** $5O_2 + Sb_2S_3 \rightarrow Sb_2O_4 + 3SO_2$

ans.   **g.** $PdCl_2 + 2HNO_3 \rightarrow Pd(NO_3)_2 + 2HCl$

17. Balance each of the following equations:

    a. $BaCO_3 + C + H_2O \rightarrow{}^2 CO + Ba(OH)_2$

    b. ${}^2 CeO_2 +{}^2 KI +{}^8 HCl \rightarrow{}^2 KCl +{}^2 CeCl_3 +{}^4 H_2O + I_2$

    c. ${}^2 Ga +{}^3 H_2SO_4 \rightarrow Ga_2(SO_4)_3 +{}^3 H_2$

    d. ${}^3 HfCl_3 + Al \rightarrow{}^3 HfCl_2 + AlCl_3$

    e. $CuO + H_2 \rightarrow Cu + H_2O$ balanced

18. Balance each of the following equations:

    a. ${}^2 PaI_5 \rightarrow{}^2 Pa +{}^5 I_2$

    b. $Ra +{}^2 C \rightarrow RaC_2$

    c. ${}^2 Re +{}^3 Br_2 \rightarrow{}^2 ReBr_3$

    d. ${}^2 Sb +{}^3 H_2O \rightarrow Sb_2O_3 +{}^3 H_2$

    e. $Zn +{}^2 CrCl_3 \rightarrow{}^2 CrCl_2 + ZnCl_2$

4:10 Indicating Physical State

It is helpful to know the physical state of substances appearing in chemical equations. The symbol (g) after a formula means that the substance is a gas. Liquids are indicated by the symbol (l), and solids by the symbol (s).

Many chemical reactions take place in solution. Water is the usual solvent. A reactant in water solution is indicated by the symbol (aq). This symbol comes from the word aqueous (Latin *aqua* = water). For example, if a water solution of sulfurous acid is warmed, it decomposes. The products of this reaction are water and sulfur dioxide, a gas.

$$H_2SO_3(aq) \rightarrow H_2O(l) + SO_2(g)$$

Physical state symbols in an equation:
(g) — gas
(l) — liquid
(s) — solid
(aq) — water solution

Some reactions in solution yield a product that is not soluble in the solvent. This product will come out of solution and may settle to the bottom of the container. This substance is called a precipitate and is indicated by the symbol (s). For example, if a solution of sodium chloride is added to a solution of silver nitrate, a precipitate of silver chloride is formed:

$$NaCl(aq) + AgNO_3(aq) \rightarrow AgCl(s) + NaNO_3(aq)$$

All equations from this point on will make use of the physical state symbols listed here. Later, (s)-solid will be modified to (c)-crystal.

The reactions noted could be used as demonstrations.

4:11 Energy and Chemical Change

Chemical changes are always accompanied by a change in energy. If heat energy is absorbed, or taken up, in a reaction, the reaction is *endothermic* (en doh THER mik). On the other hand, if heat energy is

In endothermic reactions, energy must be supplied.

In exothermic reactions, energy is given off.

given off by a reaction, the reaction is *exothermic* (ek soh THER mik).

Both endothermic and exothermic reactions require a certain minimum amount of energy to get started. This minimum amount of energy is called the *activation energy*. Without it, the reactant atoms or molecules will not unite to form the product and the reaction does not occur.

Chemical reactions have many possible sources for their activation energy. When a match is struck, friction produces enough heat to activate the reactants on the match head. In photography, light is the source of the activation energy.

Activation energy for a reaction may be supplied as heat or light.

Now let us consider the chemical view of activation energy. Suppose hydrogen is placed in a container with oxygen. The container is sealed and stored for many years. When opened, there will be no evidence that any reaction has taken place. The reaction is proceeding infinitely slowly. Yet we know that two molecules of hydrogen $(2H_2)$ will combine with one molecule of oxygen (O_2) to produce two molecules of water. If, when the two gases are first mixed, a spark is discharged in the container, the two gases will react with such speed that an explosion takes place. The spark is enough to provide the necessary activation energy. Thus, the rate of the reaction is considerably increased.

FIGURE 4-8. Light is the source of activation energy in photography. The negative image (a) was caused by light entering the camera. The positive image (b) was obtained in a later step by exposing light-sensitive paper to light passed through the negative.

a

b
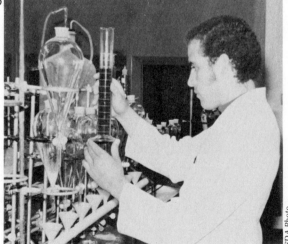

SUMMARY

1. Chemists use symbols, formulas, and equations to describe substances and the changes which they undergo.
2. A chemical symbol for an element represents one atom of that element when it appears in a formula or equation.
3. A chemical formula is a statement in chemical symbols of the composition of one formula unit of a compound. A subscript in a formula represents the relative number of atoms of an element in the compound.
4. A polyatomic ion is a stable, charged group of atoms.
5. The combining capacity of an atom or polyatomic ion is indicated by its oxidation number or charge.
6. In chemical reactions, atoms always combine in definite ratios. Their combined charges add to zero.
7. A binary compound is composed of two elements. Its name is the name of the positive element followed by the name of the negative element modified to end in -ide.
8. Some elements can have more than one possible oxidation number. A compound containing such an element can be named in two ways: (1) Prefixing each such element, as mono-, di-, tri-, and so on; or (2) showing the oxidation number in Roman numerals in parentheses after the element.
9. A compound formed from one element and one polyatomic ion is named in the same way as a binary compound. However, the ending of the name of the polyatomic ion is not changed.
10. An empirical formula represents the simplest ratio between atoms in a compound.
11. A molecular formula shows the actual number of each kind of atom in one molecule of a compound. It is always a whole-number multiple of the empirical formula.
12. A formula unit represents a definite amount of a compound.
13. The coefficient of a formula indicates the number of molecules or the number of formula units of a nonmolecular substance.
14. A chemical reaction is the process by which one or more substances are changed into one or more new substances.
15. Reactants are the starting substances in a reaction.
16. Products are the substances resulting from a reaction.
17. A chemical equation represents changes that take place in a reaction. It also shows relative amounts of reactants and products.

18. Balancing an equation means adjusting coefficients so that there are the same number of atoms of each element on both sides of the equation.

19. In a single displacement reaction, one element displaces another element. In a double displacement reaction, ions from two compounds are interchanged.

20. In a decomposition reaction, a compound breaks down into two or more simpler substances.

21. In a synthesis reaction, two or more substances combine to form a more complex substance.

22. The physical state of substances in equations is shown by (g) for gas, (l) for liquid, (s) for solid, and (aq) for a water solution.

23. A chemical change is always accompanied by an energy change. Heat energy is absorbed in an endothermic reaction and given off in an exothermic reaction.

24. Activation energy is the energy required before a chemical reaction can begin. Heat and light are forms of activation energy.

PROBLEMS

19. Balance each of the following equations:
    a. $AsCl_3(s) +^3 H_2O(l) \rightarrow^3 HCl(aq) + As(OH)_3(aq)$
    b.^{2} $Ho(s) +^6 H_2O(l) \rightarrow^2 Ho(OH)_3(aq) +^3 H_2(g)$
    c.^{2} $IrCl_3(aq) +^3 NaOH(aq) \rightarrow Ir_2O_3(s) +^3 HCl(aq) +^3 NaCl(aq)$
    d.^{2} $MoO_3(s) +^3 Zn(s) +^3 H_2SO_4(l) \rightarrow Mo_2O_3(s) +^3 ZnSO_4(aq) +^3 H_2O(l)$
    e.^{4} $Na(s) + O_2(g) \rightarrow^2 Na_2O(s)$

20. Balance the following equations:
    a. $NbI_3(s) + I_2(s) \rightarrow NbI_5(s)$ balanced
    b. $Pb(C_2H_3O_2)_2(aq) + K_2CrO_4(aq) \rightarrow PbCrO_4(s) +^2 KC_2H_3O_2(aq)$
    c. $RbCl(s) +^2 O_2(g) \rightarrow RbClO_4(s)$
    d.^{3} $SiF_4(s) +^3 H_2O(l) \rightarrow^2 H_2SiF_6(aq) + H_2SiO_3(s)$
    e. $Sn(s) +^2 KOH(aq) \rightarrow K_2SnO_2(s) + H_2(g)$

21. Substitute symbols for names and balance each of the following equations:
    a. copper(II) carbonate decomposes to copper(II) oxide and carbon dioxide gas $CuCO_3(s) \rightarrow CuO(s) + CO_2(g)$
    b. sodium reacts with water to produce sodium hydroxide and hydrogen gas $2Na(s) + 2H_2O(l) \rightarrow 2NaOH(aq) + H_2(g)$
    c. ammonium nitrite decomposes to nitrogen gas and water
    d. copper combines with sulfur to form copper(I) sulfide $2Cu(s) + S(s) \rightarrow Cu_2S(s)$ $NH_4NO_2(s) \rightarrow 2H_2O(l) + N_2(g)$

22. Substitute symbols for names and balance each of the following equations:
   a. acetic acid reacts with ammonium hydroxide to produce water and ammonium acetate $HC_2H_3O_2(aq) + NH_4OH(aq) \rightarrow H_2O(l) + NH_4C_2H_3O_2(aq)$
   b. calcium carbonate reacts with hydrochloric acid to produce calcium chloride, water, and carbon dioxide gas $CaCO_3(s) + 2HCl(aq) \rightarrow CaCl_2(aq) + H_2O(l) + CO_2(g)$
   c. ammonium nitrate decomposes to water and nitrogen(I) oxide $NH_4NO_3(s) \rightarrow 2H_2O(l) + N_2O(g)$
   d. chromium displaces hydrogen from hydrochloric acid, with chromium(II) chloride as the other product $Cr(s) + 2HCl(aq) \rightarrow H_2(g) + CrCl_2(aq)$
   e. barium hydroxide reacts with carbon dioxide to form barium carbonate and water $Ba(OH)_2(aq) + CO_2(g) \rightarrow BaCO_3(s) + H_2O(l)$

23. Balance each of the following reactions after predicting the products:
   a. copper plus silver nitrate (displacement; copper(II) compound is formed) $Cu(s) + 2AgNO_3(aq) \rightarrow Cu(NO_3)_2(aq) + 2Ag(s)$
   b. magnesium plus oxygen (synthesis) $2Mg(s) + O_2(g) \rightarrow 2MgO(s)$
   c. hydrochloric acid plus silver nitrate (double displacement) $HCl(aq) + AgNO_3(aq) \rightarrow HNO_3(aq) + AgCl(s)$
   d. magnesium plus hydrochloric acid (displacement) $Mg(s) + 2HCl(aq) \rightarrow MgCl_2(aq) + H_2(g)$

24. Balance each of the following reactions after predicting the products:
   a. iron plus oxygen (synthesis; iron(III) compound is formed) $4Fe(s) + 3O_2(g) \rightarrow 2Fe_2O_3(s)$
   b. iron plus sulfur (synthesis; iron(II) compound is formed) $Fe(s) + S(s) \rightarrow FeS(s)$
   c. calcium hydroxide plus sulfuric acid (double displacement) $Ca(OH)_2(aq) + H_2SO_4(aq) \rightarrow CaSO_4(s) + 2H_2O(l)$
   d. magnesium plus nitrogen (synthesis) $3Mg(s) + N_2(g) \rightarrow Mg_3N_2(s)$

ONE MORE STEP

See Teacher's Guide at the front of this book.

1. Try balancing each of the following equations:
   a. $FeCl_3(aq) +^3NH_4OH(aq) \rightarrow Fe(OH)_3(s) +^3NH_4Cl(aq)$
   b. $Cu_2S(s) +_{12}HNO_3(aq) \rightarrow Cu(NO_3)_2(aq) + CuSO_4(aq) +_{10}NO_2(g) +_6H_2O(g)$
   c. $CH_4(g) +^2O_2(g) \rightarrow CO_2(g) +^2H_2O(l)$
   d. $^2Ce(IO_3)_4(aq) +_{24}H_2C_2O_4(aq) \rightarrow Ce_2(C_2O_4)_3(aq) +^4I_2(aq) +_{42}CO_2(g) +_{24}H_2O(l)$
   e. $MnCl_2(s) + Br_2(l) +^4NH_4OH(aq) \rightarrow MnO_2(s) +_2NH_4Cl(aq) +_2NH_4Br(aq) +_2H_2O(l)$

2. Why are some foods and beverages stored in brown bottles?
3. Find out how light affects the emulsion on a photographic film. What chemical reactions are involved in the developing of a film?
4. Find out what is meant by the term "flash point."
5. What kind of reaction is a metathesis reaction?
6. What chemical compounds can be found in the medicine cabinet in your home? In the kitchen?

Suggested Readings for this chapter may be found in the Teacher's Guide at the front of this book.

These are special glass rods prepared by the National Bureau of Standards. Carefully measured amounts of trace elements were added to the molten glass before it was drawn into rods of uniform length and diameter. These rods will be sliced into thin pieces. By comparing glass of unknown composition with these standard glass slices, the concentration of trace elements in the glass can be determined. What units of concentration do chemists usually use in the laboratory?

The Mole _____ 5

Chapter 5 introduces gram-molecular mass and the use of this concept in manipulating formulas and equations. The first three sections explain the mole; the other sections develop applications of the mole concept to quantitative chemistry. This chapter might also be entitled, "How much?" It introduces students to the setting up and solving of chemical quantitative problems.

Chemical symbols and formulas (such as H and H_2O) are shorthand signs for chemical elements and compounds. The _symbol_ of an element may also represent one atom of the element. The _formula_ of a compound may also represent one molecule or one formula unit of the compound. The masses of the atoms are compared by using the atomic mass scale which has the "atomic mass unit" (a.m.u.) as a standard. The source of this standard will be discussed in Chapter 6.

GOAL: You will gain knowledge and understanding of the mole concept and will apply this concept in solving simple chemical quantitative problems.

Point out that elements can have formulas such as I_2, S_8, and P_4.

PARTICLE MASSES AND AVOGADRO'S NUMBER

5:1 Molecular Mass

The atomic mass of hydrogen in atomic mass units is 1, and the atomic mass of oxygen is 16. Therefore, the total mass of a water molecule (H_2O) is $1 + 1 + 16$, or 18 a.m.u. If the atomic masses of all the atoms in a molecule are added together, then the sum is the mass of that molecule. Such a mass is called a _molecular mass_. This name is incorrect when applied to ionic substances, such as sodium chloride (NaCl). Ionic substances do not exist in molecular form. A better name for this mass of ionic substances is formula mass. The sum of the atomic masses of all atoms in the formula unit of an ionic compound is called the _formula mass_ of the substance.

Another term that applies to ionic substances is _ion mass_, the mass of an ion in atomic mass units. To calculate a molecular mass, a formula mass, or an ion mass, list the atomic masses of the atoms included in the formula and add these masses.

Molecular mass of a molecule is the sum of the atomic masses of the atoms in the molecule.

Formula mass of an ionic compound is the sum of the atomic masses of the atoms in a formula unit.

Ion mass is the mass of an ion in atomic mass units.

For example, to find the formula mass of sodium sulfate (Na_2SO_4), add the atomic masses of all the atoms in the Na_2SO_4 formula unit:

$$2 \text{ Na atoms} \quad 2 \times 23 = 46 \text{ a.m.u.}$$
$$1 \text{ S atom} \quad 1 \times 32 = 32 \text{ a.m.u.}$$
$$4 \text{ O atoms} \quad 4 \times 16 = \underline{64} \text{ a.m.u.}$$
$$\text{formula mass of } Na_2SO_4 = 142 \text{ a.m.u.}$$

Formula mass can usually be rounded to the nearest whole number.

PROBLEMS

1. Calculate the molecular or formula masses of the following compounds:

  a. $C_{49}H_{100}$ *ans.*   689 a.m.u.
  b. $C_9H_{13}N$ *ans.*   135 a.m.u.
  c. TaC   *ans.*   193 a.m.u.
  d. K_2S_2 *ans.*   142 a.m.u.
  e. $LaCl_3$ *ans.*   245 a.m.u.

2. Calculate the molecular or formula masses of the following compounds:

  a. C_2H_8NBr 126 a.m.u.   **d.** $C_6H_{10}S_3$ 178 a.m.u.
  b. $C_5H_{12}O$ 88 a.m.u.   **e.** $C_3H_8SO_2$ 108 a.m.u.
  c. KH_2PO_4 136 a.m.u.

3. Calculate the molecular or formula masses of the following compounds:

  a. $Ca_3(PO_4)_2$ 310 a.m.u.   **d.** $Th(SO_4)_2$ 424 a.m.u.
  b. $Na_2Al_2(SO_4)_4$ 484 a.m.u.   **e.** US_2 302 a.m.u.
  c. TeI_2 381 a.m.u.

5:2 Avogadro's Number

There is one drawback in using the molecular masses of substances. These masses are in atomic mass units. Since an atomic mass unit is only 1.66×10^{-24} g, the mass of a single molecule is so small that it is impossible to measure in the laboratory. For everyday use in chemistry, a larger, more convenient unit, such as a gram, is needed.

In the laboratory, mass is measured in grams rather than in atomic mass units.

One helium atom has a mass of 4 a.m.u., and one nitrogen atom has a mass of 14 a.m.u. The ratio of the mass of one helium atom to one nitrogen atom is 4 to 14, or 2 to 7. If we compare the mass of two helium atoms to that of two nitrogen atoms, the ratio would be $2 \times$ 4 to 2×14, or 2 to 7. If we compare the mass of 10 atoms of each element, we will still get a 2 to 7 ratio. No matter what number of atoms we compare, if we choose equal numbers of helium and nitrogen atoms, their mass ratio will still be 2 to 7. In other words, the numbers in the atomic mass table give us the relative masses of the atoms of the elements.

The conventional laboratory unit of mass is the gram. Thus it would be convenient to choose some number of atoms (true for all elements) which would have a mass in grams equivalent to the mass of one atom in a.m.u. Chemists have found by experiment that 6.02×10^{23} atoms of an element have a mass in grams equivalent to the mass of one atom in a.m.u. For example, one atom of hydrogen has a mass of 1.0079 a.m.u.; 6.02×10^{23} atoms of hydrogen have a mass of 1.0079 g. This number, 6.02×10^{23}, is called Avogadro's number in honor of a 19th century Italian scientist.

5:3 The Mole

Avogadro's number is an internationally accepted standard. We may add it to the others we have studied: the kilogram, the meter, the second, and the degree Celsius. The symbol used to represent Avogadro's number is N_A. Expressed to the maximum precision measured, N_A is 6.022169×10^{23}. This number of things is called one *mole* of the things. Note again that one mole of particles (atoms, ions, molecules) has a mass in grams equivalent to that of one particle in a.m.u. Thus, if a mole of any particle (atom, ion, or molecule) has a mass of 4.02 g, then the particle has a mass of 4.02 a.m.u. In the same manner, if a single particle has a mass of 54.03 a.m.u., then a mole of particles will have a mass of 54.03 g.

The mass of a mole of atoms is called a *gram-atomic mass*. The mass of a mole of molecules is called a *gram-molecular mass*. The simplest unit of some substances is neither an atom nor a molecule. Sodium chloride is such a substance. Crystals of NaCl contain sodium ions and chlorine ions stacked in an orderly arrangement. However, there is no smallest unit that can be called a molecule. The relative composition of this kind of ionic compound can be indicated by an empirical formula. The mass of one mole of such a compound is found by adding the masses of the atoms indicated by the empirical formula. This mass of the substance is called the *gram-formula mass*. Salt exists only as sodium ions and chlorine ions. Avogadro's number of ions, 1 mole of either sodium ions or chlorine ions, is called one *gram-ion mass*.

It is important to realize that each of these quantities of matter (one gram-atomic mass, one gram-molecular mass, one gram-formula

You may wish to describe the use of radioactive material in determination of Avogadro's number as follows:

Polonium is a radioactive element which emits alpha particles (helium nuclei). These particles can be detected by a phototube or by eye if a luminescent screen is used. In two years, 95% of a polonium sample will decay into helium and lead. If the number of emitted particles is known, the number of particles in the sample of polonium is known. If the mass of the polonium is recorded prior to its disintegration, it is possible to determine the number of particles per unit mass. From this data the number of particles in 1 gram-molecular mass of the substance can be calculated. This number has been found to be 6.02×10^{23}.

mass, and one gram-ion mass) contains 6.02×10^{23} atoms, molecules, units, or ions. N_A, therefore, can be expressed as:

$$\frac{molecules}{mole}, \quad \frac{atoms}{gram\text{-}atomic\ mass}, \quad \frac{ions}{gram\text{-}ion\ mass}, \quad or \quad \frac{a.m.u.}{gram}.$$

N_A is not an arbitrary number, once we have decided to express relative masses in grams. If a gram-molecular mass of iodine molecules (I_2) is inspected by X ray, the actual number of I_2 molecules can be determined. This number has been found to be 6.02×10^{23} molecules. Avogadro's number also has been determined by inspection of the blue of the sky, by use of radioactive materials, and by Millikan's oil drop experiment.

Attempt to solve the following three problems using what you know about the mole.

EXAMPLE

How many atoms will a ten-gram sample of calcium metal contain?

The gram-atomic mass of calcium is 40 grams. Therefore, use the ratios $\dfrac{1\ mole}{40\ grams}$ and $\dfrac{6.02 \times 10^{23}\ atoms}{1\ mole}$.

$$\frac{10\ grams}{} \left| \frac{1\ mole}{40\ grams} \right| \frac{6.02 \times 10^{23}\ atoms}{1\ mole} = 1.5 \times 10^{23}\ atoms$$

EXAMPLE

1.2×10^{25} molecules of NH_3 will be how many moles? What mass is this?

Since 6.02×10^{23} molecules equals one mole, use the ratio

$$\frac{1\ mole}{6.02 \times 10^{23}\ molecules}.$$

$$\frac{1.2 \times 10^{25}\ molecules}{} \left| \frac{1\ mole}{6.02 \times 10^{23}\ molecules} \right. = 0.20 \times 10^2\ moles$$

$$= 20\ moles$$

Since the gram-molecular mass of NH_3 is 17 g, use $\dfrac{17\ g}{1\ mole}$.

$$\frac{20\ moles}{} \left| \frac{17\ grams}{1\ mole} \right. = 340\ grams\ of\ NH_3$$

EXAMPLE

How many moles are represented by 11.5 grams of C_2H_5OH?

One mole of C_2H_5OH has a mass of 46 grams. Using $\dfrac{1 \text{ mole}}{46 \text{ grams}}$,

$$\frac{11.5 \text{ grams}}{} \; \Big| \; \frac{1 \text{ mole}}{46 \text{ grams}} = 0.25 \text{ moles of } C_2H_5OH$$

PROBLEMS

4. Make the following conversions:
   a. 1.00×10^{23} molecules of $MgSiF_6$ to grams
   ans.   27.6 $MgSiF_6$
   b. 76.0 g HNO_3 to moles   ans.   1.21 moles HNO_3
   c. 0.400 mole H_2O to molecules
   ans. 2.41×10^{23} molecules H_2O
   d. 1.00×10^{26} molecules $NaNH_2$ to moles
   ans.   166 moles $NaNH_2$
   e. 46.0 g MnSi to molecules   ans. 3.34×10^{23} molecules MnSi
5. Make the following conversions:
   a. 3.00 moles As_2S_3 to grams 738 g As_2S_3
   b. 4.70×10^{24} molecules $CaCO_3$ to moles 7.81 moles $CaCO_3$
   c. 18.0 g HBr to moles 0.222 moles HBr
   d. 9.30 moles SiH_4 to molecules 5.60 $\times$ 10^{24} molecules SiH_4
   e. 8.00×10^{19} molecules H_2O to grams 0.00239 g H_2O

CALCULATIONS ON COMPOUNDS

5:4   Percentage Composition

A chemist often compares the *percentage composition* of an unknown compound obtained from an experiment with the percentage composition calculated from a hypothetical formula. The percentage of the total mass of a compound contributed by an element is the percentage of that element in the compound. Consider the percentage composition of the following substances: copper, sodium chloride, and ethyl alcohol. For copper, the percentage composition is 100 percent Cu because it is composed of a single element. Salt is made up of two elements, sodium and chlorine. We know they

Percentage composition may be used in the identification of some compounds.

are always present in the same ratio by mass (considered in detail in Chapter 6). The ratios in which they are present are the ratios of their atomic masses. Therefore, the percentage of sodium in any sample of sodium chloride would be $\dfrac{23 \text{ a.m.u.}}{(23 + 35.5) \text{ a.m.u.}} \times 100$, or 39.4%. The atomic mass of the element in the compound divided by the molecular mass of the compound and multiplied by 100 is the percentage of that element in the compound.

But what about compounds such as ethyl alcohol where more than one atom of an element appears? The formula for ethyl alcohol is C_2H_5OH and its molecular mass is 46. Here it can be seen that for one molecule, the total carbon content is two carbon atoms with a combined atomic mass of 24. Therefore, the percentage of carbon in the compound is $(24/46) \times 100$. The percentage of hydrogen is $(6/46) \times 100$, and that of oxygen is $(16/46) \times 100$. The three percentages should add up to 100%. Often, because we round off answers or because we are able to read the slide rule to only three significant digits, we may find that the percentages total one- or two-tenths more or less than 100%.

EXAMPLE — PERCENTAGE COMPOSITION

Find the percentage of sulfur in aluminum sulfate.

The formula for aluminum sulfate is $Al_2(SO_4)_3$. The formula mass is:

$$
\begin{array}{lll}
2 \text{ Al atoms} & 2 \times 27 = & 54 \text{ a.m.u.} \\
3 \text{ S atoms} & 3 \times 32 = & 96 \text{ a.m.u.} \\
12 \text{ O atoms} & 12 \times 16 = & \underline{192} \text{ a.m.u.} \\
& & 342 \text{ a.m.u.}
\end{array}
$$

$$\text{The percentage of S} = \frac{96 \text{ a.m.u.}}{342 \text{ a.m.u.}} \times 100 = 28\%$$

PROBLEMS

6. Find the percentage composition of:

  a. CsF   **c.** Hg_2NI **e.** $NH_4Ga(SO_4)_2$

  b. InI   **d.** $KC_{18}H_{35}O_2$

7. Find the percentage composition of:

  a. Bi_2O_3 **c.** Li_2GeO_3 **e.** Ag_2C_2

  b. CuC_2O_4 **d.** PtI_2

Margin notes:

Percent of an element in a compound =
$\dfrac{\text{mass of element} \times 100}{\text{formula mass compound}}$

Total percent of all elements in a compound equals 100%.

6. a. 87.5%, 12.5%
  b. 47.5%, 52.5%
  c. 74.0%, 2.58%, 23.4%
  d. 12.1%, 67.0%, 10.9%, 9.92%
  e. 5.00%, 1.44%, 24.9%, 22.9%, 45.7%

7. a. 89.7%, 10.3%
  b. 41.9%, 15.8%, 42.2%
  c. 10.3%, 54.0%, 35.7%
  d. 43.5%, 56.5%
  e. 90.0%, 10.0%

5:5 Empirical Formulas

We can find the empirical formula for any substance if we know the masses of the elements which make up the substance. If we know that a 2.5 g sample of a certain substance contains 0.9 g of calcium and 1.6 g of chlorine, we know, first of all, that the substance is made up of two elements. Since elements are made of atoms, and compounds are made of elements, and there is no such thing as half an atom, we can state that the elements in a compound must combine in simple ratios, such as 1 to 1, 1 to 2, 2 to 3, and so on. If the atoms of the elements are present in simple ratios, it should be possible to express the ratio of the moles of each element in the substance in small whole numbers (in a simple ratio). This means that the elements combine in simple ratios of the number of moles of each element present. In the same example, if we calculate the number of moles of calcium and the number of moles of chlorine in the compound, we can find the ratio of the number of atoms of calcium to the number of atoms of chlorine. From this we can find the *empirical formula*, which is simply the ratio of atoms in a compound.

Elements in compounds combine in simple whole number ratios.

An empirical formula is the simplest ratio of the atoms in a compound.

EXAMPLE — EMPIRICAL FORMULA

What is the empirical formula for a compound if an analysis shows that 2.50 g of the compound contain 0.900 g of calcium and 1.60 g of chlorine?

We know: The sample has a mass of 2.50 g. Calcium in the sample has a mass of 0.900 g, and the atomic mass of Ca is 40.1. Chlorine in the sample has a mass of 1.60 g, and the atomic mass of Cl is 35.5.

The sample contains:

$$\frac{0.900 \text{ g}}{} \left| \frac{1 \text{ mole}}{40.1 \text{ g}} \right. = 0.0224 \text{ moles of Ca}$$

$$\frac{1.60 \text{ g}}{} \left| \frac{1 \text{ mole}}{35.5 \text{ g}} \right. = 0.0451 \text{ moles of Cl}$$

The ratio of moles of calcium to moles of chlorine is $\frac{0.0224}{0.0451}$ which is approximately $\frac{1}{2}$. This shows that for each mole of calcium, there are 2 moles of chlorine. The empirical formula is $CaCl_2$.

We can also calculate empirical formulas from percentage composition. If we know the percentage composition of a compound to

The ratio of moles is the same as the ratio of atoms for a given formula unit because there are exactly N_A atoms in one mole of any element.

Point out that any mass could be used: 45g, 93.7g, or any other. We use 100g to simplify arithmetic.

To determine an empirical formula, change grams to moles and find the ratio of the moles.

be 40.0% carbon, 6.71% hydrogen, and 53.3% oxygen, then we know that every sample of the compound, no matter how small or how large, will have this composition. To calculate the ratio of moles of these elements, we may use a convenient amount of compound, usually 100 g, since the percentages of the elements are then equal to their occurrence in grams. In the present example, we would find 40.0 g of carbon, 6.71 g of hydrogen, and 53.3 g of oxygen in a 100-g sample. We change quantities to moles:

$$\frac{40.0 \text{ g}}{} \Bigg| \frac{1 \text{ mole}}{12.0 \text{ g}} = 3.33 \text{ moles of carbon}$$

$$\frac{6.71 \text{ g}}{} \Bigg| \frac{1 \text{ mole}}{1.00 \text{ g}} = 6.64 \text{ moles of hydrogen}$$

$$\frac{53.3 \text{ g}}{} \Bigg| \frac{1 \text{ mole}}{16.0 \text{ g}} = 3.33 \text{ moles of oxygen}$$

We can see that the ratio of carbon to hydrogen is 1 to 2, and carbon to oxygen is 1 to 1. Thus, the empirical formula is CH_2O.

	Percent	Grams in 100 gram sample	Moles	Empirical formula
C	40%	40 g	$\frac{40}{12}$ 1	
H	6.7%	6.7 g	$\frac{6.7}{1}$ 2	CH_2O (CHOH)
O	53.3%	53.3 g	$\frac{53.3}{16}$ 1	

FIGURE 5-1. Calculation of the empirical formula from percentage composition.

PROBLEMS

8. Find the empirical formulas of the following compounds:
   a. 1.67 g Ce, 4.54 g I CeI_3
   b. 31.9 g Mg, 27.1 g P Mg_3P_2
   c. 287 g Pb, 44.4 g S   PbS
   d. 9.11 g Ni, 5.89 g F NiF_2
   e. 6.27 g Ca, 1.46 g N Ca_3N_2
9. Find the empirical formulas of the following compounds:
   a. 0.0134 g Fe, 0.00769 g S, 0.0115 g O $FeSO_3$
   b. 1.21 g Al, 1.88 g N, 6.44 g O $Al(NO_3)_3$
   c. 1.39 g Co, 5.98 g I, 2.26 g O $Co(IO_3)_2$
   d. 0.463 g Tl, 0.0544 g C, 0.00685 g H, 0.0725 g O $TlC_2H_3O_2$
   e. 12.2 g Ca, 1.22 g H, 18.8 g P, 38.9 g O $Ca(H_2PO_4)_2$

10. Find the empirical formulas of the following compounds:

    a. 32.8% Cr, 67.2% Cl $CrCl_3$

    b. 75.1% Ir, 24.9% S IrS_2

    c. 27.5% Nd, 72.5% I NdI_3

    d. 58.5% Ra, 41.5% Br $RaBr_2$

    e. 26.8% Sn, 16.0% Cl, 57.2% I $SnCl_2I_2$

11. Find the empirical formulas of the following compounds:

    a. 1.10% H, 12.3% B, 86.6% F HBF_4

    b. 28.8% Mg, 14.2% C, 57.0% O $MgCO_3$

    c. 55.3% K, 38.3% B, 6.40% H $K_2B_5H_9$

    d. 46.6% Ag, 39.7% W, 13.7% O Ag_2WO_4

    e. 67.1% Zn, 32.9% O ZnO_2

5:6   Molecular Formulas

We have, thus far, calculated empirical formulas from experimental data. In order to calculate a *molecular formula*, we must know one more experimental fact, the molecular mass. In the last example in the previous section, the empirical formula calculated was CH_2O. If we know that the molecular mass of the compound is 180, how can we find the molecular formula? The molecular formula shows the number of atoms of each element in a molecule. Knowing that the elements will always be present in the ratio 1:2:1, we can calculate the mass of the empirical formula and find the number of these empirical units present in one molecular formula. In the substance CH_2O, the empirical unit has a mass of $12 + 2(1) + 16$, or 30. It will, therefore, take six of these units to make 180, or one molecular formula. Thus, the molecular formula is $C_6H_{12}O_6$.

Molecular mass is a whole number multiple of the empirical formula mass.

PROBLEMS

12. What is the molecular formula of dichloroacetic acid, if the empirical formula is CHOCl and the molecular mass is 129? $C_2H_2O_2Cl_2$

13. What is the molecular formula of cyanuric chloride, if the empirical formula is CClN and the molecular mass is 184.5? $C_3Cl_3N_3$

14. What is the molecular formula of a substance with empirical formula $TlC_2H_2O_3$ and molecular mass 557? $Tl_2C_4H_4O_6$

5:7   Hydrates

There are a large number of compounds which crystallize from a water solution with water molecules adhering to the particles of the

Hydrates contain water molecules.

crystal. These *hydrates*, as they are called, usually contain a specific ratio of water to compound. Chemists often dry these compounds by heat in order to calculate the ratio of compound to water.

EXAMPLE — HYDRATE CALCULATION

A chemist has a sample of hydrated barium iodide. He wishes to know what the ratio is between the barium iodide and the water. Barium iodide has the formula BaI_2 and water has the formula H_2O. First, he finds the mass of his sample to be 10.407 g. Then he heats the sample to drive off the water and measures the mass of the dried sample. The dry sample has a mass of 9.520 g. The 9.520 g represents barium iodide. The difference between the two masses (0.887 g) is the mass of water. These masses are then converted to moles:

$$\frac{9.520 \text{ g } BaI_2}{} \left| \frac{1 \text{ mole } BaI_2}{391.2 \text{ g } BaI_2} \right. = 0.02434 \text{ mole of } BaI_2$$

$$\frac{0.887 \text{ g } H_2O}{} \left| \frac{1 \text{ mole } H_2O}{18.0 \text{ g } H_2O} \right. = 0.0492 \text{ mole of } H_2O$$

The ratio between BaI_2 and H_2O is seen to be 1 to 2. The formula for the hydrated compound is then written $BaI_2 \cdot 2H_2O$.

PROBLEM

15. Find the formulas for the following hydrates:
    a. 0.391 g Li_2SiF_6, 0.0903 g H_2O $Li_2SiF_6 \cdot 2H_2O$
    b. 0.737 g $MgSO_3$, 0.763 g H_2O $MgSO_3 \cdot 6H_2O$
    c. 95.3 g $LiNO_3$, 74.7 g H_2O $LiNO_3 \cdot 3H_2O$
    d. 76.9% $CaSO_3$, 23.1% H_2O $CaSO_3 \cdot 2H_2O$
    e. 89.2% $BaBr_2$, 10.8% H_2O $BaBr_2 \cdot 2H_2O$

CALCULATIONS ON REACTIONS

5:8 Mass-Mass Relationships

A balanced equation is necessary for obtaining correct answers to chemical problems.

A chemical equation is simply a shorthand expression which gives information about a reaction. Once a balanced equation is written, it can be used to help solve problems involving the reaction.

EXAMPLE – MASS-MASS

How many grams of silver chloride can be produced from the reaction of 17.0 g of silver nitrate with excess sodium chloride solution?

FIRST. We must decide what chemical reaction occurs, and write a correctly balanced equation:

$$AgNO_3(aq) + NaCl(aq) \rightarrow AgCl(s) + NaNO_3(aq)$$

SECOND. We must determine how many moles of silver nitrate are in 17.0 g. We must also find the number of moles of AgCl produced by 1 mole of $AgNO_3$. We can use these two facts to find the number of moles of AgCl produced:

$$
\begin{array}{lcl}
\text{17.0 g} & & \text{yields ? grams} \\
AgNO_3(aq) + NaCl(aq) & \rightarrow & AgCl(s) + NaNO_3(aq) \\
\text{1 mole} & & \text{yields 1 mole}
\end{array}
$$

1 mole of $AgNO_3$ has mass: Ag $1 \times 108 = 108$ g
                                         N $1 \times\ \ 14 =\ \ 14$ g
                                     3 O $3 \times\ \ 16 =\ \ \underline{48}$ g
                      gram molecular mass $= 170$ g

We have 17.0 g of $AgNO_3$. One mole of $AgNO_3$ has mass 170 g. Therefore, we have 0.100 mole of $AgNO_3$.

1 mole of $AgNO_3$ yields 1 mole of AgCl
0.100 mole of $AgNO_3$ will yield 0.100 mole of AgCl.

THIRD. We know that 0.100 mole of AgCl is produced. We now change 0.100 mole into grams:

1 mole of AgCl has mass: Ag $1 \times\ 108 = 108$ g
                                      Cl $1 \times 35.5 =\ \ \underline{35.5}$ g
                   gram molecular mass $= 144$ g
0.100 mole of AgCl will have mass $0.100(144) =\ \ 14.4$ g

We conclude that 17.0 g of silver nitrate will react with sodium chloride to form 14.4 g of silver chloride. This problem can also be done by the factor-label method.

Write a balanced equation.

Find the number of moles of reactant and product.

Convert moles of product to grams.

The factor-label method is the easiest method for solution. The label can be used as a check on the answer.

17.0 g AgNO₃	1 mole AgNO₃	1 mole AgCl	144 g AgCl
	170 g AgNO₃	1 mole AgNO₃	1 mole AgCl

$$= 14.4 \text{ g of AgCl}$$

The problem we just solved involves finding the mass of product formed from a given mass of reactant. Problems of this type are called mass-mass problems. All mass-mass problems can be solved in this way. This and similar quantitative studies of chemical reactions are called *stoichiometry* (stoh kee AHM uh tree).

Stoichiometry is the quantitative study of chemical reactions.

First Step.

FIRST. Write the balanced equation.

The first step in the solution of any problem is to write a balanced equation for the *correct* reaction. In practice, this is not always easy. Several reactions may occur, the actual reaction may not be known, or all the reactant may not react. In this section, we will always assume that only one reaction occurs and that all of at least one reactant reacts.

Second Step.

SECOND. Find the number of moles of reactant and product.

Usually a specific mass of reactant is given.

(a) Express the mass of reactant in moles. This is done by dividing the mass of reactant by its molecular mass.

$$\frac{\text{mass of reactant}}{\text{molecular mass of reactant}} = \frac{\text{grams}}{\text{grams/mole}} = \frac{\text{grams}}{1} \times \frac{\text{mole}}{\text{grams}} = \text{moles}$$

(b) Inspect the balanced equation to determine how many moles of product 1 mole of reactant will yield. For instance:
$$2H_2(g) + O_2(g) \rightarrow 2H_2O(g)$$
In this reaction, 1 mole of oxygen forms 2 moles of water.

Once the equation is balanced, only the reactants and products in which you are interested should be involved in your calculations.

(c) Multiply the moles of reactant by the number of moles of product that 1 mole of reactant will form. You now know the number of moles of product formed.

Third Step.

THIRD. Express the moles of product formed in terms of grams of product formed if necessary.

To do this, multiply the number of moles by the mass of 1 mole of the substance.

$$\text{Molecular mass} \times \text{moles} = \frac{\text{grams}}{\text{mole}} \times \frac{\text{mole}}{1} = \text{grams}$$

Notice that, as you work through a problem of this kind, you first convert grams of reactant to moles of reactant, and then convert moles of product back to grams of product.

start with grams	reactants grams to moles	yield	products moles to grams	end with grams

This method is used because the balanced equation relates the number of moles of reactant to the number of moles of product formed. Now try the following two problems:

EXAMPLE – MASS-MASS

How many grams of Cu_2S could be produced from 9.90 g of CuCl reacting with an excess of H_2S gas?

FIRST. We must write the balanced equation:

$$2CuCl(aq) + H_2S(g) \rightarrow Cu_2S(s) + 2HCl(aq)$$

If we use the wrong reaction or do not balance the equation properly, we cannot get a correct answer.

SECOND. Find the number of moles of reactant and product.

(a) $\dfrac{9.90 \text{ g CuCl}}{} \left| \dfrac{1 \text{ mole}}{99.0 \text{ g CuCl}} \right. = 0.100$ mole of CuCl

(b) 2 CuCl + (_ _ _ _) → Cu_2S + (_ _ _ _)
2 moles yield 1 mole
1 mole yields 0.5 mole

Notice that, although H_2S and HCl are part of the reaction, we do not consider them in this problem.

(c) (0.100 mole CuCl) (0.5) → 0.0500 mole of Cu_2S

THIRD. We must convert 0.0500 mole of Cu_2S into grams of Cu_2S.

1 mole of Cu_2S has mass: 2 Cu 2×63.5 = 127 g
S 1×32 =   32 g
gram molecular mass = 159 g

Number of moles (0.0500) times mass of 1 mole $= 0.0500 \times 159$ g $=$ 7.95 g. We conclude that 9.90 g of CuCl will react with (an adequate amount of) hydrogen sulfide to form 7.95 g of copper (I) sulfide. We will check this answer by the factor-label method.

$$\frac{9.90 \text{ g } \cancel{CuCl}}{} \; \bigg| \; \frac{1 \text{ mole } \cancel{CuCl}}{99.0 \text{ g } \cancel{CuCl}} \; \bigg| \; \frac{1 \text{ mole } \cancel{Cu_2S}}{2 \text{ moles } \cancel{CuCl}} \; \bigg| \; \frac{159 \text{ g } Cu_2S}{1 \text{ mole } \cancel{Cu_2S}}$$
$$= 7.95 \text{ g of } Cu_2S$$

EXAMPLE — MASS-MASS

How many grams of chlorine will be needed to react completely with 10.0 g of sodium to produce NaCl?

We must be sure we have read the problem correctly. Notice that we are asked to find the mass of chlorine, not the mass of the product, sodium chloride.

FIRST. Write a balanced equation.

$$2 \text{ Na(s)} + Cl_2(g) \rightarrow 2 \text{ NaCl(s)}$$

SECOND. Change 10.0 g of sodium to moles of sodium.

(a) $\dfrac{10.0 \text{ g } \cancel{Na}}{} \; \bigg| \; \dfrac{1 \text{ mole Na}}{23.0 \text{ g } \cancel{Na}} = 0.435$ mole of Na

(b) $2 \text{ Na} + Cl_2 \rightarrow 2 \text{ NaCl}$

2 moles plus 1 mole $\rightarrow$ 2 moles

or 1 mole plus 0.5 mole $\rightarrow$ 1 mole

(c) $(0.5) (0.435) = 0.217$ mole of Cl_2 needed.

We have multiplied the number of moles of chlorine that will completely react with a mole of sodium by the number of moles of sodium we used (10.0 g $= 0.435$ moles). This gives us the number of moles (0.217 mole) of Cl_2 needed.

THIRD. Change 0.217 mole of chlorine into grams (mass) of chlorine.

Molecular mass of $Cl_2 = 2(35.5) = 71.0$ g

$$\frac{71.0 \text{ g } Cl_2}{1 \text{ mole } \cancel{Cl_2}} \; \bigg| \; \frac{0.217 \text{ mole } \cancel{Cl_2}}{1} = 15.4 \text{ g of } Cl_2$$

Check by the factor-label method:

10.0 g Na	1 mole Na	1 mole Cl$_2$	71.0 g Cl$_2$
	23.0 g Na	2 moles Na	1 mole Cl$_2$

$$= 15.4 \text{ g of Cl}_2$$

From this point use the factor-label method for conversions.

PROBLEMS

16. How many moles of H_2 can be produced from the reaction of 11.5 g of sodium with an excess of water?   *ans.* 0.250 mole

17. An excess of nitrogen reacts with 2.00 g of hydrogen to produce how many moles of ammonia? 0.661 mole

18. How many grams of oxygen are required to burn completely 18.0 g of carbon?   *ans.* 48.0 g

19. In Problem 18, how many grams of CO_2 will be formed? 66.0 g

20. In the decomposition of potassium chlorate, 16.0 g of O_2 are formed. How many grams of potassium chloride are produced?   *ans.* 24.9 g

21. The action of carbon monoxide on iron (III) oxide can be represented by the equation:

$$Fe_2O_3(s) + 3CO(g) \rightarrow 2Fe(s) + 3CO_2(g)$$

What would be the minimum amount of carbon monoxide used if 28.0 g of iron were produced? 21.1 g

22. How many grams of hydrochloric acid are required to react completely with 10.0 g of calcium hydroxide?   *ans.* 9.84 g

23. How many grams of hydrogen are produced when 5.00 g of aluminum react with excess hydrochloric acid? 0.560 g

ENERGY CHANGES

5:9   Heat Measurement

Emphasize that the heat produced by a reaction must equal the heat gained by the water in an adiabatic system.

Experimentally, the energy changes of chemical reactions are measured in a *calorimeter* (kal uh RIHM uh tuhr) (Figure 5–2). To change the temperature of a substance, heat must be added or removed. Some substances require little heat to cause a change in

A calorimeter is used to measure energy changes in chemical reactions.

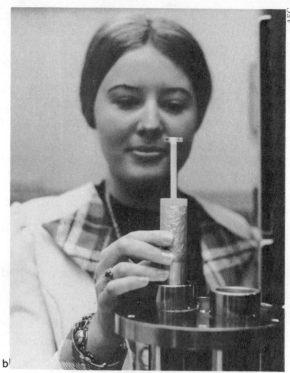

Courtesy of Central Scientific Company

a b

FIGURE 5-2. The student calorimeter (a) consists of a jacket,
stirrer, inner vessel, a seal, and
a lid. A twin-bridge calorimeter
(b) is being used here to measure heat given off during nuclear decay.

The specific heat capacity
of a substance is the heat
needed to raise the temperature of one gram of the substance 1C°.

A calorie is the amount of
heat needed to raise the
temperature of one gram of
water 1C°.

their temperature. Other substances require a great deal of heat to
cause the same temperature change. For example, one gram of water
requires one calorie of heat to cause a temperature change of one
Celsius degree. It takes only 0.215 calories to raise the temperature
of one gram of aluminum one Celsius degree. The amount of heat
needed to raise the temperature of 1 g of a substance by 1C° is called
the *specific heat capacity* of the substance. Every substance has its
own specific heat capacity. The amount of heat required to raise the
temperature of one gram of water one Celsius degree is called one
calorie. The specific heat capacity of water is 1 cal/g-C°.

Specific heat capacities are usually given in calories per gram-
Celsius degree (cal/g-C°). Appendix A-1 and A-5 lists the specific
heat capacity of some substances. For example, to heat 40 g of
water from 20°C to 36°C requires:

$$\frac{1 \text{ cal}}{\text{g-C}°} \times 40 \text{ g} \times 16\text{C}° = 640 \text{ cal.}$$

One *kilocalorie* is equal to 1000 calories. Since one calorie is the
amount of heat required to raise the temperature of one gram of
water one Celsius degree, one kilocalorie is the amount of heat

1 kilocalorie=1000 calories.

required to raise the temperature of 1000 grams (one kilogram) of water one Celsius degree.

Another heat quantity, similar to specific heat capacity, often used by chemists is the *molar heat capacity*. This quantity is the heat needed to raise the temperature of 1 mole of a substance by 1C°. In the case of a monatomic element, the term *atomic heat capacity* is used instead of molar heat capacity. To find the molar (or atomic) heat capacity of a substance, we have only to multiply the specific heat capacity of the substance by its molecular (or atomic) mass. All of the heat changes we have discussed are measured in calorimeters.

There are several kinds of calorimeters. The calorimeter most often used to measure the amount of heat absorbed or released by a chemical reaction contains water. Heat energy from a chemical reaction in a cup in the calorimeter causes a change in temperature of the water in the calorimeter. The temperature change of the water is used to measure the amount of heat absorbed or released by the reaction. The product of the specific heat capacity of the water, the temperature change of the water, and the mass of the water gives the change in heat energy. The heat energy released or absorbed is calculated using the following formula:

$$\begin{pmatrix}\text{temperature change} \\ \text{of water}\end{pmatrix}\begin{pmatrix}\text{specific heat} \\ \text{capacity of water}\end{pmatrix}\begin{pmatrix}\text{mass of} \\ \text{water}\end{pmatrix} = \begin{matrix}\text{calories} \\ \text{of heat}\end{matrix}$$

$$(\Delta T)\left(\frac{1 \text{ calorie}}{\text{g-C}°}\right)(\text{grams of water}) = \text{calories} = \text{energy change}$$

The same method can be used to calculate the change in heat energy when two dilute solutions react. The solutions are placed in a cup in the calorimeter. As the chemical reaction occurs, the temperature change is measured. Because the solutions are dilute, we can assume that the mixture has the same specific heat capacity as water, 1 cal/g-C°. By multiplying the specific heat capacity by the temperature change in C° and the mass of the solutions in grams, we can calculate the heat change (in calories) of the reaction.

5:10   Heat Calculations

Notice that throughout our discussion of calorimetry, we have assumed that the calorimeter itself does not absorb any heat. We also have assumed that no heat escapes from the calorimeter. Neither of these things is ever completely true. However, we will assume them

Molar heat capacity is the quantity of heat needed to raise the temperature of one mole of a substance 1C°.

A calorimeter represents an adiabatic system. Spend time making certain students understand the units of specific heat (cal/g-C°).

$\triangle T$ (delta T) represents the change in temperature.

It is assumed that no heat is lost or absorbed by the calorimeter.

so in order to simplify our calculations. The error introduced by actual losses of heat should be taken into account in any laboratory exercise involving calorimetry.

The law of conservation of energy requires that in an insulated system, any heat lost by one quantity of matter must be gained by another. Such a transfer of energy takes place between two quantities of matter which are at different temperatures. Heat energy flows from one to the other until the two are at the same temperature. Further, the amount of energy transferred can be calculated from the relationship:

Heat flows from warmer to cooler areas.

heat gained = mass × change in temperature × specific heat capacity
    or lost

$$H = m(\Delta T)C_p$$

Let us suppose that we have a piece of iron with a mass of 21.5 grams at a temperature of 100.0°C. We drop the metal into an insulated container of water containing 132 grams of water at 20.0°C. What will be the final temperature of the system? We know that the heat lost must equal the heat gained. Since the iron is at a higher temperature than the water, the iron will lose energy. The water will gain an equivalent amount of energy.

T_f=final temperature

The heat lost by the iron is:

$$H = m(\Delta T)C_p = (21.5 \text{ g})(100.0°C - T_f)\left(\frac{0.107 \text{ cal}}{\text{g-C}°}\right)$$

The heat gained by the water is:

$$H = m(\Delta T)C_p = (132 \text{ g})(T_f - 20.0°C)\left(\frac{1.00 \text{ cal}}{\text{g-C}°}\right)$$

Heat gained must equal heat lost:

$$(132 \text{ g})(T_f - 20.0°C)\left(\frac{1.00 \text{ cal}}{\text{g-C}°}\right) = (21.5\text{g})(100.0°C - T_f)\left(\frac{0.107 \text{ cal}}{\text{g-C}°}\right)$$

$$T_f = 21.4°C$$

Specific heat of unknowns can be calculated from experimental data.

The same type of calculation may be used to measure the specific heat of an unknown metal. If the masses of the two substances, the initial temperatures of both, and the final temperature are known, the only unknown factor is the specific heat of the metal.

The specific heat capacities of metals are fairly constant over a wide range of temperatures. In fact, the specific heat capacities of all solids and liquids are fairly constant.

In contrast, the specific heat capacities of gases vary considerably with temperature. They are also dependent on whether the gas is heated at constant volume or constant pressure. When performing heat calculations on gases, then, we must be careful to use correct data. We must use figures which represent a good average of the heat capacities of a substance over the temperature range involved. We must also check the conditions of volume and pressure stated for the change.

Specific heat capacities of solids and liquids are nearly constant.

Specific heat capacities of gases vary with temperature.

5:11   Heats of Fusion and Vaporization

When heat is added to a solid substance, the temperature of the object increases until the melting point of the substance is reached. Upon the addition of more heat, the substance begins to melt. The temperature, however, remains the same until all of the substance has melted. The heat required to melt 1 g of a particular substance is called the *heat of melting*, or *heat of fusion (Hf)* of that substance. A similar phenomenon takes place at the boiling point. The heat required to vaporize 1 g of a substance at its boiling point is called the *heat of vaporization (Hv)* of the substance.

H_f is the heat required to melt one gram of a substance at its melting point.

H_v is the heat required to vaporize one gram of a substance at its boiling point.

Steve Danison

FIGURE 5-3. As shown in the graph (a), at the melting and boiling points (b) of a substance, additional heat is required to cause a change of state.

There is no increase in kinetic energy during melting and boiling because the temperature remains constant. Any additional energy is changed to potential energy which causes the particles to move farther apart and become more disorganized.

EXAMPLE—HEATS OF FUSION AND VAPORIZATION

How much heat is necessary to convert 10.0 g of ice at −10.0°C to steam at 150.0°C? It is often helpful in problems of this type to draw a graph such as the one in Figure 5-3a. The following steps are taken to change ice to steam.

The specific heat capacity of ice is equal to 0.500 cal/g-C°.

FIRST. Ice must be heated to its melting point, 0.0°C. The specific heat capacity of ice is 0.500 cal/g-C°:

$$\left(\frac{0.500 \text{ cal}}{\text{g-C}°}\right)(10.0 \text{ g})(10.0 \text{C}°) = 50.0 \text{ cal}$$

H_f for water = 76.4 cal/g

SECOND. Ice must be melted. The heat of fusion of ice is 76.4 cal/g:

$$\left(\frac{76.4 \text{ cal}}{\text{g}}\right)(10.0 \text{ g}) = 764 \text{ cal}$$

Specific heat capacity of water is equal to 1.00 cal/g-C°.

THIRD. Water must be heated to its boiling point, 100.0°C. The specific heat capacity of water is 1.00 cal/g-C°:

$$\left(\frac{1.00 \text{ cal}}{\text{g-C}°}\right)(10.0 \text{ g})(100.0 \text{C}°) = 1000 \text{ cal}$$

H_v for water=539 cal/g

FOURTH. Water must be vaporized. The heat of vaporization of water is 539 cal/g, and the heat required is:

$$\left(\frac{539 \text{ cal}}{\text{g}}\right)(10.0 \text{ g}) = 5390 \text{ cal}$$

Specific heat capacity of steam is equal to 0.482 cal/g-C°.

FIFTH. Steam, with a specific heat capacity of 0.482 cal/g-C°, must now be heated to 150.0°C:

$$\left(\frac{0.482 \text{ cal}}{\text{g-C}°}\right)(10.0 \text{ g})(50.0 \text{C}°) = 241 \text{ cal}$$

Totaling the quantities of heat needed for each individual step, we obtain:

50.0 cal + 764 cal + 1000 cal + 5390 cal + 241 cal = 7450 cal.

Introduce molar heats of fusion and vaporization before assigning these problems.

PROBLEMS

24. How much heat is needed to melt 25.4 g of I_2 ($H_f = 3650$ cal/mole)? 0.365 kcal
25. How much heat is needed to melt 4.24 g of Pd ($H_f = 4120$ cal/mole)? 0.164 kcal
26. From the following data and that of Appendix A, calculate the heat required to raise 45.0 g of cesium metal from room tem-

perature (24.0°C) to 880°C. Specific heat capacity of solid Cs = 7.18 cal/mole-C°, specific heat capacity of liquid Cs = 8.00 cal/mole-C°, specific heat capacity of gaseous Cs = 4.97 cal/mole-C°, heat of fusion = 520 cal/mole, heat of vaporization = 21,300 cal/mole. 9.51 kcal

27. Using data from Appendices A-1 and A-5, calculate the amount of heat needed to raise the temperature of 5.58 kg of iron from 20°C to 1000°C. 585 kcal

28. Using information from the sample problem in the preceding section, calculate the heat required to change 50.0 g of ice at −32C° to steam at 400°C. 43.8 kcal

5:12   Heat of Chemical Reaction

Balanced chemical equations can be used to predict the relative amounts of reactants and products in a reaction. A balanced chemical equation can also be used to calculate the energy absorbed or released during a chemical reaction.

When carbon (for instance coal) is burned, heat is released:

$$C(s) + O_2(g) \rightarrow CO_2(g) + \text{heat (94.05 kcal)}$$

Point out that these equations are considered to be moles rather than molecules.

One mole of carbon reacts with one mole of oxygen to produce one mole of carbon dioxide and 94.05 kcal of heat. The heat released (94.05 kcal) is called the heat of reaction.

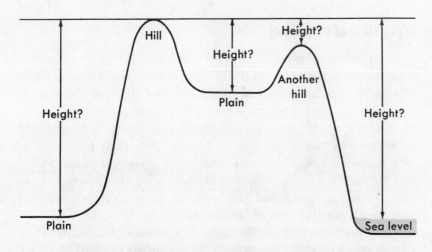

FIGURE 5-4. Heat content must be measured in relation to some arbitrary standard. How high is the hill?

Since heat is released during the reaction, the product (CO_2) must contain less energy than the reactants (C and O_2). Because we think of the heat as coming from the reactants, we arbitrarily assign each reactant a *heat content*. The heat content or *enthalpy* is represented by the symbol *H*.

We cannot measure enthalpy (heat content) directly. We can only measure changes in enthalpy. The height of a hill cannot be measured in absolute terms either. Instead, we describe the level of the surrounding plain or we say it is a certain number of meters above sea level. The figure we give depends upon what standard of reference is used. In measuring heat content, we use the heat content of a free element at 1 atmosphere pressure and 25°C as our standard. We arbitrarily define this heat content as zero. If carbon is burned in oxygen, chemical potential energy is converted into heat energy. If we assign zero heat content to the elements carbon and oxygen, the molar heat content of carbon dioxide must be −94.05 kcal per mole. Thus, carbon dioxide has a heat content or enthalpy of −94.05 kcal per mole.

The heat content of a free element is defined as zero, at 1 atmosphere and 25°C.

Chemical equations can be added and subtracted just as any other algebraic equalities. When heat (or energy) terms are included, they too can be added or subtracted. The result, in energy units, gives the energy change for the reaction obtained by the addition or subtraction.

When referring to a table of heats of formation, check to determine which convention applies. All tables in this book employ the current convention; that is, a compound produced by an endothermic reaction will have a positive heat of formation. The opposite convention was used for many years.

5:13 Heat of Formation

The preceding reaction involves the formation of a compound from its elements. The quantity of heat released or consumed when one mole of a compound is produced from the free elements is known as the *heat of formation*. This is usually expressed in terms of kilocalories per mole. A negative sign is given to the heat of formation of compounds produced by an exothermic process. This sign is used because such compounds are thought of as containing less energy than the elements from which they are formed. For the same reason, a compound produced by an endothermic reaction will have a positive heat of formation.

Heat of formation is the quantity of heat released or consumed when one mole of a compound is produced from free elements.

Knowledge of enthalpy change can help determine whether a reaction will be exothermic or endothermic.

In the previous section, we found the enthalpy (heat content) of CO_2 to be −94.05 kcal per mole. This quantity is the heat of formation of CO_2. Compounds like CO_2 with large negative heats of formation are very stable. This stability is due to the amount of energy

This is important! It is necessary if an exothermic reaction is to show a positive production of heat.

that is required to decompose them (or the energy released during their formation from the elements).

Appendix A–8 lists the heats of formation (enthalpy) for a number of compounds. The symbol used for heat of formation is ΔH_f^o. The superscript "^{o}" is used to indicate that the values given are those at one atmosphere pressure and 25°C.

Stable compounds have large negative heats of formation.

5:14   Calculation of Heat of Reaction

Let us apply the law of conservation of energy to a reaction. We can see that the total enthalpy change (ΔH^o) of a reaction is the difference between the enthalpy of the products ($\Delta H_{f\,products}^o$) and the enthalpy of the reactants ($\Delta H_{f\,reactants}^o$).

$$\Delta H^o = \Delta H_{f\;products}^o - \Delta H_{f\;reactants}^o$$

If the enthalpy for each of the reactants and products is known, it is possible to calculate the amount of heat produced or absorbed. We can then predict whether a reaction will be exothermic or endothermic.

ΔH_f° = heat of formation

ΔH° = change in enthalpy
= difference between ΔH_f° of products and ΔH_f° of reactants

Stanislao Cannizzaro

(1826–1910)

As a pioneer in the development of modern atomic theory, Stanislao Cannizzaro insisted on the distinction (then only imperfectly realized) between molecular and atomic masses. He determined atomic masses of elements in volatile compounds from the molecular masses of those compounds. He also found atomic masses of elements from a knowledge of their specific heat capacities.

Cannizzaro was devoted to organic chemistry, particularly those phases concerning compounds containing a benzene ring.

Cannizzaro's investigations were interrupted many times because of his political interests. In 1848, he became involved in a Sicilian revolution and was forced to flee to Paris. He returned to Italy and eventually was elected vice president of the senate.

EXAMPLE – ENTHALPY CHANGE

Calculate the enthalpy change in the following chemical reaction:

carbon monoxide + oxygen → carbon dioxide

First, write a balanced equation. Include all the reactants and products:

$$2CO(g) + O_2(g) \rightarrow 2CO_2(g)$$

Assume each formula unit represents one mole. We know from the law of conservation of energy that the total energy on the left side of the equation must equal the total energy of the right side of the equation. Remember that the free elements have zero enthalpy by definition. From the table of enthalpies (Appendix A-8), the total enthalpy of the reactants (2CO and O_2) is:

$$\Delta H^o_{f \text{ reactants}} = 2(-26.4 \text{ kcal}) + 0 \text{ kcal} = -52.8 \text{ kcal}$$

and the total enthalpy of the product ($2CO_2$) is:

$$\Delta H^o_{f \text{ products}} = 2(-94.05 \text{ kcal}) = -188.1 \text{ kcal}$$

The difference between the enthalpy of the reactants and the enthalpy of the product is:

$$\Delta H^o = \Delta H^o_{f \text{ products}} - \Delta H^o_{f \text{ reactants}}$$

$$\Delta H^o = -188.1 \text{ kcal} - (-52.8 \text{ kcal})$$
$$\Delta H^o = -135.3 \text{ kcal}$$

This difference between the enthalpy of the products and the enthalpy of the reactants (−135.3 kcal) is released as the *heat of reaction*.

$$2CO(g) + O_2(g) \rightarrow 2CO_2(g) + \text{heat of reaction}$$
$$-52.8 \text{ kcal} + 0 \text{ kcal} \rightarrow -188.1 \text{ kcal} + 135.3 \text{ kcal}$$

Notice that a release of heat (a positive heat of reaction) is equivalent to a negative change in enthalpy. The negative sign for ΔH^o ($\Delta H^o = -135.3$ kcal) indicates that the two moles of carbon monoxide have *released* 135.3 kcal of heat. Since there are two moles of reactant, each mole of reactant has released half this amount $\left(\dfrac{135.3}{2}\right)$

or 67.65 kcal of heat. The ΔH^o for each mole of carbon monoxide is -67.65 kcal.

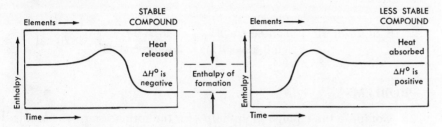

FIGURE 5-5. The heat released or absorbed during a chemical reaction is called the enthalpy change (ΔH°). If the reactants are elements and the product is a compound, ΔH° is called the enthalpy of formation. Substances with a large negative enthalpy of formation tend to be stable.

If heat is absorbed during a reaction, the products must have a greater enthalpy than the reactants; the enthalpy change must be positive (ΔH^o is positive). A positive enthalpy change indicates that a reaction is endothermic. A negative enthalpy change indicates that a reaction is exothermic. Since an enthalpy change causes a change in temperature, we measure ΔH^o quantitatively in a calorimeter.

A negative $\triangle H^\circ$ implies an exothermic reaction.

A positive $\triangle H^\circ$ implies an endothermic reaction.

EXAMPLE – MASS-HEAT PROBLEM

How much heat is produced (or absorbed) by the reaction of 6.20 g of sodium hydroxide with excess sulfuric acid?

First, we need a balanced equation:

$$2NaOH(aq) + H_2SO_4(aq) \rightarrow Na_2SO_4(aq) + 2H_2O(l)$$

Next, we need to calculate the heat of reaction:

$$\begin{aligned}
\Delta H^o &= \Delta H^o_f \text{ products} - \Delta H^o_f \text{ reactants} \\
&= [(-330{,}900 \text{ cal}) + 2(-68{,}315 \text{ cal})] - [(-217{,}320 \text{ cal}) \\
&\qquad\qquad\qquad\qquad\qquad + 2(-101{,}720 \text{ cal})] \\
&= -46{,}770 \text{ cal}
\end{aligned}$$

Since $\Delta H^o < 0$, the reaction is exothermic, and 46,770 cal are produced. However, this amount of heat is for the equation as written. That is, 46,770 cal are produced for one mole of sulfuric acid to react with two moles of sodium hydroxide. In the problem at hand, only 6.20 g of sodium hydroxide reacted giving us the following solution:

$$\frac{6.20 \text{ g NaOH}}{} \left| \frac{1 \text{ mole NaOH}}{40.0 \text{ g NaOH}} \right| \frac{46,770 \text{ cal}}{2 \text{ mole NaOH}} = 3620 \text{ cal}$$

PROBLEMS

29. Compute the change in enthalpy for the formation of 193 grams of ammonium bromide from ammonia and hydrogen bromide. -88.7 kcal

30. Compute the change in enthalpy for the decomposition of 0.772 grams of cobalt(II) carbonate into cobalt(II) oxide and carbon dioxide. 139 cal

31. Compute the change in enthalpy for the displacement of 0.0663 grams of bromine from sodium bromide by chlorine. -5.06 cal

SUMMARY

1. The symbol for an element represents one atom of the element or one gram-atomic mass of the element when it stands alone.

2. The formula for a compound can represent one molecule or formula unit, or it can represent one gram-molecular mass or gram-formula mass of the compound.

3. Masses of atoms are based on the atomic mass unit (a.m.u.). An atom of the lightest element, hydrogen, has a mass of approximately 1 a.m.u., or 1.660×10^{-24} g.

4. The molecular mass of a molecule is found by adding the atomic masses of all the atoms in one molecule.

5. Not all substances exist normally as molecules; therefore, molecular mass is not a good term for these substances. The mass of the simplest formula unit (based on the empirical formula) of a salt such as sodium chloride is called the formula mass.

6. There are 6.02×10^{23} molecules in 1 mole. This is known as Avogadro's number of molecules and is given the symbol N_A.

7. One gram-atomic mass is the mass in grams of one mole of atoms.

8. One gram-molecular mass is the mass in grams of one mole of molecules of a substance.

9. One gram-formula mass or one gram-ion mass is the mass expressed in grams of one mole of formula units or one mole of ion units.

10. The number of moles in a given mass of substance can be found by dividing the total mass by the gram-molecular mass.

11. The percentage of the total mass of a compound contributed by an element is the percentage of that element in the compound.

12. The empirical formula indicates the ratio of atoms present in a compound.

13. The molecular formula of a compound is some whole number multiple of the empirical formula.

14. Complete, correct formulas for hydrated compounds can be written by finding the molar ratio from mass data.

15. Calculations involving chemical reactions can be conveniently carried out once a correct, properly balanced equation representing the reaction has been written.

16. The balanced equation indicates the ratio of moles of reactants and products in the reaction.

17. The specific heat capacity of a substance is the heat required to raise 1 g of the substance 1C°.

18. The heat energy transferred when a quantity of matter changes temperature is:
   heat = mass × change in temperature × specific heat capacity

19. The heat of fusion is the heat required to melt 1 g of a solid substance at its melting point.

20. The heat of vaporization is the heat required to vaporize 1 g of a liquid at its boiling point.

21. The heat of condensation is the heat released when 1 g of a gas changes to a liquid at its boiling point.

22. The specific heat capacity of ice is 0.500 cal/g-C°, of water is 1.00 cal/g-C°, of steam is 0.482 cal/g-C°. The heat of fusion of water is 76.4 cal/g. The heat of vaporization of water is 539 cal/g.

23. Balanced equations can be used to calculate energy changes resulting from chemical changes.

24. The change in enthalpy (heat content) of a system is the energy absorbed or produced during a chemical reaction.

25. The change in enthalpy for a reaction is represented by the symbol ΔH^o.

26. The heat of formation of a compound is the heat released or absorbed when 1 mole of the compound is formed from its elements.

27. A stable compound has a large negative heat of formation.
28. The total enthalpy change (ΔH^o) for a reaction is the difference between the heats of formation (enthalpy) of the products and the heats of formation (enthalpy) of the reactants:

$$\Delta H^o = \Delta H^o_f \text{ products} - \Delta H^o_f \text{ reactants}$$

PROBLEMS

32. Calculate the formula mass of:
    a. K_2SO_4 174   d. AsI_5 709
    b. $CuSO_4 \cdot 5H_2O$ 250   e. $BiONO_3 \cdot H_2O$ 305
    c. $NH_4CoPO_4 \cdot H_2O$ 190
33. Calculate the molecular or formula mass of:
    a. $CuCl_2$ 134   d. $Cr_2(C_2O_4)_3 \cdot 6H_2O$ 476
    b. $Gd_2(C_2O_4)_3 \cdot 10H_2O$ 759 e. $Ca(C_9H_7O_2)_2 \cdot 3H_2O$ 388
    c. CeH_3 143
34. Convert:
    a. 10.0 g of $CaCO_3$ to moles 0.100 mole $CaCO_3$
    b. 1.00×10^{25} molecules of I_2 to grams 4.22 x 10³ g I_2
    c. 0.426 moles of H_2S_3 to molecules 2.56 x 10²³ molecules H_2S_3
    d. 26.8 moles of $PBrCl_4$ to molecules 1.61 x 10²⁵ molecules $PBrCl_4$
    e. 681 formula units of K_2CS_3 to moles 1.13 x 10⁻²¹ moles K_2CS_3
35. Find the percentage composition of:
    a. K_2CO_3 56.6%, 8.69%, 34.7%   d. $Tl_2Cr_2O_7$ 65.4%, 16.6%, 17.9%
    b. CH_3COOH 40.0%, 6.71%, 53.3%   e. $Ba(MnO_4)_2$ 36.6%, 29.3%, 34.1%
    c. $Al_2(SO_4)_3 \cdot Na_2SO_4 \cdot 24H_2O$ 5.89%, 14.0%, 69.8%, 5.02%, 5.28%
36. Find the empirical formula for the compound which is 33.3% calcium, 40.0% oxygen, and 26.7% sulfur. $CaSO_3$
37. The percentage composition of a compound is 92.3% C and 7.7% H. If the molecular mass is 78, find the molecular formula. C_6H_6
38. Find the molecular formula of a compound with percentage composition 26.7% P, 12.1% N, and 61.2% Cl and molecular mass 695. $P_6N_6Cl_{12}$
39. How many calories would be required to heat 198 kg of nickel from 25°C to 300°C? 6.67 x 10⁶ cal
40. How many calories would be required to heat 50.0 g of tin from 24.0°C to 100.0°C? 201 cal
41. How many grams of ice at 0°C would be required to cool 1000 ml of water from 100°C to 0°C? 1310 g

42. How many grams of $NaAlO_2$ can be obtained from 1.46 g of $AlCl_3$ according to the reaction: 0.898 g NaAlO₂

$$AlCl_3(aq) + 4NaOH(aq) \rightarrow NaAlO_2(aq) + 3NaCl(aq) + 2H_2O(l)$$

43. How many grams of CO_2 are obtained when 6.15 g of $Ce_2(C_2O_4)_3$ are formed according to the reaction: 209 g CO₂

$$2Ce(IO_3)_4(aq) + 24H_2C_2O_4(aq) \rightarrow Ce_2(C_2O_4)_3(aq)$$
$$+ 4I_2(aq) + 42CO_2(aq) + 24H_2O(l)$$

44. Compute the heat of the following reaction: −27.3 kcal

$$2NO(g) + O_2(g) \rightarrow 2NO_2(g)$$

45. Compute the heat of the following reaction: −138 kcal

$$4FeO(s) + O_2(g) \rightarrow 2Fe_2O_3(s)$$

ONE MORE STEP See Teacher's Guide at the front of this book.

1. Molar heat capacities are determined experimentally, but their value may be predicted with a reasonable degree of accuracy. Investigate this process and be prepared to explain its basis to the class.

2. Specific heat capacities of substances are not constant over a wide range of temperatures. Their values vary such a small amount that, except for the most exacting work, they are considered constant. Determine the change in specific heat capacity for three liquids from their freezing point to their boiling point. Include water as one of the liquids. See if you can discover the reason for this change.

3. The heat of a reaction gives only an indication of whether or not a reaction will take place. What other factor or factors must be taken into consideration?

4. If neither matter nor energy is created or destroyed in an ordinary chemical reaction before the reaction occurs, where is the energy that is given off or absorbed by the reaction?

5. Find out what the Law of Hess is and how to use it in energy calculations. Be prepared to report to the class on your findings.

6. How would heat capacity affect selection of fuels?

Suggested Readings for this chapter may be found in the Teacher's Guide at the front of this book.

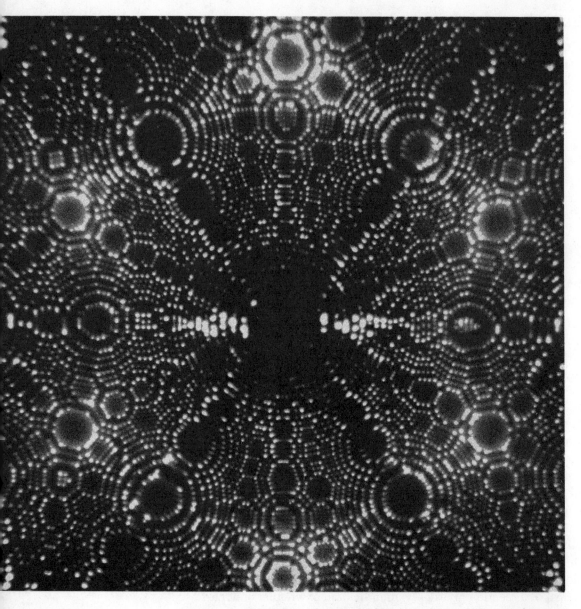

This is a photograph of individual atoms of tungsten as they are arranged in the point of a needle. Each small dot represents a single atom magnified 800,000 times. The pattern was produced as charged atoms were induced to escape from the tip of a tungsten needle in a field ion emission microscope. How large is a single atom of tungsten? What particles make up a single atom? How large is each of these subatomic particles?

Atomic Structure _____ 6

Chapter 6 contains a short historical summary of the development of atomic theory, introduces subatomic particles, and
presents Bohr's atomic model.

Much of civilization today depends on electricity. Most of our
electricity is conducted from place to place along wires made of the
element copper. Let us take a closer look at some copper. Suppose
that we take a piece of copper wire and cut it into very small pieces.
Would these pieces still be copper? Now imagine that we take one
of these very small pieces and cut it into even smaller pieces under a
microscope. How many times could we continue to divide this piece
of copper and still have particles of copper? What do we have when
we have divided the copper into the smallest possible pieces? We
mentioned earlier that the smallest piece of matter which would
still be copper is called an atom. This atom, in turn, is made up of
smaller particles such as electrons, protons, and neutrons. Why do
we believe that such small particles actually exist? What evidence is
there that they do exist? We will devote this chapter to the study
of atoms and their component parts, so that we may have a better
understanding of the units which take part in chemical reactions.

GOAL: You will gain knowledge and understanding of
atomic theory using the
Rutherford-Bohr atom as a
model.

Yes. Until one atom is left.

ATOMIC THEORY

6:1 Origin of the Atomic Theory

Our modern concept of the atom has not grown at a steady rate or
by a direct route. Certainly, the atomic theory is not yet complete.
The information we now have about the structure of the atom is a
result of the work of generations of scientists.

The Greek philosopher Democritus, around 400 B.C., proposed the
first atomic theory. His theory was based upon intuition and faith
that a simple explanation underlay the complexity of everyday
observations. Democritus thought that the world was made up of
two things, void (empty space) and tiny particles which he called

Democritus proposed the
first atomic theory.

"atoms." This word comes from the Greek word *atomos*, meaning indivisible. He also said that atoms were very small and could not be destroyed or cut up. They could not be broken up because they were the smallest possible particles which could exist. In addition, he proposed that there were many of these atoms and that they had various shapes. There was a different type of atom for each material in the world. For example, there were atoms of air, atoms of rock, and atoms of iron. However, atoms of different materials were about the same size. Atoms of solid materials were rough and would not slide easily over one another, while atoms of liquids were smooth. His theory was very general and was not supported by experimental evidence.

These beliefs about the atomic nature of matter were not accepted for centuries because of the teachings of Aristotle. Aristotle believed that matter was continuous and made up of only one substance called *hyle*. Aristotle's teachings were accepted until the

Although Aristotle made many contributions to Greek philosophical science, it took chemistry 2000 years to recover from his views on atoms.

Ernest Rutherford

(1871–1937)

Ernest Rutherford, one of the most brilliant scientists investigating atomic structure, won the Nobel Prize in chemistry for his study of radioactivity. The theories he projected in this area serve as a basis for our modern theory of radioactivity.

In his principle of atomic transmutation, he contended a radioactive atom emits electrically charged particles and forms a new atom of a different chemical element.

In 1911, Rutherford worked out the nuclear theory of the atom which led him to be known as the "father of nuclear science." From his experiments, he constructed a model in which the electrons were outside a positively charged center called the nucleus. This model is the basis of our present-day view of atomic structure.

Rutherford spent most of his 66 years teaching and doing research in New Zealand, Canada, and England.

seventeenth century, when doubts and objections began to be expressed.

Isaac Newton and Robert Boyle published articles expressing a belief in the atomic nature of elements. Their works offered no proof; they were explanations of the known, with no predictions of the unknown. It was up to an English chemist, John Dalton, to offer a logical hypothesis about the existence of atoms.

Newton and Boyle believed in an atomic theory.

6:2 Law of Conservation of Mass

During the early 1800's, Dalton was aware of certain experimental observations. Antoine Lavoisier, a French chemist, had noted that if a chemical change takes place in a closed space, the mass of the materials present before the change is equal to the mass of the materials present after the change. In all tests of chemical changes, he found that mass remains constant. He proposed the law: *Matter cannot be created or destroyed.* This statement means that, in ordinary chemical reactions, matter can be changed in many ways, but it cannot be created or destroyed. Today this law is called the *law of conservation of mass.*

Lavoisier observed constant mass in chemical reactions.

In ordinary chemical reactions, matter is not created or destroyed but may be altered.

6:3 Law of Definite Proportions

The work of another French chemist, Joseph Proust, also came to the attention of Dalton. Proust had observed that specific substances always contain their elements in the same ratio by mass. For exam-

FIGURE 6-1. The mass of the reactants (a) is equal to the mass of the products (b). This illustrates the law of conservation of matter.

a

b

Courtesy of Kodansha Ltd.

Courtesy of Kodansha Ltd.

Proust stated that substances have definite proportion by mass.

ple, common table salt is made of sodium and chlorine. The ratio of the mass of sodium to the mass of chlorine in any sample of pure salt is always the same. Regardless of where the sample is obtained, how it is obtained, or how large it is, the ratio of the mass of sodium to the mass of chlorine is always the same. This principle is known as the *law of definite proportions*.

6:4   Dalton's Hypothesis

Dalton's hypothesis is an example of an inductive process.

Dalton believed that each element is composed of atoms exactly alike.

The atoms of one element are different from the atoms of any other element.

Atoms unite in simple whole number ratios to form compounds.

Dalton's Atomic Theory:
1. All matter is composed of atoms.
2. All atoms of the same element are identical.
3. Atoms of different elements are different.
4. Atoms unite in definite ratios to form compounds.

Dalton was attempting to explain these findings when he formed the beginnings of our present atomic theory. He stated that all matter is composed of very small particles called *atoms*, and that these atoms could not be broken apart. In these two respects, Dalton's hypothesis was like that of Democritus. However, Dalton believed that atoms were simpler than particles of air or rock, and that atoms of different elements were quite unlike. In Dalton's view, each element was composed of atoms that were exactly alike, but quite different from atoms of all other elements. He stated that atoms can unite with other atoms in simple ratios to form compounds.

These last two sentences are the key to the *atomic theory*. We can see how well Dalton's hypothesis explains the two laws he was considering. If atoms could not be destroyed, then atoms must simply be rearranged in a chemical change. The total number and kind of atoms must remain the same. Therefore, the mass before a reaction must equal the mass after a reaction. Also, if the atoms of an element are always alike, then the mass of each atom of a particular element must equal the mass of every other atom of that element.

In the example of salt, according to Dalton, all sodium atoms have the same mass and all chlorine atoms have the same mass. When a sodium atom combines with a chlorine atom, salt is formed. The same is true of any other pair of these atoms. Dalton would say that since all sodium atoms are equal in mass and all chlorine atoms are equal in mass, the ratio of the mass of sodium to the mass of chlorine must be the same for any sample of salt. This same type of reasoning would hold true for any given material. Experiments have shown that Dalton's hypothesis is not entirely correct. As we will see later, not all atoms of the same element are exactly alike in mass. However, by taking this fact into consideration, and by changing the word "mass" to "average mass," we can use Dalton's hypothesis with present-day knowledge.

Atoms of one element may differ in mass. Thus we use "average mass" rather than "mass."

6:5   Law of Multiple Proportions

The development of this law is a good example of the deductive process.

Dalton saw another possibility for his hypothesis. He stated a second law based on what he believed would be true if his atomic theory were correct. This law was not based on experimental data. If two elements combine to form more than one compound substance, the ratio of masses of the one element which combine with a constant mass of the other element can be expressed in small whole numbers. This statement is called the *law of multiple proportions.* Look at the second and fourth columns of Table 6–1. Note that the fourth column is composed of small whole numbers. Do you see why these numbers cannot be fractions? Atoms cannot be divided. Therefore, a fraction of an atom cannot exist. Do you now see how Dalton could arrive at this conclusion in terms of atoms? Table 6–1 offers experimental proof of Dalton's hypothesis. It confirms his law of multiple proportions.

The law of multiple proportions states that the combining masses of one element with another are in the ratio of small whole numbers.

Table 6–1

Binary Compounds

Compound	Formula	Grams of oxygen combined with 1 gram of nitrogen	Relative masses of oxygen combined with 1 gram of nitrogen
nitrogen(I) oxide	N_2O	0.571134	1
nitrogen(II) oxide	NO	1.14227	2
nitrogen(III) oxide	N_2O_3	1.71340	3
nitrogen(IV) oxide	NO_2	2.28454	4
nitrogen(V) oxide	N_2O_5	2.85567	5

At about the same time that Dalton formed his atomic theory, J. L. Gay-Lussac, a French chemist, made an interesting observation about the reactions of gases. He noted that, under conditions of constant temperature and pressure, the volumes of reacting gases and their gaseous products were in the ratio of small whole numbers.

Combining volumes of gases are related by small whole numbers.

A few years later, Amadeo Avogadro, an Italian physicist, explained Gay-Lussac's observation on the basis of Dalton's atomic theory. Avogadro's hypothesis stated that equal volumes of gases, under the same conditions of pressure and temperature, contained the same number of molecules. Since the atoms in these molecules always remained whole when a reaction occurred, their changes

Avogadro stated that equal volumes of gases under the same conditions contain the same number of molecules.

FIGURE 6-2. This student gathers information on atomic theory from a book printed in braille.

AEC: Wescott

FIGURE 6-2. This student gathers information on atomic theory from a book printed in braille.

could be represented by simple whole number ratios. Since an equal number of molecules always occupied an equal volume, reacting volumes could also be expressed in small whole number ratios. We will consider Avogadro's hypothesis more fully in Chapter 16.

The atomic theory and the law of multiple proportions, as stated by Dalton, were tested and accepted as correct. For decades, all scientific work was based on the belief that atoms could not be broken up. Today, however, there are major exceptions to some of Dalton's statements. The most important exception is that the atom is divisible under special conditions. However, Dalton was still basically right in stating that atoms are not divided in ordinary chemical changes. We now believe that all atoms are composed of three fundamental particles: electrons, protons, and neutrons. (Other subatomic particles will be discussed in Chapter 23.) We will now consider electrons, protons, and neutrons in some detail.

Three fundamental particles are the electron, the proton, and the neutron.

THE ATOM

6:6 The Electron

Experiments by several scientists in the middle of the nineteenth century led to the conclusion that electricity existed in small units. Using a tube such as the one in Figure 6–3. it was possible to learn a great deal about the particles we now call *electrons*. In each end

Free electrons are produced in a cathode ray tube.

of the tube, there was a metal piece called an electrode. The positive terminal of a powerful source of electricity was connected to one electrode. The negative terminal was connected to the other electrode. These electrodes were called the anode (AN ohd) (positive electrode) and the cathode (KATH ohd) (negative electrode). As the air in the tube was removed, a glow in the glass around the anode could be noted. Careful observation revealed the presence of rays in the tube. Since these rays appeared to begin at the cathode and travel toward the anode, they were called *cathode rays*. Further investigation showed that the rays were made of discrete particles called electrons.

In 1897, J. J. Thomson, an English scientist, did some skillful research on these electrons. As a result, Thomson is generally credited with the discovery of electrons. He noted that electrical and magnetic fields affected the paths of the cathode rays as if they were made up of negatively charged particles. To test his observation, Thomson built a cathode ray tube which subjected cathode rays to both a magnetic field and an electrical field. By measuring the bending of the path of the cathode rays, Thomson was able to determine the ratio of the charge of the electron to its mass.

Robert Millikan, an American, obtained the first accurate measurement of the charge of the electron by using a device like the one in Figure 6–4b. He used two charged plates to exert a force opposite to the gravitational force exerted on the particle. Thus, Millikan was able to suspend a tiny drop of oil possessing a negative charge. He

You might borrow this equipment from the physics lab to demonstrate the various discharge tubes.

Cathode rays are streams of electrons.

An electron has a negative charge.

Thomson measured the ratio of charge to mass of the electron.

Millikan determined the charge on an electron.

The same principles apply to both the cathode ray tube and the TV tube.

Courtesy of Kodansha Ltd.

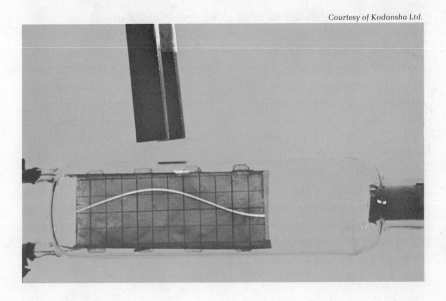

FIGURE 6-3. Thomson used a tube similar to the one shown to determine the charge-mass ratio of the electron.

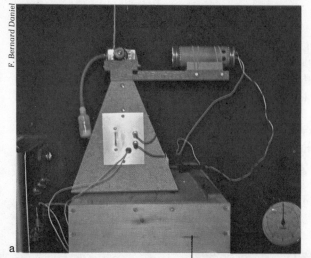

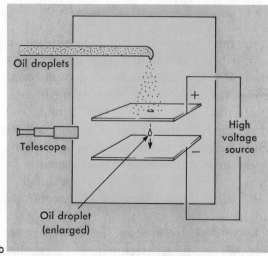

a   b

Oil droplets

Telescope

Oil droplet (enlarged)

High voltage source

+

−

Instead of oil drops, teflon balls are bombarded with electrons in this student Millikan apparatus.

FIGURE 6-4. Students, today, can determine the charge on an electron using an apparatus (a) similar to that used by Millikan (b).

e^- is the symbol for an electron, which has a charge of 1−.

The mass of the electron is 1/1837 the mass of one hydrogen atom.

To obtain protons, the gas discharge tube must be charged with hydrogen.

A proton has a charge equal in size but opposite in sign to that of an electron.

A proton has a mass 1837 times that of an electron.

calculated the strength of the charge on the drop and found that although the charges on the drops varied, they were all multiples of one small charge. He concluded (correctly) that this charge must be the charge on a single electron. This charge is now the standard unit of negative charge (1−). The electron and charge on the electron may be represented by the symbol e^-.

Using the data of Thomson and Millikan, it was possible to calculate the actual mass of the electron. Its mass was only 1/1837 the mass of the lightest atom known, the hydrogen atom.

6:7 The Proton

Protons were also discovered in an experiment involving a cathode ray tube containing hydrogen. In 1886, a scientist used a metal disc with holes in it as the cathode of a tube such as the one in Figure 6–5. To his surprise, he saw rays traveling in the direction opposite to the direction traveled by the cathode rays. These rays came from the holes on the side of the cathode away from the anode, and traveled in straight lines toward the end of the tube. He named them *canal rays*. Later it was shown that these rays possessed a positive charge. The nature of the rays was discovered by J. J. Thomson. He showed that these rays consist of particles. These particles have the same amount of electric charge as an electron, but the charge is opposite to the charge on the electron. These particles are now called *protons*. Thomson calculated that the mass of the proton was just about 1837 times that of the electron. This meant that the mass of a proton was almost the same as the mass of a hydrogen atom. The proton is now the standard unit of positive charge (1+).

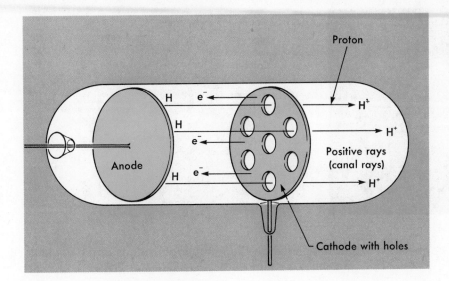

In the figure: Proton, H, e⁻, H, e⁻, H, Anode, H⁺, H⁺, H⁺, Positive rays (canal rays), Cathode with holes

6:8 The Neutron

A third particle remained unobserved for a long time. However, its existence had been predicted by Lord Rutherford, an English physicist, in 1920. The first evidence of the particle was obtained by Walter Bothe in 1930. Another English scientist, James Chadwick, repeated Bothe's work in 1932. He found high energy particles with no charge and with essentially the same mass as the proton. These particles are now known as *neutrons*. Through his work, Chadwick is credited with the discovery of the neutron.

Dalton had assumed that atoms could not be broken up. The discovery of subatomic particles led to a major revision of Dalton's atomic theory to include this new information.

Chadwick discovered the neutron.

The neutron by itself is not a stable particle.

A neutron has no charge and has approximately the same mass as a proton.

6:9 Isotopes

While working with neon, J. J. Thomson observed what seemed to be two kinds of neon atoms. They were exactly alike chemically, but slightly different in mass. The word *isotope* (I suh tohp) is used for different kinds of atoms of the same element. Today it is known that every element has isotopes. Atoms which possess the same number of protons but a different number of neutrons are isotopes.

Isotopes contain the same number of protons but a different number of neutrons.

6:10 Atomic Number

Another English scientist, Henry Moseley, was investigating the nature of X rays. He tried building a series of X-ray tubes using different metals as the anodes. He found that the wavelength of the X rays produced was characteristic of the metal used for the anode.

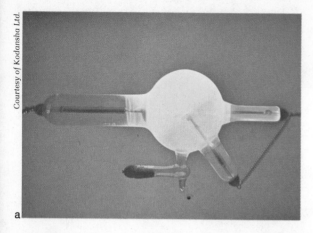

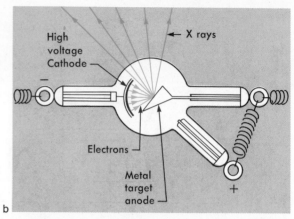

a

b

High
voltage
Cathode

← X rays

Electrons

Metal
target
anode

FIGURE 6-6. The X-ray tube (a) is similar to the type used by Moseley (b) to study X rays produced from different metal targets,

The atomic number (Z) of an element equals the number of protons in the nucleus.

The mass number (A) of an atom is the sum of the nucleons.

The wavelength depended on the number of protons in the nucleus of the atom and was constant for a given element. This number of protons is known as the *atomic number* of the element and is represented by the symbol Z. The difference in mass of the isotopes is due to different numbers of neutrons in the nucleus. Thus the number of protons determines the element and the number of neutrons determines the particular isotope of the element.

Dalton's atomic theory was again changed, this time to state that all atoms of an element must contain the same number of protons but they could contain different numbers of neutrons. The particles which make up the nucleus (protons and neutrons) are called *nucleons*. The number of nucleons in an atom is called the *mass number* of that atom. The symbol for the mass number is A. A particular kind of atom containing a definite number of protons and neutrons is called a *nuclide*.

Table 6-2

Isotopes of Hydrogen

Name	Protons	Neutrons	Mass Number
Protium	1	0	1
Deuterium	1	1	2
Tritium	1	2	3

6:11   Atomic Mass

The data from many experiments conducted since Thomson first described the electron have shown that the mass of the proton is 1837 times the mass of the electron. The proton and neutron are essentially equal in mass. Because the mass of the electron is so small, practically the entire mass of an atom is located in the nucleus. Even the simplest atom, which contains only one proton and one electron, has 1837/1838 of its mass in the nucleus. In other atoms which have neutrons in the nucleus, an even higher fraction of the total mass of the atom is in the nucleus.

The particles which make up atoms have the following masses:

$$1 \text{ electron} = 9.11 \times 10^{-28} \text{ g}$$
$$1 \text{ proton} = 1.673 \times 10^{-24} \text{ g}$$
$$1 \text{ neutron} = 1.675 \times 10^{-24} \text{ g}$$

It is possible to discuss the mass of a single atom. However, chemists have continued to use the masses of large groups of atoms. They do so because of the very small size of the particles in the atom. As discussed in Chapter 5, chemists have chosen one mole, or Avogadro's number of atoms, as a standard unit for large numbers of atoms. This number of atoms was chosen so that N_A atoms have a mass in grams what one atom has in atomic mass units. We know that the unit gram was defined as 1/1000 the mass of the international standard kilogram, but what about the atomic mass unit?

In measuring the atomic masses of the elements, an atom of one element is chosen as a standard, and the other elements are compared with it. Scientists use a carbon nuclide, carbon 12, as the standard for the atomic mass scale. The carbon-12 atom is the nuclide of carbon with 6 protons and 6 neutrons in the nucleus. One such atom is defined as having a mass of 12 atomic mass units. Similar to the mass of the standard kilogram, the mass of the carbon-12 isotope may be divided into smaller units of reference called *atomic mass units*. An atomic mass unit is defined to be $\frac{1}{12}$ the mass of the carbon-12 nuclide.

If, then, it were possible to take exactly 12 grams of carbon-12 atoms and count them, we would count Avogadro's number of atoms. Look carefully at Table 6–3. Notice that many of the elements have a mass in a.m.u.'s which is close to the total number of protons and neutrons in their nuclei. However, some do not. What causes the mass of chlorine or copper, for example, to be about halfway between whole numbers? The numbers in the table are based on the "average atom" of an element. Most elements have many isotopic forms which occur naturally. It is difficult and expensive to obtain a large amount of a single nuclide of an element. Thus, for most calculations, the *average atomic mass* of the element is used.

Nearly all the mass of an atom is in the nucleus.

These are rest masses. As the velocity increases, the mass also increases, especially near the speed of light.

Chemists generally deal in moles of atoms rather than in individual atoms.

One a.m.u. is defined as 1/12 the mass of one carbon-12 atom.

Avogadro's number (N_A) of atoms is contained in 12 grams of carbon-12.

The average atomic mass of an element is used in calculations.

This average mass can be determined if the relative amounts in which the various isotopes occur are known. For example, it has been determined that neon has two isotopes. They have masses of 20 and 22 a.m.u. They are present in every neon sample in the ratio of 9:1. In a sample of ten atoms, nine will be neon-20 and one will be neon-22. The average mass can then be found:

$$\frac{(9 \times 20 \text{ a.m.u.}) + (1 \times 22 \text{ a.m.u.})}{10} = \frac{202}{10} = 20.2 \text{ a.m.u.}$$

Similarly, chlorine isotopes with various masses are found to have an average mass of 35.453 a.m.u.

6:12   Mass Spectrometer

The measurement of the masses of isotopes and their relative amounts is performed in a device called a mass spectrometer (spek TRAHM uh tuhr). It was developed from the early tubes of J. J. Thomson. It is most similar in design to the tube used by Thomson to find the charge/mass ratio of the electron.

The sample in the form of a gas is introduced into a chamber where it is ionized by hitting it with electrons. These ions are then propelled by electrical and magnetic fields. As in the Thomson tube, the fields bend the path of the charged particles. The paths of the heavy particles are bent only a little as they pass through the fields; the paths of the lighter particles are bent more. This difference in paths results in a division of particles by relative mass. The particles are caught and recorded electrically. One drawback of the instrument is that the ionization chamber, field tube, and detection device must all be in a vacuum equal to about one hundred-millionth (1/100,000,000) of normal atmospheric pressure.

Since the strength of the fields, the speed of the particles, and their paths are known, the mass of particles can be calculated. Once the masses of the isotopes and their relative amounts have been found, the average atomic mass can be calculated. This average mass is called the *atomic mass* of an element. It is represented by the symbol M.

The mass spectrometer has other uses. It can be used in the separation of isotopes of an element. Geologists, biologists, petroleum

a

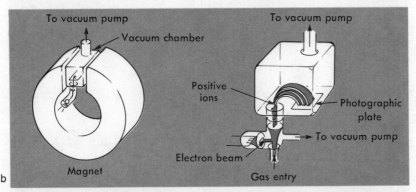

b

FIGURE 6-7. The complete mass spectrometer (a) consists of a magnet and collector end where components of the ion beam are collected and measured mass by mass (b), and an ion source region (c). Using mass spectrometers of this type, inorganic trace substances in samples of blood, lunar rocks, and pollution sources may be measured in the parts per million (ppm) range to the parts per billion (ppb) range with high precision and accuracy.

This mass spectrometer (a) can be used to measure the relative mass of minute particles as follows:

Within the metal "can" (c) is contained the sample holder, ionization filaments and suitable electrodes to provide a stable focused ion beam accelerated to 10,000 volts. Each mass component of the beam is focused on a faraday cup collector by varying the magnetic field in small known steps. The faraday cup ion current from a given mass component is converted to a voltage and measured on a strip chart recorder or with digital electronics to give a number proportional to the amount of that component present.

c

FIGURE 6-8. Mass spectra
such as those of hexane (a)
and 2,2-dimethylbutane (b) can
be used to distinguish isomers.

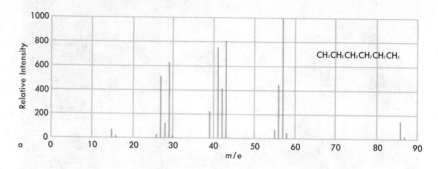

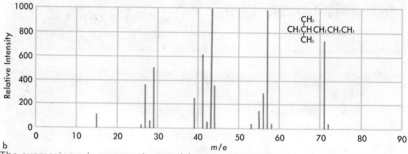

The expression *m/e* represents mass/charge which in this case is mass/one or mass.

chemists, and many other research workers use the mass spectrometer
as an analytical tool. The spectrometer is also used in research on
isomers, compounds which have the same formula but different
structures. The isomers are broken down by hitting them with electrons. The fragments are then examined. For example, hexane and
2,2-dimethylbutane have the same formula, C_6H_{14}. However, their
structures are different and they break down into different parts.
Hexane can produce five-carbon chains. The other substance cannot.
The mass of the parts determines which substance was in the chamber. In the same manner, the structures of other compounds can be
determined.

SIZE AND SHAPE OF THE ATOM AND ITS PARTS

6:13   Atomic Dimensions

In discussing the distances within and between atoms, you will
find it necessary to become familiar with a new unit of length. The
centimeter and meter are too large to be easily applied to the sizes

Table 6–3

International Atomic Masses

Element	Symbol	Atomic number	Atomic mass	Element	Symbol	Atomic number	Atomic mass
Actinium	Ac	89	227*	Mercury	Hg	80	200.59
Aluminum	Al	13	26.98154	Molybdenum	Mo	42	95.94
Americium	Am	95	243*	Neodymium	Nd	60	144.24
Antimony	Sb	51	121.75	Neon	Ne	10	20.179
Argon	Ar	18	39.948	Neptunium	Np	93	237.0482*
Arsenic	As	33	74.9216	Nickel	Ni	28	58.70
Astatine	At	85	210*	Niobium	Nb	41	92.9064
Barium	Ba	56	137.34	Nitrogen	N	7	14.0067
Berkelium	Bk	97	247*	Nobelium	No	102	255*
Beryllium	Be	4	9.01218	Osmium	Os	76	190.2
Bismuth	Bi	83	208.9804	Oxygen	O	8	15.9994
Boron	B	5	10.81	Palladium	Pd	46	106.4
Bromine	Br	35	79.904	Phosphorus	P	15	30.97376
Cadmium	Cd	48	112.40	Platinum	Pt	78	195.09
Calcium	Ca	20	40.08	Plutonium	Pu	94	244*
Californium	Cf	98	251*	Polonium	Po	84	209*
Carbon	C	6	12.011	Potassium	K	19	39.098
Cerium	Ce	58	140.12	Praseodymium	Pr	59	140.9077
Cesium	Cs	55	132.9054	Promethium	Pm	61	145*
Chlorine	Cl	17	35.453	Protactinium	Pa	91	231.0359*
Chromium	Cr	24	51.996	Radium	Ra	88	226.0254
Cobalt	Co	27	58.9332	Radon	Rn	86	222*
Copper	Cu	29	63.546	Rhenium	Re	75	186.207
Curium	Cm	96	247*	Rhodium	Rh	45	102.9055
Dysprosium	Dy	66	162.50	Rubidium	Rb	37	85.4678
Einsteinium	Es	99	254*	Ruthenium	Ru	44	101.07
Erbium	Er	68	167.26	Samarium	Sm	62	150.4
Europium	Eu	63	151.96	Scandium	Sc	21	44.9559
Fermium	Fm	100	257*	Selenium	Se	34	78.96
Fluorine	F	9	18.99840	Silicon	Si	14	28.086
Francium	Fr	87	223*	Silver	Ag	47	107.868
Gadolinium	Gd	64	157.25	Sodium	Na	11	22.98977
Gallium	Ga	31	69.72	Strontium	Sr	38	87.62
Germanium	Ge	32	72.59	Sulfur	S	16	32.06
Gold	Au	79	196.9665	Tantalum	Ta	73	180.9479
Hafnium	Hf	72	178.49	Technetium	Tc	43	98.9062*
Helium	He	2	4.00260	Tellurium	Te	52	127.60
Holmium	Ho	67	164.9304	Terbium	Tb	65	158.9254
Hydrogen	H	1	1.0079	Thallium	Tl	81	204.37
Indium	In	49	114.82	Thorium	Th	90	232.0381
Iodine	I	53	126.9045	Thulium	Tm	69	168.9342
Iridium	Ir	77	192.22	Tin	Sn	50	118.69
Iron	Fe	26	55.847	Titanium	Ti	22	47.90
Krypton	Kr	36	83.80	Tungsten	W	74	183.85
Lanthanum	La	57	138.9055	Uranium	U	92	238.029
Lawrencium	Lr	103	256*	Vanadium	V	23	50.9414
Lead	Pb	82	207.2	Xenon	Xe	54	131.30
Lithium	Li	3	6.941	Ytterbium	Yb	70	173.04
Lutetium	Lu	71	174.97	Yttrium	Y	39	88.9059
Magnesium	Mg	12	24.305	Zinc	Zn	30	65.38
Manganese	Mn	25	54.9380	Zirconium	Zr	40	91.22
Mendelevium	Md	101	258*	Element 104†		104	257*
				Element 105†		105	260*

* The mass number of the isotope with the longest known half-life.

† Names for elements 104 and 105 have not yet been approved by the IUPAC. The USSR has proposed Kurchatovium (Ku) for element 104 and Bohrium (Bh) for element 105. The United States has proposed Rutherfordium (Rf) for element 104 and Hahnium (Ha) for element 105.

of individual atoms. Therefore, another unit has found wide usage among scientists working with small dimensions, the angstrom (Å). One angstrom equals 1×10^{-10} m or 1×10^{-8} cm. Stated in terms of conventional fractions, this is one hundred-millionth (1/100,000,-000) of a centimeter. Most atoms have a diameter between 1 and 5 angstroms.

When the sizes of the parts of an atom are examined, we find that most of the atom is empty space. The radii of the nuclei of atoms vary between 1.2×10^{-5} Å and 7.5×10^{-5} Å. The radius of the electron is about 2.82×10^{-5} Å. In most atoms, the distance between the nucleus and the nearest electron is about 0.5 Å. Thus, the nucleus occupies only about one trillionth (or 10^{-12}) of the volume of an atom. To help you think about this relationship: if the nucleus of hydrogen is the size of a golf ball, the electron is roughly the size of a tennis ball, about 1.07 kilometer away.

6:14　The Rutherford-Bohr Atom

During the period 1912–1913, Lord Rutherford brought together in his laboratory a remarkable team of physicists. Included in this group was Niels Bohr, a young Dane. The beginnings of our modern concept of atomic structure were developed by this group through experiment and hypothesis. Experiments performed under Rutherford's direction showed that the atom consists of a central, positively charged nucleus surrounded in some manner by electrons. Hans

1 Å= 10^{-8}cm

Atomic diameters range from 1 Å to 5 Å.

An atom is mostly empty space.

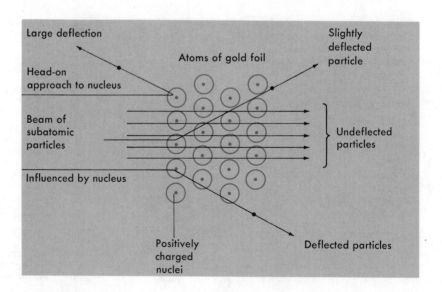

FIGURE 6-9. Most subatomic particles, when aimed at a sheet of gold foil, pass directly through. However, others are deflected or bounced back in almost same direction from which they came.

Geiger and Ernest Marsden subjected a very thin sheet of gold foil to a stream of subatomic particles. They found that most of the particles passed right through the sheet. (The atom is mostly empty space.) However, they also found that some of the particles (about 1 in 8000) were bounced back in almost the opposite direction from which they started. Rutherford explained this phenomenon as meaning that there was a very small "core" to the atom. The "core" contained all the positive charge and almost all the mass of the atom. The particles which Geiger and Marsden had shot at the foil were positively charged and weighed about 4 a.m.u. Only a highly positively charged, massive "core," or nucleus could have caused the severe bending of these particles from their normal path.

Electrons are negatively charged and attracted to the larger positive nucleus. What is there that prevents the electrons from falling into the nucleus? The discussions among these physicists, led by Rutherford and Bohr, resulted in a new idea. They thought of electrons in "orbit" around the nucleus in much the same manner as the earth is in orbit around the sun. They suggested that there is a force of attraction between the electrons and the nucleus, just as there is a force of attraction between the earth and the sun. The Rutherford-Bohr model of the atom is sometimes called the planetary atomic model.

The Rutherford-Bohr atom is a planetary model.

6:15   The Hydrogen Atom

The hydrogen atom is the simplest atom possible. It is made of a single proton in the nucleus and a single electron moving around the nucleus. Thus, according to the planetary model, this atom should be similar to a solar system consisting of a sun and one planet. J. J. Thomson did his pioneering work with *canal rays*, which are hydrogen atoms with their electron removed. Thomson did not know that the hydrogen nucleus was a single proton. We can now understand why his work ended with the calculation of the mass of a proton being about the same as the mass of a hydrogen atom.

6:16   Spectroscopy

When a substance is exposed to a certain intensity of light, heat, or some other form of energy, the atoms absorb some of the energy and are said to be excited. If atoms and molecules are in an excited state, energy changes occur. These changes can be observed. Each excited atom or molecule produces definite energy changes which

Spectroscopy depends on continuous exciting energy.

can be used to identify that kind of atom or molecule. Radiant energy of several different types can be emitted (given off) or absorbed (taken up) by excited atoms and molecules. The methods of studying substances that are exposed to some sort of continuous exciting energy are called *spectroscopy*. Originally, spectroscopy was used for studying the visible spectrum of light. There are now several types of spectroscopy. Some use the type of energy emitted by excited atoms and molecules. Others use the form of energy absorbed by atoms and molecules.

The wavelength of the light absorbed is characteristic of the substance being excited. The set of wavelengths absorbed by a substance is called the *spectrum* of that substance. The same set would be emitted by all excited particles of the same substance. We will work with absorption spectra, although emission spectra are also used.

The spectrum of a substance is the set of wavelengths absorbed or emitted by that substance.

FIGURE 6-10. Examples of line spectra are the xenon spectrum (a), the neon spectrum (b), and the hydrogen spectrum (c).

Courtesy of Kodansha Ltd.

6:17   The Bohr Model of the Hydrogen Atom

Electromagnetic radiation (energy) with a wavelength between 700 and 400 nanometers (nm) lies in the *visible spectrum*. This small band of visible radiation has given chemists and physicists a large amount of information about the elements. Bohr pointed out that the absorption of light by hydrogen at definite wavelengths means definite changes in the energy of the electron. He reasoned that the orbits of the electrons surrounding a nucleus must have a definite diameter. According to Bohr, electrons could occupy only certain orbits whose differences in energy were the same as the energy absorbed as light when the atom was excited (Section 6:20).

Each wavelength corresponds to a definite change in the energy of an electron.

You may wish to have a student do research on the general theory of blackbody radiation and the concept of energy packets or quanta.

6:18   Visible and Ultraviolet Spectroscopy

The absorption and emission spectra are the fingerprints of the elements. Each element has its own unique set of wavelengths that it absorbs or emits. Thus, the visible spectrum has been a very useful tool. Some of the elements (rubidium, cesium, helium, and hafnium) were actually discovered through its use. The visible spectrum is useful for finding the concentration of substances, for analyzing mixtures, for analysis of complex ions, and for studying indicator color range. Almost any change involving color can be measured using visible spectroscopy.

> Each element has a characteristic spectrum.

The absorption of light in the visible region can be used in another laboratory procedure called *colorimetry* (kuhl uh RIM uh tree). If a solution is colored, the intensity of its color can be compared with solutions of known strength. When the colors are of equal intensity, the solutions are at the same strength.

> Colorimetry can be used for analysis.

Ultraviolet radiation (400–200 nm) can also be used to study atomic and molecular structure. Both ultraviolet spectra and visible spectra result from electron changes. The ultraviolet spectrum of an element or compound consists of bands rather than lines because the high energy UV radiation greatly excites the electrons. The transition of the electrons from ground level to excited level causes changes in the molecule; sometimes bonds are even broken. The visible radiations are not so destructive because they have less energy than the UV radiation. Ultraviolet spectroscopy is used for the same types of analyses as visible spectroscopy.

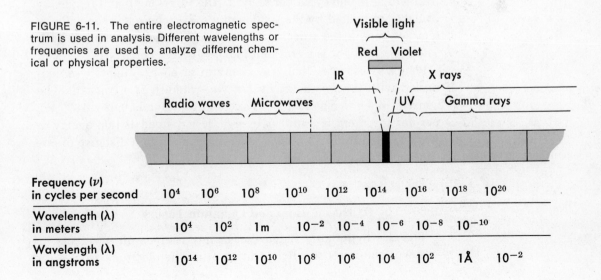

FIGURE 6-11. The entire electromagnetic spectrum is used in analysis. Different wavelengths or frequencies are used to analyze different chemical or physical properties.

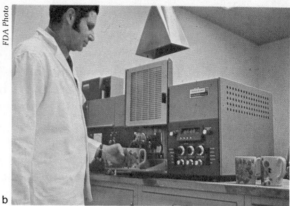

FIGURE 6-12. Spectrophotometers can be used in analytical studies. Here, FDA chemists check foods for vitamin content (a) and mugs for lead contamination (b).

QUANTUM THEORY

6:19 Planck's Hypothesis

Once Bohr had developed the basic outline of his planetary model of the atom, he made use of a new theory. The theory was the *quantum theory* which had been set forth by a German, Max Planck. Planck concluded that the theories concerning the emitting of light by objects heated to the glowing point were in error. Planck assumed that energy instead of being given off continuously is given off in little packets, or *quanta*. Quanta of radiant energy are often called *photons*. He further stated that the amount of energy radiated is indicated by the frequency of the light emitted.

The frequency of a wave is the number of cycles completed in a unit of time, usually one second. The unit of frequency is the hertz (Hz) which is one cycle per second. The wavelength and frequency of light are related by the statement $v = \lambda\nu$, where v is the velocity (cm per sec), λ the wavelength (cm), and ν the frequency (hertz). The speed of light is a constant (3.00×10^{10} cm per sec).

Planck's idea was that one quantum of energy (light) was connected with the frequency by $E = h\nu$, where h is a constant. The constant is known as Planck's constant. Its value is 6.63×10^{-27} erg per hertz. An erg is a unit of energy. It is defined as that energy or work needed to accelerate a mass of one gram in a distance of one centimeter by one cm/sec². $1 \text{ erg} = \dfrac{1 \text{ g-cm}^2}{\text{sec}^2}$

6:20 The Hydrogen Atom and Quantum Theory

Planck's hypothesis stated that energy is given off in quanta instead of continuously. Bohr thought that the electrons around the

Planck proposed that light was radiated in quanta, or photons.

Frequency is the number of cycles per unit of time.

Velocity of a wave:
$v = \lambda\nu$

Energy of a quantum:
$E = h\nu$

If you can find an old radio dial calibrated in both kilocycles and meters, it will illustrate nicely the relationship between frequency and wavelength.

nucleus of an atom could absorb or emit energy only in terms of whole numbers of photons. In other words, an electron could emit energy in one quantum or two quanta, but not in $1\frac{1}{4}$ or $3\frac{1}{2}$ quanta. He pictured the hydrogen atom as an electron circling a nucleus at a distance of about 0.53 Å.

Bohr also imagined that an electron could absorb a quantum of energy under certain conditions and move to a larger orbit. Since this represents a definite amount of energy, the next orbit must be at some definite location with respect to the first. If still more energy is added to the electron, it moves into a still larger orbit, and so on.

When an electron drops from a larger orbit to a smaller one, energy is given off. Since these orbits represent definite energy levels, the energy radiated is a definite amount. The frequency of the light emitted is dependent only on the amount of energy in the quantum and has a definite value. This emission of light has actually been observed and measured.

The size of the smallest orbit which an electron can occupy, the one closest to the nucleus, can be calculated. This smallest orbit is called the *ground state* of the electron. Bohr knew the ground state of the hydrogen electron. By applying the quantum theory to atomic structure, he calculated the frequencies that should be in the hydrogen spectrum. His results agreed almost perfectly with the actual observations of the hydrogen spectrum. Although today we use a model of the atom which differs from that of Bohr, many of the characteristics of his theory are still retained. The chief difference, as you will see in the next chapter, is that electrons do not actually move in orbits around the nucleus in the same sense that planets move in orbits around the sun. However, the idea of energy levels is still the basis of atomic structure theory. The values calculated by Bohr for the hydrogen atom are still basically correct.

Electrons absorb or emit only whole numbers of quanta.

An electron moves farther from the nucleus as it emits energy.

The ground state of an electron is the position of least energy.

Modern atomic theory differs from Bohr's in describing the path of the electron.

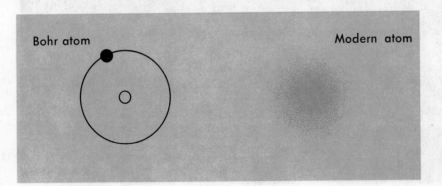

FIGURE 6-13. The modern picture of the atom indicates only the most probable location of the electron.

We can restate the discussion as follows: A wave of a certain frequency has only one possible wavelength, given by $\lambda = \dfrac{v}{\nu}$. It has only one possible amount of energy, given by $E = h\nu$, since both v and h are constants. If any one of the three quantities, frequency, wavelength, or energy, is known, we can calculate the other two.

FIGURE 6-14. A spectroscope (a), as illustrated (b), makes use of a discharge tube (c) to produce spectra (d).

F. Bernard Daniel

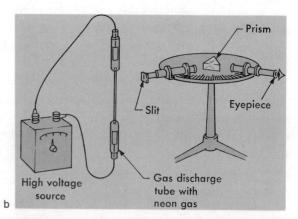

Courtesy of Kodansha Ltd.

Courtesy of Kodansha Ltd.

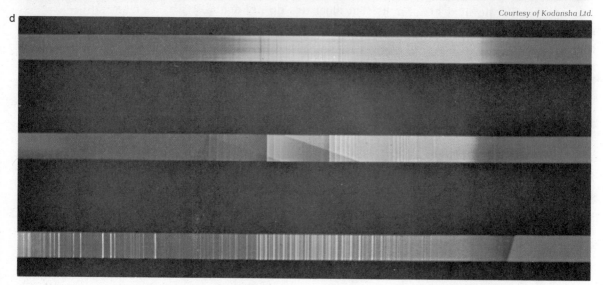

The following table is a list of several flame tests which can be used to illustrate emission of light as excited electrons return to lower energy states:

Element	Color
Na^+	Yellow
K^+	Violet
Ca^{2+}	Yellow-red
Sr^{2+}	Deep red
Li^+	Crimson
Ba^{2+}	Green-yellow
Cu^{2+}	Blue-green

The spectrum produced by a compound can be used to determine the composition of the compound. Each line in a spectrum represents one frequency of light. Because the velocity of light is always constant, each frequency means a certain energy. This energy is determined by the movement of electrons between energy levels which are specific for each element. The same set of energy levels will always produce the same spectrum.

EXAMPLE – ENERGY OF QUANTA

A certain red light has a wavelength of 600 nm. What is its frequency? What is the energy content of one photon of this light? (The velocity of light is equal to 3.00×10^{10} cm/sec.)

Solving for frequency:

$$\lambda = 600 \text{ nm} = 6.00 \times 10^{-5} \text{ cm; and}$$

$$v = \lambda \nu$$

thus, $\nu = \dfrac{v}{\lambda}$

$$\nu = \frac{3 \times 10^{10} \text{ cm}}{\text{sec}} \left| \frac{1}{6 \times 10^{-5} \text{ cm}} \right.$$

$$\nu = \frac{5 \times 10^{14}}{\text{sec}} = 5 \times 10^{14} \text{ Hz}$$

Solving for energy:

$$E = h\nu$$
$$E = \frac{6.63 \times 10^{-27} \text{ erg}}{\text{Hz}} \left| 5 \times 10^{14} \text{ Hz} \right.$$

$$E = 3.31 \times 10^{-12} \text{ ergs}$$

PROBLEMS

1. A certain violet light has a wavelength of 410 nm. What is its frequency? The velocity of light is equal to 3.00×10^{10} cm/sec.

   ans. 7.32×10^{14} Hz

2. A certain green light has a frequency of 6×10^{14} Hz. What is its wavelength?

   5000Å or 500 nm

3. What is the energy content of one quantum of the light in Problem 1?

   ans. 4.85×10^{-12} ergs

4. What is the energy content of one quantum of the light in Problem 2?

   3.97×10^{-12} ergs

6:21 Photoelectric Effect

Before leaving the quantum theory, we will consider one other observation which was explained by this theory. Recall that quanta of light energy are referred to as photons. It had been known for some time that light falling on the surface of certain substances would cause electrons to be given off. There was, however, a puzzling fact about this change. When the intensity of light (the number of photons per unit time) falling on the surface was reduced, the electrons emitted still had the same energy; there were just fewer of them. Albert Einstein pointed out that Planck's hypothesis explained this nicely.

A certain amount of energy is needed to remove an electron from the surface of a substance. If a photon of greater energy strikes the electron, the electron will move away from the surface. Since it is in motion, the electron has some kinetic energy. The kinetic energy of the departing electron is equal to the difference between the energy of the incoming photon ($h\nu$) and the work required to remove it from the surface. If light of one frequency is used, then the electrons escaping from the surface of the substance will all have the same energy. This emission of electrons is called the *photoelectric effect*. If the amount of light falling on the surface is increased, but the frequency remains the same, the number of electrons being emitted will increase. Experiments show this idea to be true. What would happen if the frequency of the light were increased? The equation $E = h\nu$ is used to supply the answer. Increased frequency means increased energy in the photon. The amount of energy that must be

Photoelectric effect refers to emission of electrons from certain substances when exposed to light of suitable frequency.

The photoelectric effect lends strong support for the quantum theory.

FIGURE 6-15.   Photoelectric cells have many practical uses. They are a part of photographic light meters (a) and security light systems (b).

The electrons are emitted from the surface with a higher energy, that is, at a greater velocity.

a

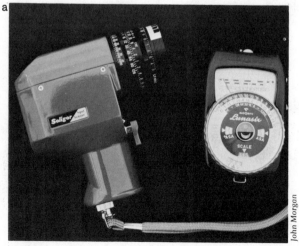

b

used to free the electron from the atom is constant for a given substance. The electrons now leave the surface with a higher energy than they did with the other frequency. This idea has also been checked by experiment.

SUMMARY

1. Democritus proposed the earliest recorded atomic theory.
2. Modern atomic theory dates from John Dalton's hypothesis which made use of the law of conservation of mass and the law of definite proportions.
3. Dalton stated: all matter is formed of indivisible particles called atoms; all atoms of one element are the same; atoms of different elements are unlike; and atoms can unite with one another in simple whole-number ratios.
4. From his atomic hypothesis, Dalton stated the law of multiple proportions.
5. Modern atomic theory differs from Dalton's atomic theory mainly because of subatomic particles and isotopes.
6. An electron is a negatively charged particle with a very small mass.
7. A proton is a positively charged particle with a mass 1837 times the mass of an electron.
8. A neutron is an uncharged particle with a mass about the same as the mass of a proton.
9. All atoms of an element contain the same number of protons in their nuclei.
10. Atoms which contain the same number of protons but different numbers of neutrons in their nuclei are isotopes of the same element.
11. The atomic number (Z) of an element is the number of protons in its nucleus.
12. The mass number (A) of an atom is the number of particles in the nucleus of that atom.
13. The atomic mass (average mass, M) of an element is the mass of an average individual atom of the element compared with $\frac{1}{12}$ the mass of the carbon-12 atom.
14. Atomic mass can be measured with the mass spectrometer.
15. Atoms are extremely small and consist mostly of space.

16. Rutherford and Bohr pictured the atom as consisting of a central nucleus surrounded by electrons in orbits.

17. Substances excited by an electric current emit light in definite wavelengths called a spectrum.

18. Visible and ultraviolet spectroscopy are used to study the wavelengths of light absorbed and emitted by electrons in atoms.

19. Planck stated that energy is radiated in discrete units called quanta. A photon is a quantum of light energy.

20. The energy of a quantum of radiation varies directly as the frequency of the radiation ($E = h\nu$).

21. The quantum theory helped Bohr explain the hydrogen spectrum, and thus, to calculate the orbits for the hydrogen atom.

22. The photoelectric effect is the loss of electrons from a substance, caused by photons falling on its surface.

PROBLEMS

See Teacher's Guide at the front of this book.

5. What did each of the following do in forming the atomic theory:
   a. Dalton   c. Rutherford   e. Moseley   g. Planck
   b. Thomson   d. Chadwick   f. Bohr

6. How would you show the law of conservation of mass with a burning candle?

7. Design an experiment to demonstrate the law of definite proportions.

8. A particular atom of argon contains 18 protons, 18 electrons, and 22 neutrons. What is the atomic number of this atom? What is its mass number?   atomic number 18
          mass number 40

9. Compute the average atomic mass of gallium, if 60% of the gallium atoms occurring in nature have mass number 69 and 40% of the atoms have mass number 71.   69.8 a.m.u.

10. Compute the average atomic mass of chromium if the relative amounts are as follows: 52.1 a.m.u.

mass number	percentage
50	4.31
52	83.8
53	9.55
54	2.38

11. How many Å are there in 2.01 cm? 2.01 x 10⁸ Å

12. What would be the wavelength of light necessary to cause electrons to leave the surface of a substance with an energy of 1.2×10^{-12} ergs? Assume the energy necessary to release the electron from the surface is 3.6×10^{-12} ergs. 4140 Å

13. How did the discovery of subatomic particles and isotopes affect Dalton's theories?

14. What are the basic differences among protons, neutrons, and electrons?

See Teacher's Guide at the front of this book.

ONE MORE STEP

1. Make a table listing as many subatomic particles as you can. For each particle, list its mass, charge, and lifetime.

See Teacher's Guide at the front of this book.

2. Make a list of the mass numbers of all known isotopes of the first twenty elements. Show those that are unstable (radioactive) in red.

3. What was the age of each of the men listed in Problem 5 on page 132 at the time of his major work?

4. Although Bohr was the first to use experimental evidence to support his hypothesis, he was not the first person to advance a planetary model for the atom. Look into the history of this idea prior to Bohr.

5. Find a description of an experiment used for determining the size of a proton or a neutron.

6. Two techniques for analysis which are closely allied with colorimetry are fluorimetry (floh uh RIHM ih tree) and nephelometry (nef uh LAHM ih tree). Investigate the uses of these two procedures.

7. Prepare a report for your class on the topic of electron paramagnetic resonance (EPR), one of the newer methods in analysis.

Suggested Readings for this chapter may be found in the Teacher's Guide at the front of this book.

Your telephone feels like a very solid object. Like all other matter, your telephone is made up of atoms. Each atom is made up of still smaller particles. Much of the space taken up by an atom is really empty space. Thus, when objects containing elements of relatively low atomic number are exposed to neutrons, many of the neutrons pass completely through and can expose a photographic film. This process is called neutron radiography. Can you think of some practical applications of this process?

Electrons and Clouds ———————————— 7

Chapter 7 introduces Schrödinger's probability equation and Heisenberg's uncertainty principle. This leads to the electron cloud and quantum numbers of the modern atomic model.

In the last fifty years, the division between matter and energy has become less and less distinct. Radiant energy is found to have many of the properties of particles. Matter, particularly in the form of very small particles, is found to display the characteristics of wave motion. The purpose of this chapter is to look more closely at this wave-particle problem.

We have seen that the frequencies predicted by Bohr for the hydrogen spectrum are "essentially" correct (Chapter 6). Note that we did not use the word "exactly." Improved equipment has shown that the hydrogen spectrum lines predicted by Bohr are not single lines. Let us examine the hydrogen spectrum with an instrument capable of spreading the lines far apart. We see that what seemed to be single lines, consist of several lines very closely spaced. Scientists have had to reexamine many of their ideas about the behavior of the particles in an atom. They have done so because of the discovery of "fine structure" of spectral lines and Bohr's use of the quantum theory in the study of atomic structure.

GOAL: You will gain an understanding of the electronic structure of the atom.

Hydrogen spectrum lines are not single lines.

Spectra of several elements are shown in Figure 6-10.

Suggestion: Demonstrate the hydrogen spectrum using a Geisler tube and a Bunsen spectroscope.

WAVES AND PARTICLES

7:1 DeBroglie's Hypothesis

In 1923, a French physicist, Louis DeBroglie, proposed a new hypothesis which became a building block for the present theory of atomic structure. DeBroglie knew of Planck's theory (radiation of a certain frequency and wavelength is composed of discrete amounts of energy called quanta). This theory appeared to give the characteristics of particles to waves. DeBroglie thought that, if Planck were correct, then it might be possible for particles to have some of the characteristics of waves.

DeBroglie suggested that particles have characteristics of waves.

Einstein had previously predicted that every particle of matter is equivalent to a discrete amount of energy. The relationship between matter and energy is given by the equation:

$$E = mv^2$$

where E is energy, m is the mass of the particle, and v is the speed of light (a constant). It was also known that every quantum of a wave has a discrete amount of energy. The energy of a quantum is given by the equation:

$$E = h\nu$$

where ν is the wave frequency and h is Planck's constant. DeBroglie thought that if particles had wave characteristics, the two expressions for energy would be equivalent.

$$mc^2 = h\nu$$

In order to make the equation apply to all cases, he substituted v, a general velocity, for c, the velocity of light. Thus,

$$mv^2 = h\nu$$

The velocity of a wave is related to the wavelength, λ, and the frequency, ν, by the expression

$$v = \lambda\nu \quad \text{and} \quad \nu = \frac{v}{\lambda}$$

Substituting v/λ for ν in the following equation:

$$mv^2 = h\nu$$

DeBroglie obtained an expression for the wavelength associated with a moving particle.

$$mv^2 = \frac{hv}{\lambda}$$

$$\lambda = \frac{hv}{mv^2} = \frac{h}{mv}$$

The expression, $\lambda = \dfrac{h}{mv}$ was DeBroglie's prediction of the wave length of a particle of mass m and velocity v. Within two years, DeBroglie's hypothesis was proven correct. Scientists demonstrated by experiment that, in some ways, an electron stream acted in the same way as a ray of light (Figure 7–1). They further showed that the wavelength of the electrons was exactly that predicted by DeBroglie.

The wavelength of a particle can be described by the expression $\lambda = \dfrac{h}{mv}$.

The Davisson-Germer experiment

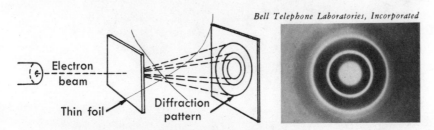

Bell Telephone Laboratories, Incorporated

Electron beam

Thin foil

Diffraction pattern

FIGURE 7-1. A diffraction pattern (shown in photo) is formed by passing a narrow beam of electrons through thin foil.

7:2 The Apparent Contradiction

Waves can act as particles, and particles can act as waves. We saw how the photoelectric effect and Bohr's planetary atom model were explained in terms of the particle properties of light. Now let us look at a light phenomenon which can be explained in terms of the wave properties of light.

Light travels at different speeds in different substances. When light passes from one substance into another it changes speed. If the light strikes the surface at an angle, it also changes direction (is bent or refracted). Every transparent substance bends light by a certain amount. The amount of bending that occurs for each substance is given by its index of refraction. The index of refraction is a ratio or comparison.

The index of refraction of a substance is determined by the degree to which light is bent as it passes at an angle from a vacuum into that substance. Each substance has a characteristic index of refraction (Figure 7–2). We can identify a substance by its index of refraction. The index of refraction of a mixture is related to the relative amounts of the two substances in the mixture. If we know the index of refraction of each of the two substances, we can determine the percentage

Light has properties of both particles and waves.

Index of refraction is a characteristic of all transparent materials.

FIGURE 7-2. Light is refracted as it passes at an angle from air into glass.

Index of refraction is measured with respect to a vacuum. However, the index with respect to air will be negligibly different in most cases.

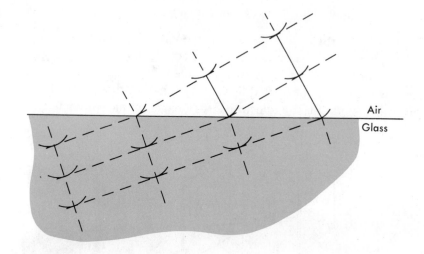

Air

Glass

composition of the mixture. For example, we may want to find the concentration of a saltwater solution. To do this we measure the index of refraction of the mixture, and compare it to the index of refraction of pure salt and that of pure water. The instrument used to measure index of refraction is called a *refractometer* (ree frak TOM uh tuhr).

A refractometer is used to measure index of refraction.

Like light, electrons also have properties of both waves and particles. However, one cannot observe both the particle and wave characteristics of an electron by the same experiment. If an experiment is carried out to show an electron's wave characteristics, the electron will act only as a wave. Another experiment, carried out to

FIGURE 7-3. A refractometer (a) is used to measure index of refraction. A pencil (b) when placed in water, which has an index of refraction of 1.33, appears to be bent.

a

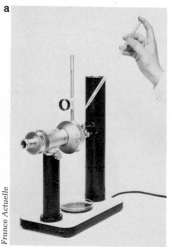

France Actuelle

b

Steve Danison

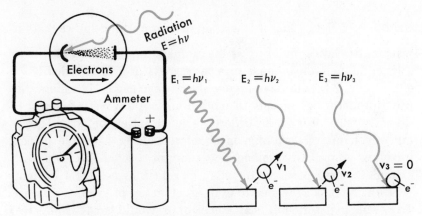

FIGURE 7-4. The photoelectric effect can be used to demon-strate that electrons have particle characteristics. Only certain electrons near the surface of the metal receive enough energy to escape.

Wave particle duality has interesting philosophical implicatons. Previous to formulation of the uncer-tainty principle, scientists assumed that there was no limit to the accuracy of any measurement other than the limits imposed by the instru-ment used in measuring. The wave-particle duality concept now places a physical limit on the possible accuracy of measurement. As the location of a minute-particle becomes more certain, its velocity becomes less certain.

show the electron as a particle, will show only that the electron is a particle (Figure 7–4). The link between these two concepts is Planck's constant, h. The whole idea of the two-sided nature of waves and particles is referred to as the *wave-particle duality of nature*. The duality applies to all waves and all particles. Scientists are not always interested in duality. For example, when scientists study the motion of an artillery shell, wave characteristics do not enter into their study for two reasons. First, the wavelength is so short that it cannot be detected; and second, the shell as a particle is all that the scientists want to study. However, with a very small particle such as an electron, a study of its wave characteristics can tell as much about its behavior as a study of its particle char-acteristics.

Electrons have wave-par-ticle duality.

UNCERTAINTY AND WAVE MECHANICS

7:3 Momentum

The product of the mass and velocity of an object is called the *momentum* of the object. In equation form, $mv = p$, where m is the mass, v is the velocity, and p is the symbol for momentum. Recall DeBroglie's equation for the wavelength of the wave associated with a particle in motion $\left(\lambda = \dfrac{h}{mv} \right)$. Substituting for mv, we can then

As momentum of an object increases, its wavelength decreases.

Newton's laws of motion:
1. Every object remains at rest or in uniform motion until an external force acts to change its motion.
2. The change in motion of an object produced by an external force varies directly with the force exerted.
3. For every action, there is an equal and opposite reaction.

write $\lambda = \dfrac{h}{p}$. Notice that it is written in a form which shows that the wavelength varies inversely as the momentum. An object may have a large momentum because of a large mass or a large velocity. In either case, it would have a very small wavelength. Therefore, the wave properties of objects in motion are not always of interest to the scientist. This is a basic difference between Newtonian and quantum mechanics. Newtonian mechanics deals with visible objects traveling at ordinary velocities. Quantum mechanics deals with extremely small particles traveling at velocities near that of light.

To the chemist, the electrons in an atom are of greatest interest. To be able to describe fully an electron, we would have to know two things: (1) where it is, and (2) where it is going. In other words, we must know the electron's present location and its momentum (mass times velocity). Remember that velocity includes not only the speed but also the direction of motion. If we know the velocity and the location of an electron at any instant, we can calculate where the electron will be after some period of time has elapsed.

PROBLEMS

1. Calculate the momentum in g-cm/sec of an electron with a velocity of 1.00×10^{10} cm/sec.   *ans.* 9.11×10^{-18} g-cm/sec
2. Calculate the momentum of a proton with a velocity of 1.40×10^8 cm/sec. 2.34×10^{-16} g-cm/sec

7:4 Measuring Position and Momentum

Werner Heisenberg further improved the ideas about atomic structure. He pointed out that it is impossible to know both the exact location and the exact momentum of an object at the same time.

Heisenberg's ideas were as follows. To locate the exact position of an electron, we must be able to "look" at it as shown in Figure 7–5. When we look at an object large enough to see with our eyes, we actually see the light waves which the object has reflected. When a sailor "looks" at an object by using radar, he (or rather the radar receiver) is actually "seeing" the radar waves reflected by the object. In other words, for us to see something, the something (object) must

Heisenberg's uncertainty principle: The exact location and momentum of an object can not be determined at the same time.

be hit by some kind of radiant energy. However, a collision between a quantum (photon) and an electron results in a large change in the energy of the electron. Let us assume now that we have "looked" at an electron, using some sort of radiant energy as "illumination," and

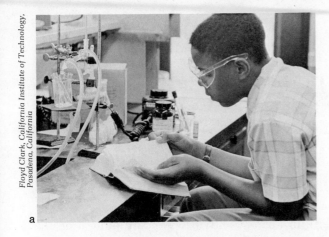

Floyd Clark, California Institute of Technology, Pasadena, California

a

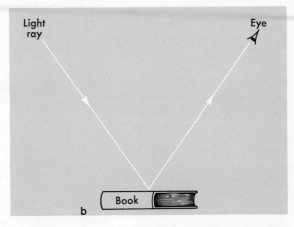

Light ray

Eye

Book

b

FIGURE 7-5. A student reading a book (a) sees the book because of reflected light waves (b).

have found the exact location of the electron. Now we would have little idea of the electron's velocity. The collision between it and the quantum of energy that was used to see it has caused its velocity to change. Thus, we would know the location of the electron, but not its velocity. On the other hand, if we measure an electron's velocity, we will change the electron's position. We would know the velocity fairly well, but not the location. Heisenberg stated that there is always some uncertainty as to the location and momentum of an electron. This last statement is known as *Heisenberg's uncertainty principle.*

The uncertainty of the location and the uncertainty of the momentum of an electron are related by Planck's constant. If Δp is the uncertainty in the momentum and Δx is the uncertainty in the location, then $\Delta p \, \Delta x \geqq h$. Thus, since h remains constant, the more certain we are of the location of the electron, the less certain we are of its momentum. The more certain we are of its momentum, the less certain we are of its location.

Momentum is a vector quantity. A vector always has both magnitude and direction. Vectors consist of two or more components. For instance, one vector consists of distance and time; another vector quantity could be constructed using distance and direction. Momentum is a vector which consists of mass and velocity.

$\Delta p \, \Delta x \geq h$

7:5 Wave Characteristics

Chemists and physicists now found themselves unable to describe the structure of the atom. Heisenberg had, in effect, told them not only that did they not know the exact motion of an electron but also that they never could know. Notice, however, that Heisenberg's principle of uncertainty treats the electron as a particle. What happens if the electron is treated as a wave? This is what the Austrian physicist, Erwin Schrödinger, did. Before considering his work, let us take another look at the properties of waves.

Thus far, three properties of waves have been discussed: wavelength, λ; frequency, ν; and velocity, v. Another wave property that

Schrödinger considered the electron as a wave.

Amplitude modulated (AM) radio waves can be used to introduce the section on wave characteristics.

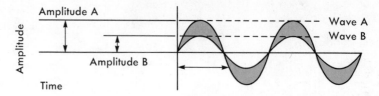

FIGURE 7-6. Wave A has the same wavelength as wave B.

is of importance is the amplitude of a wave, or its maximum displacement from zero. In Figure 7-6, two waves are plotted on the same axes. Note that the amplitude of wave A is twice that of wave B, even though they have the same wavelength.

Amplitude of a wave is its maximum displacement from a base line.

7:6 Schrödinger's Work

Schrödinger treated the electron as a wave and developed a mathematical equation to describe its wave-like behavior. Schrödinger's equation related the amplitude of the electron-wave, ψ, to any point in the space surrounding the nucleus. As he pointed out, there is no physical meaning to the values of ψ. You should avoid trying to assume one. Terms for the total energy and for the potential energy of the electron are also involved in this equation. In computing the total energy and the potential energy, certain integers must be used. These numbers are important in chemistry. For example, the term for the total energy is $2\pi^2 m e^4/h^2 n^2$. Here, m is the mass of the electron, e is the charge on the electron, h is Planck's constant, and n can take positive whole number values. The symbol n is called a quantum number. There are four such quantum numbers used in describing electron behavior. They will be studied in detail in later sections. The actual wave equation involves mathematics with which you are probably not familiar and so it will not be given.

Certain integers in Schrödinger's equation are called quantum numbers.

The physical significance of all this mathematics was pointed out by Max Born. He showed that the square of the absolute value of the amplitude, $|\psi|^2$, gave the probability of finding the electron at the point for which the equation was solved.

7:7 Wave-Mechanical View of the Hydrogen Atom

We can use Schrödinger's wave equation to determine the probability of finding the hydrogen electron in any given place. Used for this purpose, the equation provides the same results as those pre-

Schrödinger's equation can be used to "find" the hydrogen electron.

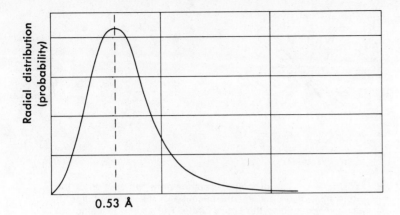

0.53 Å

FIGURE 7-7. This graph shows the probability (according to Schrödinger's equation) of finding the electron a given distance from the nucleus. The point of highest probability for the first orbital is approximately the same as Bohr found in his work with the hydrogen atom, 0.53 Å.

dicted by Bohr. We can do this as follows: Compute the probabilities of finding the electron at different points along a given line away from the nucleus. We will then find one point with a higher probability than any other (Figure 7–7). To carry the process even further, we may calculate the probabilities for thousands of points in space. There will be many points of equal probability. If we select all the points of highest probability and connect them, some three dimensional shape will be formed (Figures 7–14 and 7–15). The most probable place to find the electron will be some place on the surface of this calculated shape. Remember that this shape is only a "mental model," and does not actually exist. It is something we use in our minds to locate the electron.

There is another way of looking at this phenomenon. Consider that the electron moves about the nucleus in such a way as to pass through the points of high probability more often than through any other points. The electron is traveling at a very high rate of speed. If it were visible to the eye, it would look like a cloud formed by the electron's rapid motion, not like a small particle moving in a path. Think of the propeller of an airplane as shown in Figure 7–8. A four-blade propeller fills, at any given time, only about 20% of the circle in which it turns. However, when the propeller is turning, it appears to fill the complete circle. If we place something between the blades while the propeller is turning, we would realize that the

A surface of points of greatest probable location of the electron is a "mental model."

The position of an electron can best be represented by a cloud.

Propeller   Cloud

FIGURE 7-8. The propeller occupies only one section of the circle at a given instant but because of its rapid rotation, it effectively occupies the entire circle. The same reasoning applies to the location of an electron in an orbital.

An electron effectively occupies all the space around a nucleus.

FIGURE 7-9. The location of a car travelling at a very high rate of speed is not well defined. Like that of an electron, only the probable location of the car is known at a given time.

propeller is effectively filling the entire circle! So it is with the electron. It effectively fills all the space. At any given time, it is more likely to be somewhere on the surface of the shape described by the points of highest probability. Whereas the probability of finding the propeller outside its volume is hopefully zero, it is possible to find the electron outside of its high probability surface. Therefore, since the volume occupied by an electron is somewhat vague, it is better to refer to it as an electron cloud. Let us now look at this electron cloud so that we may learn more about its size and shape.

AEC: Hoffman

QUANTUM NUMBERS

7:8 Solution of Schrödinger's Equation

Unfortunately, the Schrödinger equation proved difficult for even the best mathematicians. It has been solved exactly only for very simple cases involving the hydrogen atom. The use of quantum numbers in the solution of the wave equation was mentioned in Section 7:6. These numbers, which change the values in the equation by whole-number steps, represent different energy states of the electron. In Schrödinger's atomic model, changes between energy states must take place by emission or absorption of whole numbers of photons just as in Bohr's model. In the simple hydrogen atom, solution of the wave equation gives us accurate energy states. In more complex atoms, however, the interaction of electrons makes solution of the equation impossible. In spite of this, we can come close to finding the electronic structure of atoms. We do this by assuming that the various electrons in a multielectron atom occupy energy states corresponding to the various single states in the simpler hydrogen atom. The different single states of the hydrogen atom are calculated by changing the quantum numbers. There are four quantum numbers (parameters), n, l, m, and s. Each electron within an atom can be described by a set of four quantum numbers. We will discuss each quantum number separately starting with n.

An electron in an atom can be described by a set of four quantum numbers.

7:9 The Principal Quantum Number

The first quantum number (n) corresponds to the energy levels (1,2,3, ... n) that Bohr suggested for the hydrogen atom. According to Bohr, an electron can have only certain energies, and can occupy only specific energy levels. These energy levels are numbered, starting with 1 and proceeding to the higher integers. The number of the energy level, referred to as n, is called the principal quantum number.

Electrons may be found in each energy level of an atom but the greatest number of electrons possible in any one level is $2n^2$. Thus, in the first level ($n = 1$), there may be at most two electrons (2×1^2). In the fourth energy level, there can be no more than 32 electrons (2×4^2). Figure 7–10, an energy level diagram, shows the relative energies of the various energy levels and indicates the maximum number of electrons possible in each level.

The principal quantum number (n) is the number of the energy level.

The maximum number of electrons in any energy level (n) is $2n^2$.

The principal quantum number (n) is a constant that can be any positive integer (1,2,3, . . .n). It refers to energy level or shell. The shells are labeled 1,2,3, . . . starting at the center and moving outward from the nucleus.

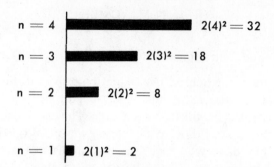

FIGURE 7-10. An energy level diagram showing the maximum number of electrons in each level from $n = 1$ to $n = 4$.

PROBLEM

3. Calculate the maximum number of electrons that can occupy the levels with $n = 3, 5, 6,$ and 8. 3. 18, 50, 72, 128

7:10 Energy Sublevels

The second quantum number is l. You may have had the idea that all electrons in one level have the same energy. This is not true. Spectrum studies have shown that an energy level is actually made up of many energy states closely grouped together. We can refer to these as *sublevels*.

Each level has a number of sublevels equal to the principal quantum number. You can expect to find one sublevel in the 1 level, two sublevels in the 2 level, three sublevels in the 3 level, and four sublevels in the 4 level. The lowest sublevel in a given level has been

The second quantum number (l) is the number of a sublevel in n.

Each energy level (n) has n sublevels.

The second quantum number (l) is a constant which is related to n, the first quantum number. It is an integer which can take on the values $0, 1, 2, \ldots (n-1)$. It is associated with orbital (or energy sublevel) shape. The sublevels are commonly designated as $s\ (l = 0)$, $p\ (l = 1)$, $d\ (l = 2)$, $f\ (l = 3), \ldots$

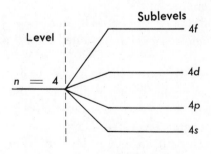

FIGURE 7-11. The $n = 4$ energy level contains s, p, d, and f sublevels.

named *s*; the second, *p*; the third, *d*; and the fourth, *f*. Thus, the first level has only an *s* sublevel. The second level has *s* and *p* sublevels, while the third has *s*, *p*, and *d* sublevels.

As an example, consider the *n* = 4 level. Instead of the single energy line as was shown in Figure 7–10, the *n* = 4 level should look as in Figure 7–11 with all sublevels shown.

We can now redo the energy level diagram. Figure 7–12 shows the various sublevels for each of the levels. Notice the overlapping in the third and fourth levels. There is even more in the fourth and fifth, fifth and sixth, and so on. What this means, in effect, is that the 4*s* sublevel is of lower energy than the 3*d* sublevel. These will be of interest later when we consider how the levels become filled with electrons in the atoms of various elements.

Sublevels are named *s*, *p*, *d*, and *f*.

The *n* = 4 level contains four sublevels.

Sublevels of different energy levels may overlap.

The letters *s,p,d,* and *f* stand for sharp, principal, diffuse, and fundamental. These terms were originally spectroscopy labels for different series of spectral lines emitted by the elements.

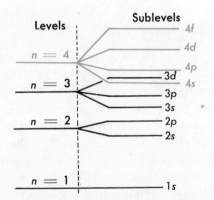

FIGURE 7-12. An energy level diagram showing levels and sublevels. Notice the overlapping of sublevels between *n* = 3 and *n* = 4.

7:11 Orbitals

The third quantum number is *m*. Research has shown that the 1*s*, 2*s*, and 3*s* sublevels have space for only one pair of electrons. The 2*p* and the 3*p* sublevels can contain three pairs, and the 3*d* sublevel can contain five pairs. In general, any *s* sublevel may contain one pair of electrons; any *p* sublevel, three pairs; any *d* sublevel, five pairs; and any *f* sublevel, seven pairs. Each of the pairs in a given sublevel has a different place in space and makes up one *orbital*.

We can now redraw the energy level diagram with the orbitals shown. Each short line in Figure 7–13 represents an orbital capable of containing a pair of electrons.

The third quantum number (*m*) represents the number of orbitals in a sublevel.

Each orbital may contain a pair of electrons.

The third quantum number (m) is an integer which is related to l, the second quantum number. It can take on the values $0, \pm1, \pm2, \ldots (\pm l)$. It is associated with direction in space of an orbital. Each sublevel has the following number of possible orbitals:

s, one orbital ($m = 0$)
p, three orbitals ($m = 0, \pm1$)
d, five orbitals ($m = 0, \pm1, \pm2$)
f, seven orbitals
($m = 0, \pm1, \pm2, \pm3$)

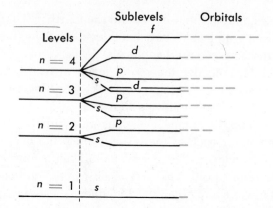

FIGURE 7-13. Each sublevel can be divided into one or more orbitals.

7:12 Effect on the Charge Cloud

We now want to see how these various energy levels and sublevels affect the electron charge cloud described in Section 7:7. In general, the size of the charge cloud is proportional to n, the principal quantum number. The larger the value of n, the larger the cloud. However, there are also other factors which govern the size of the cloud. Electrons are not only repelled by each other, they are also attracted by the positively charged nucleus. At the same time, other electrons serve to screen the effect of the nucleus. That is, when electron "A" is between the nucleus and electron "B", electron "A" reduces the attraction of the nucleus for electron "B." Thus, it is difficult to assign the size of the charge cloud to any single factor.

A geometric model of the cloud will be helpful later in thinking about relationships among atoms even though it is not entirely

The size of the charge cloud depends primarily on n.

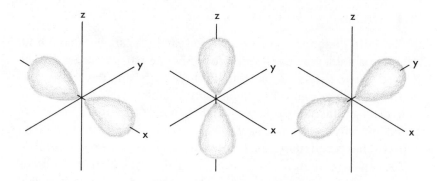

FIGURE 7-14. The probability shapes of the three $2p$ orbitals.

accurate. The general probability function of Schrödinger (Section 7:6) predicts that the total charge cloud of all the electrons in any sublevel or energy level can be thought of as spherical. However, orbitals have characteristic probability shapes of their own. For example, as shown in Figure 7–14, the three 2p orbitals can be directed along the three-dimensional, mutually perpendicular x, y, and z axes.

The shape of the charge cloud depends on *l*. The effective charge cloud of an energy level or sublevel can be thought of as spherical.

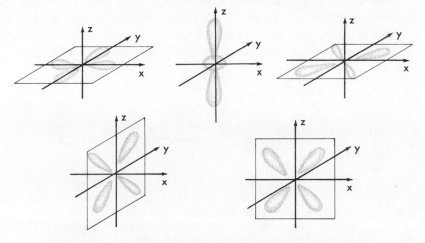

FIGURE 7-15. The probability shapes of the five 3d orbitals.

As shown in Figure 7–15, the five 3d orbitals also have probability shapes which have relationships among themselves. Notice that these, as well as the 2p orbitals, when filled and combined, have a spherical charge cloud, the cloud of the energy level.

Each orbital has a characteristic shape.

The third quantum number, m, indicates the direction in space of the orbital. There are three possible values for m when discussing a p sublevel. They correspond to orbitals aligned along the x, y, and z axes. These orbitals are alike in size and shape and differ only in direction. As a result, the electrons occupying them have the same energy. Orbitals representing electrons of the same energy are said to be *degenerate* (dih JEHN uh rayt).

The direction of the orbital in space depends on *m*.

Degenerate orbitals represent electrons of the same energy.

PROBLEMS

4. Using a 3 mm dowel and clay, construct all three p orbitals on one set of axes.

5. How many orbitals are there in a d sublevel?

6. How many orbitals are there in an f sublevel?

7:13 Distribution of Electrons

So far, we have been discussing energy levels and charge clouds, with only brief mention of the way in which electrons are arranged throughout the energy levels. The atom is electrically neutral. For each proton in the nucleus, there is one electron in the charge cloud. Thus, as the atomic number increases, the number of electrons increases. Let us see how they are arranged.

The energy levels in an atom can be thought of as an empty, multistoried rooming house, in which the choice double rooms are on or near the ground level. Electrons, as tenants, will tend to fill the better (lower) rooms first, one at a time. Then they double up in these

In an atom, the number of protons in the nucleus of an atom equals the number of electrons in the charge cloud.

Two electrons can occupy the same orbital only if they have opposite spins. The magnetic fields of force produced by a moving charge can be used to explain this.

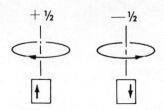

FIGURE 7-16. The fourth quantum number (s) has only two possible values, + ½ and − ½. Two electrons can occupy the same orbital only if they have opposite spins.

better rooms before going to the next level. Let us consider the first "tenant," the electron from the hydrogen atom. It will occupy the position of least energy, the 1s orbital. What about a different set of room tenants, the electrons of the helium atom?

Before we can answer this question and similar ones, we must consider a principle which helps to explain the arrangement of the electrons. This principle is called Pauli's exclusion principle. It states that no two electrons in an atom can have the same set of quantum numbers. The quantum numbers mentioned so far (n, l, and m) are those that describe relative cloud size (n), shape of the cloud (l), and direction of the cloud (m). A fourth quantum number (s) describes the spin of the electron, clockwise or counterclockwise. If two electrons occupy the same orbital, they must have opposite spins, since the other quantum numbers will be identical (Figure 7–16). Note that the values of the fourth quantum number, although fractions, differ by a whole number amount.

Now consider the helium atom. Both electrons of a helium atom take positions in the 1s orbital, and thus have opposing spins. We call this a $1s^2$ electron configuration (read as one-s-two).

Pauli's exclusion principle: No two electrons in an atom can have the same set of quantum numbers.

The quantum number (s) describes the spin of an electron.

The fourth quantum number (s) is independent of the other three quantum numbers. It has a value of either + ½ or − ½. It describes the direction of rotation of an electron on its axis.

The electrons of lithium ($Z = 3$) fill both positions in the 1s orbital and one position in the 2s orbital. We designate this as $1s^2 2s^1$ (Figure 7–17).

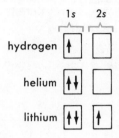

FIGURE 7-17. Filling the 1s and 2s orbitals of hydrogen, helium, and lithium.

Let's move on to the seven electron nitrogen atom, and see how the electrons are distributed. We would expect two electrons in the 1s orbital, two in the 2s, and three in the 2p. These can be indicated as in Figure 7–18, where each arrow represents an electron. The opposing arrows indicate opposite spins. Notice that, just as tenants,

Wolfgang Pauli

(1900–1958)

As theorists, few physicists could match Vienna-born Wolfgang Pauli. As a young man he had the opportunity to study with Max Born and Niels Bohr.

In 1945, Pauli was awarded the Nobel Prize for his exclusion principle which enabled physicists to prepare a more useful description of the electronic structure of atoms.

Some of his other theories helped explain atomic spectra, the behavior of electrons in metals, and how metals are affected by magnetic fields.

In 1940, he was appointed to the chair of theoretical physics at the Institute for Advanced Studies in Princeton, New Jersey. He became a naturalized citizen of the United States in 1946, but later he returned to Zurich, Switzerland.

each electron takes an empty "room" (orbital), if possible, rather than pair with another. This is reasonable when you realize that the electrons repel each other, and that all orbitals in a given sublevel of a normal atom are degenerate. Since each orbital has a different orientation in space, electrons in different orbitals are farther apart than electrons in the same orbital.

The electrons in the oxygen atom are arranged as shown in Figure 7-18. The eighth electron enters the partially filled $2p$ orbital.

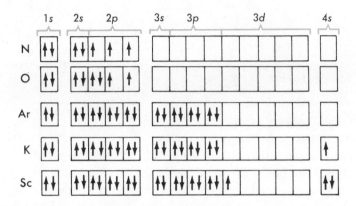

FIGURE 7-18. A section of the periodic table in which the $2p$, $4s$, and $3p$ orbitals are being filled.

7:14   The Diagonal Rule

Everything works very well until we finish the electron configuration of argon: $1s^2 2s^2 3s^2 3p^6$. Where will the electrons of the next element, potassium ($Z = 19$), go? You may remember that in the first energy level diagram (Figure 7–12), the $4s$ level had lower energy than that of the $3d$. Thus, in this case, the $4s$ level fills first. The potassium configuration, therefore, is $1s^2 2s^2 2p^6 3s^2 3p^6 4s^1$. Calcium has the configuration $1s^2 2s^2 2p^6 3s^2 3p^6 4s^2$. Scandium, however, returns to begin the filling of the $3d$ orbitals, and has a configuration

of $1s^2 2s^2 2p^6 3s^2 3p^6 4s^2 3d^1$.

In many of the atoms with higher atomic numbers, the sublevels are not regularly filled. It is of little value to learn each configuration. However, there is a rule of thumb which will give a correct configuration for most of the atoms in the ground state. (As with most rules of thumb, it is not always correct.) This model is called the diagonal rule and is shown in Figure 7–19. Electrons tend to arrange themselves by energy levels. If you follow the diagonals, listing the orbitals passed, you can find the electron configuration of

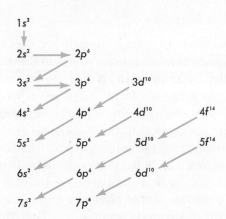

FIGURE 7-19. Illustration of the diagonal rule.

It is important to make it clear that this rule is only an approximation. You may wish to cite some exceptions: Cr, Cu, Nb, Mo, Tc, Ru, Rh, Pd, Ag, La, Ir, Pt, Au, Ac.

most atoms. As an example, suppose you are to find the electron configuration of zirconium $(Z = 40)$. Begin with the 1s level, drop to the 2s and move over to the 2p. Follow the diagonal to 3s and move to 3p. Follow the diagonal to 4s. Move back up to the tail of the next diagonal (3d) and follow it through 4p and 5s. Move back to the tail of the next diagonal at 4d, and place the remaining two electrons. Thus, the electron configuration is $1s^2 2s^2 2p^6 3s^2 3p^6 4s^2 3d^{10} 4p^6 5s^2 4d^2$. A quick addition of the superscripts gives a total of 40, which is the atomic number (Z). For a review of the quantum numbers see Figure 7–20.

The diagonal rule is used to approximate electron configuration.

PROBLEM

7. Write the electron configurations of the elements with $Z = 1$ through $Z = 20$. Electronic configuration of all the elements is given on pages 165 and 166.

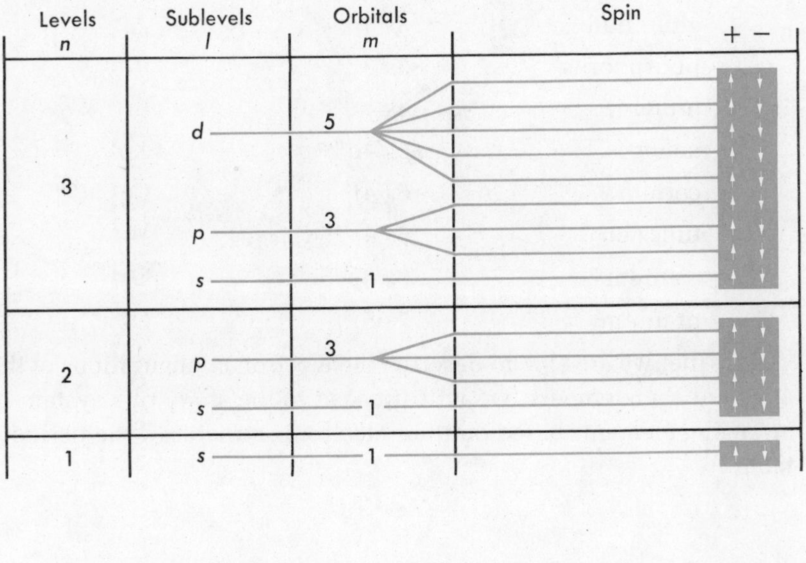

Levels n	Sublevels l	Orbitals m	Spin $+ \; -$
3	d	5	
	p	3	
	s	1	
2	p	3	
	s	1	
1	s	1	

FIGURE 7-20. Energy level diagram.

7:15　Electron Dot Diagrams

Usually only the electrons in the outer level of atoms are involved in chemical change.

In studying electrons in atoms, our primary concern will be the electrons in the outer level. It is often useful to draw these electrons around the symbol of an element. We let the symbol stand for the nucleus and all electrons not in the outer level. We will use again some examples we used for the electron configurations in the previous section. For hydrogen, the diagram is (H·), showing the nucleus and one electron; for helium, (He:). The two electrons for helium are shown together on the same side, because they are both in the same orbital. The electron dot diagram for oxygen is (:Ö:). Here we see that there are two sets of paired electrons and two unpaired electrons. One pair of electrons is in the 2s orbital, the other pair in either the $2p_x$, the $2p_y$, or the $2p_z$ orbital. One of the unpaired electrons is in each of the 2p orbitals not already filled by the second pair. Note that the 1s electrons do not appear on the diagram because they are not in the outer level. The diagram for calcium is (Ca:). The paired electrons are those in the 4s sublevel. For cadmium, (Cd:), the paired electrons are those in the 5s sublevel. In the cadmium diagram, we followed the rule for showing only the electrons in the outer level, even though they are not the last electrons added. In the case of cadmium, the last electrons added (the highest energy electrons) are the 4d electrons. Several other electron dot diagrams are shown in Table 7–1.

In the electron dot diagram, dots indicate outer level paired or unpaired electrons.

Table 7–1

Electron Dot Diagrams for Some Elements

Element	Configuration Ending	Dot Diagram
carbon	. . . $2s^2 2p^2$	·C̈·
aluminum	. . . $3s^2 3p^1$	Al:
phosphorus	. . . $3s^2 3p^3$	:Ṗ·
bromine	. . . $4s^2 3d^{10} 4p^5$	:B̈r:
xenon	. . . $5s^2 4d^{10} 5p^6$	:Ẍe:
cerium	. . . $6s^2 4f^2$	Ce:
tungsten	. . . $6s^2 4f^{14} 5d^4$	W:
osmium	. . . $6s^2 4f^{14} 5d^6$	Os:
uranium	. . . $7s^2 5f^4$	U:

Students who can write dot diagrams easily will have less trouble later predicting bonding and molecular formation.

Now that we are able to describe the electron configurations of the atoms of the elements, we will proceed to the study of a system of arranging elements based on their electronic structure—the periodic table.

SUMMARY

1. DeBroglie first pointed out the wave-particle duality of nature: the idea that all particles exhibit some wave characteristics, and vice versa.
2. The momentum of an object is the product of its mass and velocity. Momentum varies inversely as its wavelength.
3. To describe an electron's behavior completely, we must know where it is, how fast it is going, and in what direction it is going.
4. An electron's future location could be found from its present location and its momentum.
5. Heisenberg's uncertainty principle states that because the process of observation changes an electron's position or its velocity, it is impossible to know both the position and the momentum of an electron at the same time.
6. The more certain we are of the position of an electron, the less certain we are of its momentum, and vice versa. The amount of the uncertainty is related by Planck's constant.
7. Waves have the characteristics of wavelength, frequency, velocity, and amplitude.
8. Schrödinger developed a wave equation which describes the behavior of an electron as a wave.
9. The solution set of the wave equation can be used to calculate the probability of finding an electron at a particular point.
10. Because of the electron's high velocity, it effectively occupies all of the volume defined by the path through which it moves. This volume is called the electron cloud.
11. In the solution of the wave equation, certain whole-number parameters, called quantum numbers, are introduced.
12. The principal quantum number ($n = 1,2,3$ . . .) is the number of the energy level and describes the relative electron cloud size.
13. Each energy level has as many sublevels as the principal quantum number. The second quantum number ($l = s,p,d,f$ . . .) describes the shape of the cloud.
14. The third quantum number, m, describes the direction in space of each orbital.
15. The fourth quantum number, s, describes the spin of the electron.
16. Each orbital may contain a maximum of one pair of electrons. Electrons in the same orbital have opposite spins.
17. Pauli's exclusion principle states that no two electrons in an atom can have the same set of quantum numbers.

18. Electrons tend to occupy the lowest empty orbital of an atom first.
19. Use of the diagonal rule will provide the correct electron configuration for most atoms.
20. Since the chemist is primarily concerned with the electrons in the outer level, electron dot diagrams are useful constructions which can be made when the electron configurations are known.

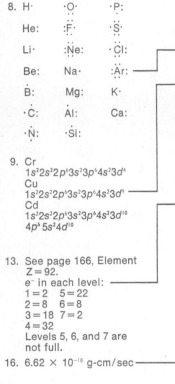

8. H·   ·Ö·   ·P̈:

     He: :F̈·   ·S̈:

     Li·   :N̈e: ·C̈l:

     Be: Na·   :Är:

     Ḃ: Mg: K·

     ·Ċ: Al: Ca:

     ·N̈:   ·Si:

9. Cr
     $1s^2 2s^2 2p^6 3s^2 3p^6 4s^2 3d^4$
     Cu
     $1s^2 2s^2 2p^6 3s^2 3p^6 4s^2 3d^9$
     Cd
     $1s^2 2s^2 2p^6 3s^2 3p^6 4s^2 3d^{10}$
     $4p^6 5s^2 4d^{10}$

13. See page 166, Element
     Z = 92.
     e^- in each level:
     1 = 2   5 = 22
     2 = 8   6 = 8
     3 = 18 7 = 2
     4 = 32
     Levels 5, 6, and 7 are
     not full.

16. 6.62×10^{-18} g-cm/sec

PROBLEMS

8. Draw the electron dot diagrams of the elements whose electron configurations were calculated in Problem 7.
9. Write the electron configuration for a chromium atom; a copper atom; a cadmium atom.
10. How many electrons in one atom may have $n = 5$?   50   4 (or 2 pairs)
11. How many paired electrons are there in an atom of boron? an atom of sulfur? —14 (or 7 pairs) an atom of fluorine? ¬ 8 (or 4 pairs)
12. How many electrons are not shown in the electron dot diagrams of the elements from $Z = 3$ to $Z = 10$? $2e^-$
13. Write the electron configuration for uranium. Compute the number of electrons in each level. Calculate the levels which are not full of electrons.
14. What elements are composed of atoms having the following electron configurations:
     a. $1s^2 2s^2 2p^6 3s^2 3p^6 4s^2 3d^5$ Mn
     b. $1s^2 2s^2 2p^6 3s^2 3p^6 4s^2 3d^{10} 4p^6 5s^2 4d^4$ Mo
15. What wavelength would be associated with a 1360 kg automobile traveling at a rate of 90.0 km per hour? 1.95×10^{-36} cm
16. What is the uncertainty in the momentum of an electron if its position has been determined to an accuracy of $\pm$ 0.1 Å?
17. Draw electron dot diagrams for the elements with Z equal to 33, 51, and 83.   ·N̈:   ·P̈:   ·Äs: ·S̈b: ·Bï:
18. What are the actual values that the fourth quantum number (s) can take? $\pm \frac{1}{2}$

ONE MORE STEP

See Teacher's Guide at the front of this book.

1. The uncertainty principle has some interesting philosophical implications. Investigate this aspect of the principle.
2. Classical physics would predict that only the three quantum numbers should be necessary to describe the motion of the electron in three-dimensional space. What necessitates a fourth?

3. Try to find a pictorial representation of the *f* orbitals.
4. Look up experiments which have been performed with the electron, one demonstrating its properties as a wave, and one demonstrating its properties as a particle. Prepare a report to your class on the procedure and consequences of these experiments.
5. Look up the Schrödinger wave equation and investigate the meaning of each of the symbols in it.

Suggested Readings for this chapter may be found in the Teacher's Guide at the front of this book.

Over one hundred elements are known today. Most of them are found in varying amounts in nature. The most abundant elements found in the earth's crust are silicon and oxygen. There they are found chemically combined, often in the form of silicon dioxide. Sand is a form of silicon dioxide. It is used in the manufacture of glass bottles. What are some other common elements? How do they occur in nature? What are some ways in which elements can be classified?

Chapter 8 introduces and develops the periodic table and reveals some of the periodic characteristics of the elements based upon their electronic structure.

The element sodium reacts violently with water. Potassium reacts still more violently with water. An experienced chemist can reasonably predict that the elements rubidium, cesium, and francium will react in a similar manner. How can he do this? The chemist can make such predictions without additional experimenting because he knows that all of these elements have a similar atomic structure. He knows that they have a similar structure because of their arrangement (classification) in the first column of the periodic table. What is the periodic table?

GOAL: You will gain an understanding of the periodic table and the relationship between the periodic properties of the elements and their electronic structure.

Warning: students should not try this experiment without your supervision; it is dangerous.

EARLY ATTEMPTS AT CLASSIFICATION

8:1 Dobereiner and Newlands

Early in the nineteenth century, men began to seek ways to classify the elements in order to simplify their study. One of the earliest attempts at classification was by Johann Dobereiner, a German chemist, in 1817. Dobereiner observed that the properties of the three metals calcium, barium, and strontium were very similar. He also noted that the atomic mass of strontium was about midway between those of calcium and barium. He formed what he termed a _triad_ of these three elements. In later years, Dobereiner and other chemists found several other groups of three elements with similar properties.

Properties of elements are in Appendix A.

Dobereiner discovered groups of three related elements.

Table 8–1

Some of Dobereiner's Triads

Name	Atomic Mass	Name	Atomic Mass	Name	Atomic Mass
Calcium	40	Chlorine	35.5	Sulfur	32
Barium	137	Iodine	127	Tellurium	127.5
Average	88.5	_Average_	81.3	_Average_	79.8
Strontium	87.6	Bromine	79.9	Selenium	79.2

In 1863, John Newlands, an English chemist, suggested another classification. He arranged the elements in order of their increasing atomic masses. He noted that there appeared to be a repetition of similar properties every eight elements. Therefore, he arranged the elements known at that time into seven groups of seven each. Newlands referred to his arrangement as the *law of octaves*.

Newlands suggested groups of seven based on atomic masses.

Table 8–2

Newlands' Law of Octaves

1	2	3	4	5	6	7	8
Li	Be	B	C	N	O	F	Na
Na	Mg	Al	Si	P	S	Cl	K
K							

The law of octaves was proposed to explain the property similarities which occurred with every eighth element when the elements were arranged in order of increasing atomic weight.

8:2   Mendeleev's Periodic Table

Just six years after Newlands' proposal, Dmitri Mendeleev, a Russian chemist, proposed a similar classification (Table 8–3). He suggested, as had Newlands, that the properties of the elements were a function of their atomic masses. However, Mendeleev felt that similar properties occurred after periods of varying length. Although he placed seven elements each in his first two periods, he placed seventeen elements in the next two.

Mendeleev's predictions made his proposal seem superior to Meyer's.

Finally, in 1871, Mendeleev and the German chemist Lothar Meyer, each working alone, made up an eight-column table of the elements. However, Mendeleev had to leave some blank spots in order to have all the elements with similar properties in the same column. To explain these blank spots, Mendeleev suggested there must be other elements that had not yet been discovered. On the basis of his arrangement, Mendeleev predicted the properties and atomic masses of the unknown elements. Today, these elements are known, and Mendeleev's predictions have been found to be very nearly correct.

Mendeleev suggested periods of varying lengths based on atomic masses.

Mendeleev left blanks in his table for undiscovered elements.

Mendeleev's table revealed that the properties of the elements are repeated in an orderly way, if the elements are arranged in order of their increasing atomic masses. Mendeleev regarded the properties of the elements as a periodic function of their atomic masses. This statement was called the *periodic law*.

Mendeleev's periodic law: properties of elements are periodic functions of their atomic masses.

Table 8-3

Mendeleev's Periodic Table of the Elements

Legend:
- ∨ Known to the ancients
- (shaded box) Known to Mendeleev
- (outlined box) Atomic numbers reversed
- XXXX (hatched) Unknown to Mendeleev; date element was discovered
- (hatched box) Dobereier's triads

Columns (or Groups)

Rows (or Periods)	0	I	II	III	IV	V	VI	VII	VIII
1		Hydrogen 1.0079							
2 (7 elements)	Neon 20.179 1898	Lithium 6.941	Beryllium 9.01218	Boron 10.81	Carbon 12.011	Nitrogen 14.0067	Oxygen 15.9994	Fluorine 18.99840 1886	Helium 4.00260 1895
3 (7 elements)	Argon 39.948 1894	Sodium 22.98977	Magnesium 24.305	Aluminum 26.98154	Silicon 28.086	Phosphorus 30.97376	Sulfur 32.06	Chlorine 35.453	
4 (17 elements, 3 unknown)	Krypton 83.80 1898	Potassium 39.098 / Copper 63.546	Calcium 40.08 / Zinc 65.38	Scandium 44.9559 1879 / Gallium 69.72 1875	Titanium 47.90 / Germanium 72.59 1886	Vanadium 50.9414 / Arsenic 74.9216	Chromium 51.996 / Selenium 78.96	Manganese 54.9380 / Bromine 79.904	Iron 55.847 Cobalt 58.9332 Nickel 58.70
5 (17 elements, 1 unknown)	Xenon 131.30 1898	Rubidium 85.4678 / Silver 107.868	Strontium 87.62 / Cadmium 112.40	Yttrium 88.9059 / Indium 114.82	Zirconium 91.22 / Tin 118.69	Niobium 92.9064 / Antimony 121.75	Molybdenum 95.94 / Iodine 126.9045	Technetium 99 1937 / Tellurium 127.60	Ruthenium 101.07 Rhodium 102.9055 Palladium 106.4
6 (17 elements, 4 unknown)	Radon 222 1900	Cesium 132.9054 / Gold 196.9665	Barium 137.34 / Mercury 200.59	Lanthanum* 138.9055 / Thallium 204.37	Hafnium 178.49 1923 / Lead 207.2	Tantalum 180.9479 / Bismuth 208.9804	Wolfram 183.85 / Polonium 209 1898	Rhenium 186.207 1925 / Astatine 210 1940	Osmium 190.2 Iridium 192.22 Platinum 195.09
7 (2 elements known)		Francium 223 1939	Radium 226.0254 1898	Actinium** 227 1899	Thorium 232.0381	Protactinium 231 1917	Uranium 238.029		

* The Lanthanide Series
** The Actinide Series

Mendeleev knew nothing of the noble gases.

Table 8–4

Periodic Properties

H	Li	Be	B	C	N	O	F	Na	Mg	Al	Si	P	S	Cl	K	Ca

Mendeleev knew these elements had similar properties and he rearranged them.

Note that Mendeleev did not know where to place hydrogen.

H						H
Li	Be	B	C	N	O	F
Na	Mg	Al	Si	P	S	Cl
K	Ca					

He noted that the properties of the elements are repeated in an orderly way.

8:3 The Modern Periodic Law

There was a problem with Mendeleev's table. If the elements were arranged according to increasing atomic masses, tellurium and iodine seemed to be in the wrong columns. Their properties were different from those of other elements in the same column. However, they were next to each other, and switching their positions put them in the columns where they belonged according to their properties. If the switch were made, however, Mendeleev's basic assumption that the properties of the elements were a periodic function of their atomic masses would be in error. Mendeleev assumed that the atomic masses of these two elements had been poorly measured. He thought that new mass measurements would prove his hypothesis to be correct. However, new measurements simply confirmed the original masses. What was the reason for this apparent reversal? Why were there exceptions?

The errors in Mendeleev's table cast doubt on his periodic law.

Soon, new elements were discovered, and two other pairs showed the same kind of reversal. Cobalt and nickel were known by Mendeleev, but an accurate determination of their atomic masses had not been made. When such a determination was made, it was found that their positions in the table were reversed. Also, when argon was discovered, the masses of argon and potassium were reversed.

Table 8-5

Mendeleev's Prediction

Ekasilicon* *Predicted properties*	Germanium *Actual properties*
1. Atomic mass = 72	1. Atomic mass = 72.60
2. High melting point	2. Melting point = 958°C
3. Density = 5.5 g/cm³	3. Density = 5.36 g/cm³
4. Dark gray metal	4. Gray metal
5. Will obtain from K_2EsF_6	5. Obtain from K_2GeF_6
6. Slightly dissolved by HCl	6. Not dissolved by HCl
7. Will form EsO_2	7. Forms oxide (GeO_2)
8. Density of EsO_2 = 4.7 g/cm³	8. Density of GeO_2 = 4.70 g/cm³

Henry Moseley (Section 6:10) found the reason for these apparent exceptions to the rule. As a result of Moseley's work, the periodic law was revised. It now had as its basis the atomic numbers of the elements instead of the atomic masses. Today's statement of the periodic law is: *the properties of the elements are a periodic function of their atomic numbers.*

Mendeleev predicted the existence of six undiscovered elements:

ekaboron
   (scandium)
ekaaluminum
   (gallium)
ekasilicon
   (germanium)
ekamanganese
   (technetium)
dvimanganese
   (rhenium)
ekatantalum
   (polonium)

Moseley's revision: properties of the elements are periodic functions of their atomic numbers.

THE MODERN PERIODIC TABLE

8:4 The Modern Basis

The atomic number of an element indicates the number of protons in the nucleus of each atom of the element. The atomic number also indicates the number of electrons (negative charges) surrounding the nucleus of the atom.

Certain electron arrangements are periodically repeated. If we place elements with similar electron configurations in the same column and list the elements in order of their increasing atomic masses, we can form a table of the elements similar to Table 8-6. This is called the *periodic table* of the elements.

We can construct Table 8-6 in the following manner: We use the diagonal rule (Section 7:14) to determine the order of filling the sublevels. Each s sublevel contains two electrons; each p sublevel contains six electrons arranged in three pairs, or orbitals; each d sublevel

Elements with similar electron configurations are listed in columns.

---

* One of the blank spaces in Mendeleev's table appeared below silicon. Mendeleev assumed such an element existed but had not yet been discovered. He called this element ekasilicon (later named germanium) and predicted some of its properties.

PERIODIC CLASSIFICATION OF THE ELEMENTS
(BASED ON $^{12}C = 12.0000$)

Light Metals · Transition Metals · Nonmetals

IA	IIA	IIIB	IVB	VB	VIB	VIIB	VIIIB			IB	IIB	IIIA	IVA	VA	VIA	VIIA	VIIIA
1 H 1.0079																	2 He 4.00260
3 Li 6.941	4 Be 9.01218											5 B 10.81	6 C 12.011	7 N 14.0067	8 O 15.9994	9 F 18.99840	10 Ne 20.179
11 Na 22.98977	12 Mg 24.305											13 Al 26.98154	14 Si 28.086	15 P 30.97376	16 S 32.06	17 Cl 35.453	18 Ar 39.948
19 K 39.098	20 Ca 40.08	21 Sc 44.9559	22 Ti 47.90	23 V 50.9414	24 Cr 51.996	25 Mn 54.9380	26 Fe 55.847	27 Co 58.9332	28 Ni 58.70	29 Cu 63.546	30 Zn 65.38	31 Ga 69.72	32 Ge 72.59	33 As 74.9216	34 Se 78.96	35 Br 79.904	36 Kr 83.80
37 Rb 85.4678	38 Sr 87.62	39 Y 88.9059	40 Zr 91.22	41 Nb 92.9064	42 Mo 95.94	43 Tc 97	44 Ru 101.07	45 Rh 102.9055	46 Pd 106.4	47 Ag 107.868	48 Cd 112.40	49 In 114.82	50 Sn 118.69	51 Sb 121.75	52 Te 127.60	53 I 126.9045	54 Xe 131.30
55 Cs 132.9054	56 Ba 137.34	71 Lu 174.97	72 Hf 178.49	73 Ta 180.9479	74 W 183.85	75 Re 186.207	76 Os 190.2	77 Ir 192.22	78 Pt 195.09	79 Au 196.9665	80 Hg 200.59	81 Tl 204.37	82 Pb 207.2	83 Bi 208.9804	84 Po 209	85 At 210	86 Rn 222
87 Fr 223	88 Ra 226	103 Lr 256	104 257	105 260													

Lanthanide series

57 La 138.9055	58 Ce 140.12	59 Pr 140.9077	60 Nd 144.24	61 Pm 145	62 Sm 150.4	63 Eu 151.96	64 Gd 157.25	65 Tb 158.9254	66 Dy 162.50	67 Ho 164.9304	68 Er 167.26	69 Tm 168.9342	70 Yb 173.04

Actinide series

89 Ac 227	90 Th 232.0381	91 Pa 231	92 U 238.029	93 Np 237	94 Pu 244	95 Am 243	96 Cm 247	97 Bk 247	98 Cf 251	99 Es 254	100 Fm 257	101 Md 258	102 No 255

Table 8-6 **The Modern Periodic Table**

Table 8–7

Electronic Configurations of the Elements

	Z	Element	1 s	2 s p	3 s p d	4 s p d f	5 s p d f	6 s p d	7 s	
	1	H	1							1st row
nmetal st row	2	He	2							
	3	Li	2	1						
	4	Be	2	2						
	5	B	2	2 1						2nd row
	6	C	2	2 2						
metals d row	7	N	2	2 3						
	8	O	2	2 4						
	9	F	2	2 5						
	10	Ne	2	2 6						
	11	Na	2	2 6	1					
	12	Mg	2	2 6	2					
	13	Al	2	2 6	2 1					
	14	Si	2	2 6	2 2					3rd row
	15	P	2	2 6	2 3					
metals d row	16	S	2	2 6	2 4					
	17	Cl	2	2 6	2 5					
	18	Ar	2	2 6	2 6					
	19	K	2	2 6	2 6	1				
	20	Ca	2	2 6	2 6	2				
	21	Sc	2	2 6	2 6 1	2				
	22	Ti	2	2 6	2 6 2	2				
	23	V	2	2 6	2 6 3	2				
nsition	24	Cr	2	2 6	2 6 5	1 *				
ements	25	Mn	2	2 6	2 6 5	2				
st row	26	Fe	2	2 6	2 6 6	2				
	27	Co	2	2 6	2 6 7	2				4th row
	28	Ni	2	2 6	2 6 8	2				
	29	Cu	2	2 6	2 6 10	1 *				
	30	Zn	2	2 6	2 6 10	2				
	31	Ga	2	2 6	2 6 10	2 1				
	32	Ge	2	2 6	2 6 10	2 2				
	33	As	2	2 6	2 6 10	2 3				
metals	34	Se	2	2 6	2 6 10	2 4				
h row	35	Br	2	2 6	2 6 10	2 5				
	36	Kr	2	2 6	2 6 10	2 6				
	37	Rb	2	2 6	2 6 10	2 6	1			
	38	Sr	2	2 6	2 6 10	2 6	2			
	39	Y	2	2 6	2 6 10	2 6 1	2			
	40	Zr	2	2 6	2 6 10	2 6 2	2			
	41	Nb	2	2 6	2 6 10	2 6 4	1 *			
ansition	42	Mo	2	2 6	2 6 10	2 6 5	1 *			
ements	43	Tc	2	2 6	2 6 10	2 6 5	2			5th row
nd row	44	Ru	2	2 6	2 6 10	2 6 7	1 *			
	45	Rh	2	2 6	2 6 10	2 6 8	1 *			
	46	Pd	2	2 6	2 6 10	2 6 10	*			
	47	Ag	2	2 6	2 6 10	2 6 10	1 *			
	48	Cd	2	2 6	2 6 10	2 6 10	2 *			
	49	In	2	2 6	2 6 10	2 6 10	2 1			
	50	Sn	2	2 6	2 6 10	2 6 10	2 2			
	51	Sb	2	2 6	2 6 10	2 6 10	2 3			

*The asterisk indicates configurations which differ from that predicted by the diagonal rule.

Table 8–7 (continued)

	Z	Element	1 s	2 s p	3 s p d	4 s p d f	5 s p d f	6 s p d	7 s
nonmetals 5th row	52	Te	2	2 6	2 6 10	2 6 10	2 4		
	53	I	2	2 6	2 6 10	2 6 10	2 5		
	54	Xe	2	2 6	2 6 10	2 6 10	2 6		
	55	Cs	2	2 6	2 6 10	2 6 10	2 6	1	
	56	Ba	2	2 6	2 6 10	2 6 10	2 6	2	
	57	La	2	2 6	2 6 10	2 6 10	2 6 1	2 *	
	58	Ce	2	2 6	2 6 10	2 6 10 1	2 6 1	2	
	59	Pr	2	2 6	2 6 10	2 6 10 3	2 6	2	
	60	Nd	2	2 6	2 6 10	2 6 10 4	2 6	2	
	61	Pm	2	2 6	2 6 10	2 6 10 5	2 6	2	
	62	Sm	2	2 6	2 6 10	2 6 10 6	2 6	2	
Lanthanide series	63	Eu	2	2 6	2 6 10	2 6 10 7	2 6	2	
	64	Gd	2	2 6	2 6 10	2 6 10 7	2 6 1	2 *	
	65	Tb	2	2 6	2 6 10	2 6 10 9	2 6	2	
	66	Dy	2	2 6	2 6 10	2 6 10 10	2 6	2	
	67	Ho	2	2 6	2 6 10	2 6 10 11	2 6	2	
	68	Er	2	2 6	2 6 10	2 6 10 12	2 6	2	
	69	Tm	2	2 6	2 6 10	2 6 10 13	2 6	2	
	70	Yb	2	2 6	2 6 10	2 6 10 14	2 6	2	
	71	Lu	2	2 6	2 6 10	2 6 10 14	2 6 1	2	
	72	Hf	2	2 6	2 6 10	2 6 10 14	2 6 2	2	
	73	Ta	2	2 6	2 6 10	2 6 10 14	2 6 3	2	
	74	W	2	2 6	2 6 10	2 6 10 14	2 6 4	2	
Transition elements 3rd row	75	Re	2	2 6	2 6 10	2 6 10 14	2 6 5	2	
	76	Os	2	2 6	2 6 10	2 6 10 14	2 6 6	2	
	77	Ir	2	2 6	2 6 10	2 6 10 14	2 6 7	2	
	78	Pt	2	2 6	2 6 10	2 6 10 14	2 6 9	1 *	
	79	Au	2	2 6	2 6 10	2 6 10 14	2 6 10	1 *	
	80	Hg	2	2 6	2 6 10	2 6 10 14	2 6 10	2	
	81	Tl	2	2 6	2 6 10	2 6 10 14	2 6 10	2 1	
	82	Pb	2	2 6	2 6 10	2 6 10 14	2 6 10	2 2	
	83	Bi	2	2 6	2 6 10	2 6 10 14	2 6 10	2 3	
	84	Po	2	2 6	2 6 10	2 6 10 14	2 6 10	2 4	
nonmetals 6th row	85	At	2	2 6	2 6 10	2 6 10 14	2 6 10	2 5	
	86	Rn	2	2 6	2 6 10	2 6 10 14	2 6 10	2 6	
	87	Fr	2	2 6	2 6 10	2 6 10 14	2 6 10	2 6	1
	88	Ra	2	2 6	2 6 10	2 6 10 14	2 6 10	2 6	2
	89	Ac	2	2 6	2 6 10	2 6 10 14	2 6 10	2 6 1	2 *
	90	Th	2	2 6	2 6 10	2 6 10 14	2 6 10	2 6 2	2 *
	91	Pa	2	2 6	2 6 10	2 6 10 14	2 6 10 2	2 6 1	2 *
	92	U	2	2 6	2 6 10	2 6 10 14	2 6 10 3	2 6 1	2 *
	93	Np	2	2 6	2 6 10	2 6 10 14	2 6 10 4	2 6 1	2 *
	94	Pu	2	2 6	2 6 10	2 6 10 14	2 6 19 6	2 6	2 *
	95	Am	2	2 6	2 6 10	2 6 10 14	2 6 10 7	2 6	2
Actinide series	96	Cm	2	2 6	2 6 10	2 6 10 14	2 6 19 7	2 6 1	2 *
	97	Bk	2	2 6	2 6 10	2 6 10 14	2 6 10 8	2 6 1	2? *
	98	Cf	2	2 6	2 6 10	2 6 10 14	2 6 10 9	2 6 1	2? *
	99	Es	2	2 6	2 6 10	2 6 10 14	2 6 10 10	2 6 1	2? *
	100	Fm	2	2 6	2 6 10	2 6 10 14	2 6 10 11	2 6 1	2? *
	101	Md	2	2 6	2 6 10	2 6 10 14	2 6 10 12	2 6 1	2? *
	102	No	2	2 6	2 6 10	2 6 10 14	2 6 10 13	2 6 1	2? *
	103	Lr	2	2 6	2 6 10	2 6 10 14	2 6 10 14	2 6 1	2? *
	104		2	2 6	2 6 10	2 6 10 14	2 6 10 14	2 6 2	2? *
	105		2	2 6	2 6 10	2 6 10 14	2 6 10 14	2 6 3	2?

Row labels (right side): 5th, 6th, 7th

*Configurations which differ from that predicted.

contains ten electrons, or five orbitals; and each f sublevel contains fourteen electrons, or seven orbitals. We then align the elements with similar electron structures or configurations. The first configuration in Table 8–8, hydrogen $(Z = 1)$, consists of one electron in the 1s sublevel. The second configuration, helium $(Z = 2)$, consists of two electrons in the 1s sublevel. Two electrons completely fill the 1s sublevel, so additional electrons will go into the 2s sublevel. The third element, lithium $(Z = 3)$, consists of two electrons in the 1s sublevel and one electron in the 2s sublevel. Lithium is similar to hydrogen in that it has only one electron in its outer-most sublevel. Therefore, it is placed in the same column as hydrogen. The next element, beryllium $(Z = 4)$, has a configuration consisting of two electrons in the 1s sublevel and two electrons in the 2s sublevel. It might belong in the column with helium, except that the two electrons in helium's outermost level represent all of the electrons the $n = 1$ level can hold.

Even though the beryllium and helium configurations are similar, the two electrons in the 2s sublevel of beryllium do not fill the second level. Recall that the $n = 2$ level has a p sublevel, as well as its s sublevel. Beryllium, therefore, starts a new column (Table 8–8). Boron $(Z = 5)$ has a configuration composed of two 1s electrons, two 2s electrons, and one 2p electron. It heads a new column. Carbon $(Z = 6)$, nitrogen $(Z = 7)$, oxygen $(Z = 8)$, and fluorine $(Z = 9)$ atoms have structures containing two, three, four, and five electrons, respectively, in the 2p sublevel. Each of these elements heads a new column.

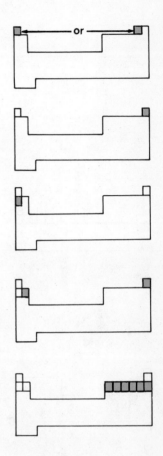

Table 8–8

Elements 1–10

Z	Element	1	2	
		s	s	p
1	H	1		
2	He	2		
3	Li	2	1	
4	Be	2	2	
5	B	2	2	1
10	Ne	2	2	6

Suggestion: Ditto, mimeograph, or buy blank periodic tables and have the students fill them in as this section is discussed or studied. An overhead projector will be a great help.

The atoms of neon $(Z = 10)$, the tenth element, contain six 2p electrons (Table 8–9). The second level $(n = 2)$ is now full, so neon is placed in the same column as helium. Sodium atoms $(Z = 11)$ have the same outer level configuration as lithium atoms, one s electron $(3s^1)$. Thus, sodium is placed under lithium. The atoms of the

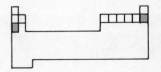

Table 8-9

Elements 11-20

Z	Element	1	2	3	4
		s	s p	s p	s
(10)	(Ne)	2	2 6		
11	Na	2	2 6	1	
12	Mg	2	2 6	2	
18	Ar	2	2 6	2 6	
19	K	2	2 6	2 6	1
20	Ca	2	2 6	2 6	2

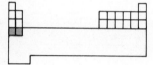
elements magnesium (Z = 12) through argon (Z = 18) have the same outer structures as the atoms of the elements beryllium through neon, and are also placed in the appropriate columns. Atoms of potassium (Z = 19) and calcium (Z = 20) have outer structures that are similar to sodium and magnesium.

8:5   The Transition Elements

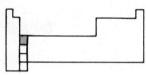
The scandium (Z = 21) configuration introduces a new factor into the arrangement. It has two electrons in the outer level (4s²) and is similar to the calcium configuration. However, the scandium atom has, in addition to a filled 4s sublevel, one electron in the 3d sublevel. It is, therefore, placed in a new column, which is labeled (IIIB). For the atoms of elements titanium (Z = 22) through nickel (Z = 28), additional electrons are added in the 3d sublevel, which is not the outer level. Each of these elements heads a new column

Table 8-10

Some Transition Elements

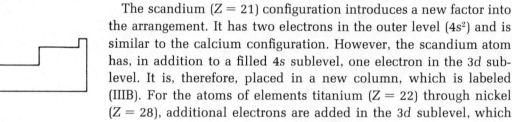

Z	Element	1	2	3	4
		s	s p	s p d	s p
(20)	(Ca)	2	2 6	2 6	2
21	Sc	2	2 6	2 6 1	2
22,	Ti	2	2 6	2 6 2	2
23	V	2	2 6	2 6 3	2
24	Cr	2	2 6	2 6 5	1
25	Mn	2	2 6	2 6 5	2
26	Fe	2	2 6	2 6 6	2
27	Co	2	2 6	2 6 7	2
28	Ni	2	2 6	2 6 8	2
29	Cu	2	2 6	2 6 10	1
30	Zn	2	2 6	2 6 10	2
(31)	(Ga)	2	2 6	2 6 10	2 1

(columns IIIB to VIIIB) (Figure 8–1). Note that the atoms of copper and zinc have filled inner levels, and are again completing the filling of the 4s sublevel. All structures in column IB have filled inner levels and one electron in the outer level. All structures in column IIB have filled inner levels and two electrons in the outer level. In columns IIIA through VIIIA, electrons are added to the p sublevel until there are a total of eight electrons in the outer level.

The transition elements head the B columns.

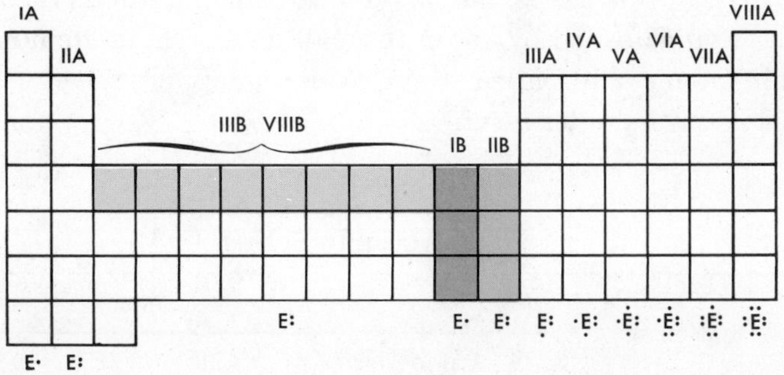

FIGURE 8-1. Structure of the periodic table.

The next electron is added to the next s sublevel whether the inner level is filled or not. The process is continued until all of the elements are placed in the main part of the table.

Table 8–11

The Lanthanide Series

Z	Element	1	2	3	4	5	6
		s	s p	s p d	s p d f	s p d	s
55	Cs	2	2 6	2 6 10	2 6 10	2 6	1
56	Ba	2	2 6	2 6 10	2 6 10	2 6	2
57	La	2	2 6	2 6 10	2 6 10 1	2 6 1	2
58	Ce	2	2 6	2 6 10	2 6 10 2	2 6 1	2
59	Pr	2	2 6	2 6 10	2 6 10 3	2 6	2
60	Nd	2	2 6	2 6 10	2 6 10 4	2 6	2
61	Pm	2	2 6	2 6 10	2 6 10 5	2 6	2
62	Sm	2	2 6	2 6 10	2 6 10 6	2 6	2
63	Eu	2	2 6	2 6 10	2 6 10 7	2 6	2
64	Gd	2	2 6	2 6 10	2 6 10 7	2 6 1	2
65	Tb	2	2 6	2 6 10	2 6 10 9	2 6	2
66	Dy	2	2 6	2 6 10	2 6 10 10	2 6	2
67	Ho	2	2 6	2 6 10	2 6 10 11	2 6	2
68	Er	2	2 6	2 6 10	2 6 10 12	2 6	2
69	Tm	2	2 6	2 6 10	2 6 10 13	2 6	2
70	Yb	2	2 6	2 6 10	2 6 10 14	2 6	2
71	Lu	2	2 6	2 6 10	2 6 10 14	2 6 1	2
72	Hf	2	2 6	2 6 10	2 6 10 14	2 6 2	2
73	Ta	2	2 6	2 6 10	2 6 10 14	2 6 3	2
74	W	2	2 6	2 6 10	2 6 10 14	2 6 4	2
75	Re	2	2 6	2 6 10	2 6 10 14	2 6 5	2
76	Os	2	2 6	2 6 10	2 6 10 14	2 6 6	2

The elements in both columns IA & IB contain only one e⁻ in the outer level. However, column IA metals contain 8 e⁻ in the next to outer level and column IB metals contain 18 e⁻ in this level. The column IA metals (alkali metals) easily lose the single outer electron and form extremely stable ions which have a stable noble gas configuration. Column IB metals (coinage metals) are non-corrosive and relatively unreactive because loss of the single outer level electron does not result in the formation of an appreciably more stable ion.

8:6　The Lanthanides and Actinides

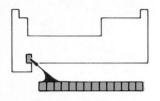

Lanthanides add electrons to the 4f sublevels.

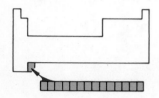

Actinides add electrons to the 5f sublevels.

The lanthanide series contains the elements lanthanum ($Z = 57$) through ytterbium ($Z = 70$); all have a predicted structure with two electrons in the outer level. In this series, electrons are being added to the $4f$ sublevel instead of to a sublevel of the sixth or outer level (Table 8–11).

The actinide series contains actinium ($Z = 89$) through nobelium ($Z = 102$). In this series, the $5f$ sublevel is being filled (Table 8–12). The columns headed by boron through neon, which are nonmetals, contain atoms with filled s sublevels and progressively filling p sublevels in the outer level.

Table 8–12

The Actinide Series

Z	Element	1 s	2 s p	3 s p d	4 s p d f	5 s p d f	6 s p d	7 s
83	Bi	2	2 6	2 6 10	2 6 10 14	2 6 10	2 3	
84	Po	2	2 6	2 6 10	2 6 10 14	2 6 10	2 4	
85	At	2	2 6	2 6 10	2 6 10 14	2 6 10	2 5	
86	Rn	2	2 6	2 6 10	2 6 10 14	2 6 10	2 6	
87	Fr	2	2 6	2 6 10	2 6 10 14	2 6 10	2 6	1
88	Ra	2	2 6	2 6 10	2 6 10 14	2 6 10	2 6	2
89	Ac	2	2 6	2 6 10	2 6 10 14	2 6 10	2 6 1	2
90	Th	2	2 6	2 6 10	2 6 10 14	2 6 10	2 6 2	2
91	Pa	2	2 6	2 6 10	2 6 10 14	2 6 10 2	2 6 1	2
92	U	2	2 6	2 6 10	2 6 10 14	2 6 10 3	2 6 1	2
93	Np	2	2 6	2 6 10	2 6 10 14	2 6 10 4	2 6 1	2
94	Pu	2	2 6	2 6 10	2 6 10 14	2 6 10 6	2 6	2
95	Am	2	2 6	2 6 10	2 6 10 14	2 6 10 7	2 6	2
96	Cm	2	2 6	2 6 10	2 6 10 14	2 6 10 7	2 6 1	2
97	Bk	2	2 6	2 6 10	2 6 10 14	2 6 10 8	2 6 1	2?
98	Cf	2	2 6	2 6 10	2 6 10 14	2 6 10 9	2 6 1	2?
99	Es	2	2 6	2 6 10	2 6 10 14	2 6 10 10	2 6 1	2?
100	Fm	2	2 6	2 6 10	2 6 10 14	2 6 10 11	2 6 1	2?
101	Md	2	2 6	2 6 10	2 6 10 14	2 6 10 12	2 6 1	2?
102	No	2	2 6	2 6 10	2 6 10 14	2 6 10 13	2 6 1	2?
103	Lr	2	2 6	2 6 10	2 6 10 14	2 6 10 14	2 6 1	2?

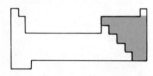

Periods are horizontal rows of elements.

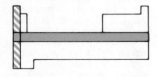

Groups are vertical columns of elements.

The atoms of some elements do not have the exact electron configurations predicted for them. The differences, however, involve only one or two electrons. For purposes of constructing the table, we will assume that all elements have the predicted configurations.

All elements in a horizontal line are referred to as a *period*. All elements in the same vertical column are referred to as a *group* and are labeled IA through VIIIA and IB through VIIIB.

8:7   Octet Rule

When an s electron is the highest energy level electron in an atom, it is in the outer level. The same is true of a p electron. However, d and f electrons, theoretically, can never be in the outer level of a neutral atom (see diagonal rule). Since s sublevels hold two electrons and p sublevels hold six, the largest number of electrons an atom normally has in its outer level is eight. One of the basic empirical rules in chemistry is that an atom with eight electrons in its outer level is particularly stable. This rule is called the *octet rule*. Although the helium atom has only two electrons in its outer level, it, too, is one of these exceptionally stable elements. Its outer level is also the first level and can hold only two electrons. Thus, it has a full outer level. From now on, we will consider the octet rule to include helium.

The octet rule should be learned as "four pairs" of electrons.

Eight electrons in the outer level of an atom represent a stable arrangement.

Helium is included in the octet rule.

SURVEYING THE TABLE

8:8   Electron Configurations

The periodic table was originally constructed by placing elements with similar properties in a column. We now know that chemical properties are determined by the electron configuration of atoms. By reversing the procedure in which the table was constructed, the table may be used to "read" the configuration of an element. Thus, the written configuration of any element in Group IA will end in s^1. This configuration means that the outer level of each atom of Group IA elements contains one electron. The coefficient of s^1 is easily found from the table because the number of the period indicates the level. For example, potassium is in the fourth period of Group IA. Thus, the written electron configuration for the outer level of potassium is $4s^1$. The superscript, the 1 in s^1, is given by the group number. The coefficient, the 4 in $4s^1$, is given by the period number. Find lithium in the periodic table. How does its written electron configuration end? What is the written electron configuration for its outer level? Find Group II in the periodic table. What is the ending for the written electron configuration for all elements in this group? What is the written electron configuration for the outer level for each of the elements in this group? The same procedure can be used for Groups IIIA through VIIIA where endings, instead of s^1 or s^2, are p^1 through p^6 preceded by a coefficient which is the same as the number of the period.

The periodic table can be used to determine electron configuration of an element.

Atoms in the same period have the same principal quantum number.

Students should develop some facility in using the periodic table to "read" electron configurations.

IA, IIA : s^1, s^2

IIIA — VIIIA : $p^1 - p^6$

For Groups IIIB through IIB, the endings are d^1 through d^{10} preceded by a coefficient which is one less than the period number. For the lanthanides, the endings are f^1 through f^{14} preceded by a coefficient which is two less than the period number. For transition elements, remember that the d sublevel is always preceded by an s sublevel one level higher.

We may also explain some of the departures from the ground states predicted by the diagonal rule. To understand these exceptions, it is necessary to know that there is a special stability associated with certain electron configurations. You already know that eight electrons in the outer level have a special stability. Added stability is also gained any time a sublevel is filled or half filled. Thus, chromium is predicted to have two electrons in its $4s$ sublevel and four electrons in its $3d$ sublevel. Actually, it has one electron in its $4s$ sublevel and five electrons in its $3d$ sublevel. Note that by changing one electron between two very closely spaced sublevels. we attain two half-full sublevels instead of one full sublevel and one with no special stability. Copper has a similar change. Copper is predicted to have two $4s$ electrons and nine $3d$ electrons. Actually, it has one electron in its $4s$ sublevel and ten electrons in its $3d$ sublevel. One full and one half-full sublevel are more stable than one full sublevel and one with no special stability as predicted. Most of the deviations from predicted configurations can be explained in this way.

> Deviations from the diagonal rule are periodic and explainable.

> Full or half-full sublevels are particularly stable.

8:9 Metals and Nonmetals

Groups IA and IIA of the periodic table contain the most active metals. Many of the columns in the table have family names. Group IA, except hydrogen, is called the *alkali metal family*. Group IIA is called the *alkaline earth metal family*.

On the other side of the table are the nonmetals, in Groups VIA, VIIA, and VIIIA. Group VIA is called the *chalcogen family*. Group VIIA is known as the *halogen family*. Group VIIIA is called the *noble gases*.

One characteristic of *metals* is the presence of only a few electrons in the outer level. *Nonmetals* have more electrons in the outer level. There are exceptions. However, as a general rule, elements with three or less electrons in the outer level are considered to be metals. Elements with five or more electrons in the outer level are considered to be nonmetals. There are some elements which have properties of both metals and nonmetals. These elements are called the *metalloids*. Boron is an example.

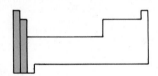

> Most active metals: groups IA and IIA.

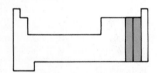

> Most active nonmetals: Group VIA and VIIA.

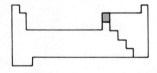

> Metalloids are elements which have both metallic and nonmetallic properties.

Suggestion: ask students to list typical metallic and nonmetallic properties they are familiar with, such as: electrical conductivity, hardness, and metallic lustre. This will set the stage for later development of these properties in terms of bonding and electrons.

a   b

The elements of Groups IB through VIIIB are called the *transition elements*. Since all atoms of transition elements have one or two electrons in the outer level, they all show metallic properties. The elements 57 through 70 and 89 through 102 have a similar characteristic* (Table 8–7). Most of these atoms have two electrons in the outer level (some have only one electron), and the elements are therefore classified as metals.

The elements of Groups IIIA through VA include both metals and nonmetals. At the top of the table, each of these groups contains nonmetallic elements. The metallic character of the elements increases toward the bottom of the table, and the last member of each family is distinctly metallic.

FIGURE 8-2. Two of the characteristics of metals are conductivity and malleability. Thus, metals may be used in the manufacture of motors (a) and food containers (b).

Transition elements are metals.

Metals generally have fewer electrons in the outer level than nonmetals.

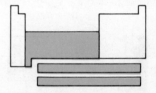

Metallic character increases down the table.

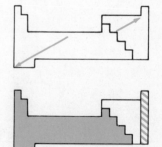

PROBLEMS

1. Classify the following elements as metals, metalloids, or nonmetals:
   a. cadmium metal
   b. calcium metal
   c. californium metal
   d. carbon nonmetal
   e. dysprosium metal
   f. oxygen nonmetal
   g. praseodymium metal
   h. thallium metalloid
2. Are there more metals or nonmetals in the periodic table?
   There are more metals.

Most of the elements are metallic.

8:10 Review—Periodic Table

Now look at the periodic table as a whole. Metals are located on the left and nonmetals on the right. Note again that most of the elements are metallic; that is, their atoms contain one, two, or three

* Elements 57 through 70 are called the lanthanide series.

electrons in the outer level. The most stable atoms are those of the noble gases. In general, when atoms of elements unite to form molecules or compounds, their structures become more stable.

8:11   The Sodium-Chlorine Period (Period 3)

We can see the periodic nature of the elements by looking at a row of the periodic table. The third period begins with sodium. Chlorine is the next to last element in this period. The compound formed by sodium and chlorine, sodium chloride or common table salt, is very stable. However, there are no sodium chloride molecules. Instead, each cube of sodium chloride, small or large, is one unit. A solid salt crystal will not carry an electric current because the individual ions are tightly bound and cannot move freely. However, when salt is dissolved or melted, it will carry a current. The individual sodium and chlorine ions are free to move. If we look at the periodic table and the electron arrangement of these two elements, we can see why this happens.

Sodium chloride is an ionic compound.

8:12   The Reaction of Sodium and Chlorine

Sodium and chlorine are located at opposite ends of the third row of the table. Sodium is found at the left of the table, and is a metal. Therefore, it tends to lose its single 3s sublevel electron and form an ion. The sodium ion (NA$^+$) has a positive charge and a stable configuration which resembles neon.

The configuration of Na$^+$ is similar to neon.

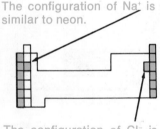

The configuration of Cl$^-$ is similar to argon.

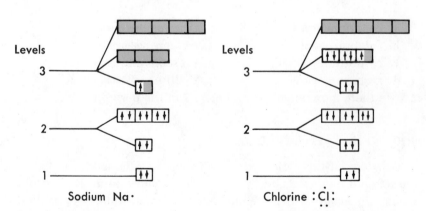

FIGURE 8-3. Both sodium and chlorine atoms contain unfilled third levels.

Chlorine is at the right of the table in column VIIIA. It is a non-metal. Its atoms contain seven electrons in the outer level. The chloride ion (Cl⁻) has a negative charge and is formed when the chlorine atom gains one electron. The configuration of the chloride ion is the same as that of the noble gas, argon.

Note that both sodium and chlorine have partially filled third levels. This means that the outer electrons which take part in reactions are separated from the nucleus by two levels, or ten electrons, in both sodium and chlorine. The chlorine nucleus contains seventeen protons; the sodium nucleus contains only eleven protons. The outer electrons (the electrons which take part in reactions) of the chlorine atom are attracted by six more protons than are the outer electrons of the sodium atom. Therefore, the chlorine electrons are held more tightly, and the chlorine atom is smaller than the sodium atom.

The chlorine atom is smaller than the sodium atom.

The sodium atom holds its single outer electron very loosely. When chlorine and sodium react, the more positive chlorine nucleus almost completely removes the single outer electron from the sodium atom. This change results in a positively charged sodium ion. The sodium ion is smaller than the sodium atom. It is very stable because its outer level resembles the outer level of the stable noble gas, neon.

The sodium ion is smaller than the sodium atom.

When salt is formed, the chlorine atom gains an electron and becomes the negatively charged chloride ion. Compare the size of the chloride ion and the chlorine atom (Figure 8–6). The chloride ion is larger because it has gained an electron and a resulting negative

Courtesy of Kodansha Ltd.

Rick Kocks

FIGURE 8-4. Sodium and chlorine combine chemically to form sodium chloride. Sodium is very reactive and is stored in an inert liquid (a). Chlorine is very reactive and is used in purification of municipal water supplies (b).

The chloride ion is larger than the sodium atom.

charge. However, the positive charge on the nucleus has remained the same because the number of protons in its nucleus has not changed. The ion is stable because it has an outer level similar to that of the noble gas, argon.

We have noted that the sodium ion is smaller than the sodium atom. Notice that the magnesium ion is even smaller than its atom. In losing two outer electrons, the unbalanced nuclear positive charge is larger. Aluminum, when it loses three electrons, also acts as a metal. The nonmetals sulfur and chlorine form ions which are larger than their respective atoms. The elements silicon and phosphorus do not lose or gain electrons readily, and tend to form compounds by sharing their outer electrons.

Covalent and ionic bonds are discussed in the next chapter. It would probably be advisable to avoid consideration of bond formation in this chapter. Concentrate instead on the properties of atoms as a function of their structure.

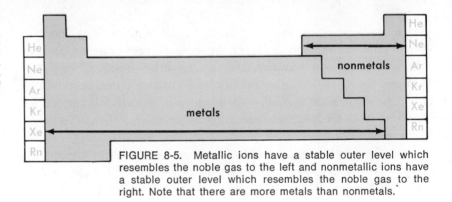

FIGURE 8-5. Metallic ions have a stable outer level which resembles the noble gas to the left and nonmetallic ions have a stable outer level which resembles the noble gas to the right. Note that there are more metals than nonmetals.

We can make a generalization which will apply to any element in any row of the periodic table. In general, metallic ions on the left and in the center of the table are formed by loss of electrons, and are smaller than the atoms from which they are formed. Nonmetallic ions are located on the right side of the table, and are larger than the atoms from which they are formed. Notice that metallic ions have a stable outer level which resembles the noble gas at the end of the preceding period. Nonmetallic ions have an outer level resembling the noble gas to the right.

Metallic and nonmetallic ions have a noble gas configuration.

8:13 Predicting Oxidation Numbers

Those electrons which are involved in the reaction of atoms with each other are the outer and highest energy electrons. Now that you know electron configurations and the tendency toward noble gas

METALS   NONMETALS

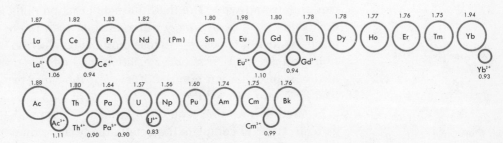

FIGURE 8-6. This chart indicates the relative size of atomic
and ionic radii of metals and nonmetals.

Oxidation numbers can be predicted from electron configurations.

Group IA : 1+

Group IIA : 2+

Transition elements tend to have more than one possible oxidation number.

Nonmetals tend to gain electrons.

structures, it is possible for you to predict what oxidation numbers atoms will have.

Consider the metals in Group IA. Each atom has one electron in its outer level, and it will tend to lose only this outer electron. Group IA metals have an oxidation number of 1+. Note that the hydrogen atom could attain the helium configuration by gaining one electron. If this happened, we would say that hydrogen had a 1− oxidation number. Hydrogen does indeed exhibit a 1− oxidation number in some compounds. In Group IIA the same kind of reasoning leads to a prediction of 2+ oxidation number for the alkaline earth metals. So far all of our predictions are accurate, and these two columns exhibit the oxidation numbers predicted for them.

Beginning with Group IIIB, we have atoms in which the highest energy electrons are not in the outer level. For instance, scandium has the configuration $1s^2 \ 2s^2 \ 2p^6 \ 3s^2 \ 3p^6 \ 4s^2 \ 3d^1$. Scandium's outer level is the fourth level containing two electrons. Its highest energy electron, however, is the one in the $3d$ sublevel. For the transition elements, it is possible to lose not only the outer level electrons, but also some lower level electrons. Most of the transition elements exhibit oxidation numbers varying from 2+ (representing loss of the two outer s electrons) up to as many as 7+. Scandium, we would predict, should show only 2+ and 3+. Actually, the element has only the 3+ oxidation number. Titanium should show 2+, 3+, and 4+, and it does. As we continue across the fourth row, vanadium has a maximum oxidation number of 5+, chromium a 6+ oxidation number, and manganese a 7+ oxidation number. Iron, however, has only 2+ and 3+ oxidation numbers. Recall that a half-full sublevel represents a particularly stable configuration. To take iron higher than 3+ would mean breaking up a half-full $3d$ sublevel.

Group IIIA elements lose three electrons and have an oxidation number of 3+. Thallium, in addition to the 3+ oxidation number, exhibits a 1+ oxidation number. If we look at its configuration, we can understand why. The thallium configuration ends $6s^2 \ 4f^{14} \ 5d^{10} \ 6p^1$. There is such an energy difference between the $6s$ and the $6p$ electrons, that it is possible to lose only the $6p$ electron for an oxidation number of 1+. If stronger reaction methods are used, thallium also has an oxidation number of 3+. For the same reason, tin and lead in Group IVA exhibit a 2+ and 4+ oxidation number.

In Groups VA, VIA, and VIIA, there is a general tendency to gain electrons to complete the octet already more than half filled in the outer level. These elements show oxidation numbers of 3−

(Group VA), 2– (Group VIA), and 1– (Group VIIA). It is also possible for these elements to lose electrons and have positive oxidation numbers that are predictable. The tendency to lose electrons increases as we pass down the columns. This tendency will be discussed in more detail later.

PROBLEM

3. Explain the deviations from the diagonal rule for the electron configurations of molybdenum, palladium, and gadolinium.

4. Explain the deviations from the diagonal rule for the electron configurations of gold, curium, and thorium.

5. Predict all possible oxidation numbers for the following elements and state your evidence: argon, europium, aluminum, antimony, and bromine.

6. Predict all possible oxidation numbers for the following and state your evidence: uranium, sodium, silicon, cerium, and cobalt.

7. Check the actual oxidation numbers of the elements in Problem 5. Explain any deviations from your predictions.

8. Repeat Problem 7 with the elements of Problem 6.

See Teacher's Guide at the front of this book.

5. $Ar = 0$; $Eu = 2+$; $Al = 3+$; $Sb = 3+, 5+$; $Br = 1-$

6. $U = 2+, 3+, 4+, 5+, 6+$; $Na = 1+$; $Si = 4+, 4-$; $Ce = 2+$; $Co = 2+$

7. Ar, Al, Sb, Br, as predicted; Eu, also 3+

8. Na, Si as predicted; U, no 2+; Ce, no 2+ (3+ or 4+ instead); Co, also 3+

PERIODIC PROPERTIES

8:14　Groups

We can see the periodic nature of the elements in the groups as well as in the periods of the table. The elements in the first group— hydrogen, lithium, sodium, potassium, rubidium, cesium, and francium—all contain one s electron in the outer level. A group is often called a *family* because of the similarity of the elements within it. The family is usually given a name. We have already mentioned the alkali metal family and the halogen family. The members of a family have a similar arrangement of outer electrons and thus tend to react similarly. For instance, lithium, sodium, and potassium all lose one electron to chlorine and form chlorides (LiCl, NaCl, KCl). Hydrogen is also found in this group. It, too, forms a chloride, hydrogen chloride. Let us take a closer look at hydrogen.

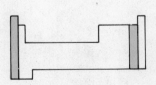

Members of a chemical family (group) react similarly.

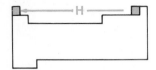

FIGURE 8-7. Hydrogen burns in chlorine to form the gas hydrogen chloride (a). Hydrogen also reacts with oxygen to form water which can be seen condensing on the cooled flask (b).

8:15 Hydrogen

Hydrogen, like the alkali metals, has only one outer electron. Because of its unique properties, it is usually considered to be in a family by itself. There are three general ways in which the hydrogen atom can react. It may lose its one electron to become a positive hydrogen ion. However, a positive hydrogen ion is simply a bare proton. Remember from Section 6:7 that a proton is about one trillionth the size of an atom. Because of its small size, the hydrogen ion has some unique characteristics. These will be considered in Section 14:10 (Hydrogen Bonding) and Section 20:1 (Acids). The second way a hydrogen atom can react is by sharing its single outer electron. Most nonmetals react with hydrogen to form compounds involving shared electrons. These compounds and their formation will be studied in more detail in Chapter 9.

The third way hydrogen can react is to gain an electron. When this happens, the atom becomes a hydride ion, H^-. Such a reaction can take place only between hydrogen and atoms of elements which give up electrons easily. Only the most reactive metals lose electrons easily. The metals of Groups IA and IIA form ionic hydrides. In these compounds, the radius of the hydride ion averages about 1.42 Å. From Figure 8–6, we can see that the hydride ion is larger than the fluoride ion. Such a radius indicates that the single proton of the hydride ion has a very weak hold on the two electrons. We would expect, then, that the ionic hydrides would not be highly stable. Experiment confirms this belief. The ionic hydrides are found

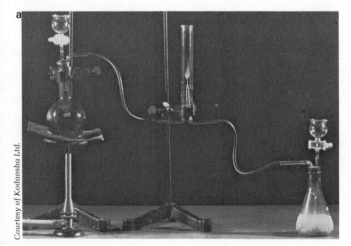

to be quite reactive compounds. By sharing or gaining electrons, hydrogen attains the stable outer level configuration of helium.

There is a fourth type of bonding involving hydrogen. It involves the formation of bridges between two atoms by hydrogen atoms. The best examples of these compounds are found with the element boron and some of the transition metals. A study of such compounds is beyond the scope of this book. Since they are not common compounds, they make up only a small fraction of the chemistry of hydrogen.

Hydrogen reacts in four different ways.

8:16 Alkali Metals

The metals in Group IA are very reactive. If we know that one member of a family will form a compound with a certain element or ion, we can predict that other members of the family will form similar compounds. However, the members of a family are not the same in every way. Notice that the outer electron of lithium is much nearer the nucleus than the outer electron of sodium. Notice also that there are many more electrons between the outer electron and the nucleus in sodium than between the outer electron and the nucleus of lithium. Increasing the number of electrons between the outer level and the nucleus has a *shielding effect* on the attraction of the nucleus for the outer electrons. Both the distance from the nucleus to outer electrons and the shielding effect tend to cause the larger atoms to lose their electrons more readily.

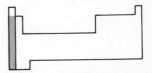

As the atomic numbers of the alkali metals increase:
1. *the atoms become larger*
2. *the outer electron is farther from the nucleus*
3. *the lower level electrons shield the effect of the larger nucleus*
4. *the outer electrons are held less tightly*
5. *the atoms become more active.*

Table 8–13

Alkali Metal Compounds

Alkali metal	Acetate ($C_2H_3O_2^-$)	Iodate (IO_3^-)	Hexafluorosilicate (SiF_6^-)	Sulfate (SO_4^{2-})
Li^+	$LiC_2H_3O_2$	$LiIO_3$	Li_2SiF_6	Li_2SO_4
Na^+	$NaC_2H_3O_2$	$NaIO_3$	Na_2SiF_6	Na_2SO_4
K^+	$KC_2H_3O_2$	KIO_3	K_2SiF_6	K_2SO_4
Rb^+	$RbC_2H_3O_2$	$RbIO_3$	Rb_2SiF_6	Rb_2SO_4
Cs^+	$CsC_2H_3O_2$	$CsIO_3$	Cs_2SiF_6	Cs_2SO_4

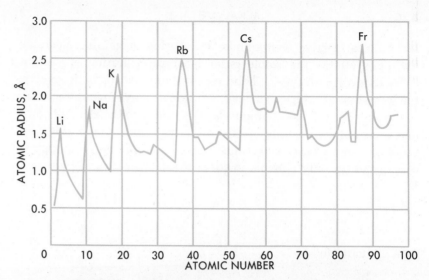

FIGURE 8-8. The atomic radii are related to the size of the nucleus. Note that the alkali metals have the largest atomic radii and the halogens have the smallest atomic radii.

As the atoms of alkali metals increase in size, the nucleus increases in positive charge. However, the increased attraction of the larger nucleus does not counterbalance the two previously mentioned forces in the alkali metal family. As a result, we find that the alkali metal atoms lose their electrons more readily as we proceed down the column. This indicates that the most active metal would be francium, which is in the lower left corner of the periodic table.

8:17 Lithium

The reactions of the alkali metals involve essentially the formation of the 1+ ions. In general, the reactivity increases with increasing atomic number, with one exception: lithium reacts more vigorously with nitrogen than any other alkali metal does. Lithium is exceptional in other ways, too. It has the same charge in its ionic form as the other alkali metals, but the unusual behavior is due to its smaller size. The ratio of charge to radius is often a good indication of the behavior of an ion. In its charge/radius ratio, lithium more closely resembles the magnesium ion (Mg^{2+}) of Group IIA than it does the next member of its own family, sodium (Na^+). This *diagonal relationship* is not unusual among the lighter elements. One example of this relationship is that lithium burns in air to form the oxide, Li_2O, as does magnesium to form MgO. The other alkali metals form the peroxide, M_2O_2, or the superoxide, MO_2 (where M =

Na, K, Rb or Cs). Another example of this relationship concerns the solubilities of compounds. The solubility of lithium compounds is similar to that of magnesium compounds, but not to that of sodium compounds.

The lithium atom also differs from the other alkali metal atoms in some physical properties. Unlike all the other alkali metals which dissolve in each other in any proportions, lithium is insoluble in all but sodium. It will dissolve in sodium only above 380°C. In other respects, lithium metal is similar to the other members of its family. For example, it is a soft, silvery metal with a low melting point, as are the other alkali metals except cesium. Cesium is yellow. All of the alkali metals will dissolve in liquid ammonia to give faintly blue solutions. These solutions are found to be electrical conductors.

Lithium is physically similar to other members of Group IA.

The alkali metals form binary compounds with almost all nonmetals. In these compounds, nonmetals are in the form of negative ions. In solution, the lithium ion, because of its high charge/radius ratio, attracts water molecules far more strongly than any other alkali ion.

There are two other 1+ ions which, because of their size, behave in quite similar fashion to the alkali ions. These are the ammonium ion (NH_4^+) and the thallium (I) ion (Tl^+). Their compounds, in solid form as well as in solution, follow much the same patterns as the alkali metal compounds.

NH_4^+ and Tl^+ behave similarly to the alkali family.

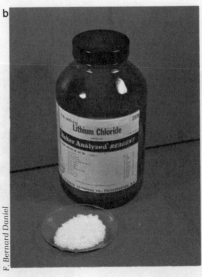

Courtesy of Kodansha Ltd.

F. Bernard Daniel

FIGURE 8-9. Lithium, like the other alkali metals, is very reactive and must be stored in an inert liquid (a). Lithium forms binary compounds such as lithium chloride (b) which is used in soldering aluminum and in bottling mineral water.

8:18 Carbon and Silicon

The elements of Group IVA have atoms with four electrons in the outer level. These elements generally react by sharing electrons. However, the tendency to lose electrons increases as atomic number of Group IVA elements increases. There are a few compounds in which carbon in the form of a *carbide* ion (C^{4-}) can be considered to exist. Silicon, the next member of this family, although nonmetallic, does not form distinctive 4— ions under any conditions. However, there are compounds in which silicon is present as 4+ ions.

The major part of the chemistry of carbon is classed as *organic chemistry*. Exceptions to this classification are usually the element carbon itself, carbonic acid and its salts, carbides, cyanides, and the oxides and sulfides of carbon. Most organic compounds involve the sharing of electrons between a carbon atom and one or more other carbon atoms. The tendency to form "chains" of similar atoms is called *catenation*. Only carbon exhibits catenation to any great extent.

Carbon is found in nature in two different molecular forms: diamond and graphite. In diamond, each carbon atom shares electrons with the four nearest carbon atoms. In graphite, the sharing is to the nearest three carbon atoms. The difference in structure leads to quite different properties for these two forms of carbon. We will study these differences in Chapter 13.

Silicon shows only a slight tendency toward catenation, much less so than carbon. However, the chemistry of silicon, like that of carbon, is characterized by electron sharing. Silicon is the second

FIGURE 8-10. Carbon exists in two molecular forms. These are diamond (a) and graphite (b) which is used in the manufacture of pencils.

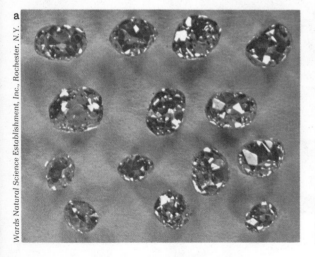

a

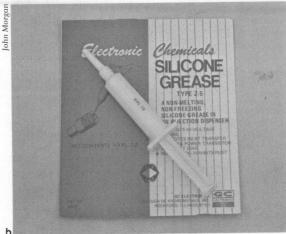

b

most plentiful element in the earth's crust. (Oxygen is the most plentiful.) It is found in a very large number of minerals in the form of silicon bound to oxygen atoms in a variety of complex ways. In these compounds, called silicates, each silicon atom is surrounded by four oxygen atoms with which it shares electrons. Transistors and synthetic motor oils are two recent developments of silicon chemistry. As you might gather from this brief description of their chemistries, carbon and silicon differ more than any other two vertically neighboring elements in the periodic table.

Transistors are discussed more fully in Chapter 13.

FIGURE 8-11. Some crystalline forms of silicon are shown in (a). Because they are good electrical insulating materials, some silicon compounds can be used to manufacture products which prevent high-voltage arcing (b).

Carbon and silicon have as many differences as similarities.

8:19 Oxygen

Oxygen is the most plentiful element in the earth's crust. It combines with all other elements except helium, neon, and argon. Since it has six electrons in the outer level of its atoms, it can gain two electrons to achieve the stable configuration of neon. In so doing, it becomes the oxide ion, O^{2-}. It also can react by sharing electrons. With metals which tend to lose electrons readily, oxygen forms ionic oxides. With nonmetals, oxygen tends to share electrons. The behavior of these oxides when dissolved in water depends on their structure. Ionic oxides generally react with water to produce basic solutions. However, oxides formed by the sharing of electrons tend to react with water to form acidic solutions. There are some oxides which produce either acidic or basic solutions, depending on what other substances are present. Such oxides are called *amphoteric* oxides.

Oxygen may gain or share electrons in reacting.

Like carbon, oxygen exhibits more than one molecular form in the free state. Oxygen usually occurs in the form of diatomic oxygen molecules (O_2). There is another molecular form of oxygen called

F. Bernard Daniel

Paul Nesbit

a

b

FIGURE 8-12. Diatomic oxygen makes up 20% of the earth's air and is necessary for respiration in animals (a). Small amounts of triatomic oxygen, ozone, may be formed in air as a result of lightning (b).

O_3 is ozone.

ozone. Ozone is the triatomic form of oxygen (O_3). The free oxygen which you breathe in from air is O_2. Ozone can be formed in the laboratory or commercially by subjecting O_2 to a silent electrical discharge. It is formed in small amounts by lightning. It is also formed naturally in the upper atmosphere by ultraviolet radiation from the sun. Ozone is highly reactive. It is used in chemical synthesis. In Europe, it is the principal chemical used in water purification.

Henry Gwyn-Jeffreys Moseley
(1887–1915)

Henry Moseley was the first to discover a definite way of determining the atomic numbers of elements. This he accomplished by using different metals as targets in an X-ray tube. His research enabled scientists to determine the atomic number of unknown elements and to correct Mendeleev's periodic table.

As a teacher at the University of Manchester, Moseley also spent time investigating radioactivity.

His efforts in this field were halted, however, when the British government sent him to serve as an ordinary foot soldier in the First World War. He was killed in the fighting in Gallipoli at the age of 28. Because of this loss, Britain restricted its scientists to noncombat duties during World War II.

8:20　Halogens

The effective nuclear charge of all elements in a column is roughly the same.

Group VIIA contains fluorine, chlorine, bromine, iodine, and astatine. The elements of this group are called the *halogen* (salt forming) family. In many chemical reactions, the halogen atoms gain one electron and become negatively charged ions with a stable outer level containing eight electrons. As in other families already discussed, the three factors which determine the reactivity of the halogens are: the distance between the nucleus and the outer electrons, the shielding effect of inner level electrons, and the size of the positive charge on the nucleus. Fluorine atoms contain fewer inner level electrons than the other halogens, so the shielding effect is at a minimum. The distance between the fluorine nucleus and its outer electrons is less than in the other halogens. Thus, its nucleus has the greatest tendency to attract other electrons.

The astatine nucleus has the largest number of protons and the largest positive charge. However, the increased charge on the nucleus is not sufficient to counterbalance the distance and shielding effects. Thus, of all halogen atoms, the astatine nucleus has the least noticeable affinity for outer electrons. Little is known of astatine's chemical properties.

Notice that fluorine is active because the atoms of fluorine have a great tendency to gain one electron and become negative ions. The atoms of the most active metal are active because they hold the single outer electron loosely and have a great tendency to lose it. The groups between IA and VIIA vary between these two extremes. In general, on the right side of the table, we find that the nonmetallic elements become more active as we move from the bottom to the

Halogens gain an electron in reactions.

As the atomic numbers of the halogens increase:
1. the atoms become larger
2. the outer levels are farther from the nucleus
3. the intervening electrons shield the effect of a larger nucleus
4. the nucleus has less attraction for electrons of other atoms
5. the atoms become less active

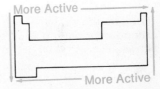

Fluorine is the most active element.

FIGURE 8-13. Hydrogen fluoride can be used to etch glass. A design is cut into the paraffin coating on a glass plate (a). The uncoated part of the plate is exposed to hydrogen fluoride. The result is an etched plate (b).

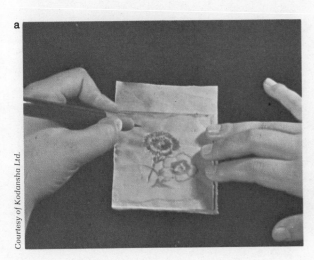

Courtesy of Kodansha Ltd.

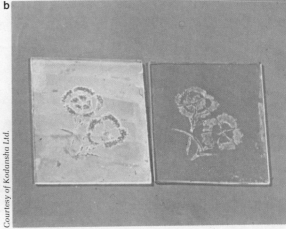

Courtesy of Kodansha Ltd.

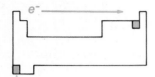

The most active elements are in the upper right and lower left of the periodic table.

Halogen atoms can form compounds among themselves.

top. On the left-hand side of the table, the metals become more active as we move from the top to the bottom. The most active elements are located at the upper right-hand and lower left-hand corners of the periodic table.

8:21   Fluorine and Chlorine

The halogens are the most reactive nonmetallic family. They react almost always by forming negative ions or sharing electrons. As in many other families, the first member differs the most from the rest of the family. In the case of fluorine, the difference is due mainly to the small size of the fluorine atom. Like hydrogen, halogen atoms can form bridges between two other atoms. An example of such a compound is BeF_2. The halogens also form a large number of compounds among themselves. Examples are ClF, ClF_5, BrF_5, IF_5, IF_7, $BrCl$, and ICl_3. Fluorine is the most reactive of all the chemical elements. It reacts with all other elements except helium, neon, and argon.

Chlorine, though less abundant than fluorine in the earth's crust, is more commonly found in both the laboratory and industry. Chlorides of most elements are available commercially. These compounds are quite often used in the laboratory as a source of the positive ions bound with the chloride ions.

FIGURE 8-14. Chlorine is a good bleaching agent. Much of the color of the flower (a) disappears when the flower is exposed to chlorine (b).

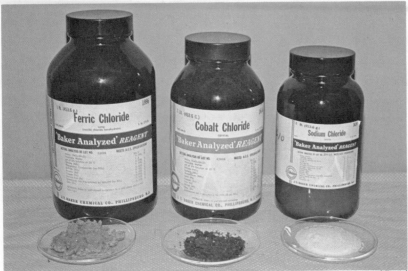

FIGURE 8-15. Some chlorides commonly used in the laboratory are iron(III) chloride, cobalt(II) chloride, and sodium chloride.

F. Bernard Daniel

The commercial preparation of chlorine led to one of the major water pollution crises of the early 1970s. The chlorine was produced by running an electric current through a solution of sodium chloride in water. One of the substances used to conduct current in the apparatus was mercury. The leakage of mercury into nearby watercourses caused a public outcry. Manufacturers had either to extract the mercury from their waste water before dumping, or to switch to another method of producing chlorine. Both the extraction methods and alternate manufacturing methods had to be developed by chemists. There are many other pollution problems which must be given special attention by chemists in the near future.

Ohio Environmental Protection Agency: Richard Ulry

FIGURE 8-16. Chemists play an important role in preventing and solving problems of pollution.

8:22   Noble Gases

For many years after their discovery, the noble gases, helium, neon, argon, krypton, xenon, and radon, were believed to be chemically unreactive or *inert*. However, in 1962, the first compound involving one of the "inert" gases was synthesized. Since these gases are not inert, we will refer to them as the noble gases. The first compound made was xenon hexafluoroplatinate ($XePtF_6$).

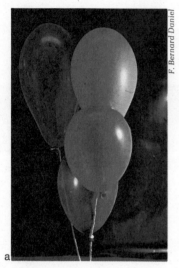

FIGURE 8-17. Helium, because it does not burn and is less dense than other noble gases can be used to elevate a balloon (a). Noble gases such as neon are also used to make many commercial signs (b).

Other compounds of xenon were soon produced. Once the techniques were learned, the compounds could be made with increasing ease. Xenon difluoride (XeF_2) was first made by combining xenon and oxygen difluoride (OF_2) in a nickel tube at 300°C under pressure. The same crystalline compound can now be made by mixing xenon and fluorine in an evacuated glass container and exposing the container to daylight. The equation can be written:

$$Xe(g) + F_2(g) \xrightarrow{\text{light}} XeF_2(s)$$

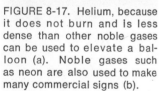

9. a. iron
   b. nickel
   c. fermium
   d. fluorine
   e. gold. Silver is actually more active. This is a good example of the danger of oversimplified generalizations. Gold, although it appears below silver in the periodic table, is very much less active than silver.

PROBLEMS

9. Which elements from the following pairs would you predict to be more active?
   a. cobalt, iron
   b. copper, nickel
   c. fermium, mendelevium
   d. fluorine, oxygen
   e. gold, silver

10. Which elements from the following pairs would you predict to be more active?

a. hafnium, zirconium   **d.** potassium, calcium

b. lithium, sodium   **e.** arsenic, selenium

c. nitrogen, phosphorus

SUMMARY

1. The many attempts to classify the elements in a systematic manner include Dobereiner's triads, Newlands' law of octaves, and Mendeleev's and Meyer's tables.

2. The modern periodic law states: The properties of the elements are a periodic function of their atomic numbers.

3. Today's periodic table is based on the electron configurations of the atoms.

4. All elements in a horizontal line of the table are called a period; all elements in a vertical line are called a group or family.

5. The most stable atoms have eight electrons in the outer level. Helium atoms are stable with two electrons in the outer level.

6. The periodic table may be used to predict electron configurations.

7. Full and half-full sublevels represent states of special stability.

8. Elements with one, two, or three electrons in the outer level tend to be metals. Elements with five, six, seven, or eight outer electrons tend to be nonmetals.

9. The periodic table, together with the octet rule, may be used to predict oxidation numbers.

10. The most active metals are listed toward the lower left-hand corner of the table. The most active nonmetals are listed toward the upper right-hand corner.

11. Hydrogen is often considered to be in a family by itself because of the unique way in which it can react.

12. The alkali metals (Group IA) are the most active metals and react by losing one electron.

13. Carbon and silicon (Group IVA) have four electrons in the outer level and react by sharing electrons.

14. Oxygen (Group VIA) is distinctly nonmetallic and reacts by gaining two electrons or by sharing electrons.

15. The halogens (Group VIIA) are the most active nonmetallic elements and usually react by gaining one electron.

16. The noble gases (Group VIIIA) have very stable outer electron configurations and are much less reactive than most of the other elements.

PROBLEMS

11. Classify the following elements as metals or nonmetals:
    a. chromium metal
    b. fluorine nonmetal
    c. gold metal
    d. helium nonmetal
    e. iron metal

12. Classify the following elements as metals or nonmetals:
    a. neodymium metal
    b. nitrogen nonmetal
    c. tantalum metal
    d. hydrogen nonmetal
    e. lithium metal
    f. fluorine nonmetal
    g. silicon nonmetal

13. a. actinium
    b. plutonium
    c. berkelium
    d. carbon
    e. fluorine

13. From their relative positions in the periodic table, predict which element from the following pairs is more active:
    a. actinium, lanthanum
    b. americium, plutonium
    c. berkelium, terbium
    d. carbon, silicon
    e. chlorine, fluorine

14. a. gallium
    b. neptunium
    c. oxygen
    d. cesium
    e. bromine

14. From their relative positions in the periodic table, predict which element from the following pairs is more active:
    a. gallium, germanium
    b. neptunium, plutonium
    c. nitrogen, oxygen
    d. rubidium, cesium
    e. bromine, iodine

ONE MORE STEP

1. Sections 8:1 and 8:2 give a start. Kauffman (see Suggested Readings in Teacher's Guide) also has some information.

See Teacher's Guide at the front of this book.

1. Make a chart showing the history of the classification of elements. Include date, person, and contribution.

2. Obtain a reproduction of Mendeleev's original table, and list the errors it contains.

3. Mendeleev made predictions about five elements in addition to germanium. Find out what these elements were and how accurate his predictions were.

4. Both Moseley and Lavoisier lost their lives for political causes. Find out what these causes were.

5. In the past few years, much research has been done on compounds of the noble gases. Find an article about one of these projects and report on it to the class.

6. The names of the elements have an interesting history. Develop a table showing how each name was derived.

7. What property of metalloids has led to their use in transistors?

8. Lithium is often listed as more reactive than sodium, contrary to predictions. See if you can find out why.

See Teacher's Guide at the front of this book.

Suggested Readings for this chapter may be found in the Teacher's Guide at the front of this book.

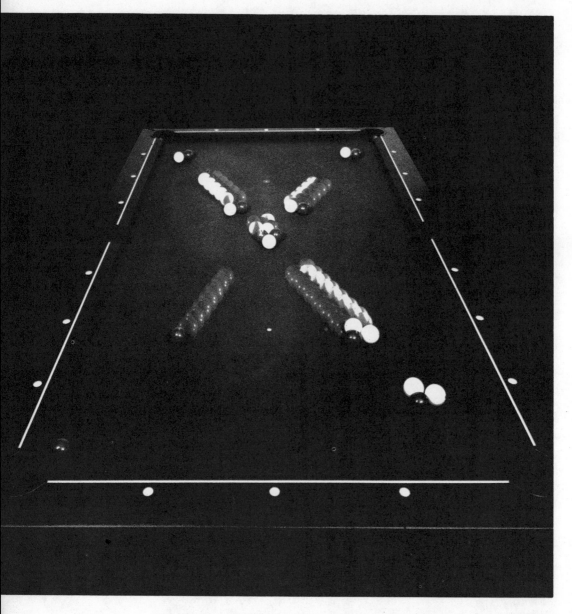

The interactions of some atoms and parts of atoms can be compared to the interactions of these billiard balls. This is an example of the use of a scientific model. Because atoms are much too small to be studied individually, chemists often use models of atoms in an attempt to understand and explain atomic phenomena. Have you ever built a model in any of your scientific studies? If so, what was its purpose?

Chemical Bonding

Chapter 9 introduces chemical bonding and examines the factors which help determine the nature of the bond.

In Chapter 8, we looked at the ways atoms could react. We found that some atoms tend to give up electrons and become positive ions, while other atoms tend to gain electrons and become negative ions. We also discovered that some atoms tend to share electrons. In the present chapter, we want to investigate these processes in detail.

GOAL: You will gain an understanding of chemical bonding and factors which affect bonding.

ATOMS AND ELECTRONS

9:1 Determining Ionization Energy

An atomic model such as Bohr's model of the atom can be used to predict the energy needed to remove the most loosely held electron from an atom. The model can be tested by determining this energy experimentally and comparing this value with the predicted energy value.

First ionization energy: energy needed to remove the most loosely held electron in an atom.

The determinations involve shooting electrons at a vapor. If a substance is vaporized in a space between two electrodes (Figure 9–1), no current will flow through the vapor from one electrode to the other because the individual atoms of the vapor have no charge.

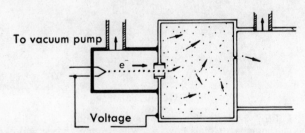

FIGURE 9-1. A device for determining the ionization energy of a vaporized substance. The dotted line represents an electron beam. The central chamber contains vapor which is ionized by the electrons.

If this vapor is bombarded with a stream of electrons, some of the bombarding electrons will collide with atoms and "knock loose" electrons from atoms. This process leaves positively charged ions. The positive ions will move toward the negative electrode, and a current will be detected. In this way, it is possible to determine that the vapor has been ionized.

To determine the energy necessary to cause a current, the energy of the bombarding electrons is increased gradually until a current is detected. The energy of the electrons which first caused the ionization can be considered the energy necessary to remove completely an electron from an atom of the element being bombarded, leaving a positive ion. This energy is called the *first ionization energy* of that element. It is often measured in electronvolts (eV)*.

9:2 First Ionization Energies

The first ionization energies (energy needed to remove the first electron) of the first ninety-five elements are graphed in Figure 9–2. Note that the ionization energies, like many other properties

The energies shown on the graph are first ionization energies. Subsequent ionization energies give experimental evidence for the existence of energy levels and sublevels.

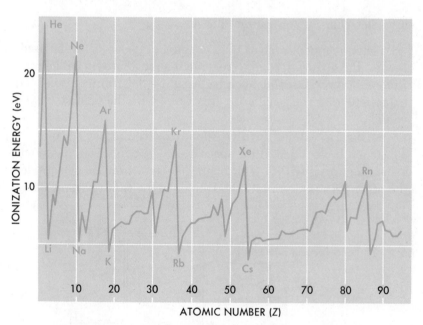

FIGURE 9-2. Ionization energies are periodic in relation to atomic number. Metals have a low ionization energy and nonmetals have a high ionization energy.

* One electronvolt is the kinetic energy acquired by an electron in passing through a potential difference of 1 volt in a vacuum.

of the elements, are periodic. In fact, the relative difference between the ionization energies of two elements can be predicted by referring to the position of the two elements in the periodic table.

The ionization energy tends to increase with increasing atomic number in any horizontal row. In any column, in contrast, there is a gradual decrease in ionization energy with increase in atomic number. Note, for example, the gradual decrease in ionization energy in the alkali metal series (lithium through cesium) or in the noble gas series (helium through radon).

In any row of the table, the metals are those elements with a low ionization energy. Metals are located at the left side of the table. Elements with a high ionization energy are nonmetals. They are found at the right side of the table.

Today, we use these ionization energies as evidence for the existence of energy levels in the atom. However, our theories of structure are based on experimental results such as ionization energies and atomic spectra. The experimental evidence came first, then the model of structure.

Table 9–1

First Ionization Energies (in electronvolts)

H 13.60							He 24.59
Li 5.39	Be 9.32	B 8.30	C 11.26	N 14.53	O 13.62	F 17.42	Ne 21.57
Na 5.14	Mg 7.65	Al 5.99	Si 8.15	P 10.49	S 10.36	Cl 12.97	Ar 15.76
K 4.34	Ca 6.11						

Note that the colored areas are maximum nodes and that the ionization energy falls off immediately as each node is passed and gradually builds up to the next maximum. This corresponds to the formation and filling of each new level.

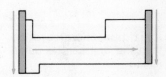

Look at Table 9–1. Notice that the ionization energies decrease as you go down a column of the periodic table (for instance, lithium, sodium, potassium). The increased distance of the outer electrons and the shielding effect of the other electrons are enough to overcome the increased nuclear charge of the element with greater atomic number. Remember that the number of electrons in the outermost sublevel remains the same for all elements in a column of the periodic table.

In passing across a row of the periodic table, we can see several differences from the expected trend of increasing ionization energy. This increase in ionization energy in going from the left side of the table to the right side is a result of the increasing nuclear charge. Look at the second row. There is a small decrease from beryllium $(1s^2 2s^2)$ to boron $(1s^2 2s^2 2p^1)$. This shows that a p sublevel has a higher energy than an s sublevel. In beryllium, the first ionization energy is determined by removing an s electron. In boron, it is determined by removing a p electron. Since the p electron already has a greater energy, less energy is needed to remove it.

There is another slight decrease from nitrogen $(1s^2 2s^2 2p^3)$ to oxygen $(1s^2 2s^2 2p^4)$. The nitrogen p sublevel is half-full (a state of special stability) and a large amount of energy is needed to break up the sublevel. In oxygen, on the other hand, there is one electron over the half-full state, and removing one electron puts the atom in the special state. Thus, oxygen has a lower ionization energy than nitrogen.

Ionization energies are determined by the same factors as activity.

These regularities may appear familiar. The ionization energy is determined by the same factors which we discussed in detail in Chapter 8 in connection with the periodic table. The factors are:

1. size of nuclear charge
2. distance between the nucleus and outer electrons
3. shielding effect
4. sublevel of electrons

The fourth factor, the effect of s & p sublevels, causes the slight drop from beryllium to boron and from magnesium to aluminum. Electrons in the p sublevel have slightly more energy and therefore require less additional energy to be removed from the atom.

Ionization energies other than the first can be determined.

9:3   Multiple Ionization Energies

It is possible to measure the subsequent (second, third, etc.) ionization energies of an atom. These measurements give us the same kind of evidence for atomic structure that the first ionization energies give. For example, in aluminum, the second ionization energy is about three times as large as the first, the third is about one and two-thirds times as large as the second, while the fourth is about four times as large as the third. The difference between the first and second ionizations is great in aluminum because the first ionization involves a p electron and the second involves an s electron. The third electron's ionization energy is greater than the second (even though both are in an s sublevel) because the nuclear charge of the atom has remained constant as we removed electrons. Consequently, the remaining electrons are more tightly held. But the jump between third and fourth ionization energies is large. Why? Look at the electron configuration. Aluminum has the configuration $1s^2 2s^2 2p^6 3s^2 3p^1$. To remove a fourth electron, a level closer to the nucleus must be broken. The $2s^2 2p^6$ level with eight electrons is very stable.

We have considered only the aluminum atom, but the same kind of information can be obtained from similar data for other elements. This information can be used as evidence for our theories of atomic structure (Table 9–2).

Emphasize that the theories came from experimental evidence.

Table 9–2

Ionization Energies (in electronvolts)

Element	1st	2nd	3rd	4th	5th	6th
Hydrogen	13.60					
Helium	24.59	54.42				
Lithium	5.39	75.64	122.42			
Beryllium	9.32	18.21	153.85	217.66		
Boron	8.30	25.16	37.92	259.30	340.13	
Carbon	11.26	24.38	47.86	64.48	391.99	489.84

Ionization energy is the energy necessary to remove completely an electron from an atom.

9:4 Electron Affinities

Consider now, not the ease of electron removal, but the attraction of an atom for additional electrons. The attraction of an atom for an electron is called the *electron affinity*. It is influenced by the same factors which affect the ionization energy. In general, the greater the electron affinity, the greater the ionization energy. Metals have the lowest electron affinity. Nonmetals have the greatest electron affinity (Table 9–3).

Electron affinity: attraction of an atom for an electron.

Table 9–3

Electron Affinities (in electronvolts)

H 0.77							He −0.56
Li 0.58	Be −0.68	B 0.16	C 1.25	N −0.29	O 1.47	F 3.45	Ne −1.03
Na 0.50	Mg 0.69	Al 0.33	Si 1.40	P 0.70	S 2.07	Cl 3.61	Ar −1.23
K 0.91	Ca 1.00						

9:5 Electronegativity

Both electron affinity and ionization energy deal with isolated atoms. They make no reference to other particles. Chemists need a comparative scale relating the abilities of the elements to attract electrons when their atoms combine. The relative tendency of an atom to attract shared electrons to itself when bound with another atom is called its *electronegativity*. The elements can be assigned electronegativities on the basis of a number of experimental tests.

Many of the chemical properties of the elements can be systematized in terms of electronegativities. For example, the strength of the bond between two atoms increases with the difference in their electronegativities. To illustrate this, the strengths of the bonds between hydrogen and the halogens are listed in Table 9–4, with the values of the electronegativity differences.

Electronegativity: tendency of an atom to attract shared electrons.

Bond strength increases with difference in electronegativity.

The strength of the bond between the two atoms increases as the electronegativity difference increases.

Table 9–4

Bonds Between Hydrogen and Halogens

Bond	Bond Strength (kcal/mole)	Electronegativity Difference
H—F	127.9	1.80
H—Cl	96.68	0.80
H—Br	81.05	0.62
H—I	65.06	0.28

Electronegativity varies with electron affinities and ionization energies.

The electronegativities of the elements are influenced by the same factors which affect the ionization energies and the electron affinities. In fact, it is possible to construct an electronegativity scale using only the first ionization energies and the electron affinities of the elements. Examination of Table 9–5 shows that the variation in electronegativity in the periodic table follows the same pattern as the ionization energies and the electron affinities. The most active metals (left and down) have the lowest electronegativities. The most active nonmetals (right and up) have the highest electronegativities. Consider a reaction between two elements. Do the elements react by the loss and gain of electrons or do they share electrons? Their relative attraction for electrons determines how they react. We can use the electronegativity scale to determine their relative attraction for electrons. Since electronegativity represents a comparison of the same property for each of the elements, it is a dimensionless number.

Table 9–5

Electronegativities

H 2.20																

Li 0.96	Be 1.50			B 2.02	C 2.56	N 2.81	O 3.37	F 4.00

These are average values obtained from numerous experiments. The electronegativity of an element is affected in slightly different amounts by the different atoms with which it may combine. It is therefore necessary to combine the experimental results from several different compounds.

Na 0.96	Mg 1.29											Al 1.63	Si 1.94	P 2.04	S 2.46	Cl 3.00
K 0.84	Ca 1.02	Sc 1.28	Ti 1.44	V 1.54	Cr 1.61	Mn 1.57	Fe 1.74	Co 1.79	Ni 1.83	Cu 1.67	Zn 1.60	Ga 1.86	Ge 1.93	As 2.12	Se 2.45	Br 2.82
Rb 0.85	Sr 0.97	Y 1.16	Zr 1.27	Nb 1.23	Mo 1.73	Tc 1.36	Ru 1.42	Rh 1.87	Pd 1.78	Ag 1.57	Cd 1.52	In 1.69	Sn 1.84	Sb 1.83	Te 2.03	I 2.48
Cs 0.82	Ba 0.93	*Lu 1.20	Hf 1.23	Ta 1.33	W 1.88	Re 1.46	Os 1.52	Ir 1.88	Pt 1.86	Au 1.98	Hg 1.72	Tl 1.74	Pb 1.87	Bi 1.76	Po 1.76	At 1.96
Fr 0.86	Ra** 0.97															

*La 1.09	Ce 1.09	Pr 1.10	Nd 1.10	Pm 1.07	Sm 1.12	Eu 1.01	Gd 1.15	Tb 1.10	Dy 1.16	Ho 1.16	Er 1.17	Tm 1.18	Yb 1.06
**Ac 1.00	Th 1.11	Pa 1.14	U 1.30	Np 1.29	Pu 1.25	Am 1.2	Cm	Bk	Cf	Es	Fm	Md 1.2	

⟵——— estimated ———⟶

PROBLEMS

1. Arrange the following elements in order of the increasing force with which the outer electrons are held: bismuth, chlorine, neon, tellurium, thallium. *ans.* Tl,Bi,Te,Cl,Ne

2. Arrange the following elements in order of increasing force between nucleus and outer electrons: arsenic, gallium, germanium, radium, sulfur. Ra, Ga, Ge, As, S

3. Explain each of the maxima in Figure 9–2. See Teacher's Guide.

BOND TYPES

9:6 Bond Character

As you might expect, electrons are transferred between atoms when the difference in electronegativity between the atoms is quite high. If the electronegativity difference between two reacting atoms is small, we might expect a sharing of electrons. At what point in electronegativity difference does the changeover occur? The answer is not a simple one. For one thing, the electronegativity of an

Bond character between atoms depends upon electronegativity differences.

atom varies slightly depending upon the atom with which it is combining. Another factor involved is the number of other atoms with which the atom in question is combining. Thus, chemists have constructed a scale showing the percent of transfer (or sharing) of electrons depending on the electronegativity difference between two atoms. Such a scale is shown in Table 9–6.

Table 9–6

Character of Bonds

Electronegativity Difference	0.00	0.65	0.94	1.19	1.43	1.67	1.91	2.19	2.54	3.03
Percent Ionic Character	0%	10%	20%	30%	40%	50%	60%	70%	80%	90%
Percent Covalent Character	100%	90%	80%	70%	60%	50%	40%	30%	20%	10%

Emphasize that the character of the bonds — ionic to covalent — is on a continuum. The use of 1.67 as the breaking point is simply a convenience for working with compounds. Most covalent bonds will have some ionic character and vice versa.

When two atoms combine by transfer of electrons, ions are the result. The opposite charges of the ions cause them to be attracted to each other. When two elements combine in this manner, they are said to form an *ionic bond*. If two elements combine by sharing electrons, they are said to form a *covalent bond*.

Ionic bonds: transfer of electrons.

Covalent bonds: sharing of electrons.

From Table 9–6 you can see that two atoms with electronegativity difference of about 1.67 would form a bond that is 50% ionic and 50% covalent. For our purposes, we will consider an electronegativity difference of less than 1.67 as indicating a covalent bond. A difference of 1.67 or greater indicates an ionic bond. However, almost all bonds have some of both sets of characteristics.

Nearly all bonds have both covalent and ionic characteristics.

9:7 Ionic Bonds

We have discussed sodium chloride, an excellent example of a compound with an ionic bond. Most of the properties of *ionic compounds* (compounds containing ionic bonds) are best explained by assuming a complete transfer of electrons. If a chloride ion and a sodium ion are brought together, there will be an attractive force between them. If the ions are brought almost into contact, the force will be great enough to hold the two ions together. The electrostatic force which holds two ions together due to their differing charges is the ionic bond.

An ionic bond is an electrostatic bond.

Elements can be assigned oxidation numbers for ionic bonding. Sulfur, for example, with six electrons in the outer level, will tend to gain two electrons. Thus, it attains the stable eight-electron configuration. The oxidation number of sulfur for ionic bonding is (2−). The negative two is its electrical charge after gaining two electrons.

Ionic compounds are characterized by high melting points. A sampling of 139 different ionic compounds showed an average melting point of 1060°C, with two-thirds of the compounds melting between 640°C and 1480°C. Ionic compounds also show electrical conductivity in the molten state. They tend to be soluble in water and they usually crystallize in sharply defined particles.

Characteristics of compounds with ionic bonds:
1. high melting point
2. soluble in water
3. well-defined crystals
4. molten form conducts electricity.

9:8 Ionic Radii

We saw in Chapter 8 that a sodium ion is smaller than a sodium atom. We also found that a chloride ion is larger than a chlorine atom. Chemists have developed values for the radii of many ions. These values are found from a combination of experimental data and simplifying assumptions.

Chemists have determined length of ion radii.

Table 8-6 in Chapter 8 lists the ionic radii of many ions. By summing the radii of two ions in a compound we may find the internuclear distance of the two ions in a crystal of the compound.

Courtesy of Lederle Laboratories

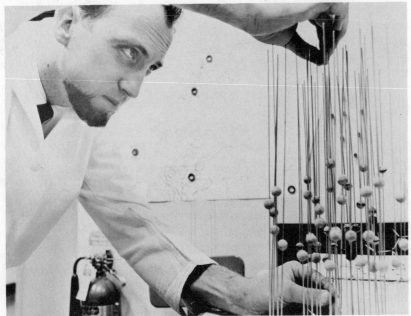

FIGURE 9-3. This scientist is examining a crystal model. The structure of ionic compounds can be analyzed by means of X-ray crystallography.

Remember that the radii are not fixed. One reason for their variability is the "fuzziness" of the electron cloud. Another reason is the affect each ion has on all of its neighbor ions.

9:9 Covalent Bonds

A molecule is formed through covalent bonds.

When two or more atoms bond covalently, the resulting particle is called a *molecule*. The line joining the nuclei of two bonded atoms in a molecule is called the *bond axis*. Ordinarily, the orbitals formed by the bonding electrons are symmetrical about the bond axis. If one atom is bonded to each of two other atoms, the angle between the two bond axes is called the *bond angle*. The distance between nuclei along the bond axis is called the *bond length*. This length is not really fixed, because the bond acts much as if it were a stiff spring. The atoms vibrate as though the bond were alternately stretching and shrinking.

Covalent bonds act like stiff springs.

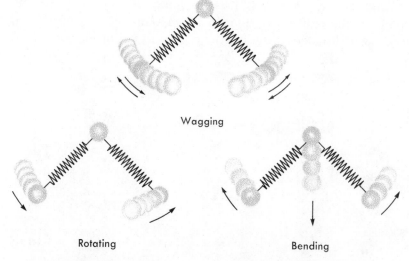

Wagging

Rotating

Bending

FIGURE 9-4. In addition to simple vibrations, covalent bonds undergo rotating, wagging, and bending vibrations.

Bonds also undergo bending, wagging, and rotational vibrations. These movements cause the bond angles and lengths to change constantly. However, the amplitudes of these vibrations are not large. Thus, the bond lengths and bond angles which we measure are accurate, though average, values. We may think of them as the values

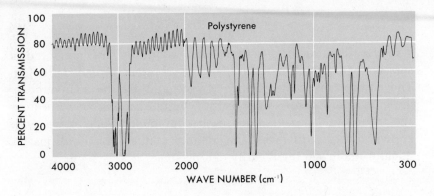

FIGURE 9-5. The infrared spectrum of polystyrene.

The polystyrene 2600 cm^{-1} peak is commonly used as a standard reference in IR spectroscopy.

for a molecule completely at rest. However, molecular vibration does not entirely cease, even at absolute zero.

Much of what we know about the structure of molecules has been learned from infrared spectroscopy. The infrared wavelengths lie in a region of the electromagnetic spectrum between radio waves and waves of visible light. The wavelengths vary from 700 nm to over 50,000 nm. A vapor, solution, or clear crystal of a compound can be identified by the infrared radiation it absorbs or transmits. Each compound has its own infrared spectrum which is different from that of any other compound.

The infrared spectrum indicates energy changes in the bonding between the particles of the compound. Since the atoms of the molecule can stretch, twist, wag, and bend around the bonds joining them, radiation of the proper energy will be absorbed. The energy absorbed must agree in frequency with the natural frequency of vibration of the molecule.

Infrared spectroscopy can be used to identify compounds.

Point out IR spectroscopy as one more experimental process available to help understand the structure of the atom. Stress its usefulness as an identifying process.

FDA Photo

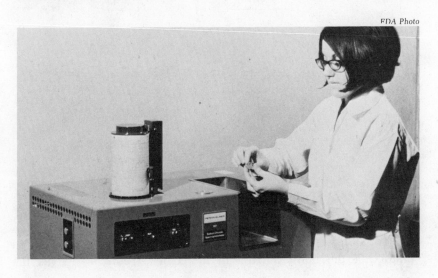

FIGURE 9-6. This chemist is using an infrared spectrophotometer to establish the identity of a material separated from a cosmetic.

In the IR (infrared) *spectrometer*, a sample of the compound is subjected to a continuously changing wavelength of IR radiation. The absorption of the various wavelengths by the compound is measured and recorded graphically. A unique continuous absorption spectrum can be plotted for each compound. Comparison with known spectra will reveal the identity of the compound, just as fingerprints reveal the identity of a person.

9:10   Covalent Radii

Chemists have determined
molecular bond lengths.

It is possible, by experiment, to determine the internuclear distance between two atoms that are bonded together. For example, consider iodine monochloride, ICl. What are the radii of the iodine and chlorine atoms in this molecule? The internuclear distance in ICl is found to be 2.30 Å. The internuclear distance in Cl_2 is 1.98 Å, and in I_2 it is 2.66 Å. One-half of each of these values might be taken as the radii of the chlorine and iodine atoms: 0.99 Å and 1.33 Å. The sum of the iodine and chlorine radii would then be 2.32

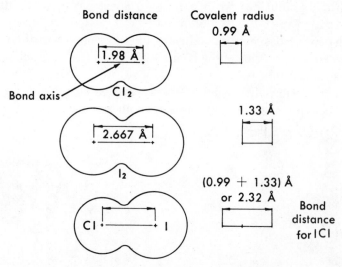

FIGURE 9-7. One method of predicting bond distance.

A, which is in fairly good agreement with the observed bond distance in ICl. However, these radii, called the *covalent radii*, are only approximate; the value for hydrogen is even less reliable than that for other atoms. Nevertheless, these radii are very useful in predicting the bond lengths in molecules. Table 9–7 gives the covalent radii for some common atoms; Table 9–8 gives the bond lengths for some molecules. See for yourself how well the predicted bond lengths agree with the measured ones.

Table 9-7

Covalent Radii (in Angstroms)

Atom	Radius	Atom	Radius	Atom	Radius
H	0.28	Ge	1.22	S	1.04
Be	1.06	Sn	1.40	Se	1.17
Mg	1.40	Pb	1.44	Te	1.37
B	0.88	N	0.70	F	0.64
Al	1.26	P	1.10	Cl	0.99
Ga	1.26	As	1.21	Br	1.14
In	1.44	Sb	1.41	I	1.33
C	0.77	Bi	1.52	Ti	1.36
Si	1.17	O	0.66		

These radii are experimentally determined and are actually averages obtained from a number of different compounds.

Table 9-8

Experimental Molecular Shapes

Molecule	Bond	Length
$(H_3Si)_2NN(SiH_3)_2$	Si—N	1.73 Å
	N—N	1.46 Å
O_3	O—O	1.28 Å
OF_2	O—F	1.41 Å
CH_4	C—H	1.09 Å
Diamond	C—C	1.54 Å
NH_3	N—H	1.01 Å
H_2O	H—O	1.01 Å
HF	H—F	0.92 Å
ClBr	Cl—Br	2.14 Å
CH_3I	C—H	1.10 Å
	C—I	2.14 Å
H_2SAlBr_3	S—Al	2.43 Å
$TiCl_4$	Ti—Cl	2.19 Å
BCl_3	B—Cl	1.74 Å
B_2H_6	B—H	1.19 Å

Remember that covalent radii are used to find the internuclear distance between atoms bonded to each other. Like electronegativities, covalent radii are average values. The radius of a particular atom is not constant. Its size is influenced by the other atom or atoms to which it is bonded.

The radius of an atom is influenced by atoms to which it is bonded.

PROBLEMS

4. Classify the bonds between the following pairs of atoms as principally ionic or covalent:

a. boron and carbon **d.** hydrogen and chlorine

b. cesium and fluorine **e.** magnesium and nitrogen

c. fluorine and silicon

ans. Ionic **b, c;** covalent **a, d, e.**

5. Classify the bonds between the following pairs of atoms as principally ionic or covalent:

a. beryllium and fluorine **d.** chlorine and sodium

b. bromine and strontium **e.** hydrogen and iodine

c. chlorine and lithium Ionic a, b, c, d; covalent e

6. Predict the oxidation number of the following elements, using only the periodic table as a guide: astatine, germanium, mercury, polonium, tin.

ans. At, 1−; Ge, 4+; Hg, 2+; Po, 2−; Sn, 4+.

7. Predict the oxidation number of the following elements, using only the periodic table as a guide: francium, hafnium, neodymium, rubidium, tellurium. Fr, 1+; Hf, 2+; Nd, 2+; Rb, 1+; Te, 2−

Friedrich August Kekulé

(1829–1896)

German chemist Friedrich Kekulé was considered by many the most brilliant of his day for his ideas on the linking of atoms. He was the first to speculate on the existence of bonds between atoms and he drew structural diagrams similar to those we use now.

Kekule explained that in substances containing several carbon atoms, it must be assumed that some of the bonds of each carbon atom are bonded to other carbon atoms.

This concept led Kekulé to propose a ring structure as the logical arrangement for the atoms composing benzene. At this time, many felt that this was the "most brilliant piece of prediction in all of organic chemistry."

Many of our present theories on the structures of compounds were formulated by Kekulé.

quadrivalence of carbon and the linkage of carbon atoms formulae

1. Ethyl chloride
2. Ethyl alcohol
3. acetic acid
4. acetamide
5. methyl formate
6. methyl cyanide

9:11 Polyatomic Ions

There are a large number of ionic compounds that are made up of more than two elements. In these compounds, one of the ions consists of two or more atoms bonded together by covalent bonds and possesses an overall charge.

For example, consider one oxygen atom and one hydrogen atom bonded together covalently (OH⁻). The hydrogen atom is stable with two electrons in its outer level. The hydrogen atom contributes only one electron to the octet of oxygen. The other electron required for oxygen to have a stable octet is the one which gives the 1— charge to the ion. Although the two atoms are bonded together covalently, the combination still possesses an ionic charge. Such a group is called a *polyatomic ion*. The polyatomic ion used as an example here is the hydroxide ion. Polyatomic ions form ionic bonds just as other ions do. Table 4–3 gives some of the more common polyatomic ions with their charges.

A polyatomic ion contains covalently bonded atoms which together have a charge.

The term polyatomic ion is used throughout this text in place of the term radical. We reserve the term radical for the free radical of organic chemistry.

9:12 van der Waals Radii

When atoms are not bonded to each other either ionically or covalently, they cannot come closer than a certain minimum distance. This limitation occurs because electrons of one atom repel the electrons of other atoms. Therefore, two atoms or molecules can never occupy the same space at the same time.

In effect, colliding free atoms and molecules act as if they had a rigid outer shell. This shell limits the closeness with which they may approach other atoms or molecules. Since the molecular bond consists of shared electrons, bonded atoms come closer together than atoms which are not bonded. The radius of this imaginary rigid shell of an atom is called the *van der Waals radius* (Figure 9–8), after the Dutch physicist of the same name.

Nonbonded atoms are held apart by electron repulsion.

van der Waals radius: distance of closest approach of nonbonded atoms.

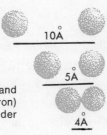

FIGURE 9-8. Balanced repulsive (electron-electron and nucleus-nucleus) forces and attractive (nucleus-electron) forces determine the van der Waals forces and the van der Waals radius (point of closest approach).

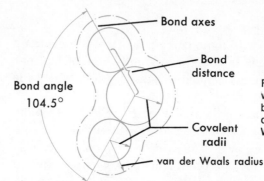

Bond axes

Bond distance

Bond angle
104.5°

Covalent radii

van der Waals radius

FIGURE 9-9. Diagram of a water molecule showing the bond axes and bond angle, the covalent radii and the van der Waals radius.

Figure 9–9 shows the relationship between the various dimensions which are needed to describe a water molecule. If we know these dimensions, we can construct a physical model which represents a molecule to scale. The heavy circles represent the covalent radii of the oxygen and hydrogen atoms in the water molecule. The outer dashed line represents the approximate closest approach of the other non-bonded atoms or molecules, or the van der Waals radii. The straight lines passing through the centers of the atoms are the bond axes.

Table 9-9

van der Waals Radii (in Angstroms)

Atom	Radius	Atom	Radius	Atom	Radius
H	1.20	Si	2.00	Br	1.95
He	1.79	P	1.90	Kr	1.98
C	1.70	S	1.85	Sb	2.20
N	1.50	Cl	1.80	Te	2.20
O	1.40	Ar	1.92	I	2.15
F	1.35	As	2.00	Xe	2.18
Ne	1.60	Se	2.00		

THE METALLIC BOND

9:13   Special Properties of Metals

Metals bond through sharing free electrons.

There is another important kind of bond. The properties of the metals are not explained by any of the bonding properties already considered. One of the properties of metals is the ability to conduct electricity quite readily. The conduction is an indication that in

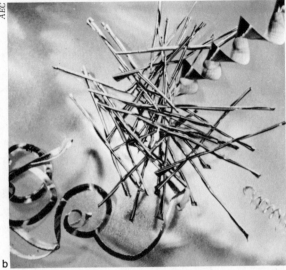

Ames Laboratory

a

AEC

b

FIGURE 9-10. The ductility of chromium can be improved by addition of trace amounts of other elements (a). The resulting alloys can be cut and formed into many shapes (b).

metals there is a ready source of electrons. It has been found that the outer electrons of atoms in a piece of metal are neither shared nor donated to other atoms, but are free to circulate in higher energy orbitals common to the entire piece of metal. These electrons are called *free electrons* and they form a *metallic bond*.

Atoms of most metals have few electrons in the outer level, usually one, two, or three; and most of the outer level orbitals are empty. Since the energy differences between these outermost unoccupied orbitals are small, electrons are free to occupy much of the space between metallic atoms. The outer electrons are free to move about in a piece of metal at random.

9:14 Metallic Properties

The properties of metals are determined by the number of outer electrons available. Group IA metals have only one outer electron per atom and are soft. Group IIA metals have two outer electrons and are harder than Group IA metals. In the transition elements, however, electrons from the partially filled d orbitals take part in the metallic bond, and some of these metals are very hard.

The number of electrons available for metallic bonding in an element determines the physical properties of the element. Group IA elements have one free electron. Group IIA elements have two free electrons. Groups IIIB through VIB elements have three through

The number of electrons available for metallic bonding determines the properties of metals.

As the number of free electrons increases, the metals become harder and stronger.

Five intermetallic compounds of potassium and mercury are known: KHg, KHg_2, KHg_3, KHg_5. KHg_{13}.
No simple bonding theory such as we use in dealing with ordinary salts and oxides has been developed to explain this.

Transition elements are the hardest and strongest elements.

six free electrons. In the elements of Groups VIIB and VIIIB the number of free electrons remains at six because all of the d sublevel electrons of these elements do not contribute to the metallic bond. The number of free electrons per atom begins to decrease with the metals of Groups IB and IIB. In Groups IIIA through VIIIA, the non-metals, the metallic properties decrease rapidly.

The strong metallic bond (free electrons per atom) of our structural metals, such as iron, chromium, and nickel, makes them hard and strong. In general, the transition elements are the hardest and strongest elements. It is possible to strengthen some of the elements with fewer free electrons by combining them with other metals to form alloys. These alloys have properties different from those of pure elements.

Table 9–10

Chemical Bond Summary

INTER ATOMIC BONDS

Bond Type	Generally Formed Between	Bond Formed By	Properties Associated With Bond Type	Examples of Substances Utilizing Bond Type
Covalent	Atoms of nonmetallic elements of similar electronegativity	Sharing of electron pairs	Stable non-ionizing molecules—not conductors of electricity in any phase	OF_2, C_2H_6, $AsCl_3$, $GeCl_4$, C, SiC, Si
Ionic	Atoms of metallic and nonmetallic elements of widely different electronegativities	Electrostatic attraction between ions resulting from transfer of electrons from one atom to another	Charged ions in gas, liquid, and solid. Solid is electrically non-conducting. Gas and liquid are conductors. High melting points.	NaCl, K_2O BaS, LiH, CdF_2, $BaBr_2$, $ErCl_3$, CdO, Ca_3N_2
Metallic	Atoms of metallic elements	Common exchange of outer electrons between atoms of low electronegativity	Electrical conductors in all phases—lustrous—very high melting points.	Na, Au, Cu, Zn, Ac, Be, Gd, Fe, Dy

SUMMARY

1. Ionization energy is the energy necessary to remove an electron from an atom, leaving a positive ion.
2. Ionization energy is determined by: (1) the size of the nuclear charge, (2) the shielding effect of inner-level electrons, (3) the distance between the nucleus and the outer electrons of an atom, and (4) the sublevel of the electrons.
3. First ionization energy is the energy required to remove the first electron from an atom.
4. Second, third, and subsequent ionization energies also provide support for our theories of atomic structure.
5. Ionization energies are often measured in electron volts. An electronvolt is the kinetic energy acquired by one electron accelerated by a potential difference of one volt in a vacuum.
6. Electron affinity is the attraction of an atom for electrons.
7. Metals have low ionization energies and electron affinities. Nonmetals have high ionization energies and electron affinities.
8. The relative tendency of an atom to attract electrons to itself in a bond with another atom is called its electronegativity.
9. The greater the difference in electronegativity between two atoms, the stronger the bond between them.
10. Ionic compounds are characterized by high melting points, solubility in water, and crystalline form.
11. Ionic bonds are formed between atoms with a great difference in electronegativity, and involve a transfer of electrons.
12. The ionic radius for an ion is the best estimate chemists can make of the effective size of an ion.
13. Covalent bonds are formed between atoms with slight differences in electronegativity, and involve sharing of electrons.
14. The bond axis is the line joining the nuclei of two bonded atoms. The length of the bond axis is called the bond length. The angle between two bond axes is called the bond angle.
15. The infrared (IR) spectrometer can be used to determine molecular structure because radiation of this wavelength (between 700 and 50,000 nm) is absorbed in characteristic patterns by the chemical bonds of molecular substances.
16. Covalent radii are used to determine the distance between bonded atoms.
17. Polyatomic ions possess an overall charge just as other ions but they are composed of groups of atoms bonded together by covalent bonds.

18. Polyatomic ions form ionic bonds just as other ions do.
19. Electron clouds act as hard spheres when two non-bonded atoms approach each other. The radius of this imaginary sphere is called the van der Waals radius of the atom.
20. A metallic bond is a bond between atoms with few electrons in the outer level or levels. These bonds result in the circulation of free electrons and allow metals to carry an electric current. They arise because the difference between the energy levels in outer levels of metals is small, and the electrons are free to occupy almost all the space between the metallic atoms.
21. The relatively high number of free electrons of such metals as iron, chromium, and nickel makes these metals very hard and strong. In general, the transition elements are the hardest and strongest elements.

PROBLEMS

8. Predict the bond lengths indicated in the following substances:
   a. Cl—Cl in Cl_2 1.98Å   d. H—Br in HBr 1.42Å
   b. N—H in NH_3 1.01Å   e. C—C in CH_3CH_3 1.53Å
   c. C—N in $(CH_3)_3N$ 1.47Å   The actual experimental measurements are given here.

9. O_2^- $NHOH^-$ $PH_2O_2^-$

   N_3^- $N_2H_3^-$ PHO_3^{2-}

   NH_2^- C_2^{2-} SeO_3^{2-}

   NH^{2-} $N_2O_2^{2-}$

9. By use of appropriate reference materials, make a list of five stable polyatomic ions other than those listed in Table 4–3.

10. Construct a graph of free electrons versus atomic number for the elements of $Z = 21$ through $Z = 30$.

11. Make a list of ten elements exhibiting more than two possible oxidation numbers. See Teacher's Guide.

12. Explain the differences in the six ionization energies of carbon (Table 9–2). See Teacher's Guide.

13. What type of bond would you expect to find between xenon and fluorine in XeF_4? ionic

14. Compute the first ionization energies of the first ten elements in kilocalories per mole. (1 kilocalorie per mole = 4.34×10^{-2} eV) See Teacher's Guide.

15. Why are most ionic compounds brittle? See Teacher's Guide.

16. Arrange the bonds in problem 8 in increasing order of covalent bond character. H—Br, N—H, C—N, Cl—Cl, C—C

17. Which atom in each of the following pairs of atoms would have the lower first ionization energy?
   a. Al, B Al   d. Ar, K K
   b. Na, K K   e. K, Ca K
   c. O, C C

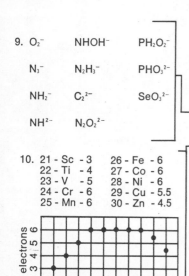

10. 21 - Sc - 3   26 - Fe - 6
    22 - Ti - 4   27 - Co - 6
    23 - V   - 5   28 - Ni - 6
    24 - Cr - 6   29 - Cu - 5.5
    25 - Mn - 6   30 - Zn - 4.5

free electrons

atomic number
21   23   25   27   29   31

18. Using the data in Table 9-2, why does the energy jump so much for the fourth boron electron and the fifth carbon electron?

Those electrons come from a lower energy level and are held more tightly.

ONE MORE STEP
See Teacher's Guide at the front of this book.

1. Predict the ionization potentials for elements with atomic numbers of 31 through 38.

2. Find an equation used to calculate electronegativities and try it on several elements.

3. Investigate the methods used by chemists for determining bond lengths.

4. What experimental data is used in determining covalent, ionic, and van der Waals radii? What simplifying assumptions are made in each case?

5. One factor affecting ionic radius, bond energy, and electronegativity of an atom is the *coordination number* of the atom. Prepare a report on this concept.

Suggested Readings for this chapter may be found in the Teacher's Guide at the front of this book.

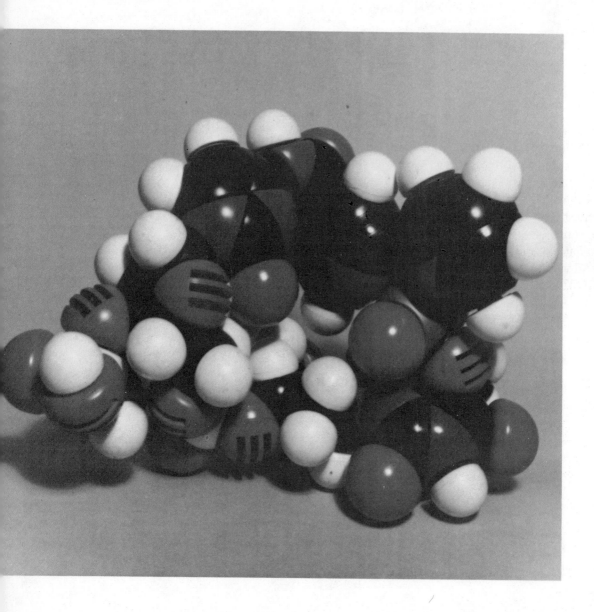

In order to visualize the shapes and sizes of molecules and atoms, scientists have constructed space-filling molecular models. This particular model shows heavy metals attached to an important biological molecule that is found in ribonucleic acid (RNA). What information does this type of model convey that a 2-dimensional drawing does not?

Molecular Shape —————————————— *10*

Chapter 10 introduces atomic and molecular orbitals and describes the relationship between chemical bonding and molecular structure.

There are several ways of approaching the structure of molecules in order to describe their shape. We will consider only two of these hypotheses. The first of these that we will consider takes into account only the repulsive forces of electron pairs surrounding an atom. The second method considers different ways in which atomic orbitals can combine to form orbitals surrounding more than one nucleus. The electrons occupying these combined orbitals then serve to bind the atoms together.

GOAL: You will gain an understanding of the relationship between chemical bonding and molecular structure.

ELECTRON CLOUDS

10:1 Pair Repulsion Electron pairs spread as far apart as possible.

Each bonding pair and unshared pair in the outer level of an atom forms a charge cloud which repels all the other charge clouds. In part, this repulsion is due to the fact that all electrons have the same charge, and thus exert an electrostatic repulsion upon each other. However, a more important factor is the *Pauli exclusion principle*. This principle states that, although electrons of opposite spin may occupy the same small volume of space, electrons of the same spin may not do so. The repulsions resulting from the Pauli principle are much greater than the electrostatic ones at small distances. Because of these repulsions, atoms cannot be compressed.

The repulsions between the charge clouds in the outer level of atoms determine the arrangement of atomic and molecular orbitals, and thus, the shape of molecules. As a result, the following rule may be stated: Electron pairs spread as far apart as possible. If there are

That atoms cannot be compressed is explained by:
1. electron cloud repulsion
2. Pauli exclusion principle

Atomic and molecular orbitals are determined by repulsion of charge clouds.

In each of these shapes, the molecules are as far apart as possible in 1-, 2-, and 3-dimensional shapes. These shapes are basic in determining molecular shape.

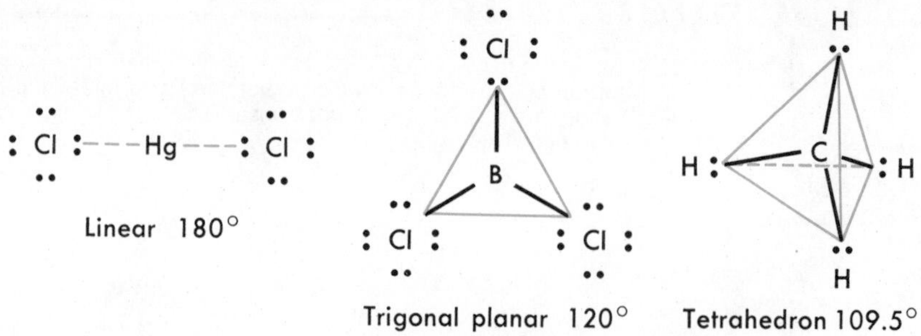

: Cl :---Hg---: Cl :

Linear 180°

Trigonal planar 120°   Tetrahedron 109.5°

FIGURE 10-1. Electron pairs spread as far apart as possible.

Linear arrangement: two electron pairs on opposite sides of the nucleus.

Planar arrangement: three electron pairs in a plane with the nucleus.

only two electron pairs in the outer level, they will be on opposite sides of the nucleus. The arrangement is called *linear*. If there are three electron pairs, the axes of their charge clouds will be 120° apart. This arrangement is called *planar* and the electron pairs lie in the same plane as the nucleus. If the outer level contains four electron pairs, the axes of the charge clouds will be farthest apart when they intersect at an angle of 109.5°. Of course, these axes will not all lie in the same plane. The easiest way to see them is to imagine a regular *tetrahedron* (teh truh HEE druhn). A tetrahedron is a figure having four faces, each of which is an equilateral triangle. The nucleus is at the center and the axes extend out to the corners. Figure 10–1 shows some examples in which each electron pair in the outer level is used in bonding to another atom. Can you see a relationship between the number of bonds formed and the resulting molecular shapes?

Tetrahedral arrangement: four electron pairs at a 109.5° angle to each other.

Electron pair repulsion:
The charge clouds generated by unshared electron pairs are pear-shaped and repel other unshared pairs most strongly. Shared electron pairs are elongated and repel other unshared pairs with much less force than an unshared pair repels.
Using these facts, bond angles can be predicted.
At the present time, experimental measurement is still necessary to confirm the bond angle and molecular shape predicted, but this approach does give qualitatively correct predictions.

FIGURE 10-2. The atom on the left has a charge cloud composed of three nonbonded electron pairs. The atom on the right is bonded to two other atoms. The resulting bonding charge clouds are slenderized and repel each other less than nonbonding charge clouds.

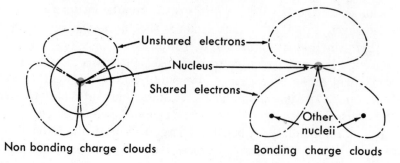

Non bonding charge clouds   Bonding charge clouds

The shared and unshared electron pairs of a charge cloud determine its shape. An unshared pair is acted upon essentially by only one nucleus. Its charge cloud is like a very blunt pear (Figure 10–2) with its stem end at the nucleus. A pair of bonding electrons moves in the field of two nuclei, and the charge cloud is much more slender (Figure 10–2).

The electron pair repulsions in a molecule may not all be equal. The repulsion between two unshared pairs is greatest. The repulsion between two different bonding pairs is least. The repulsion between an unshared pair and a bonding pair is intermediate between the other two cases:

unshared-unshared > unshared-shared > shared-shared

The shapes of the molecules of the compounds CH_4, NH_3, H_2O, and HF illustrate this repulsion. In each of these compounds, one atom has four electron pairs around it. We expect the axes of all four charge clouds to point approximately toward the corners of a tetrahedron (Figure 10–3).

CH₄ — Tetrahedron   NH₃ — Trigonal pyramid   H₂O — V shape

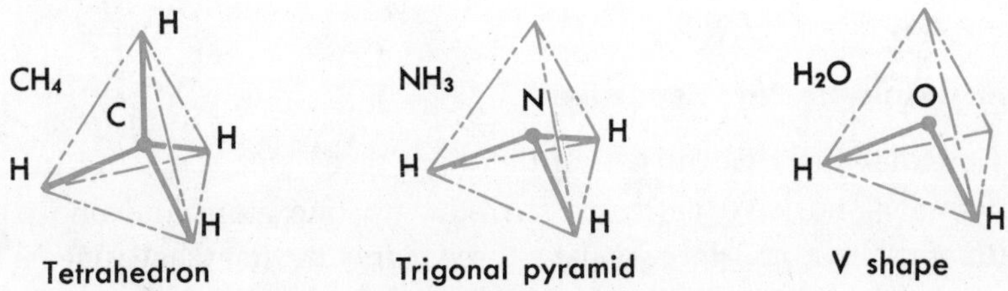

FIGURE 10-3. Bonding and nonbonding electron pairs are present in these methane, ammonia, and water molecules.

In CH_4 molecules, all of the electron pairs are bond pairs, so their repulsions are equal and the bond angle is in fact 109.5°. In NH_3 molecules, there is one unshared pair and three bond pairs. The unshared pair repels the other three more than they repel each other, so that they are at an angle of 107° to each other. In H_2O molecules, two unshared pairs are present, both of which are repelling the bond pairs. This results in a still greater reduction in the bond angle which is, in fact, 104.5°. In the HF molecule, there is only one bond axis and consequently no bond angle. Note that in the four molecules discussed, each has four electron pairs and the arrangement of the

The shape of a charge cloud is determined by shared and unshared electron pairs.

Electron pair repulsion strengths may not be equal.

These shapes occur with slight variation in many compounds.

pairs is similar. The differences in the molecules result from the greater repulsions between the unshared and the bond pair of electrons.

Table 10–1

Experimental Molecular Shapes

Molecule	Bond	Angle
$(H_3Si)_2NN(SiH_3)_2$	Si—N—Si	130°
O_3	O—O—O	117°
OF_2	F—O—F	103°
CH_4	H—C—H	109°
Diamond	C—C—C	109°
NH_3	H—N—H	107°
H_2O	H—O—H	105°
CH_3I	H—C—H	112°
	H—C—I	107°
BCl_3	Cl—B—Cl	120°

10:2 Multiple Pair Repulsions

Consider the case in which there are three electron pairs in the outer level but two pairs are shared with one atom and one pair with another atom. Here we have three pairs forming what appears to be two bonds. Mutual repulsion forces the bonds as far apart as possible, and we get a linear molecule (Figure 10–1 and Figure 10–3). In a situation involving four bonding pairs, two shared with one atom and two shared with another atom, we also get a linear molecule. If only two of the four pairs are shared doubly (two, one, and one), there are three bonds repelling and the bond angles will be 120°.

In most compounds, the outer level is considered full with four pairs or eight electrons. In atoms in which the outer level could possibly contain more than eight electrons (outer level three or greater), it is possible to force more than eight electrons into that level. A number of nonmetals, notably the halogens, form compounds in which the outer level is expanded to 10, 12, or even 14 electrons. Such an arrangement would also be true of noble gas compounds. For example, in xenon tetrafluoride (XeF_4), xenon has eight electrons of its own in its outer level together with four from

FIGURE 10-4. (a) Structure proposed for XeF$_2$. (b) Structure proposed for XeF$_4$.

(a) Trigonal bipyramidal   (b) Octahedral

the fluorine atoms (one from each). The structures proposed for these compounds are shown in Figure 10–4.

COMBINING ATOMIC ORBITALS

10:3   Combined Orbitals in Carbon Compounds

Molecular shape can also be described by considering the different ways s and p orbitals can overlap when electrons are shared. This method can best be seen by looking at the element carbon. However, the same principles can be applied to any atom forming covalent bonds.

A carbon atom can form four equivalent bonds. The carbon compound family is unique. Carbon atoms can link covalently to other carbon atoms. Carbon atoms can also link covalently to atoms of many other elements but it is the linking of carbon atom to carbon atom which gives rise to the large number of carbon compounds. There are more carbon compounds than the total of non-carbon compounds.

In Chapter 7, we described the geometric structure of atomic electron orbitals. We described the s orbital as spherical, no matter

s and *p* orbitals may overlap when electrons are shared.

Carbon atoms can link covalently to other carbon atoms.

Additional material on carbon (organic) chemistry can be found in Chapter 24.

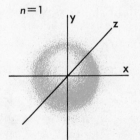 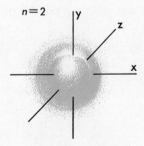

FIGURE 10-5. The s orbital is always spherical whether $n=1$, $n=2$, 3, or 4.

what level the electrons occupy. We described the three p orbitals (p_x, p_y, p_z) as being dumbbell-shaped.

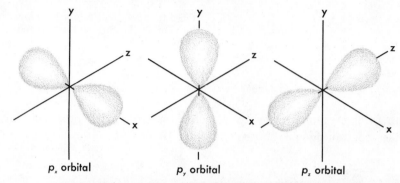

p_x orbital p_y orbital p_z orbital

FIGURE 10-6. The three p orbitals are dumbbell shaped and are arranged at right angles to each other.

10:4 Sigma and Pi Bonds

The theory of such bonding is called the linear combination of atomic orbitals (LCAO) theory.

A *covalent bond* is formed when an orbital of one atom overlaps an orbital of another atom. For example, a bond may be formed by the overlap of two s orbitals. Such a bond is called a *sigma* bond and is designated σ_s.

The overlap of two s orbitals is a sigma bond (σ_s).

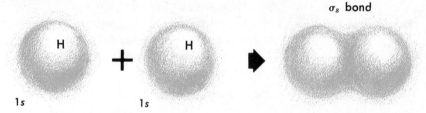

σ_s bond

1s   1s

FIGURE 10-7. Overlapping of 1s orbitals to form a sigma s (σ_s) bond between two hydrogen atoms.

The overlap of an s and a p orbital is a sigma bond (σ_{sp}).

Another type of bond is formed by the overlap of an s orbital of one atom with a p orbital of another atom (σ_{sp}).

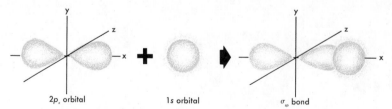

2p, orbital   1s orbital σ_{sp} bond

FIGURE 10-8. A σ_{sp} bond is formed by the overlap of a 1s orbital of hydrogen with a 2p orbital of some other atom.

Yet another type of bond is formed when two p orbitals overlap. Since p orbitals are not spherical, there are two possibilities.

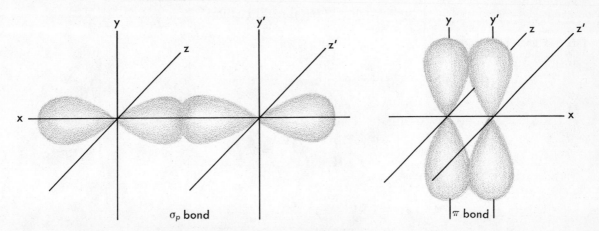

FIGURE 10-9. Two types of bond can be formed at the p orbital level. An end-to-end overlap is called a σ_p (sigma p) bond, and sidewise overlap is called a π (pi) bond.

If two p orbitals overlap along an axis in an end-to-end fashion a sigma type (σ_p) bond is formed (Figure 10–9 a). If, however, the two p orbitals overlap sideways with their axes parallel, as in Figure 10–9 b, they form what is called a pi type (π) bond.

The orbitals are distorted to do this.

The end-to-end overlap of two p orbitals is a sigma bond (σ_P).

Two p orbitals with parallel overlap is a pi bond (π).

10:5 Hybrid Orbitals

We would expect the carbon atom with four outer electrons to have both s and p orbitals available for bonding. However, it has been discovered that carbon does not usually form pure s and pure

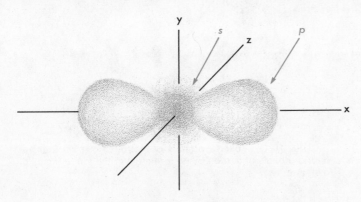

FIGURE 10-10. An s and p orbital available for bonding.

p type bonds. Instead, the s and p orbitals of carbon merge to form four equivalent hybrid orbitals. If one s and three p orbitals merge, four sp^3 (read s-p-three) hybrid orbitals are formed. The sp^3 orbitals are arranged in tetrahedral fashion.

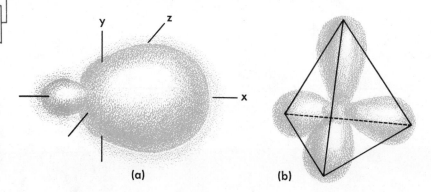

(a)　　　　　　　(b)

FIGURE 10-11. (a) The shape of one sp^3 hybrid orbital. (b) Four sp^3 hybrid orbitals of one carbon atom.

10:6　Geometry of Carbon Compounds

The bonding of four hydrogen atoms to one carbon atom to form *methane* involves the overlap of the s orbital of each hydrogen atom with one of the sp^3 hybrid orbitals of a carbon atom.

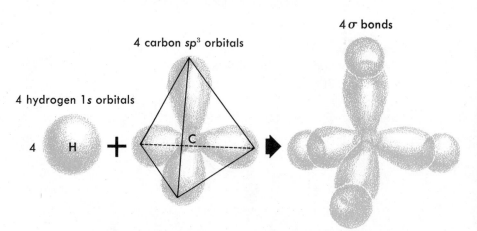

4 hydrogen 1s orbitals　　　4 carbon sp^3 orbitals　　　4 σ bonds

FIGURE 10-12. Four 1s orbitals of hydrogen overlap four sp^3 hybrid orbitals of carbon in the formation of the four σ bonds of methane.

A three dimensional representation of the structural formula of methane would be:

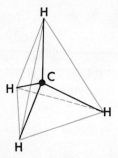

FIGURE 10-13. A three-dimensional representation of the structural formula of methane.

The solid black lines represent shared pairs of electrons (covalent bonds). There is an angle of 109.5° between each carbon-hydrogen bond axis. The angle between the bonds results in a chain which is not straight as will be pictured in structural formulas later.

A chain of carbon atoms is formed by the overlap of an orbital of one carbon atom with an orbital of another carbon atom. The carbon-carbon single bond is an end-to-end sigma (σ) type bond.

Methane is formed with four hybrid *sigma* bonds.

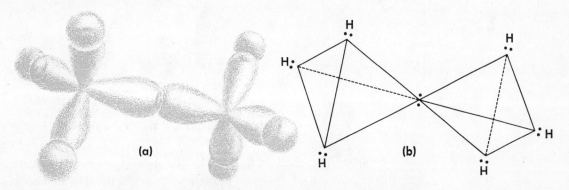

(a)   (b)

FIGURE 10-14. (a) The σ type carbon-carbon sp^3-sp^3 bond and six σ hydrogen-carbon $1s$-sp^3 bonds of ethane. (b) A geometric representation of an ethane molecule.

The other three sp^3 orbitals of each carbon atom bond with hydrogen s orbitals. A three dimensional structural formula of *ethane* would be:

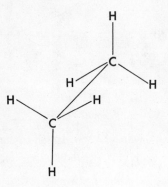

FIGURE 10-15. A three-dimensional representation of the structural formula of ethane.

Note the *trans* positions of the hydrogen atoms. Although free rotation about the single bond is allowed, the *trans* position is the most stable.

10:7   Multiple Bonds

In some compounds one s orbital and two p orbitals merge to form sp^2 hybrid orbitals. The sp^2 hybrid orbitals are arranged in planar fashion with 120° between each orbital. The third p orbital is not hybridized. It is perpendicular to the plane of the sp^2 hybrids.

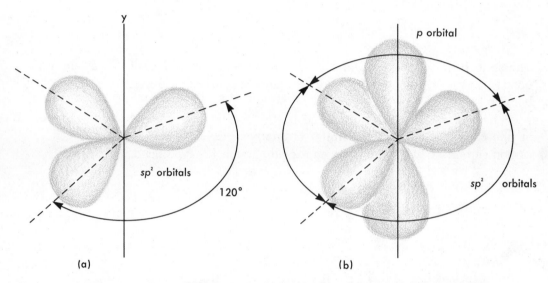

FIGURE 10-16. (a) The planar shape of sp^2 hybrid orbitals. (b) A carbon atom with one pure p orbital and three sp^2 hybrid orbitals.

The carbon-carbon double bond in *ethene* ($H_2C{=}CH_2$) is formed by the σ overlap of two sp^2 orbitals and the π overlap of two p orbitals. Thus, the two carbon atoms are sharing two pairs of electrons.

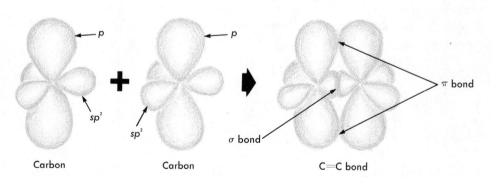

FIGURE 10-17. The σ and π overlap of the carbon-carbon double bond in ethene.

The six atoms of ethene lie in one plane. The structural formula shows the angular orientation of the bonds in the plane.

H   H
 \   121.6°→   /
  \   /   ↓116.7°   FIGURE 10-18. A three-dimen-
   C ══════════ C   sional representation of the
  /   \   structural formula of ethene.
 /   \
H   H

The carbon-carbon triple bond in *acetylene* (HC≡CH) is formed when one *s* orbital and one *p* orbital merge to form an *sp* hybrid.

The electron clouds of the two π bonds would appear cylindrical when taken together.

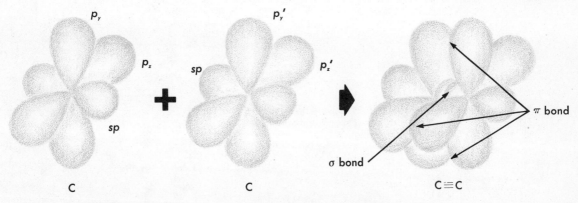

FIGURE 10-19. The σ bond and two π bonds of the carbon-carbon triple bond in acetylene (ethyne).

This leaves two pure *p* orbitals perpendicular to each other and the hybrids. Two of the *sp* orbitals overlap head-on to form a σ type bond, and the two *p* orbitals in each atom overlap sideways to form π type bonds. In acetylene, the two carbon atoms share three pairs of electrons.

Double and triple bonds are less flexible than single bonds. One of the bonds in a double or triple bond can be more easily broken than a single bond. Because second and third bonds are more easily broken, molecules containing multiple bonds are usually more reactive than molecules containing only single bonds.

Multiple bonds appear to make compounds more reactive.

10:8 Benzene

Each of the six carbon atoms in a *benzene* (C_6H_6) ring is thought to have three sp^2 hybrid orbitals and one *p* orbital.

Note that the unhybridized orbital is perpendicular to the
plane of the three hybridized
orbitals.

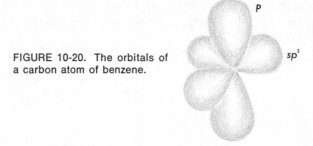

FIGURE 10-20. The orbitals of
a carbon atom of benzene.

Sigma type bonds are formed by the overlap of the sp^2 orbitals of
six carbon atoms forming a ring of single bonds.

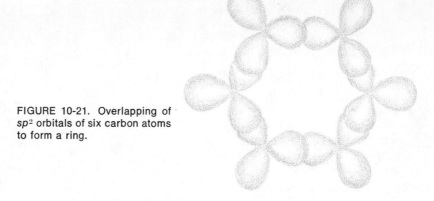

FIGURE 10-21. Overlapping of
sp^2 orbitals of six carbon atoms
to form a ring.

The double bonds of the benzene ring are formed by the π type
overlap of the p orbitals of the carbon atoms.

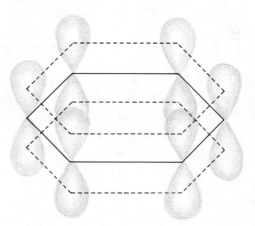

FIGURE 10-22. Mutual sharing of π electrons by p orbitals of
benzene ring atoms.

However, one of the characteristics of benzene is that the π electrons can be shared all around the ring. Since the π electrons are shared equally among all the carbon atoms, they are said to be delocalized (not in a specific area). This delocalization of π electrons among the carbon atoms (as in benzene) results in greater stability of the compound.

The symbol for benzene is The inner circle indicates the

unsaturated (uhn SACH uh rayt uhd) character of all the carbon atoms of the benzene ring. Unsaturated compounds are those containing double or triple bonds between carbon atoms.

Whenever multiple p orbital overlap can occur, the molecule is said to contain a conjugated system. Conjugated systems can occur in chains as well as in rings of atoms. Again, the conjugated system imparts a special stability to the molecule.

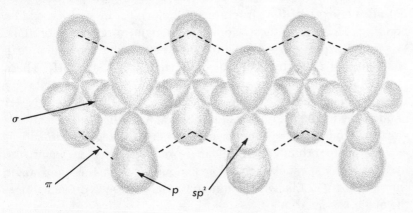

FIGURE 10-23. Delocalization of π electrons in a conjugated alkene molecule.

10:9   Combined Orbitals in Inorganic Compounds

The ground state electron configuration of carbon ends in $2s^2 2p^2$. In the bonding discussed in Section 10:6, each of the four electrons was placed in a separate orbital. We treated the carbon atom as if it were in the state $2s^1 2p^3$. We assumed that this was the configuration in order that hybridization of orbitals could occur.

What about other atoms? For example in beryllium, which has two outer electrons $(2s^2)$, only two orbitals need be hybridized. We would expect sp hybridization to lead to linear bonding orbitals. Analysis bears out this prediction with molecules having a central atom ending in an s^2 configuration. For boron $(2s^2 2p^1)$ and other

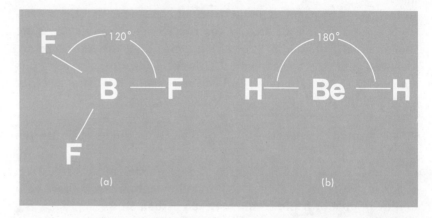

(a)   (b)

atoms with three outer electrons, we would predict sp^2 hybridization. Again, analysis bears out the prediction of trigonal planar bond arrangements.

For elements of Groups VA, VIA, and VIIA, hybridization does not always explain the structures of molecules. In such cases, the bonding electrons in these atoms are thought to occupy p orbitals. We would expect these atoms to bond at 90° angles. How, then, can we explain the structures of molecules such as H_2O and NH_3? These molecules contain simple σ_{sp} bonds only. Since p orbitals are mutually perpendicular, the expected H—O—H and H—N—H bond angles are 90°. However, hydrogen atoms will repel each other's electron clouds. They cannot get close enough together to satisfy exactly the p orbital-p orbital angle of 90°. Thus, in water, the hydrogen atoms repel each other enough to open the bond angle from 90° to 105°. Likewise in ammonia, with three hydrogen atoms, the angle is spread to 107°.

Again experimental evidence backs up or precedes theory.

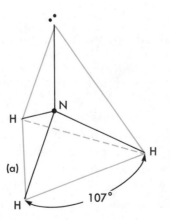

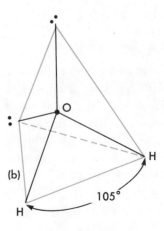

FIGURE 10-25. Three-dimensional representations of the structural formulas of ammonia (a) and water (b).

10:10   Resonance

We have been assuming that compounds can be represented by a single structural formula. However, many molecules and polyatomic ions cannot be described by one formula.

For example, consider the nitrate ion (NO_3^-). The theory of electron cloud repulsion would predict 120° O—N—O bond angles and a planar ion. Experiments have shown this prediction to be true.

Now, suppose we attempt to draw an electron dot diagram for the nitrate ion. If we let electrons originally associated with oxygen atoms be represented by (x), the electron dot structure for an oxygen atom would be:

Compounds cannot always be represented by a single structural formula.

FIGURE 10-26. The electron dot structure of an oxygen atom.

Ida Tacke Noddack

(1896–   )

An intense interest in the periodic table led Ida Tacke Noddack to two important discoveries. A gap in the table under manganese had led most researchers to assume that the new element would have properties similar to manganese.

The 25-year-old Berlin chemist and her soon-to-be husband Walter Noddack investigated the properties of the neighbors of manganese and determined that there would be discrepancies between manganese and the next elements in the family. In 1925 through X-ray spectra, they were able to identify the element which is now known as rhenium in a sample of the mineral columbite. Later they prepared the element and determined its properties.

In 1934 she proposed, counter to the great Enrico Fermi, that heavy nuclei bombarded by neutrons break down into isotopes of known elements but not neighbors or transuranium elements. Five years later her belief in nuclear fission was confirmed by others.

Likewise, if nitrogen electrons are represented by (o), the electron dot structure for nitrogen would be:

FIGURE 10-27. The electron dot structure of a nitrogen atom.

One possible electron dot diagram for the nitrate ion can be seen in Figure 10–28. The extra electron is shown by the symbol (●).

FIGURE 10-28. A possible electron dot diagram of the nitrate ion.

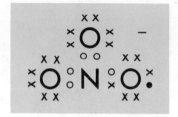

Note that the nitrogen atom has only six electrons in its outer level. We know that most atoms tend to satisfy the octet rule in compound formation. How, then, can we properly explain the structure of the nitrate ion?

In Figure 10–29 an electron dot diagram is shown which satisfies our requirements. One of the oxygen atoms shares two pairs of electrons with the nitrogen. If the nitrate ion were actually constructed, as in Figure 10–29, we would expect the oxygen atom which is doubly bonded to the nitrogen to be a little closer to the nitrogen than the other two oxygen atoms. However, analysis has shown that all three N—O bonds are the same length.

In NO_3^-, all bond lengths are equal.

FIGURE 10-29. Another possible electron dot diagram of the nitrate ion.

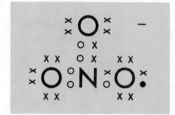

To account for this observation, we introduce a concept called *resonance*. Using the idea of resonance, we can draw several equivalent diagrams for the distribution of electrons in a molecule or ion.

In fact, we draw all possible diagrams which obey the rules about full outer levels and the number of bonds an atom can form. We then consider the actual structure of the particle to be the average of all these possibilities. Thus for the nitrate ion:

Resonance: equivalent alternative structures for a molecule or polyatomic ion which lead to "average" bond lengths.

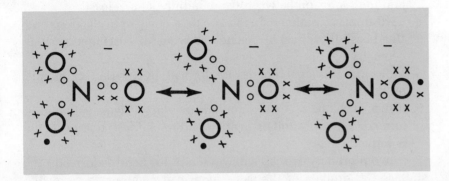

FIGURE 10-30. An electron dot diagram of the resonance structure of the nitrate ion.

If we "average" these three structures in our minds, we can see that we will end up with three equal N—O bonds, each about one and one third times the normal single bond strength. Because each bond is slightly stronger than a single bond, each bond length is slightly shorter than a single N—O bond. Since they are equivalent, the bond lengths will be the same, and the bond angles will be equal, 120°. Note that the different forms are shown to be equivalent by the double ended arrows connecting them.

SUMMARY

1. The shape of molecules can be approximated by assuming the mutual repulsion of electron pairs. This repulsion results because all electrons have the same electrostatic charge and are subject to the Pauli exclusion principle. Electron pairs spread as far apart as possible.

2. The shape of a molecule containing three or more atoms is determined by the number of bonding and nonbonding pairs. If the central atom has two bonding pairs and no nonbonding pairs, the molecule is linear. If there are three bonding pairs and no nonbonding pairs, the molecule is pyramidal. If there are four bonding and no nonbonding pairs the molecule is tetrahedral.

3. The actual bond angles vary from predicted angles because a bonding electron pair does not repel another bonding pair as strongly as it repels an unshared electron pair. The repulsion between two unshared electron pairs is most; the repulsion between an unshared pair and a bonding pair is intermediate; and the repulsion between two bonding pairs is least.

4. Two atoms sometimes share more than one pair of electrons and this possibility must be considered when discussing molecular geometry.

5. Molecular covalent bonds are formed by overlap of atomic orbitals: s–s, s–p, and p–p.

6. If two s orbitals or s and p orbitals overlap, a sigma (σ) bond is formed. If two p orbitals overlap end-to-end, a sigma (σ) bond is formed.

7. If two p orbitals overlap sideways, a pi (π) bond is formed.

8. s and p orbitals of the same atom can combine to form hybrid orbitals. One s and three p orbitals merge to form four tetrahedral sp^3 hybrids. One s and two p orbitals merge to form three planar sp^2 hybrid orbitals. One s and one p orbital merge to form two linear sp hybrid orbitals.

9. Hybrid orbitals form molecular sigma bonds.

10. A carbon-carbon double bond is formed by the sigma overlap of two sp^2 orbitals and the π overlap of two p orbitals.

11. A triple bond is formed by the sigma overlap of two sp orbitals and the π overlap of four p orbitals.

12. Delocalization of π electrons in conjugated chain and ring compounds produces stability.

13. In the concept of resonance, we assume that the actual distribution of electrons in a particle is the average of all correct structures that can be written for that compound.

PROBLEMS

1. Predict the bond angles indicated in the following compounds:

   a. H—Te—H in H_2Te 90°　　　　　**d.** Cl—As—Cl in $AsCl_3$ 98°
   b. H—P—H in PH_3 93°　　　　　　 **e.** F—C—F in $CClF_3$ 109°
   c. C—P—C in $P(CH_3)_3$ 99°

2. Hybridization is the formation of equivalent orbitals by electrons from different energy sublevels.

2. What is meant by the term "hybridization"?

See Teacher's Guide at the front of this book.

3. Draw the resonance structures for the carbonate ion (CO_3^{2-}).

4. What is the major difference between σ and π bonds?

5. Why is benzene a particularly stable compound?

6. What kinds of orbital arrangements contribute to the bonding in ethene ($H_2C{=}CH_2$)?

7. Predict the shapes of the following molecules:
   a. H_2CO planar   d. SF_6 octahedral
   b. SO_2 planar   e. S_2Cl_2 3-dimensional
   c. BF_3 planar

8. Conjugated systems, such as benzene, are often considered as "averages" of resonant forms. Draw the resonance forms for benzene and a related compound, naphthalene ( ). — See Teacher's Guide at the front of this book.

9. In the HCN molecule, the H—C bond is a single bond and the C—N bond is a triple bond. Predict the shape of the molecule, the hybridization of the carbon atom, and the type (σ, π) of each bond.

10. Predict shapes for the following ions:
    a. IO_3^- triangular pyramid   d. SO_4^{2-} tetrahedral
    b. ClO_4^- tetrahedral   e. PO_4^{3-} tetrahedral
    c. SiF_6^{2-} octahedral

11. The substance phosphorus pentachloride occurs as PCl_5 molecules in the gas phase. As a solid, it is an ionic compound, $PCl_4^+PCl_6^-$. Describe the shape and bonding in each of these species.

    11. PCl_5 — trigonal bipyramid, dsp^3 hybrid on P

    PCl_4^+ — Tetrahedral, sp^3 hybrid on P

    PCl_6^- — octahedral, d^2sp^3 hybrid on P

12. The substance H_2Se is a molecular compound. Sketch a cross-sectional view of the molecule and label its various dimensions. — See Teacher's Guide.

ONE MORE STEP

1. Using library resources, find the following bond angles:
   a. C—C=C in CH_3CHCH_2 125°   d. O—N—O in NO_2 134°
   b. F—C—F in CF_3I 108°   e. O—N—O in NO_2^- 115°
   c. H—N—N in HN_3 113°

2. Find out the geometry of d^2sp^3 hybrid orbitals. See if you can discover some compounds or ions containing such hybrids.

3. Predict the shape of cyclohexane (C_6H_{12}). From references, determine the two shapes of cyclohexane. Make models of the two shapes to illustrate why one form is more stable than the other. — See Teacher's Guide at the front of this book.

4. Predict shapes for the molecules:

   a. H_2C=C=CH_2 and   b. H_2C=C=C=CH_2

5. Read the story of the development of molecular structure theories. Prepare a report for your class on why chemists have so many different explanations for molecular structure.

Suggested Readings for this chapter may be found in the Teacher's Guide at the front of this book.

Construction materials with greatly improved mechanical strength and durability properties can be prepared from an irradiated mixture of plastics and waste materials such as crushed glass bottles. This material has three times the compressive strength of ordinary concrete and is being studied for use in manufacture of drain and sewage piping. What are some factors which determine the properties of materials?

Structure and Properties of Molecules ____ 11

Chapter 11 introduces molecular structure and its relationship to molecular properties. It also includes a description of some of the procedures used by chemists in analytical research.

The behavior of compounds depends to a large extent on the shape and structure of their molecules. The reactivity of molecules also depends on the strengths of the bonds formed between the atoms in the compound. We will now investigate how some of the properties of similar compounds differ because of the varying molecular shapes and structures.

GOAL: You will gain an understanding of the properties of molecular compounds and their relationship to molecular shape and structure.

VARIATIONS IN SHAPE

11:1 Isomers

The existence of two or more substances with the same molecular formula, but different structures, is called *isomerism* (i SAHM eh rihz uhm). The different structures are called *isomers* (I soh muhrs). Since isomerism is so common in organic chemistry, we will study the isomers of carbon compounds.

Isomers have the same molecular formula but different structures.

Consider the compound with the formula C_4H_{10}. There are two structures which can be written for this formula (Figure 11–1). They are not resonance forms because there is a different arrangement of bonds and atoms in the two structures. In resonance forms, all we change is electron distribution. Isomers of this type are called *structural isomers* or skeleton isomers, since it is the carbon chain or "skeleton" which is altered. In Chapter 24, we will study the naming of these compounds.

Isomers are *not* resonance forms.

Point out different ways in which isomerism can take place: structural, geometric, positional, and functional.

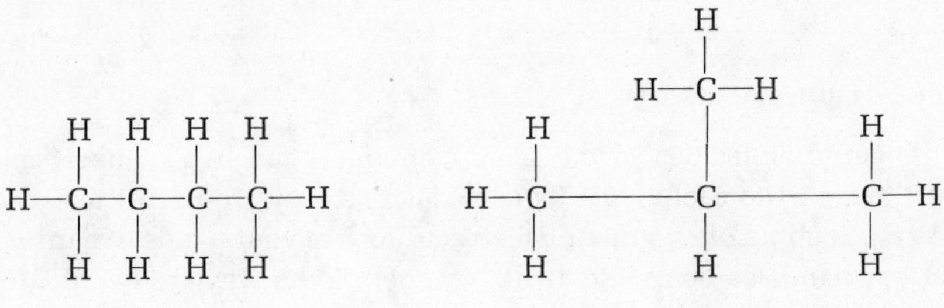

FIGURE 11-1. Structural isomers of butane.

butane

isobutane

Look at Figure 11–2. Note that the formation of a π bond prevents the atoms on each end of the bond from rotating with respect to each other. Compounds containing double bonds exhibit a kind of isomerism called *geometric isomerism*. We will use the compound butene (C_4H_8) to illustrate geometric isomers. In Figure 11–2, note that in the *cis* form of 2-butene, the CH_3 groups (and the hydrogen atoms) are on the same side of the double bond. In the *trans* form, they are on opposite sides.

Cis- and *trans-* are two forms of geometric isomerism.

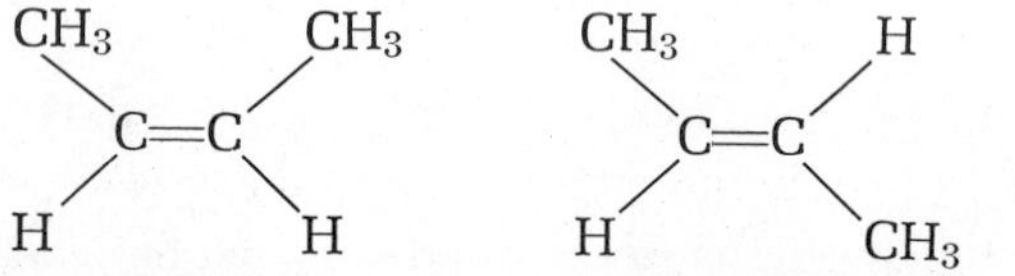

FIGURE 11-2. Geometric isomers of 2-butene.

$$\underset{\text{cis-2-butene}}{\overset{\displaystyle CH_3 \qquad CH_3}{\underset{\displaystyle H \qquad\qquad H}{C=C}}} \qquad\qquad \underset{\text{trans-2-butene}}{\overset{\displaystyle CH_3 \qquad H}{\underset{\displaystyle H \qquad\qquad CH_3}{C=C}}}$$

If we introduce a third kind of atom into a hydrocarbon molecule, we find two more kinds of isomers, *positional* and *functional*. In positional isomerism, the newly introduced particle may take two or more positions in the molecule, leading to two or more isomers. This possibility is shown in Figure 11–3.

Isomers may be: skeleton, geometric, positional, functional, or optical.

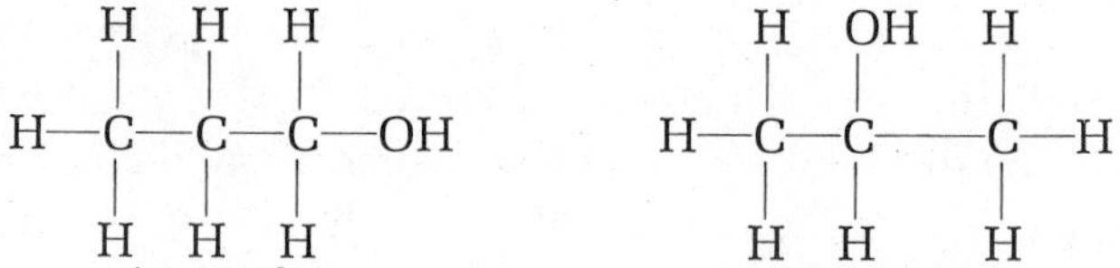

FIGURE 11-3. Positional isomers of propanol.

$$\underset{\text{1-propanol}}{H-\overset{\displaystyle H}{\underset{\displaystyle H}{C}}-\overset{\displaystyle H}{\underset{\displaystyle H}{C}}-\overset{\displaystyle H}{\underset{\displaystyle H}{C}}-OH} \qquad\qquad \underset{\text{2-propanol}}{H-\overset{\displaystyle H}{\underset{\displaystyle H}{C}}-\overset{\displaystyle OH}{\underset{\displaystyle H}{C}}-\overset{\displaystyle H}{\underset{\displaystyle H}{C}}-H}$$

In Figure 11–4 the possibility of a new atom being bonded in two different ways illustrates functional isomerism.

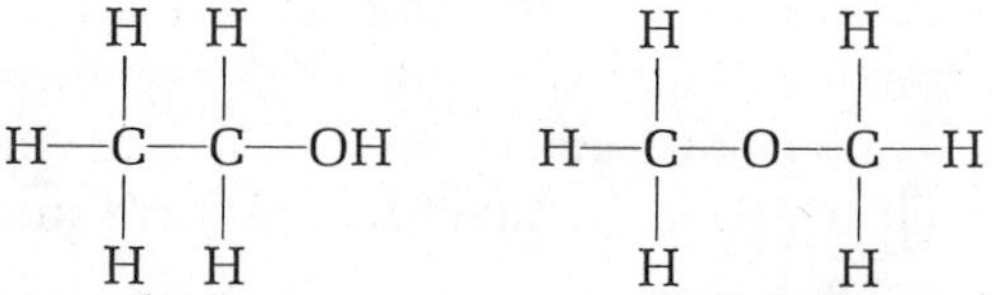

FIGURE 11-4. Functional isomers.

$$\underset{\text{ethanol}}{H-\overset{\displaystyle H}{\underset{\displaystyle H}{C}}-\overset{\displaystyle H}{\underset{\displaystyle H}{C}}-OH} \qquad\qquad \underset{\text{dimethyl ether}}{H-\overset{\displaystyle H}{\underset{\displaystyle H}{C}}-O-\overset{\displaystyle H}{\underset{\displaystyle H}{C}}-H}$$

11:2 Optical Activity

Asymmetrical molecules do not have a plane of symmetry.

Organic molecules of the same compound can be asymmetrical with respect to each other. This means that they are mirror images. As an example of asymmetrical objects, look at your hands. We think of our hands as being identical. Yet there is no way we can rotate our left hand in order to make it look exactly like our right hand.

The left hand is a mirror image of the right hand. They have an asymmetrical relationship. So do the molecules of 2-butanol. Figure 11–5 shows two different arrangements of the bonds and atoms in 2-butanol. It is impossible to rotate the one to look exactly like the

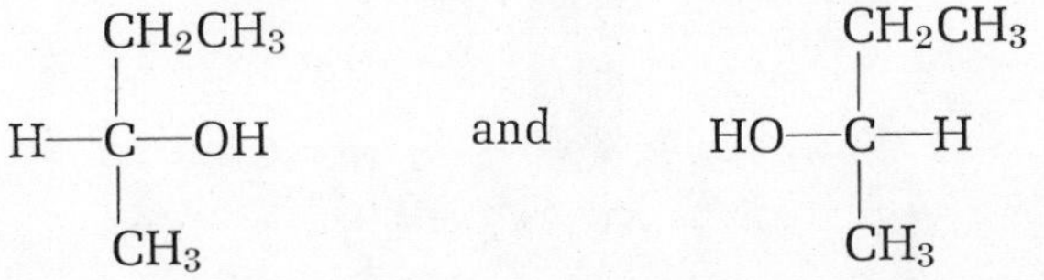

$$
\begin{array}{ccc}
CH_2CH_3 & & CH_2CH_3 \\
| & & | \\
H\!-\!\!C\!-\!OH & \quad\text{and}\quad & HO\!-\!\!C\!-\!H \\
| & & | \\
CH_3 & & CH_3
\end{array}
$$

The use of polarimetry for quantitative analysis arises from the equation:

$$[\alpha] = \frac{\alpha}{l \times d}$$

where $[\alpha]$ = specific rotation of the substance, α = observed rotation, l = length of the tube, and d = density for a pure liquid or concentration for a solution in g/cm^3.

FIGURE 11-5. The two forms of 2-butanol are optically active.

other. Asymmetrical molecules are said to be *optically active*. They have the property of rotating the plane in which polarized light is vibrating.

Asymmetric molecules of the same substance are optically active.

The electromagnetic waves in a beam of light vibrate in all directions, not just up and down or sideways. However, it is possible, using the proper kind of filter, to obtain light in which all the vibrations are taking place in the same plane. Such light is called *polarized* light (Figure 11–6).

Polarized light vibrates in only one plane.

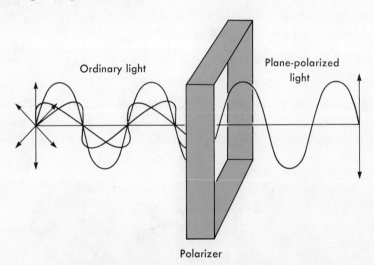

FIGURE 11-6. Nonpolarized light vibrates in several planes at once; polarized light vibrates in only one plane.

An optically active substance with asymmetrical molecules will rotate the plane in which polarized light is vibrating when the light is passed through the substance. The amount of rotation is a characteristic of the substance through which the light is passing. This property is a useful analytical tool. An instrument called a

Optically active compounds have asymmetric molecules.

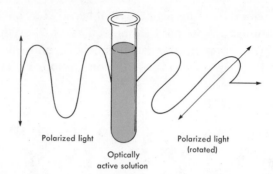

Polarized light

Optically
active solution

Polarized light
(rotated)

FIGURE 11-7. Every optically active substance rotates the plane of light vibrations in a light beam by a specific angle characteristic of the substance.

A dextrorotatory substance (Latin: *dexter*, right) rotates light to the right. A levorotatory substance (Latin: *laevus*, left) rotates light to the left.

A polarimeter measures the amount that a compound rotates polarized light.

polarimeter (poh lah RIM eht ehr) is used to measure the amount of rotation of polarized light passing through a solution of an unknown substance.

The sugars dextrose and levulose were named for their optical activity. Dextrose rotates light to the right and levulose rotates light to the left. In the example in Figure 11–5, one form of 2-butanol would rotate plane polarized light in one direction. The other form would rotate it in the other direction.

Dextrose rotates light to the right. Levulose rotates light to the left.

The symbols + and − are used to indicate rotations to the right and to the left, respectively. Thus the enantiomers for 2-butanol are known as (+)-2-butanol and (−)-2-butanol.

11:3 Polarity

If a covalent bond is formed between two atoms, and one of the atoms attracts a shared pair more strongly than the other, the resulting bond is said to be *polar*. Since one atom in the bond will

FDA Photo

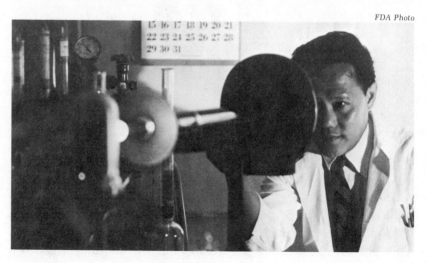

FIGURE 11-8. This chemist is using a polarimeter to determine the rotation of light due to the presence of vitamin E in a food sample.

attract the electrons more strongly, there will be a partial negative charge near the end of the bond containing this atom. In the bond, the atom with the higher electronegativity will have a partial negative charge and the other atom will have a partial positive charge. Polar bonds, unless symmetrically arranged, produce polar molecules.

A polar molecule is sometimes called a *dipole*. A dipole has asymmetrical charge distribution. A dipole has some interesting properties which are determined by its strength. The strength of a dipole is indicated by the product of the positive and negative charges and the distance between the centers of these charges. This product is called the *dipole moment* of the molecule. Molecules made of two atoms covalently bonded, but with large differences in electronegativity, will have a large dipole moment. Partial charges within a molecule are indicated by the sign δ (delta). A water molecule would be represented as follows:

$$\delta^+ \ H \!:\! \overset{\cdot\cdot}{\underset{\cdot\cdot}{O}} \!:\ \delta^-$$
$$\text{bond angle } 105° \quad \searrow H \ \delta^+$$

Table 11–1 lists a number of common solvents in order of increasing dipole moment. (The first three are nonpolar.)

Polar bonds may produce polar molecules.

Dipole: a polar molecule.

A large difference in electronegativity will produce a strong dipole movement.

Table 11–1

Polarity of Solvents

	Increasing Polarity	
Cyclohexane	C_6H_{12}
Carbon tetrachloride	CCl_4
Benzene	C_6H_6
Toluene	C_7H_8
Ethoxyethane	$C_4H_{10}O$
l-Butanol	$C_4H_{10}O$
l-Propanol	C_3H_8O
Ethanol	C_2H_6O
Methanol	CH_4O
Ethyl acetate	$C_4H_8O_2$
Water	H_2O
Propanone	C_3H_6O

Dipole moment is a measure of the polarity of a compound. A compound is polar when its molecules are composed of dissimilar atoms and the electrons involved in the bond formation are shared unequally between these dissimilar atoms. The name, dipole moment, was originated by Petrus Josephus Debye, a professor at Cornell University. The symbol, $\leftrightarrow$, stands for dipole moment. The arrow points toward the negative end of the dipole. The following is an example of a calculation involving an extremely polar molecule composed of a proton and an electron at a distance of 1 Å.

Charge on an
electron $= 4.8 \times 10^{-10}$ e s u
One Å $= 10^{-8}$ cm

Dipole moment $= 4.8 \times 10^{-10}$ esu $\times 10^{-8}$ cm
$= 4.8 \times 10^{-18}$ esu-cm

To simplify this, a new unit, the Debye (10^{-18} esu-cm), is used. Our dipole would have a dipole moment of 4.8 Debye. Water, a highly polar substance, has a dipole moment of only 1.84, so our example is a highly polar compound.

PROBLEM

1. d, a, e, c, b

1. The following pairs of atoms are all covalently bonded. Arrange the pairs in order of decreasing polarity of the bonds. (See Table of Electronegativities, Chapter 9.)
   a. boron and nitrogen
   b. carbon and sulfur
   c. hydrogen and selenium
   d. iodine and technetium
   e. nitrogen and oxygen

CHROMATOGRAPHY

11:4 Fractionation

Chromatography is a separation method which depends on polarity of substances.

Suggestions for adsorbents: Alumina is good, others are Fuller's earth, calcium oxide, calcium carbonate, calcium phosphate, talc, and starch.

Sometimes it is necessary to separate several materials from a mixture and identify them individually. A convenient method of separation based on the polarity of substances is a process called *chromatography* (kroh muh TAHG ruh fee). In chromatography, a fluid containing a number of substances is allowed to pass through a medium which has an attraction for polar materials. The different substances in the fluid will travel at different rates due to their varying polarity. Thus, they can be separated. These separations are called fractions because they are parts of the whole. The overall separation of parts from a whole by any process may be called *fractionation*.

Often, different fractions have different colors. For this reason, this method of separation is called chromatography (writing with color). The mechanical adaptation of fractionation, gas chromatography, does not use color. But since it also depends upon fractionation, the name chromatography is still applied.

FIGURE 11-9. Column chromatography can be used to separate substances (a) and (b) for identification.

Argonne National Laboratory

Dennis Brack-Black Star

11:5 Column Chromatography

In column chromatography, a glass column called a *chromatogram* is used to carry out the separation. The glass tube is packed with a specially prepared material such as calcium carbonate. Other packings now in use are magnesium or sodium carbonate, activated charcoal, ion exchange resins, clays, gels, and many organic compounds.

A solution of the material to be fractionated is added to the top of the column. Then, fresh solvent is caused to percolate through the column. The solvent may be water, an acid, an alcohol, or other organic or inorganic substance.

Each substance in the fluid travels at a different rate down the tube and the substances are separated. The rate of travel depends upon the attraction of each substance for the packing, its attraction for the solvent, and the concentration of the solvent. If the substance has a high attraction for the packing, only a high concentration of solvent will dislodge it. As the solvent moves down the tube, it becomes less concentrated, and the solute becomes more attracted to the packing again. Those substances with less attraction for the packing are carried farther, even by the less concentrated solvent. By constant percolation, the substances are separated into zones.

After this separation, it is necessary to recover the material in each separate zone for identification. One method involves forcing the zones out the bottom of the tube, one at a time. Each zone is dissolved and then purified by evaporation. A second method involves continued percolation of solvents of increasing polarity until each zone comes out the bottom along with the solvent. Identification is then made by any number of methods.

Suggested solvents, beginning with the least polar: petroleum ether, CCl_4, cyclohexane, CS_2, ether, acetone, benzene, chloroform, alcohol, water, pyridine, and acid.

Column separations depend on percolating a solvent through a packing substance.

The use of a glass tube adsorbent column sometimes becomes very involved. However, the separation of fountain pen ink on filter paper is a quick demonstration which gives more consistently evident and predictable results. See annotation on next page. See also One More Step, problem 2 on page 257.

Robert C. Smoot

FIGURE 11-10. (a) Separation of permanganate and dichromate ions on a column of alumina using $0.5M$ HNO_3 as a solvent. (b) Separation of fluorescein and methylene blue on a column of alumina using ethanol as a solvent. (c) Separation of chlorophylls and xanthophylls on cellulose using ligroin as a solvent.

Separation by this method (using a glass column) is a daily operation in many biochemical labs because the operation can be made quantitative and the separated materials are recovered.

The greatest difficulty in using this method is making the correct choice of solvent and packing. Column chromatography is used now for extremely delicate separations involving such products as vitamins, proteins, hormones, and other substances which are not easily separated by other methods.

11:6   Surface Chromatography

Paper chromatography uses strips of paper rather than columns.

Paper chromatography is an adaptation of column chromatography in which the separations are carried out on strips of paper rather than in glass columns.

Strips of paper are placed in a box or bell jar in which the atmosphere is saturated with water vapor or solvent vapor. A drop of the solution to be separated is placed at the top of the paper. The paper is then overlapped into solvent at the top of the box. The solvent moves down the paper by capillary action, separating the constituents of the drop. The paper may be placed into solvent at the bottom of the box. In this case, the drop of the solution would be placed at the bottom of the paper and the solvent would ascend the paper. In either case, the separations are seen as a series of colored spots on the paper strip. If the separated fractions happened to be colorless, they can be sprayed after separation by a liquid which will produce colored compounds. Some of these compounds may fluoresce under ultraviolet light.

Demonstration: Obtain a large test tube and a cork. Attach a strip of filter paper to the cork. Place a little water in the bottom of the test tube and arrange the filter paper so the bottom tip is immersed in the water at the bottom of the test tube when the cork is inserted. Place a drop of ink on the filter paper just below the cork and let the tube stand upright. Observe.

Robert C. Smoot

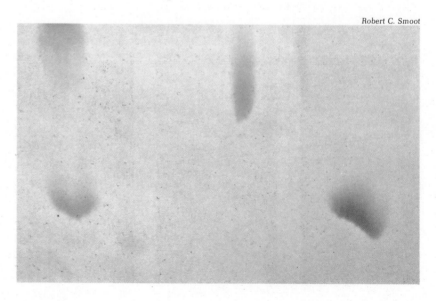

FIGURE 11-11. Paper chromatography can be used to separate substances for identification.

For example, consider the separation of Ag^+, Pb^{2+} Hg_2^{2+}. Let us see how it might be done with a paper chromatogram. The chromatogram is prepared, using a butanol-benzoylacetone solvent and a drop of the solution. The solvent will move to within 1 or 2 cm of the end of the paper. Then the chromatogram is sprayed with potassium chromate. A brick-red spot (Ag_2CrO_4) which fades to a pale yellow when held over ammonia indicates Ag^+. A bright yellow spot ($PbCrO_4$) which becomes orange with ammonia indicates Pb^{2+}. An orange spot which blackens with ammonia indicates Hg_2^{2+}.

If further resolution is needed, the paper can be turned 90°. Each spot is then used as an originating spot. The same solvent, or a second solvent, may be used. For example, a solution containing Ba, Pb, Cu, U, and Fe ions could be resolved by the use of butanol-benzoylacetone first, and by then turning the paper and using butanol-trichloroacetic acid as the second solvent.

Paper chromatography is simple, fast, and has a high resolving power. With this method, for example, it has been possible to separate the constituents of blood, urine, and antibiotics.

The development of specially treated papers such as cellulose phosphate has made this method even more valuable.

Luis Alvarez

(1911–   )

The son of a father famous in medicine, Luis Alvarez lost little time in establishing himself in the world of science. Following his degrees at the University of Chicago, he worked on radar research and development at M.I.T. and nuclear physics at Los Alamos before attaining a full professorship at the University of California, Berkeley, at age 34.

Over the next 22 years he received awards or medals from eight different scientific groups capped in 1968 by the Nobel Prize in physics. The prize was awarded for his work on subatomic particles, in particular the discovery of a large number of resonance states through the use of the hydrogen bubble chamber and modern data analysis techniques. Dr. Alvarez continues to teach and do research at Berkeley.

Any great difficulty with paper chromatography separation arises out of its extremely small scale. This makes quantitative determinations difficult. In addition, a control is needed to determine which spots belong to which compound. Even with these difficulties, the method is still extremely useful. One way of extending the usefulness of paper chromatography is to combine it, when possible, with an electric field. By utilizing the effect of both solvent and electric field, it is possible to separate substances which are inseparable by either method alone.

Another chromatographic method combines some of the techniques of both column and paper chromatography. In *thin layer chromatography*, a glass plate is coated with a very thin layer of packing, such as would be used in column chromatography. A spot of an unknown substance is applied as in paper chromatography; the glass plate is placed in an atmosphere of solvent vapor and solvent. The procedure from this point is just the same as the procedure for paper chromatography.

Thin layer chromatography uses glass plates instead of columns.

A number of reagent manufacturers presently produce excellent demonstration kits for thin layer chromatography.

FIGURE 11-12. Various oil soluble dyes are separated by thin-film chromatography.

Bell & Howell Company

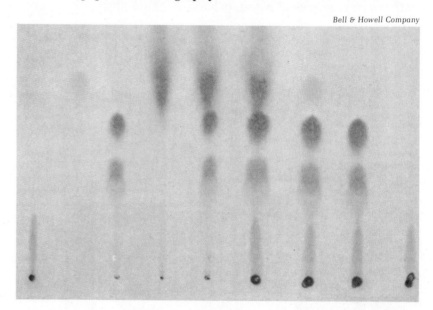

11:7 Gas Chromatography

Volatile liquids and mixtures of gases or vapors can also be analyzed by a chromatographic process. The gases to be analyzed are carried along by an inert gas such as helium. The gases are fractionated by a method similar to column chromatography. They are

Gas chromatography is used to analyze mixtures of gases.

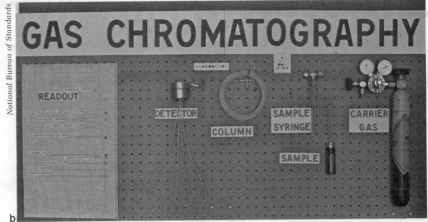

then carried by the inert helium through a tube fitted with an electrocouple. The varying amounts of contamination in the helium produce varying amounts of current. These variations are recorded by a needle on a moving sheet of graph paper. The amount of gas present in each fraction can be determined by counting the squares under the curve produced.

FIGURE 11-13. (a) A view of the inside of a gas chromatograph with the separation column in place. (b) A schematic representation of an experiment using gas chromatography.

Gas chromatography is very sensitive and rapid but it is, of course, limited to volatile liquids and gas mixtures or vapors at the temperature of operation. Also, gas chromatography has been used mostly in organic chemistry because inorganic substances vaporize at higher temperatures.

COMPLEX IONS

11:8 Ligands

As an ionic compound dissolves in water, its ions become hydrated. The surface ions of the crystal become surrounded by firmly attached H_2O molecules, and the water molecule-ion clusters thus

A complex ion is formed by ions or polar molecules clustered around a positive central ion.

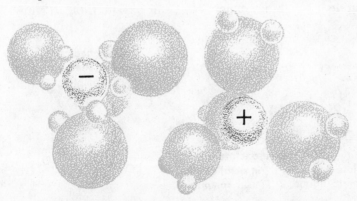

FIGURE 11-14. When a salt dissolves in water, molecules cluster around the dissolved anions and cations.

formed enter solution. The stability of these clusters is greatest when they have at their center a small ion of high charge. Since positive ions are usually smaller than negative ions, the groupings we are concerned with have a positive ion at the center. Polar molecules or negative ions cluster around the central ion and form a *complex ion*.

The molecules or negative ions which are attached to the central positive ion are known as *ligands*. The number of ligands around a central positive ion in a complex is called the *coordination number*. By far, the most common coordination number found in complexes is 6. These complex ions are described as *octahedral* because the ligands may be thought of as lying at the vertices of a regular octahedron with the central positive ion in the middle.

The coordination number 4 is also common. These complexes may be *square-planar*, with the ligands at the corners of a square and the central positive ion in the center. Others may be *tetrahedral*, with the ligands at the vertices of a regular tetrahedron and the central positive ion in the middle.

The coordination number 2 is found in complexes of Ag(I), Au(I), and Hg(II). Complex ions with coordination number 2 are always *linear*. The ligands are always located at the ends and the positive ion in the middle of a straight line.

Ligands can be either molecules or negative ions. Molecular ligands are always polar and always have an unshared pair of electrons which can be shared with the central ion. The most common ligand is water. Ammonia (NH_3) is also a very common ligand. Many negative ions also can act as ligands in complexes. Some of the most important are: fluoride, F^-; chloride, Cl^-; bromide, Br^-; iodide, I^-; cyanide, CN^-; thiocyanate, CNS^-; and oxalate $C_2O_4^{2-}$ (Figure 11–15).

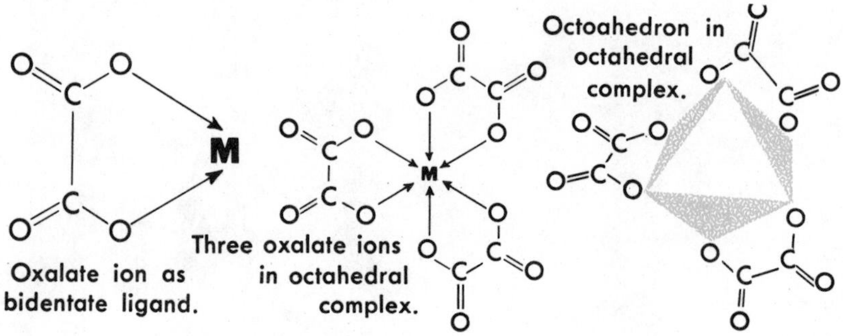

A coordination number indicates the number of ligands.

The most common coordination numbers are 6 and 4.

Water is the most common ligand.

Oxalate ion as bidentate ligand.

Three oxalate ions in octahedral complex.

Octoahedron in octahedral complex.

FIGURE 11-15. The oxalate ion ($C_2O_4^{2-}$) is an example of a bidentate ligand.

The oxalate ion is interesting because the positive ion can attach to it at two of the terminal oxygen atoms. Such a ligand is called *bidentate* (bi DEHN tayt) ("two-toothed"). Since a bidentate ligand attaches at two points, two bidentate ligands can form a tetrahedral complex, and three bidentate ligands can form an octahedral complex. *Tridentate* and *quadridentate* ligands also are known.

A bidentate ligand attaches at two points.

The number of coordinated groups is determined in part by the size and charge of the central ion. However, coordination numbers cannot at present be predicted from purely theoretical considerations.

11:9 Isomers of Complexes

It is possible to have more than one kind of ligand in the same complex. For example, platinum(IV) may form an octahedral complex with four ammonia molecules and two chloride ions, which has the formula $[Pt(NH_3)_4Cl_2]^{2+}$. The coordination number is 6. Since two ligands are of one kind and four are of another kind, there are two uniquely different ways of arranging the ligands. These arrangements are shown in Figure 11–16. Note that in one structure, the chloride ions are at opposite corners of the octahedron, while in the other they are at adjacent corners. Thus, there are *cis* and *trans* isomers of $[Pt(NH_3)_4Cl_2]^{2+}$.

Complex ions can exhibit isomerism.

Another example of isomerism in complexes is:

$Co(NH_3)_4Cl_2$

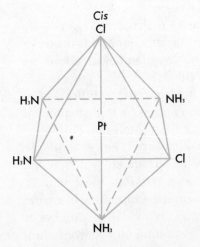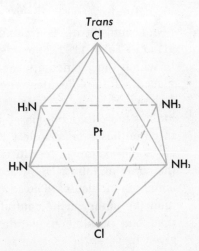

FIGURE 11-16. This octahedral complex may exist in two forms. The two forms have the same formula but different molecular structure and are called *cis-* and *trans*-isomers.

In naming a complex ion, the ligands are named first, followed by the name of the central ion. Each type of ligand is preceded by a prefix designating the number of molecules or ions of that particular ligand present in the complex. The prefixes used are *di-, tri-, tetra-,*

Note that it is possible to have a complex with a net charge of zero in a coordination compound.

Table 11–2

Some Common Ligands

Ligand	Name
OH^-	hydroxo
Br^-	bromo
Cl^-	chloro
F^-	fluoro
I^-	iodo
S^{2-}	thio
CN^-	cyano
$S_2O_3^{2-}$	thiosulfato
$C_2O_4^{2-}$	oxalato
H_2O	aquo
NH_3	ammine
CO	carbonyl
NO	nitrosyl

A more extensive list may be found in the IUPAC report, Nomenclature of Inorganic Chemistry.

penta-, and hexa-. The names for some of the common ligands are given in Table 11–2. The order given in the table represents the order in which the ligands appear in a name. Note that negative ions are placed before molecules. The name of the complex ion ends in -ate if the complex as a whole possesses a negative charge. If the central ion has more than one possible oxidation number, a Roman numeral in parentheses must follow the name of the central ion. Following are some examples to illustrate the method used. For example, in the complex ion $Cr(NH_3)_5Cl^{2+}$, the two ligands are chloride ion and ammonia molecules. The chloride is placed first, then the ammonia, then the name of the central ion, chromium. Chromium has more than one possible oxidation number, so its oxidation number is given in parentheses after its name. The ending on the word chromium remains unchanged since the ion as a whole is positive. The name of the complex ion is written as one word. Thus, the name of this ion is chloropentamminechromium(III) ion. If two more chloride ions are added, we obtain a compound of formula $[Cr(NH_3)_5Cl]Cl_2$. Note that when a question about composition could arise, the whole complex is placed in brackets. This compound would be named chloropentamminechromium(III) chloride.

Complex ions are named in order.
1. *negative ligands*
2. *molecular ligands*
3. *central ion*
4. *Roman numeral, if needed*
5. *-ate ending, if the ion is negative*

SiF_6^{2-}	hexafluorosilicate ion
$PtCl_6^{2-}$	hexachloroplatinate(IV) ion
$Ni(NH_3)_6Br_2$	hexamminenickel(II) bromide
$Na_2Sn(OH)_6$	sodium hexahydroxostannate(IV)
$Ag_3Fe(CN)_6$	silver hexacyanoferrate(III)

Note that the Latin stems are used for some metals. Some of these Latin stems are given in Table 11–3.

Table 11–3

Latin Stems Used in Some Metal Complexes

Metal	Latin Stem	Metal	Latin Stem
copper	cuprate	lead	plumbate
gold	aurate	silver	argentate
iron	ferrate	tin	stannate

11:10   Bonding in Complexes

Almost any positive ion might be expected to form complexes. In practice, the complexes of the metals of the first two groups in the periodic table have little stability. By far the most important and most interesting of the complexes are those of the transition metals. The transition metals have partially filled d orbitals which can become involved in bonding. These positive ions are small because of the strong attractive force of the nucleus for the inner electrons, and they have high oxidation numbers. The combination of small size and high charge results in a high charge density on the central ion, and this is particularly favorable to complex ion formation.

In an isolated ion of one of the metals of the first transition series, the five $3d$ orbitals all have the same energy. No energy is absorbed if an electron is transferred from one of the $3d$ orbitals to another. However, in the complex, the ligands affect the energies of the different $3d$ orbitals. In an octahedral complex, the d orbitals are split into a higher energy group of two orbitals and a lower energy group of three orbitals.

Ligands are either negative ions or polar molecules, while the central atom is ordinarily a positive ion. This suggests that the bonding forces in a complex are electrostatic, just as they are in a salt

Transition metals form complex ions.

There can be ligand field splitting into other groupings. See reference by Cotton in the Suggested Readings for this chapter.

FIGURE 11-17. The color change in this reaction is caused by the replacement of one ligand by another and the formation of a different complex according to the equation: $[Co(H_2O)_6]^{2+} + 4Cl^- \rightarrow [CoCl_4]^{2-} + 6 H_2O$.

Ronald Graves

crystal. In fact, there are strong similarities between the structures of salts and the structures of complex ions. On the other hand, the ligands usually have an unshared pair of electrons which they are capable of donating. The central ion always has unoccupied orbitals into which electron pairs might be placed. This suggests that the bonds are covalent. In fact, the name *coordinate covalent bond* has been given to covalent bonds in which both of the electrons in the shared pair come from the same atom. The bonds of most complex ions have characteristics of both covalent and ionic bonding types. The extent to which the bond has covalent or ionic character differs from one complex to another.

Complex ions form predominantly through covalent bonding.

VAN DER WAALS FORCES

11:11 Weak Forces

Van der Waals forces are due to attractions of protons and electrons in separate atoms.

A random sampling of 20 compounds formed by covalent bonding shows a melting point range of almost 3000C°! How can we account for such a wide variation?

We know that the electrostatic attraction between oppositely charged ions holds together the particles of ionic crystals. What sort of force holds together the molecules in solid hydrogen or the molecules of boron tribromide? The forces involved in these cases are called *van der Waals forces*. Johannes van der Waals was the first to take these forces into account in calculations concerning gases. These forces are sometimes referred to as weak forces because they are much weaker than chemical bonds. They involve the attraction of the electrons of one atom for the protons of another.

van der Waals attraction can result from
1. **dipole-dipole forces**
2. **dipole-induced dipole forces**
3. **dispersion forces**

The first source of van der Waals attraction which we will consider is that of dipole-dipole. Two molecules, of the same or different substances, which are both permanent dipoles due to the electronegativity difference between their constituent atoms will be attracted to each other (Figure 11–18). This would be the case between two trichloromethane molecules or between a trichloromethane and an ammonia molecule.   Water molecules are another example.

While chemical bonds range from about 50 to 200 kcal/mole, dipole-dipole forces are <30 kcal/mole.

FIGURE 11-18. Dipole-dipole interaction.

In the second case, we have the attraction of a dipole for a molecule that is ordinarily not a dipole. When the dipole approaches the normal molecule, its partial charge either attracts or repels the electrons of the other particle. For instance, if the negative end of the dipole approaches a normal molecule, the electrons of the normal molecule are repelled by the negative charge. The electron cloud of the normal molecule is distorted by bulging away from the approaching dipole (Figure 11–19). As a result, the normal molecule is itself transformed into a dipole. We say it has become an *induced dipole*. Since it is now a dipole, it can be attracted to the *permanent dipole*. Interactions such as these are called *dipole-induced dipole forces*.

A nonpolar molecule may become an induced dipole.

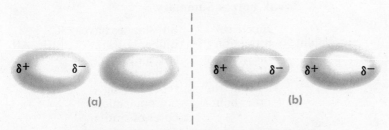

FIGURE 11-19. Dipole-induced dipole interaction.

The case of two nonpolar molecules being attracted must also be taken into account. For instance, there must be some force between hydrogen molecules; otherwise it would be impossible to form liquid and solid hydrogen. Consider a hydrogen molecule with its molecular orbital including both nuclei. We know intuitively that the electrons occupying that orbital must be somewhere. If they are both away from one end of the molecule for an instant, then the

Two nonpolar molecules may be attracted to each other.

nucleus is exposed for a short time, and that end of the molecule has a partial positive charge for that instant. At this instant, the temporary dipole can induce a dipole in the molecule next to it and an attractive force results (Figure 11–20). The forces generated in this way are called *dispersion forces*.

Dispersion forces result from temporary dipoles.

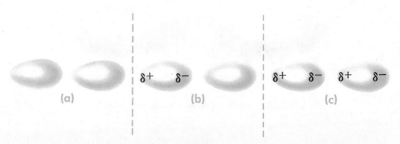

FIGURE 11-20. Dispersion forces.

Ionic solids are bound by electrostatic attraction also.

The various kinds of interactions making up the van der Waals forces affect each other, but we are only interested in the net result. Liquids and solids exist because of these intermolecular forces. These forces are effective only over very short distances. They vary roughly as the inverse of the sixth power of distance. In other words, if the distance is doubled, the attractive force is only 1/64 as large.

The van der Waals forces are effective only over very short distances.

Table 11–4

Weak Forces Summary

INTERMOLECULAR BONDS Molecules contain covalently bonded atoms					
	Dipole	Polar covalent molecules	Electrical attraction between dipoles resulting from polar bonds	Substances have higher boiling and melting points than those having nonpolar molecules of similar size $100 < mp < 600$	ICl, SO_2, $BiBr_3$, AlI_3, SeO_3
	Dispersion Forces	Nonpolar molecules	Weak electrical fluctuations which destroy spherical symmetry of electronic fields about atoms	Substances have low melting and boiling points	Cl_2, CH_4, N_2, O_2, F_2, Br_2, Cl_2, He, Ar

SUMMARY

1. Isomers are compounds with the same formula but a different arrangement of atoms and bonds.

2. Double bonds prevent rotation of groups about a bond and cause the formation of isomers called geometric isomers.

3. Positional isomers are compounds in which an atom or group of atoms may take more than one position in an otherwise unchanged molecule.

4. Functional isomers are hydrocarbon compounds in which a third kind of atom may be connected to the rest of the molecule in two or more ways.

5. Optical isomers are compounds whose molecules are asymmetrical. They have the property of rotating a plane of polarized light.

6. A polar bond is one in which a shared pair of electrons is attracted more strongly to one of the atoms, causing one end of the bond to be positively charged and the other end to be negatively charged. Asymmetrical polar bonds in a molecule cause the molecule to be polar. Such a molecule is called a dipole.

7. Chromatography (writing with color) is a method of separating substances into identifiable chemical fractions by differences in their polarity. This technique includes column chromatography, paper chromatography, thin layer chromatography, and gas chromatography.

8. The central positive ion with attached negative ions or polar molecules is called a complex ion.

9. The molecules or negative ions attached to the central ion are called ligands.

10. The number of ligands surrounding the central ion is the coordination number of a complex.

11. Complexes which contain six, four, or two ligands are most common.

12. A complex containing six ligands is an octahedral complex, one containing four ligands is either a square-planar or a tetrahedral complex, and one containing two ligands is a linear complex.

13. Ligands donate a pair or several pairs of electrons to the central ion. A ligand which donates two pairs of electrons is called a bidentate ligand; one which donates three pairs of electrons is tridentate.

14. Water is the most common ligand. Ammonia is also a common ligand.

15. Complex ions which contain more than one type of ligand may have these ligands arranged in different ways. The different arrangements, which contain the same number and the same kinds of ligands, are isomers.

16. Complex ions are named by stating the number and kind of ligand followed by the name of the central ion. The name is written as one word.

17. Small positive ions with a large nuclear attractive force form excellent central ions. The transition metal ions are good examples of these.

18. In the transition metal complexes, the *d* orbitals of the central ion are not all at the same energy level.

19. The bonds of complex ions have both ionic and covalent bonding characteristics.

20. The weak forces that result from the attraction of the nucleus of one atom for the electrons of another atom are called van der Waals forces.

21. Van der Waals forces are the net result of dipole-dipole, dipole-induced dipole, and dispersion effects.

PROBLEMS

2. a, b, e, d, c

2. The following pairs of atoms are all covalently bonded. Arrange the pairs in order of decreasing polarity of the bonds.
   a. arsenic and oxygen   d. oxygen and fluorine
   b. chlorine and silicon   e. phosphorus and bromine
   c. nitrogen and chlorine

3. See Teacher's Guide.

3. Draw the isomers of the compound with the formula C_6H_{14}.

4. Both — selective adsorption; Paper — capillary action; Column—solvent runs through adsorbent

4. How are column and paper chromatography similar? How are they different?

5. What shape would you expect the $[Al(H_2O)_6]^{3+}$ complex to have? Sketch it. octahedral

central ion—center of complex; coordination number — number of ligands; ligand — coordinated group

6. Identify: central ion, ligand, coordination number.

7. What factors determine the coordination number? size and charge

empty *d* orbitals to accept e^-; large charge-to-radius ratio

8. Why do transition metals make good central ions?

9. What forces hold molecular substances in the liquid and solid forms? van der Waals forces

10. See Teacher's Guide.

10. Define geometric, positional, and functional isomerism.

ONE MORE STEP   See Teacher's Guide at the front of this book.

1. Find a description and make a model of the following molecules:
   a. PCl_5 c. Nb_2Cl_{10} e. Al_2Cl_6
   b. IF_7 d. B_2H_6

2. Try to separate the amino acids from the milk protein casein on a paper chromatogram. This problem will entail a considerable amount of library research before you begin the laboratory procedure. First, the casein must be precipitated from the milk. Then, the protein must be hydrolyzed to amino acids. Finally, the chromatogram can be prepared.

3. In preparing paper chromatograms, identification of unknowns is aided by the measurement of R_f values. These values concern the distance an unknown has advanced compared to the distance the solvent has advanced. How are these values useful in identification?

4. Look up the structure of chlorophyll. Determine the central ion and its coordination number. What is the coordinated group, and what is its spatial orientation about the central ion?

5. Look up the structure of hemoglobin. Determine the central ion and its coordination number. What is the coordinated group, and what is its spatial orientation about the central ion?

6. Medicine and industry use certain materials called *chelating agents*. What are they and how are they related to complexes?

7. A number of organic compounds are used in the analysis of inorganic ions because they form complex ions. Investigate the substances used in detecting nickel, aluminum, and zirconium by such a method.

Suggested Readings for this chapter may be found in the Teacher's Guide at the front of this book.

Moving water and wind help us to visualize liquids and gases as being composed of very small particles in constant motion. It is more difficult to imagine that solids also are composed of tiny moving particles. This motion increases with temperature, causing warm solids to expand slightly as the particles move farther apart. How do designers of massive structures such as bridges and highways make allowance for this expansion?

Kinetic Theory

Chapter 12 introduces the Kinetic Theory. It also leads to an understanding of the ideal gas, the ideal gas equation, the relationship between the four physical states of matter, and relates them to the mole concept studied in Chapter 5.

The *kinetic theory* is a theory which explains the effect of heat and pressure on matter. Two assumptions are basic. First, all matter is composed of submicroscopic particles (*atoms*, *ions*, or *molecules*). Second, these small particles are *in constant motion*. One further assumption is made in the kinetic theory. It is assumed that all collisions are *perfectly elastic*. That is, there is no change in the total energy of two molecules before and after their collision. It may be difficult to imagine that all particles in a great structure such as the Golden Gate Bridge are in constant motion. However, as we shall see, many of the properties of matter are necessary results of such a constant motion. As early as the mid-seventeenth century, the famous English inventor Robert Hooke proposed that there were ultimate particles in nature which were in constant motion. In order to have some concept of the sizes of the quantities involved, we will first discuss oxygen.

GOAL: You will gain an understanding of the kinetic theory and its relationship to the states of matter.

The kinetic theory is based on three assumptions:
1. All matter is composed of particles.
2. The particles of matter are in constant motion.
3. All collisions are perfectly elastic.

In an ideal gas, these particles are assumed to be points which do not attract each other.

PARTICLE MOTION

12:1 Oxygen Molecules in Motion

At 0°C, the average velocity of an oxygen molecule is 4.61×10^4 cm/sec. This is equivalent to just over 1600 kilometers per hour. At this speed, the molecules collide with each other frequently. We can determine the average number of collisions a molecule undergoes in a unit of time by finding the average distance a molecule travels before colliding with another molecule. This is called the

Even at room temperature molecules are moving extremely rapidly.

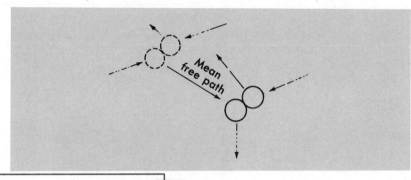

Mean = arithmetic mean or more commonly, the average

$M = \dfrac{S}{N}$, where

S = sum of numbers in a set
N = number of elements in a set

FIGURE 12-1. The mean free path of a molecule is the distance it travels between collisions.

The mean free path of a molecule is the average distance a molecule travels between collisions.

FIGURE 12-2. Individual molecules of a gas are much too small to be seen. However, effects of unequal pressure resulting from collisions of air molecules can readily be seen in this tornado-damaged community.

mean free path of the molecule (Figure 12–1). For oxygen at 0°C, the mean free path is 7.29×10^{-6} cm. Since the diameter of the oxygen molecule is about 3.39 Å, an oxygen molecule at 0°C will travel, on the average, about 215 times its own diameter before colliding with another molecule.

This travel corresponds to a little over six billion collisions per second per molecule. We give these figures for oxygen as examples of the speed, the distance of travel, and the number of molecular collisions in a gas. These factors vary with the temperature and the mass of the particles composing the gas.

W. Keith Turpie

12:2 Pressure

In addition to colliding with other molecules, the molecules of a gas collide with the walls of the container in which the gas is confined. When a gas molecule collides with the wall of a container, it exerts a force on the container. It is the force of collision and the number of collisions with the walls of a container that cause gas pressure (Figure 12–3). This pressure is measured in terms of force

Gas pressure results from collision of molecules with the walls of a container.

Emphasize that air pressure is equal in all directions in a container such as illustrated in Figure 12-3.

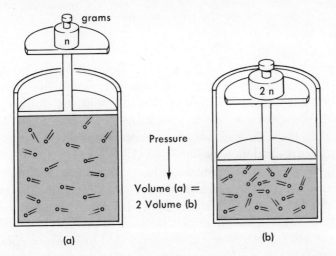

FIGURE 12-3. Pressure results from the collisions of molecules with the walls of a container and is measured as force per unit area. When the volume of the gas in a piston (a) is halved, the number of collisions with the walls of the piston is increased (b) and the pressure is doubled.

per unit area. The molecules and atoms of the gases present in the air are constantly hitting the surface of the earth and everything on it. As a result, you and everything surrounding you are subject to a certain pressure from the molecules of the air. The amount of pressure exerted by the air has been used as a scientific standard of pressure. The standard is known as *one atmosphere*, and is defined as the average pressure of the air at sea level under normal conditions. Since conditions in the air depend upon many weather factors, it is difficult to define "normal" conditions at sea level. Therefore, one atmosphere also has been defined in terms of a system which can be reproduced in the laboratory.

One atmosphere is the average normal air pressure at sea level.

MEASURING PARTICLE MOTION

12:3 Measuring Pressure

In measuring gas pressure, an instrument called a *manometer* (mah NAHM uh tuhr) is used. There are two types of manometers (Figure 12–4). In the first type, the air exerts pressure on the column

A manometer is an instrument used to measure pressure.

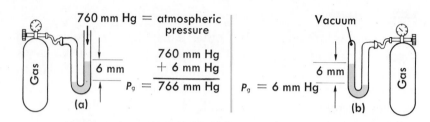

Demonstration: The two types of manometer can be illustrated easily with glass tubing and a KMnO$_4$ solution.

FIGURE 12-4. Figure (a) is an open arm manometer and Figure (b) is a closed arm manometer.

of liquid in one arm of the U-tube. The gas being studied exerts pressure on the other arm. The difference in liquid level between the two arms is a measure of the gas pressure relative to the air pressure. If you know the density of the liquid in the manometer, you can calculate the difference between the pressure exerted by the gas and the pressure exerted by the air.

A barometer is a manometer used to measure air pressure.

One atmosphere (atm) pressure will support a column of mercury 760 mm high.

The other type of manometer has a vacuum above the liquid in one arm. The pressure measured with an instrument of this type does not depend on the pressure of the air, and is called the *absolute pressure*. This manometer can be used to measure the pressure of the air itself. Such a manometer (one used to measure atmospheric pressure) is called a *barometer* (buh RAHM uht uhr). The instrument used to define an atmosphere is a barometer. *One standard atmosphere* is defined as the pressure necessary to support a column of mercury 760 mm high.

FIGURE 12-5. Barometers are manometers used to measure atmospheric pressure. The mercury barometer (a) is used in the laboratory because it is very precise. The aneroid barometer (b) is less precise but more convenient to use in everyday living.

The unit of pressure most often used in the laboratory is the torr. A torr is the pressure exerted by a column of mercury 1 mm high.

$$1 \text{ torr} = \frac{1}{760} \text{ atm}$$

$1 \text{ torr} = \frac{1}{760} \text{ atm} = 1\text{mm Hg}$

Even with a manometer of the first type, it is possible to calculate the absolute pressure of a gas. However, a barometer must be available to measure the atmospheric pressure on the outside arm of the manometer. A barometer is a special form of manometer.

The total pressure affecting the mercury must be considered.

The following examples show some typical calculations involving pressure.

EXAMPLE — PRESSURE

The manometer in Figure 12–4(a) is filled with mercury. The difference between mercury levels in the two arms is 6 mm. What is the total pressure, in atmospheres, of the gas in the container? The air pressure is 760 torr.

The total pressure of a gas is equal to the pressure of the air above the open column plus the pressure of the column of mercury: in this case, 760 + 6, or 766 torr. Since 760 torr equal 1 atmosphere (atm), the pressure is:

$$\frac{766 \text{ torr}}{} \left| \frac{1 \text{ atm}}{760 \text{ torr}} \right. = 1.01 \text{ atm}$$

EXAMPLE — PRESSURE

Suppose the difference in height of the two mercury levels in the manometer in Figure 12–4(b) is 238 mm. What is the pressure, in atmospheres, of the gas in the container?

Since the column of mercury is 238 mm high and 1 mm of mercury is 1 torr, the pressure is:

$$\frac{238 \text{ torr}}{} \left| \frac{1 \text{ atm}}{760 \text{ torr}} \right. = 0.313 \text{ atm}$$

PROBLEMS

1. A manometer such as the one in Figure 12–4(a) is filled with mercury and connected to a container of oxygen. The level of mercury is 6 mm higher in the arm of the tube connected to the container of oxygen. Atmospheric pressure is 749 torr. What is the pressure, in atmospheres, of the oxygen?   0.978 atm

2. A manometer like the one in Figure 10–4(b) is filled with mercury and connected to a container of helium. The difference in the height of mercury in the two arms is 86 mm. What is the pressure, in atmospheres, of the helium? 0.11 atm

12:4 Kinetic Energy

The average speed of molecules or atoms in a gas depends only on the temperature and the mass of the particles. How are temperature and particle mass related?

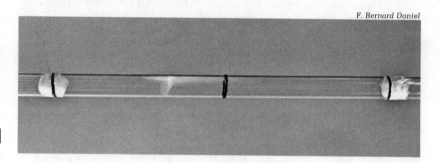

F. Bernard Daniel

FIGURE 12-6. When hydrochloric acid vapor reacts with ammonium hydroxide vapor, a white substance, ammonium chloride, is formed. The cotton in one end of this tube is saturated with HCl, the cotton in the other end is saturated with NH_4OH. Which end of the tube contains hydrochloric acid?—
HCl is on the right

Kinetic energy is the energy a body possesses because of its motion. The *kinetic theory* states that the average kinetic energy of molecules or atoms in a gas is the same for all particles at a particular temperature. The kinetic energy of a particle is equal to $\frac{1}{2}mv^2$, where m is its mass and v its velocity. The formula relating kinetic energy, mass, and velocity shows that, at a given temperature, an atom or molecule with small mass will move faster than an atom or molecule with large mass.

$$K.E. = \frac{1}{2}mv^2$$

FIGURE 12-7. The kinetic energy of a body is related to its mass and velocity.

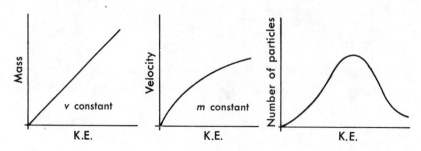

EXAMPLE – KINETIC ENERGY

For example, what is the ratio of the velocity of helium atoms to that of argon atoms at the same temperature?

Since their temperatures are the same we can consider that their average kinetic energies are the same. Thus,

$$\tfrac{1}{2}m_{He}v_{He}^2 = \tfrac{1}{2}m_{Ar}v_{Ar}^2$$

$$\frac{v_{He}^2}{v_{Ar}^2} = \frac{m_{Ar}}{m_{He}}$$

$$\frac{v_{He}}{v_{Ar}} = \frac{\sqrt{m_{Ar}}}{\sqrt{m_{He}}}$$

$$\frac{v_{He}}{v_{Ar}} = \frac{\sqrt{40}}{\sqrt{4}} = \frac{\sqrt{10}}{1} = 3.16$$

PROBLEMS

3. What is the ratio of the speed of hydrogen molecules to that of oxygen molecules when both gases are at the same temperature? Remember that both elements are diatomic. 4/1

4. What is the ratio of the speed of helium atoms to the speed of radon atoms when both gases are at the same temperature? 7.45/1

12:5 Temperature

It has been found that a decrease in the temperature of a substance causes the molecules of the substance to move more slowly, and that an increase in temperature causes the molecules to move faster. *Temperature*, then, is a measure of the average molecular motion, or a measure of the average kinetic energy of the molecules of a substance.

If molecular motion of a gas decreases as the temperature decreases, it should in theory be possible to lower the temperature to a point where all molecular motion ceases. This temperature, the temperature at which all molecular motion should cease, is known as *absolute zero*. It is −273.15°C. This value is usually rounded to −273°C.

Temperature is a measure of the average kinetic energy of the molecules of a substance.

Absolute zero is −273°C or 0°K.

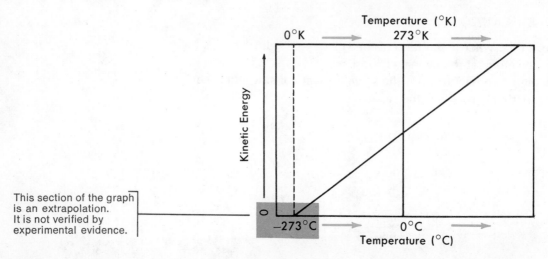

This section of the graph
is an extrapolation.
It is not verified by
experimental evidence.

FIGURE 12-8.   Theoretically, the kinetic energy of an ideal gas
is zero at −273° C.

Give students practice
problems on °C to °K and °K
to °C conversions.

To make a useful scale for measuring very low temperatures, scientists have agreed on a system known as the absolute, or *Kelvin*, scale. The zero point of the Kelvin scale is absolute zero. The divisions, or degrees, are the same size as those of the Celsius scale. Consequently,

$°K = °C + 273$

$$°K = °C + 273$$

12:6   Heat Transfer

Temperature is a measurement which can be used to determine the direction of flow of heat energy. Heat energy always flows from the warmer object to the cooler one. Kinetic theory explains this phenomenon in terms of collisions of molecules having unequal

Temperature knowledge can
aid in determining the direction of heat flow.

John Morgan

b

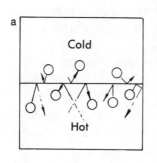

FIGURE 12-9. Kinetic energy
is transferred from the hotter
object to the colder object (a).
Heat travels from the hot water
to the cool spoon (b).

kinetic energy. The excess kinetic energy of the particles in the warmer object is passed on to the particles of the cooler object as they collide (Figure 12–9a. The particles of the cooler object gradually receive more kinetic energy. Soon, the average kinetic energy of both objects is the same.

12:7 The States of Matter

Matter exists in four states: *solid, liquid, gas,* and *plasma.* Thus far, our discussion of the kinetic theory has been limited to gases (Figure 12–11). However, the kinetic theory can also be used to explain the behavior of solids and liquids. Plasmas must be treated as a special case.

In gases, the particles are independent of each other and move in a straight line. Change of direction occurs only when one particle collides with another, or when a particle collides with the walls of the container. Gas particles, then, travel in a completely random manner. Since they travel until they collide with a neighbor (a considerable distance) or with the walls of their container, gases assume the shape and volume of their container.

FIGURE 12-10. This water droplet is undergoing its first stage of transformation into snow.. Water exists in all three fundamental states of matter — solid, liquid, and gas — within a narrow temperature range.

General Electric Research & Development Center

Solid Liquid Gas

FIGURE 12-11. The particles of a solid vibrate about a fixed point; the particles of a liquid vibrate about a moving point; the molecules of a gas travel in straight lines.

The particles of a liquid possess a motion somewhat between the motions of particles of a solid and a gas. A liquid particle has what appears to be a vibratory type of motion. The point about which the seeming vibration occurs often shifts as one particle slips past another. These differences in the amount of space between particles allow the particles to change their relative positions continually. Thus, liquids, although they have a definite volume, assume the shape of their container.

In solids, a particle occupies a relatively fixed position in relation to the surrounding particles, and appears to vibrate about a fixed

Liquid particles appear to vibrate about moving points.

Solid particles appear to vibrate about fixed points.

George Washington Carver
(1864–1943)

George Washington Carver was born in slavery. Before his death, he became one of the foremost agricultural chemists in the world. Largely self-educated, Carver was 35 years old when he received his masters degree at Iowa State University.

Carver is perhaps best known for his work with sweet potatoes and peanuts. He developed more than 100 products from sweet potatoes and over 300 from peanuts in his laboratory at Tuskegee Institute.

However, he also made use of other agricultural products to develop building materials and household goods. As he prepared imitation marble from sawdust and rugs from vegetable stalks, he was probably the forerunner of today's recycling ecologist.

Not only a chemist, Carver was also a pianist and an accomplished artist. His talent led him to study everything from dyes to fungi. Although many of his contemporaries scoffed because he failed to produce any scholarly papers, his experiments have contributed greatly to the welfare of people all over the world.

point. For example, a molecule of oxygen gas at 0°C travels an average distance equal to 215 times its own diameter before colliding with another molecule. In a solid, however, the particles are closely packed and travel a distance equal to only a fraction of their diameters before colliding. Unlike liquids, most solids have their particles arranged in a definite pattern. Solids, therefore, have both a definite shape and a definite volume.

Most solids have a definite orderly arrangement.

The arrangement of particles is important to the chemist. In the following chapters, we will discuss some of the special characteristics of solids, liquids, and gases.

12:8   Plasma

When matter is heated to very high temperatures (>5000°C), the collisions between particles are so violent that electrons are knocked away from atoms. Such a state of matter, composed of electrons and positive ions, is called a *plasma*.

A plasma state is composed of electrons and positive ions.

Most of the universe consists of plasma. Stars are in a plasma state. Outer space is not really empty. It is occupied by an extremely thin plasma. The Van Allen radiation belts which surround the earth are composed of plasma. Matter in a neon tube or in a cyclotron is in the form of plasma. Scientists are doing intense research on the character of plasmas because a type of nuclear reaction called fusion occurs only in plasmas. The fusion reaction, if it can be controlled, promises to be an energy source for mankind second only to the sun.

FIGURE 12-12. Matter exists as plasma in a cyclotron (a). Matter also exists as plasma in stars such as the sun (b).

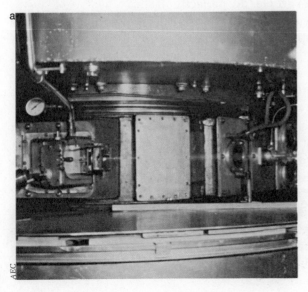
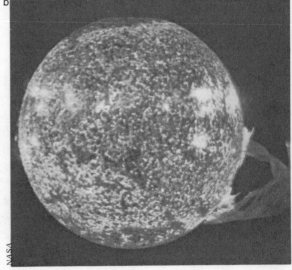

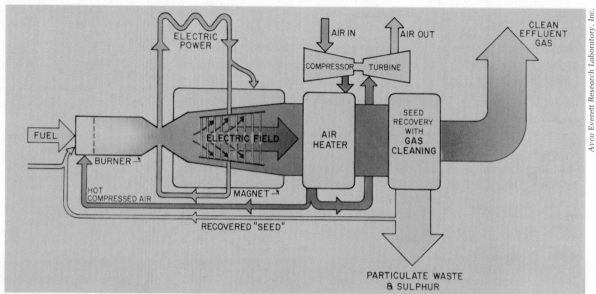

FIGURE 12-13.   A flow chart for a magnetohydrodynamic system for generating electricity.

Electric and magnetic fields affect the plasma state.

See Suggested Reading for this chapter in the Teacher's Guide at the front of this book.

Since plasma consists of charged particles traveling at high speeds, it is greatly affected by electrical and magnetic fields. Therefore, the study of plasmas is called *magnetohydrodynamics* (mag NEET oh hi droh di NAM iks). It is an area which is almost as complicated as its name.

SUMMARY

1. The kinetic theory explains the effects of heat and pressure on matter. This theory assumes that: (1) all matter is composed of particles; (2) these particles are in constant motion; (3) collisions between these particles are perfectly elastic.

2. At 0°C, an oxygen molecule travels at just over 1600 kilometers per hour in straight lines for a distance of 7.29×10^{-6} cm, a distance about 215 times its own diameter. At this temperature, it has more than six billion collisions per second.

3. A gas exerts pressure on its container because the gas molecules are constantly colliding with the walls of the container.

4. One atmosphere is the average pressure of the atmosphere at sea level under normal conditions.

5. One standard atmosphere is the pressure necessary to support a column of mercury 760 mm high. One mm of Hg exerts a pressure of 1 torr. Therefore, 760 torr = 1 atm.

6. A manometer is an instrument used to measure gas pressure.

7. Kinetic energy is the energy a body possesses because of its motion. It is related to the mass and the velocity of the body.

8. Temperature is a measure of the average kinetic energy of the molecules of a substance.

9. The Kelvin temperature scale is convenient for very low temperatures. It has the same unit degree as the Celsius scale, but a zero point at absolute zero ($°K = °C + 273$).

10. Heat energy flows from an object of higher temperature to one of lower temperature until both are at the same temperature.

11. The particles of a gas travel at random in a straight-line manner.

12. The particles of a solid appear to be vibrating about a point which is fixed with respect to neighboring particles.

13. The particles of a liquid appear to be vibrating about a point which constantly changes its position with respect to neighboring particles.

14. A plasma consists of electrons and positive ions in random motion. It is strongly affected by electrical and magnetic fields.

PROBLEMS

5. The manometer in Figure 12–4(a) is filled with mercury. The difference in the mercury level in the arms is 12 mm. What is the pressure, in atmospheres, of the gas in the container if the air pressure is 740 torr? 0.989 atm

6. In the closed manometer in Figure 12–4(b), assume that the height of the levels differ by 400 mm Hg. What is the pressure of the gas in the container? 400 torr

7. Convert the following temperatures from one temperature scale to another as indicated:
   a. 828°K to °C 555°C   c. 16°C to °K 289°K   e. 62°C to °K 335°K
   b. 751°C to °K 1024°K   d. 3°K to °C −270°C

8. At a certain temperature the velocity of oxygen molecules is 0.076 m/sec. What is the velocity of helium atoms at the same temperature? 0.215 m/sec

9. Suppose you have two vials, one containing ammonia and the other containing chlorine. When they are opened across the room from you, which would you expect to smell first? ammonia

10. What is the mean free path of an atom or molecule?

10. average distance it travels between collisions

11. With regard to molecular motion, what are the differences in the states of matter?— ⌈ gas — molecules move independently; liquid — molecules vibrate about a moving point; solid — molecules vibrate about a fixed point ⌋

ONE MORE STEP

1. Compute the kinetic energy of an oxygen molecule at 0°C, and of an automobile with a mass of 1500 kg traveling at 50 km/hr.

1. Oxygen — 5.65×10^{-14} ergs/molecule
   Automobile — 1.45×10^{12} ergs

2. Calculate the velocity of a hydrogen molecule at 0°C. 1.84×10^5 cm/sec

3. Investigate the workings of an aneroid barometer. Are there other instruments used to measure pressures in addition to manometers? ⌉ See Teacher's Guide at the front of this book.

4. Prepare a report for your class on the topic of plasmas. ⌋

Suggested Readings for this chapter may be found in the Teacher's Guide at the front of this book.

All true solids are crystalline. However, the crystal structure of many solids is so small that it can be seen only with a microscope. Salt, sugar, quartz, and gemstones are familiar crystalline materials. Perfect crystals are rare but defects in them can be useful, as in the case of transistors. In the U-tube shown here, crystals are being grown by the gel diffusion method. What is rock candy? How are its crystals grown?

Chapter 13 introduces crystal theory through a study of unit cells. Three of these unit cells are discussed and their relationship to the space lattice and to the seven crystal systems is developed. The chapter ends with a study of variation and crystal defects.

Have you ever examined table salt under a magnifying glass? If so, you would have seen that the crystals appear to be little cubes. The lengths of the edges may vary, but the angles between the surfaces are always exactly 90°. Suggestion: Obtain a microscope and allow students to observe salt crystals under low power.

GOAL: You will gain an understanding of crystal structure and its relationship to properties of solids.

CRYSTAL STRUCTURE

13:1 Crystals Wooden models of the various crystal structures are available and can be helpful in the study of this chapter. It is also possible to have one or more students construct such models from styrofoam.

All true solid substances are crystalline. Apparent exceptions to this statement can be explained in either of two ways. In some cases, substances we think of as solids are not solids at all. In other cases, the crystals are so small that the solid does not appear crystalline to the unaided eye. The study of the solid state, then, is really a study of crystals.

No exceptions have been found to Steno's Law. If an exception is found, it must either be explained or the law must be altered.

A study of crystals is a study of the solid state.

The systematic study of crystals began with Nicolaus Steno, in 1669. He observed that corresponding angles between faces on different crystals of the same substance were always the same. This was true regardless of the size or source of the crystals.

Steno's Law:

All crystals of the same substance have the same angles between faces.

Steno's observation has been extended to all intensive properties (density, refractive index, face angles, and other similar properties). It can now be stated that the extensive properties of crystals vary while the intensive properties remain the same. (See Section 3:4 to refresh your memory on the difference between intensive and extensive properties.) For example, a single crystal of the mineral beryl, $Be_3Al_2Si_6O_{18}$, weighing more than 40 tons was once unearthed in New Hampshire. This huge crystal was found to be identical in intensive properties with any other beryl crystal, even one weighing perhaps one tenth gram.

Extensive properties of crystals of the same substance may vary; intensive properties of crystals of the same substance are the same.

273

FIGURE 13-1. Beryl crystals.

An obvious inference is that all crystals of a certain substance must be made up of similar small units. These units are then repeated over and over again in the growth of the crystal. Thus a *crystal* is defined as a rigid body in which the constituent particles are arranged in a repeating pattern. The shape and properties of these small repeating units are determined by the bonds between the particles. Therefore, the bonding in the crystal partially determines the properties of the crystal.

The units which make up crystals are too small to be seen. However, even before any experimental methods existed for studying their structure, scientists were able to suggest that crystals form by

Crystals are composed of small units repeated over and over.

Properties of crystals are partially determined by the bonding.

FIGURE 13-2. How a crystal breaks (a) is related to crystal structure (b).

a

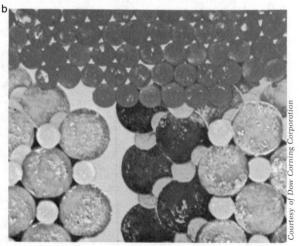

b

repetition of identical units. Such suggestions were possible because examples of structures built up by repetition of smaller units existed all around them. For example, consider the patterns on wallpaper, drapery fabrics, or dress goods. These patterns are applied by rollers which repeat the design with each revolution. In a crystal, the forces of chemical bonding play the same role that the roller does in printing. They cause the basic pattern to be repeated

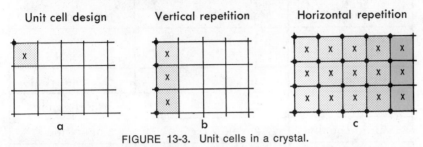

FIGURE 13-3. Unit cells in a crystal.

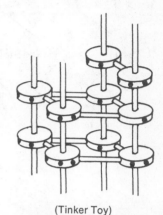

(Tinker Toy)

Suggestion:
A three dimensional model of a lattice or a unit cell can be constructed easily using a toy construction set composed of sticks and drilled disks.

over and over again. However, the "design" of a crystal must be composed of atoms, molecules, or ions instead of ink. A major difference between crystals and wallpaper is that the units in crystals are three-dimensional, whereas those in the wallpaper are two-dimensional.

There is a relationship between the characteristics of the repeating units and the external shape of the crystal. Long ago, *crystallographers* (kris tuh LAHG ruh fuhrs) (scientists who study crystals) classified crystals on the basis of their external shapes into seven "crystal systems." These are shown in Table 13–1.

FIGURE 13-4. Crystal structures can be likened to a repeat wallpaper pattern (a) or a repeat fabric design (b).

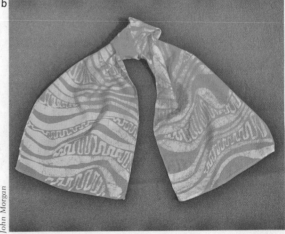

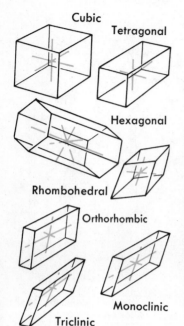

Cubic
Tetragonal
Hexagonal
Rhombohedral
Orthorhombic
Triclinic
Monoclinic

Table 13–1

The Seven Crystal Systems

Lengths of the Unit Cell Axes	Angles Between the Unit Cell Axes	Crystal System
all equal	all = 90°	cubic
2 equal 1 unequal	all = 90°	tetragonal
3 equal 1 unequal	1 = 90° 3 = 60°	hexagonal
all equal	all ≠ 90°	rhombohedral
all unequal	all = 90°	orthorhombic
all unequal	2 = 90°, 1 ≠ 90°	monoclinic
all unequal	all ≠ 90°	triclinic

Suggestion: Have students make a set of crystal system models from styrofoam, transparent plastic, or wood.

13:2 The Unit Cell

The unit cell is the simplest unit of repetition in a crystal.

Each substance which crystallizes does so according to a definite network arrangement. The simplest unit of repetition in this arrangement is called the unit cell. It is possible to have more than one kind of unit cell with the same shape.

Consider the different kinds of outline for *three-dimensional* unit cells. Fourteen such outlines are possible (Table 13–2).

Table 13–2

The Unit Cells

Unit Cell	Outlines
Cubic	simple, body-centered, face-centered
Tetragonal	simple, body-centered
Orthorhombic	simple, single face-centered, body-centered, face-centered
Monoclinic	simple, single face-centered
Triclinic	simple
Trigonal	simple
Hexagonal	simple

13:3 Typical Unit Cells

Cubic cells are the simplest unit cells.

The simple cubic cell has only one member (atom, ion, or molecule). Why should this be true, when apparently there is a particle at every vertex (corner of the cube)? Eight unit cells share one vertex. Thus, the particle at one vertex occupies only one-eighth of each cell. Since each cell has eight vertices, each cell must have the equivalent of one whole particle of its own.

The simple cubic cell has one member, or eight "⅛ members."

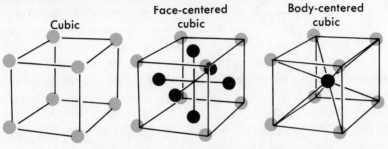

FIGURE 13-5. Three cubic unit cells.

Suggestion: Have students construct permanent models of the three cubic unit cells from clothes hangers, thread, and glue.

The face-centered cubic (FCC) cell has one-eighth particle at each vertex. In addition, it shares half of a particle with a neighboring unit cell in each of its six faces. This sharing gives a total of four particles for the FCC.

FCC cell has four members.

The body-centered cubic (BCC) cell has a slightly different setup. Here, the body-centered particle is found entirely in the unit cell. Adding this particle to the one-eighth particle at each vertex gives a unit cell with two members.

BCC cell has two members.

There are many familiar substances which have the simple structures outlined above. Iron, for example, is generally found as BCC. However, when it is heated to between approximately 900°C and 1400°C, it becomes FCC. This transition is important in heat treatment or tempering of iron.

There are fourteen different unit cells:
 1. Triclinic
 2. Monoclinic
 3. Side-centered monoclinic
 4. Orthorhombic
 5. End-centered orthorhombic
 6. Face-centered orthorhombic
 7. Body-centered orthorhombic
 8. Hexagonal
 9. Rhombohedral
10. Tetragonal
11. Body-centered tetragonal
12. Cubic
13. Face-centered cubic
14. Body-centered cubic

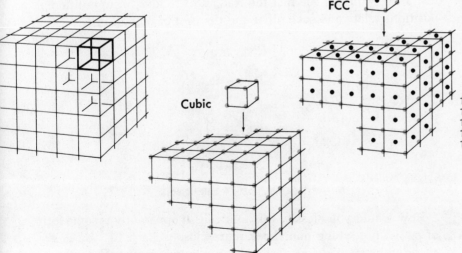

FIGURE 13-6. The space lattice is a mental concept.

Note the closeness of the packing of the particles in each of the unit cells. In the simple cubic cell, each particle has six immediate neighbors. In the face-centered cell, each has twelve; and in the body-centered, each has eight. The three-dimensional assemblage of unit cells repeated over and over in a definite network arrangement is called a *space lattice*.

Keep in mind that the particles in the cells are not so far apart as indicated in the diagrams. They are represented as dots simply for clarity in those diagrams. Actually, the particles are extremely close together (Figure 13–8).

Important!

It should also be pointed out that the space lattices and unit cells have no real physical existence. The crystal is built of atoms, ions, or molecules. The space lattice is a mental concept, or frame of reference, which helps us to understand the facts of crystal structure.

FIGURE 13-7. For clarity, crystals are diagrammed as dots and line rather than as spheres even though the spheres are more realistic.

13:4　A Complex Unit Cell

Many substances, such as sodium chloride, crystallize in a structure similar to that pictured in Figure 13–8. If you study the illustration, you can see that the Na^+ and Cl^- ions occupy different positions relative to each other and the unit of repetition.

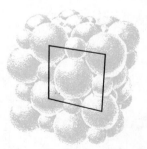

FIGURE 13-8. A salt crystal.

How would you classify this unit cell? It apparently is some form of cubic, but which one? Look more closely. Each Cl^- ion is surrounded by six Na^+ ions. Each Na^+ ion in turn is surrounded by six

---

A space lattice is a three dimensional network of unit cells.

The space lattice and unit cell are mental models. Neither actually exists within the crystal.

Suggestion: A more realistic model can be constructed using styrofoam spheres, rubber bands, and toothpicks. Punch a hole through the sphere with a thin, long, sharp object and thread a rubber band through this hole. Secure the rubber band with a toothpick which is pushed into the sphere.

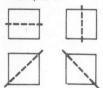

A crystal is symmetric if the parts of the crystal can be interchanged in an orderly way to produce a resulting crystal which looks just like the original crystal. To check for symmetry, observe the following planes:

in a square

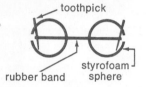

in an equilateral triangle.

Cl⁻ ions. If you consider either alone, you can see that the unit of repetition is face-centered cubic. Thus, the unit cell can be considered FCC, regardless of the fact that more than one kind of particle is present.

The particles of matter which lie within the cells are arranged in a symmetrical fashion. This symmetry is related to the symmetry of the cell itself. When the combinations of space lattices and symmetry arrangements are analyzed mathematically, it turns out that there are only 230 basically different kinds of internal arrangements in crystals.

Sodium chloride crystals are face-centered cubic.

There are 230 different kinds of internal arrangements in crystals.

13:5 Closest Packing

Let us examine in detail some of the simpler and more common types of arrangement in crystals. The elements usually have rather simple structures. If we place a group of spheres as close together as we can on a table and hold them so that they cannot roll apart, we can then place another layer upon the first one in an equally close arrangement. If we continue with more layers, a close-packed structure results. This structure is the kind found in the majority of the metals. It is difficult to visualize the lattice in such a structure, since the lattice is really only a system of imaginary lines. However, the experienced eye will detect that the lattice is either hexagonal or face-centered cubic in the close-packed arrangement (Figure 13-10). FCC is the one more frequently found in metals. Another structure, particularly found in the metals of the first group of the periodic table, is based on a body-centered cubic lattice. This structure is not quite so closely packed as the other two because, while the openings between the atoms are smaller, there are more openings.

FIGURE 13-9. This crystal model represents the cubic closest packed structure of a copper crystal. Crystals of many metals have this same structure.

The closest packed arrangement is hexagonal or FCC.

Examples of actual crystal structure in the metals:

Cubic closest packed

Ag	Cu	Pt
Al	Ni	Ca
Au	Pb	Ir
Pd	Rh	

Hexagonal closest packed

Cd	Os	Sb	Be
Mg	Zn	As	Dy
Er	Ho	Lu	Re
Ru			

Body-centered cubic

Ba	Ta	Nb	Rb
Cs	Mo	V	
K	Cr	W	

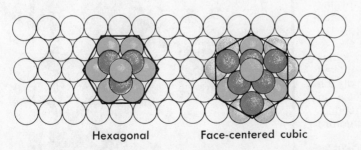

Hexagonal   Face-centered cubic

FIGURE 13-10. A closest-packed arrangement of spheres can be either hexagonal or face-centered cubic.

Properties of steel are determined by the arrangement of carbon in the iron crystal lattice.

Suggestion: Have students recall that not all compounds are composed of molecules. Have someone explain how, on the basis of knowledge of the structure of a sodium chloride crystal, the empirical and true formula of salt can be determined. By this time some students possibly will have forgotten that all compounds are not composed of molecules.

Iron, a metal, has a body-centered structure at ordinary temperatures. At higher temperatures, it has a face-centered cubic structure. This fact is of great practical importance. Iron, in its common form of steel, always contains a small amount of carbon. The carbon atoms are smaller than iron atoms, and at elevated temperatures they fit nicely into the open spaces in the face-centered structure. When the iron cools, it changes to the body-centered cubic form, and the carbon atoms can no longer fit into the small spaces which are now available. The result is either that the iron lattice is distorted by the oversize carbon atoms, or that the carbon separates out of the iron as iron carbide, Fe_3C. The final structure is determined by the percentage of iron and the rate of cooling.

Iron and Fe_3C crystals exist in many sizes and shapes because of the various conditions under which they are formed. These differences result in the great versatility of steel as an industrial material. They also account for the fact that the properties of steel can be greatly changed by heat treatment.

The simpler salts, such as those formed by the elements of Group I (the alkali metals except for Cs) and the elements of Group VII (the

William Henry Bragg

(1862–1942)

The achievements of William Henry Bragg are really achievements of his son, William Lawrence Bragg, as well. The father-son team won the Nobel Prize for their brilliant analysis of the structure of crystals.

This work included the study of the arrangement of crystal particles, made possible by their development of the X-ray spectrometer. With this, they were able to plot the positions of atoms and molecules in crystals with accuracy. The result led to much greater understanding of the forces operating between particles in crystals; and, as theories were extended, to the general knowledge of the structure of matter.

Both were knighted by the King of England for their outstanding accomplishments in science.

a

b

halogens), always have structures based on the FCC lattice. Figure 13-11(b) shows a model of the sodium chloride structure, which is typical of this class of compounds. The same model would serve for other members of the group and also for many other binary compounds, like MgO and CaO. However, to be accurate, the relative sizes of the positive and negative ions in the model should vary with each compound. Note that it is impossible to distinguish an individual molecule of NaCl.

FIGURE 13-11. The lattice structure of the sodium chloride crystal model (a) resembles the framework of a large building (b).

Simpler salts usually have a FCC lattice.

13:6 Nonmetallic Elements

There are two modifications of carbon—diamond and graphite. Their crystalline structures are illustrated in Figure 13-12. You can see that in graphite the atoms within each layer have a hexagonal

Diamond and graphite are different crystalline forms of carbon.

FIGURE 13-12. Diamond and graphite are different crystalline forms of the same element.

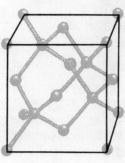

Diamond

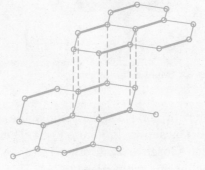

Graphite

The carbon atoms in diamond are bound together by strong covalent bonds. The molecules of molecular compounds are held to each other by much weaker van der Waals forces. To melt diamond or other compounds having a covalent lattice crystalline structure, the individual covalent bonds must be broken. This requires energy and such compounds melt at high temperatures.

General Electric Research and Development Center

Courtesy of Kodansha Ltd.

a

b

FIGURE 13-13. Carbon (a) and iodine (b) are crystalline substances.

Graphite is composed of layers of hexagonally arranged atoms.

arrangement. The atoms in a particular layer are held close together by strong covalent bonds. The layers, however, are relatively far apart and are held to each other only by weak van der Waals forces.

In diamond, each carbon atom is bonded covalently to four other carbon atoms. The four atoms are at the vertices of a tetrahedron. This repeated arrangement forms a face-centered cubic lattice.

Nonmetallic elements which have relatively low melting points, like sulfur or iodine, form crystals in which the lattice positions are occupied by molecules. The atoms within the molecules are held together by covalent bonds. The molecules are attached to other molecules by weak van der Waals forces.

Molecules may be held in crystal lattices by van der Waals forces.

Suggestion: Ask students to explain why the sulfur ring is puckered. For the answer, refer them to p. 219 (repulsion of bonding and nonbonding electron pairs).

FIGURE 13-14. The sulfur molecule is composed of a ring of eight sulfur atoms.

In sulfur crystals, the S_8 molecule contains eight atoms arranged in a ring as shown in Figure 13-14. The atoms within the molecule are much closer to each other (2.08 Å) than they are to the atoms of neighboring molecules (3.7 Å). This lattice is orthorhombic.

13:7   Macromolecules

In order to melt most compounds that occur in the form of discrete molecules, we need overcome only the van der Waals forces. Observations in the laboratory show that discrete molecular compounds have very low melting points. They range from −272°C to about 100°C. There are some very large molecules which melt at even higher temperatures, but here we are concerned with the rule, not the exception. Still, we have not accounted for covalently bound substances with melting points in the range 1000°C to 3000°C. An example is silicon carbide which melts at about 2700°C. In silicon carbide, each carbon atom is surrounded by four silicon atoms to which it is covalently bonded. Each of these silicon atoms, in turn, is surrounded by four carbon atoms to which it is covalently bonded. Thus, each atom in the crystal is bonded to its four nearest neighbors. We may think of the entire crystal as one giant molecule. In fact, this type of structure is often called a macromolecule. There are many substances composed of macromolecules. All of these substances have very high melting points. In order to melt the substance, you must break covalent bonds. These bonds are, on the average, about ten times stronger than van der Waals forces.

Macromolecules are giant crystalline molecules that have high melting points.

F. Bernard Daniel

John Morgan

FIGURE 13-15. Silicon carbide (a) is a black macromolecular substance. Because of its hardness, it is often used in the manufacture of grinding wheels (b).

VARIATIONS IN CRYSTALS

13:8   Crystal Defects

You should not assume that the repetition of the unit cell arrangement is perfect in all crystals. Actually, a perfect crystal is a rarity. Most crystals contain defects of one or more types. We will cover only two basic types.

Defects in crystals are common.

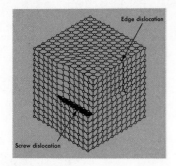

FIGURE 13-16. Most crystals have defects.

This fact is important in the production of transistors. For instance, arsenic- and indium-doped germanium crystals can be made which have the correct structure for developing semiconducting (transistor) properties.

Edge and screw dislocations are due to uneven crystal growth.

Transistors are made from deliberate crystal imperfection.

Transistors depend upon an excess or shortage of electrons.

The first type of defect involves the unit cell structure. Look at a plane of a simple crystal such as sodium chloride. The positive and negative ions alternate in such a crystal lattice. However, it is entirely possible that one of the ions may be removed from its proper position and occupy a space where no ion usually occurs. This change causes an imperfect crystal. Another possibility is that an ion is missing completely from its position in the lattice. In the event that a defect of this type occurs, for every positive ion missing there must be a negative ion missing, in order to preserve the electrical neutrality of the crystal. It is sometimes possible for extraneous ions, atoms, electrons, or even molecules to occupy these spaces vacated by the normal ions of the crystal.

The second basic type of defect concerns the manner in which the unit cells are joined. These defects are called *dislocations*. In some crystals, an extra layer of atoms extends part of the way into a crystal. The resulting crystal is said to have an *edge dislocation*, which is shown in Figure 13-16. It is also possible for the particles to be slightly out of position, due to unequal growth while the crystal was forming. Such a defect is termed a *screw dislocation*.

13:9   Transistors

Sometimes, defects are valuable. For example, in the manufacture of transistors, perfect crystals are "doped." That is, impurities are deliberately added. Silicon and germanium (Group IVA) are the most common elements used in transistors. A pure crystal of either of these elements will conduct very little electricity. However, if a small amount of another element is added, current will readily flow through the resulting "doped" crystal.

A closer look at the bonding of these elements reveals why this occurs. Silicon and germanium, each with four electrons in the outer level, crystallize in a structure similar to that of the diamond. Thus, all four electrons are involved in bonding.

Arsenic atoms have five electrons available for bonding and gallium has three. If arsenic atoms are introduced into a crystal of germanium, extra electrons are present. When a voltage is applied, the extra electrons in the lattice will move (Figure 13-17). If on the other hand, gallium atoms are introduced, the crystal will be short of electrons. The resulting electron deficient lattice, however, will also conduct electricity. It does so by moving electrons into the "holes" created by the gallium atom. This phenomenon is illustrated in Figure 13-17. Note that in both types of doping, the crystal is still electrically neutral.

Since their development in the late 1940's, transistors have been used increasingly in place of vacuum tubes in electronic circuits. Because of their small size, long life, and resistance to shock, they have revolutionized the communications industry. Computers, transistor radios, heart pacemakers, space probes, and microwave ovens are only a few of the many devices that transistors have either made possible or improved.

FIGURE 13-17. Doped crystals of germanium are good electrical conductors because of either an extra electron or a "hole."

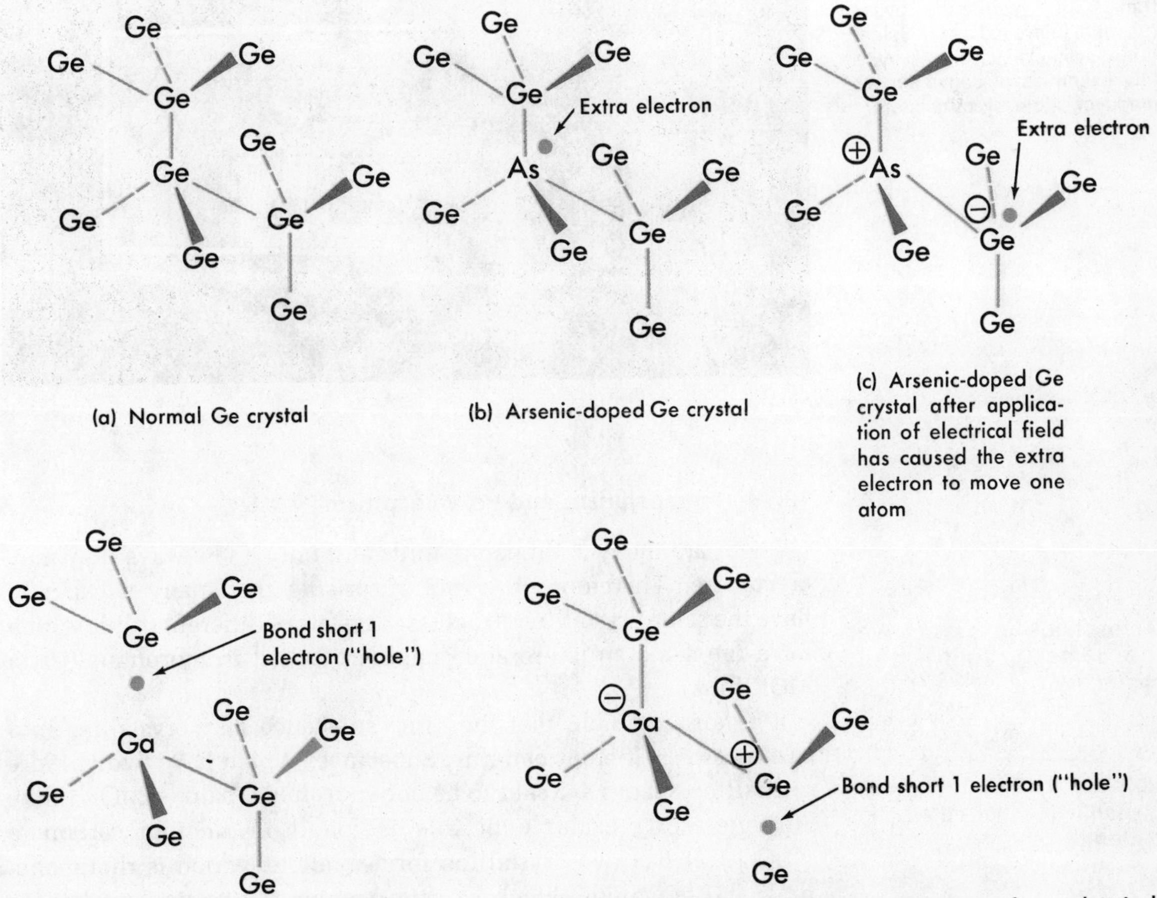

(a) Normal Ge crystal

(b) Arsenic-doped Ge crystal

(c) Arsenic-doped Ge crystal after application of electrical field has caused the extra electron to move one atom

(d) Gallium-doped Ge crystal

(e) Gallium-doped Ge crystal after application of an electrical field has caused the "hole" to move two bonds

John Morgan

Steve Damison

a

b

FIGURE 13-18. Tiny hearing aids contained in eyeglass frames (a), microwave ovens (b), and improved communications systems (c) are only a few examples of conveniences made possible by transistors.

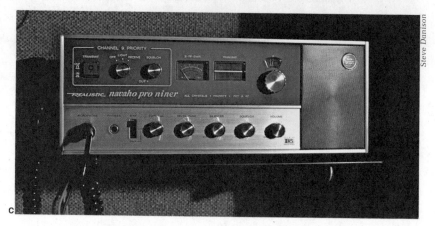

Steve Damison

c

13:10 Isomorphism and Polymorphism

There are many solid compounds and only a few ways they may crystallize. Therefore, it is not surprising that many substances have the same crystalline structure. Crystals of different solids which have the same structure and shape are called *isomorphous* (i suh MOR fuhs).

It is also possible that the same substance may crystallize into two or more different patterns. Substances which have two or more crystalline shapes are said to be *polymorphous* (pahl ee MOR fuhs). An interesting example of this is found in calcium carbonate ($CaCO_3$). It has two crystalline forms: calcite, which is rhombohedral; and aragonite, which is orthorhombic. Surprisingly calcite is isomorphous with crystalline $NaNO_3$, while aragonite is isomorphous with crystalline KNO_3.

a

b

FIGURE 13-19. Sulfur is a polymorphous substance. Two crystalline forms of sulfur are monoclinic sulfur (a) and rhombic sulfur (b).

13:11 Hydrated Crystals

If solids crystallize from water solutions, molecules of water may be incorporated into the crystal structure. For some ionic substances, the attraction between the charged ions and the polar water molecules is so high that the water molecules become chemically bonded to the ions. Ions which are chemically bonded to water atoms are called *hydrated ions*. Crystals containing hydrated ions are called *hydrated crystals*. It is also possible for ions to be surrounded by, or coordinated with, solvent molecules other than water.

Many common chemical compounds are normally hydrated. It is possible, however, to rid many hydrated crystals of water molecules.

Hydrated ions are chemically bonded to water molecules.

FIGURE 13-20. When blue hydrated copper sulfate (a) is heated, white anhydrous copper sulfate (b) is obtained. The anhydrous form turns blue when water is added. This color change can be used as a test for water.

a

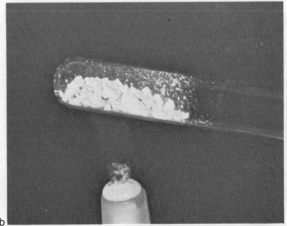

b

Water can be removed from hydrated crystals by heating.

Common drying agents: calcium chloride, conc. H_2SO_4, sodium hydroxide, magnesium chloride.

Hydrates are named with numerical prefixes.

This can be done by raising the temperature or lowering the pressure, or by a combination of increased temperature and decreased pressure. The resulting compound, without the water molecules, is said to be *anhydrous*. Anhydrous means without water. Some anhydrous compounds gain water molecules so easily that they can be used to remove water from other substances. They are called drying agents. Drying agents are referred to by chemists as *dehydrating agents* or *desiccants* (DES ih kants).

Formulas for hydrated compounds place the water of hydration following a raised dot after the regular formula. For example, $CuSO_4 \cdot 5H_2O$ is the formula for a hydrate of copper sulfate that contains 5 moles of water for each mole of copper sulfate. The name of the compound is copper(II) sulfate pentahydrate. Such compounds are named just as regular compounds except that the water is included. The regular name is followed by the word *hydrate* to which a prefix has been added to indicate the relative molar proportions of water and compound. The prefixes are listed in Table 13–3.

Table 13–3

Prefixes Used in Naming Hydrates

Prefix	Moles of Water	Name	Formula
mono-	1	monohydrate	$XY \cdot 1H_2O$
di-	2	dihydrate	$XY \cdot 2H_2O$
tri-	3	trihydrate	$XY \cdot 3H_2O$
tetra-	4	tetrahydrate	$XY \cdot 4H_2O$
penta-	5	pentahydrate	$XY \cdot 5H_2O$
hexa-	6	hexahydrate	$XY \cdot 6H_2O$
hepta-	7	heptahydrate	$XY \cdot 7H_2O$
octa-	8	octahydrate	$XY \cdot 8H_2O$
nona-	9	nonahydrate	$XY \cdot 9H_2O$
deca-	10	decahydrate	$XY \cdot 10H_2O$

Hygroscopic substances pick up water from the air.

Efflorescent substances release water to the air.

The ions of some anhydrous substances have such a strong attraction for water molecules that the dehydrated crystal will recapture and hold water molecules from the air. Such a substance is called a *hygroscopic* (hi gruh SKAHP ihk) substance. Some substances are so hygroscopic that they take up enough water of hydration from the air to dissolve and form a liquid solution. These substances are said to be *deliquescent* (del ih KWES uhnt). The opposite process can also occur. Water of hydration may be spontaneously released to the air. A substance which releases water molecules to the air from a crystal is said to be *efflorescent* (ef luh RES uhnt).

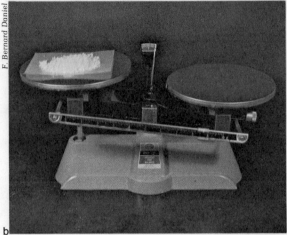

a   b

FIGURE 13-21. Calcium chloride (a) is deliquescent. The decahydrate of sodium carbonate ($Na_2CO_3 \cdot 10\ H_2O$) (b) is efflorescent.

SUMMARY

1. Corresponding angles between faces on different crystals of the same substance are always the same, regardless of the size or source of the crystals. This is Steno's law.
2. All crystals of a particular substance are composed of similar very small units which are repeated over and over.
3. A crystal is a rigid body in which particles are arranged in a repeating pattern. The smallest unit of the pattern which is repeated is called the unit cell.
4. There are seven crystal systems: cubic, tetragonal, hexagonal, rhombohedral, orthorhombic, monoclinic, and triclinic.
5. The repetition of the unit cell in a crystal forms an imaginary lattice called a space lattice.
6. Three unit cells have been discussed: the simple cubic cell, the face-centered cubic cell, and the body-centered cubic cell.
7. Many substances form crystals with a close-packed structure composed of layers of spheres packed closely together.
8. Molecular substances form crystals in which the molecules are held together by weak van der Waals forces. These substances have low melting points and low boiling points.

9. Some substances form macromolecular crystals which are characterized by very high melting points.

10. Crystal defects are lapses in the regular repetition of the unit cell arrangement. Defects can be a result either of missing particles which leave a hole or of extraneous particles. Other defects are edge dislocations and screw dislocations.

11. The transistor is an example of a practical application of a crystal defect.

12. Crystals which have the same structure and shape but different components are said to be isomorphous.

13. Substances which have two or more crystalline shapes are said to be polymorphous.

14. Ions which are chemically bonded to water molecules are called hydrated ions. Crystals containing hydrated ions are called hydrated crystals.

15. Chemical compounds which are normally hydrates are said to be anhydrous when the water molecules are removed. Anhydrous compounds which gain water molecules easily are called dehydrating agents because they dehydrate (remove water from) other substances.

16. A hygroscopic substance is one in which the ions have such a strong attraction for water molecules that the substance will capture and hold water molecules from the air.

17. A deliquescent substance is so hygroscopic that it takes enough water of hydration from the air to dissolve and form a liquid solution.

18. A substance which spontaneously releases water of hydration to the air from a crystal is called an efflorescent substance.

PROBLEMS

1. Find the maximum distance between particles in a face-centered cubic unit cell if the ionic radius is 2.19 Å. 10.6 Å

2. Find the maximum distance between particle centers in a body-centered cubic unit cell if the ionic radius of all particles in the lattice is 2.19 Å. 8.76Å

There is a 1:1 correspondence between Na^+ and Cl^- ions.

3. From the photo of the NaCl lattice, show why NaCl is the simplest formula.

4. From a table of ionic radii, determine the distance between the Na^+ ion and the Cl^- ion in the NaCl crystal. 2.82 Å

5. In Section 13:10, calcium carbonate is shown to have two crystalline forms, each isomorphous with different compounds. — See Teacher's Guide.
   What explanation could you offer for this situation?

6. Find the percentage of water in a crystal of $CuSO_4 \cdot 5H_2O$. 36.0% H_2O

7. For $NiSO_4 \cdot 7H_2O$, determine the following information:
   a. the name of the compound
   b. the percentage of water
   c. the percentage of oxygen

   a. nickel sulfate
      heptahydrate
   b. 44.8% H_2O
   c. 62.6% O

8. Answer Parts a, b, and c in Question 7 for $Ba(OH)_2 \cdot 8H_2O$.

   a. barium hydroxide
      octahydrate
   b. 45.7% H_2O
   c. 50.8% O

9. Answer Parts a, b, and c in Question 7 for $Na_2CO_3 \cdot 10H_2O$.

   a. sodium carbonate
      decahydrate
   b. 62.9% H_2O
   c. 72.7% O

ONE MORE STEP

1. Look up the lives of W. E. Bragg and W. L. Bragg. Write a report
   on the processes they used to determine crystal structure.

2. Write a report on how transistors work.

3. Make models (either clay or ball and stick) of each crystal system.
   Collect crystals which illustrate each system.

   See Teacher's Guide at the
   front of this book.

4. Try to figure out why the S_8 molecule is a puckered ring instead
   of planar.

   Suggested Readings for this chapter may be found in
   the Teacher's Guide at the front of this book.

In this scene, water is present in the form of a solid, liquid, and a gas. As the temperature of solid water (ice) is raised to its melting point, particles leave the crystal structure, forming a liquid. Molecules of liquid water evaporate into the air. These molecules collect on tiny dust particles in the atmosphere forming droplets of water which will eventually fall back to earth. How are liquids changed to solids? How do they evaporate? What is vapor pressure?

Liquids ————————————————————— 14

Chapter 14 introduces the study of liquids by developing the idea of vapor pressure in relationship to phase diagrams.

If the temperature of a solid is raised, according to the kinetic theory, the velocity of the particles should increase. As the temperature increases, the particles collide with each other with a greater force. Thus, they are forced farther apart. Almost all solids and liquids expand when they are heated because of this increase in velocity. If the temperature of a solid is raised sufficiently, the particles will move far enough apart to slip over one another. When such a change takes place, we say the solid has melted. The temperature at which a solid melts is called the *melting point* of that solid.

The reverse is true of liquids. There will be some temperature (and pressure) at which the particles travel so slowly that they can no longer slip past one another. That temperature is called the *freezing point* of the liquid. All pure liquids have a definite freezing point and all pure solids have a definite melting point. For a particular substance, the freezing point of the liquid form is the same temperature as the melting point of the solid form.

GOAL: You will gain an understanding of the properties of liquids and their relationship to molecular structure and the kinetic theory.

For a substance, freezing point of the liquid state = melting point of solid state.

VAPOR PRESSURE

14:1 Unusual Kinetic Energies

The average kinetic energy of atoms or molecules in a gas is a constant for all substances at a given temperature. This average kinetic energy can be calculated for any particular temperature. If we were to measure the kinetic energy of the individual atoms or molecules in a gas, we would find that few had the predicted kinetic energy. Some molecules would have more and some would

Average K.E. of particles is constant for a given temperature.

Boltzmann distribution law.

Few gas molecules have the average K.E.

have less kinetic energy than the average. Most would have a kinetic energy close to the calculated amount. However, we would sometimes find a molecule with a kinetic energy considerably above or below the average. It is these few molecules that we will now discuss.

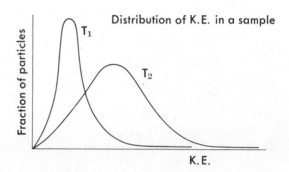

FIGURE 14-1. Few molecules have exactly the average kinetic energy of a sample.

FIGURE 14-2. Substances in the form of gases can be introduced into a system directly from an outside source (a) and can be directed through the system by a series of valves (b).

14:2   Vapor Equilibrium

All that has been said about the collisions of particles in a gas is also true of particles in a solid or a liquid. A molecule in a liquid, because of several rapid collisions with other molecules, might gain

kinetic energy considerably above the average. If that molecule is on the surface of the liquid and its kinetic energy exceeds the attractive force of nearby molecules, it may escape from the surface. The same process may also occur at the surface of a solid. The molecules which escape from the surface of a solid or a liquid form a vapor or a gas. This vapor is made up of molecules or atoms of the substance in the gaseous state.

Particles escaping from solids or liquids form a vapor.

The molecule of a solid or liquid which has escaped the surface behaves as a gaseous molecule. It is possible for this molecule to collide with the surface of the liquid it left. If its kinetic energy is sufficiently low at the time of such a collision, the molecule may be captured by the liquid and again become a part of the liquid. However, in an open container the chance of the molecule returning to the surface it left is small.

If the solid or liquid is in a closed container, then the chances of the molecule returning are greatly increased. In fact, a point will be reached where just as many molecules return to the surface as leave the surface. There will be a constant number of molecules in the solid or liquid phase, and a constant number of molecules in the vapor phase. Such a situation is known as an *equilibrium condition*. It is a special kind of equilibrium, a *dynamic equilibrium*. It is called dynamic because molecules are continuously escaping from and returning to the surface. Only the overall result remains constant. When a solid or a liquid is in equilibrium with its vapor, the gaseous phase of the system is said to be *saturated* with the vapor of that solid or liquid.

In a closed container, the vapor phase is in equilibrium with its solid or liquid phase.

At equilibrium, the vapor phase is saturated.

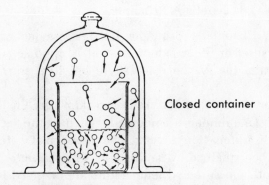

Closed container

FIGURE 14-3. A system is in equilibrium when the number of molecules escaping the surface is equal to the number of molecules reentering the liquid.

Equilibrium is an important concept in chemistry. We introduce the equilibrium concept here. Closely related to this concept is Le Chatelier's principle. For further development, see Chapter 19.

The change of molecules from liquid to vapor is represented in equation form:

$$X_{(l)} \rightarrow X_{(g)}$$

where X represents any vaporizable substance, such as water.

The opposite process can be represented by:

$$X_{(l)} \leftarrow X_{(g)}$$

The two equations can be combined:

$$X_{(l)} \rightleftarrows X_{(g)}$$

A change such as this is called a *reversible change*. The reversible change has reached equilibrium when the change is occurring at the same rate in both directions.

The vapor phase exerts a pressure. This pressure is dependent on the temperature. The higher the temperature, the higher the *vapor pressure*. A liquid and its vapor will reach equilibrium at a given pressure for any particular temperature. This shifting of the equilibrium was observed by the Frenchman Le Chatelier and was described by him in 1884.

14:3   Le Chatelier's Principle

Le Chatelier's principle is: If stress (change in temperature, pressure, or other external force) is applied to a system at equilibrium, the system readjusts (if possible) so that the stress is reduced.

For example, an ice skater can skim over the ice with little effort. The skate runners are not really touching the ice but are traveling on a thin film of liquid water. The presence of water in the liquid state can be explained by Le Chatelier's principle.

Both pressure and temperature are involved in this example. We will discuss pressure first. The entire weight of the skater is directed onto the ice through the runners on the skates. The surface area of the runners which is in contact with the ice is probably less than 15 cm².

Steve Danison

FIGURE 14-4. This skater glides across the ice on a thin film of water which forms under the blades of her skates.

stress
ice → water
  pressure
solid → liquid

  stress
ice → water
  temp.

Have students think in the pattern:

What is the stress? How can the stress be relieved? How does the equilibrium shift so as to accomplish the relief of stress?

Thus, the runners exert a great pressure on the ice at the points of contact. Ice (solid) occupies a greater volume than water (liquid). Therefore, the change of ice to water will tend to reduce the pressure (stress) caused by the runners. Increased pressure causes a reduction in volume.

Temperature also plays an important role in skating. Friction between the ice and the runners of the skates warms the runners. According to Le Chatelier's principle, this stress (increased temperature) will be relieved by the change of less energetic ice molecules into more energetic water molecules. The blades will be cooled by this change. Increased temperature causes an increase in molecular motion. Both the increased pressure and the increased temperature enable the skater to glide with very little friction over the ice.

Le Chatelier's principle applies to any equilibrium system. It is introduced here in relation to a solid-liquid equilibrium system.

14:4 Measuring Vapor Pressure

Many techniques are available to measure vapor pressure. Figures 14-5a and 14-5b show two such methods of finding the vapor pressures of substances. The method of Figure 14-5b is especially useful

FIGURE 14-5. Vapor pressure can be measured with the simple apparatus in (a) or the more elaborate apparatus in (b).

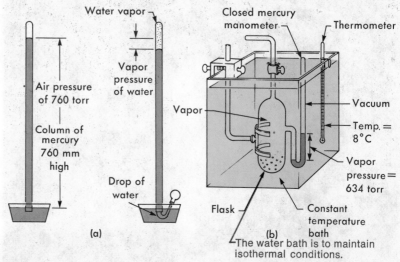

for finding the vapor pressure of solids at elevated temperatures. Table 14–1 gives the vapor pressures of some substances near room temperature.

Table 14–1

Vapor Pressures of Some Liquids at 25°C

Substance	Vapor Pressure (torr)
Mercury (Hg)	0.00185
Bromine (Br$_2$)	206
Carbon disulfide (CS$_2$)	357
Sulfur dioxide (SO$_2$)	3000
Acetone (CH$_3$COCH$_3$)	221
Carbon tetrachloride (CCl$_4$)	109
Turpentine (C$_{10}$H$_{16}$)	5.09

Vapor pressure of a substance is constant for a given temperature.

PHASE CHANGES

14:5 Melting Point

Consider the phenomenon of melting. In a mixture of solid and liquid phases, there will be a dynamic equilibrium between the molecules of the solid and liquid. However, the average number of molecules in the two phases will remain the same. Remember, though, that each of these phases is also in equilibrium with its vapor. Since there is only one vapor, the solid and liquid have the

Section 14-5 is the first of several sections which lead toward the development of the phase diagram. See pages 298-304.

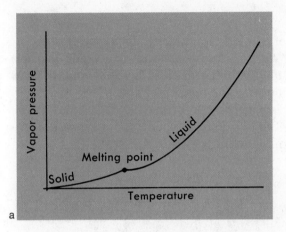

F. Bernard Daniel

a

b

FIGURE 14-6. The vapor pressures of the solid and liquid phases of a substance are equal at the melting or freezing point (a). Pictured is an apparatus used for melting point determinations (b).

same vapor pressure (Figure 14–6a). At the melting point of any substance, the vapor pressure of the solid and the vapor pressure of the liquid must be equal. In fact, the *melting point* is often defined as the temperature at which the vapor pressure of the solid and the vapor pressure of the liquid are equal.

Temperature at which the vapor pressure of the solid and vapor pressure of the liquid are equal is the melting point.

14:6 Sublimation

Examples of sublimation:
Snow disappears from ground on a cold day without melting.
Frozen clothes gradually become soft and flexible as ice sublimes.
Dry ice sublimes to CO_2.

Some solids have a vapor pressure great enough at room temperature to vaporize after a passage of time if not kept in a closed container. Such a substance will change directly from the solid to the gaseous state, without passing through the liquid state. This process is known as *sublimation* (suhb lih MAY shun). Dry ice (solid CO_2) and moth crystals are two examples of such substances.

Sublimation: phase change directly from solid to gas.

FIGURE 14-7. Dry ice (a) and mothballs (b) are examples of substances which sublime.

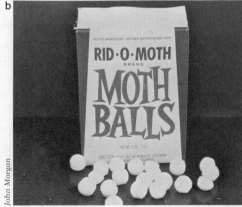

a

b

F. Bernard Daniel

John Morgan

14:7 Boiling Point

As the temperature of a liquid is increased, the vapor pressure of that liquid increases. When the vapor pressure of a liquid reaches atmospheric pressure, the liquid begins to boil. The *normal boiling point* of a liquid is defined as the temperature at which the vapor pressure of the liquid is equal to that of the standard atmospheric pressure, or 760 torr. Boiling point is a function of pressure. At lower pressures, the boiling point is lower.

Boiling point is the temperature at which the vapor pressure of a liquid is equal to atmospheric pressure.

FIGURE 14-8. The boiling point of a liquid can be determined in the laboratory with this apparatus.

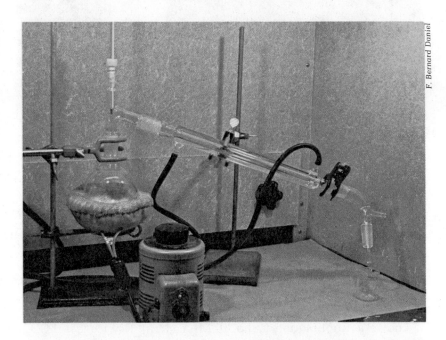

Note that at the boiling point, bubbles of vapor can form *below* the surface of the liquid.

We have seen that adding heat to a liquid at its boiling point will cause it to change to a gas rapidly by boiling. In a like manner, if we remove heat from a gas at the boiling point of that substance, the gas will change to a liquid.

The boiling point of a liquid is also the condensation point of the vapor phase of the liquid. A liquid and its vapor can be at equilibrium only in a closed container. The molecules leaving the surface of a liquid have little chance of returning if the liquid container is open to the air. When a liquid is exposed to the air and gradually disappears due to the constant escape of molecules from its surface, the liquid is said to *evaporate*.

Evaporation is the escape of molecules from the surface of a liquid.

Volatile substances evaporate rapidly.

Different liquids boil at different temperatures. A liquid which boils at a low temperature and evaporates rapidly at room tempera-

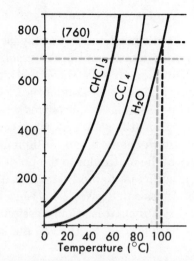

This is the second stage in the development of a phase diagram.

FIGURE 14-9. The boiling temperature decreases as the atmospheric pressure decreases.

ture is said to be *volatile* (VAHL uht uhl). Examples of volatile liquids are carbon tetrachloride and ether. Liquids which boil at high temperatures and evaporate slowly at room temperature are said to be *nonvolatile*. Some of these are molasses, glue, and mercury.

Nonvolatile substances evaporate slowly and boil at high temperatures.

FIGURE 14-10. Rubbing alcohol, gasoline, and acetone are volatile substances (a). Examples of nonvolatile materials (b) are pancake syrup, honey, and cooking oil.

14:8 Liquefaction of Gases

We have considered the condensation of gases to liquids only for substances which are normally solids or liquids at room temperature. What about substances that are normally gases at room temperature? Can they be condensed? Yes, under the correct conditions. The condensation of substances which are normally gases is called *liquefaction* (lik wuh FAK shun). A gas must be below a certain temperature before it can be liquefied. Cooling reduces the kinetic energy of the molecules to the point where the van der Waals attraction is sufficient to bind the molecules together. It is also necessary to compress some gases. The van der Waals forces are effective for only short distances. Compression forces the molecules of these gases close enough for the van der Waals forces to take effect.

Liquefaction is the condensation of gases.

Gases may be liquefied by cooling and/or pressure.

Table 14–2

Critical Temperature and Pressure

Substance	Critical temperature (°K)	Critical pressure (atm)
Water (H_2O)	647.4	218.3
Sulfur dioxide (SO_2)	430.7	77.8
Carbon dioxide (CO_2)	304.2	72.9
Oxygen (O_2)	154.8	50.1
Nitrogen (N_2)	126.3	33.5
Hydrogen (H_2)	33.2	12.8

FIGURE 14-11. In this industrial plant, air is liquified and separated into its components by trapping each gas as it boils at a characteristic temperature.

Air Products and Chemicals, Inc.

—For every gas, there is a temperature above which no amount of pressure will result in liquefying the gas. This point is called the *critical temperature* (T_c) of the gas. The *critical pressure* (P_c) is the pressure that will cause the gas to liquefy at the critical temperature. This critical point for several gases is given in Table 14–2.

Many gases have critical temperatures above normal room temperature. Sulfur dioxide, for example, has a critical temperature of 430.7°K. It can be liquefied by pressure alone if the temperature is not allowed to exceed 430.7°K. The critical point of a gas is an indication of the strength of the attractive forces between its atoms or molecules. The low critical temperature of hydrogen indicates weak forces between its atoms.

T_c = Temperature above which no pressure will liquefy a gas.

P_c = Pressure needed to liquefy a gas at T_c.

Critical point indicates the relative strength of attractive forces between particles.

Suggestion: Have students attempt to explain why the attractive forces differ (as indicated by the varying T_c and P_c) on the basis of the structure of these molecules. Note that this is fairly complicated; the higher T_c for SO_2 is due to both van der Waals attraction and polarity.

14:9　Phase Diagrams

Much of the information we have discussed can be shown in a graphic form called a *phase diagram*. Figure 14-12 shows the graph for water. The line labeled Solid-Vapor represents the vapor pressure

Phase diagrams graphically represent changes of state at varying temperatures and pressures.

Note: The slope of the solid-liquid line is exaggerated slightly to emphasize that the triple point is slightly above 0°C.

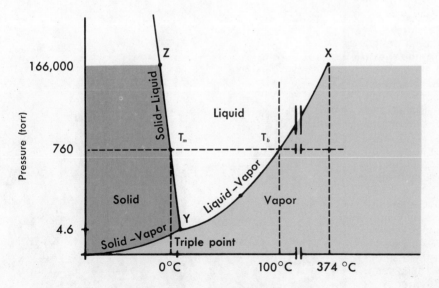

FIGURE 14-12. A phase diagram for water.

of ice at temperatures from −100°C to point Y. The line labeled Liquid-Vapor represents the vapor pressure of the liquid at temperatures from point Y to 374°C. Point Y is called the *triple point*. All three phases are in equilibrium at this temperature and pressure

At a given pressure the triple point is the temperature at which all three phases of a substance are in equilibrium.

(0.01°C and 4.58 torr). Above the critical point, X, there is no vapor pressure curve, since the liquid and gaseous states are the same at pressures and temperatures above this point.

T_b is the boiling point and T_m is the melting point. Note that the melting point occurs where the Solid-Liquid equilibrium line is cut by the pressure line corresponding to standard atmospheric pressure. However, it is important to realize that the vapor pressure of the liquid and solid (see point T_m in Figure 14–12) is not equal to atmospheric pressure at this point. The line YZ simply indicates the pressure-temperature conditions under which the solid and liquid can be in equilibrium. Only the solid-vapor and liquid-vapor lines represent vapor pressure information. The boiling point is that temperature at which the liquid-vapor equilibrium curve is cut by the pressure line of one atmosphere (see dotted lines crossing at T_b in Figure 14–12).

Norbert Rillieux
(1806–1894)

Norbert Rillieux was born in the United States and educated in Paris. At the age of 24, he was teaching applied engineering at École Centrale. It was his interest in chemistry and steam engineering which returned him to the United States and led him to a process that revolutionized the sugar industry.

The crystallization of sugar from cane syrup had been done by hand-ladling it from vat to vat until the liquid evaporated. Rillieux in 1846 made use of the reduced boiling point of a liquid under a vacuum and developed a multiple vacuum evaporator. This produced a cheaper, better, and more automated process of crystallizing sugar. The same concept is used in the manufacture of condensed milk, soap, and glue. It is also useful in the recovery of wastes from distilleries and paper factories.

Stung by what he perceived as unequal treatment, Rillieux returned to Paris. Late in life he adapted his process to sugar beets as well as cane, but he never returned to his native country.

PROPERTIES OF LIQUIDS

14:10   Hydrogen Bonding

In a number of substances, the predicted melting and boiling points differ from the observed ones. Remember that these changes of state can be predicted from a knowledge of atomic and molecular structure. It is the structure which affects interatomic and intermolecular forces. Many of the substances which do not behave as predicted have two things in common. They contain hydrogen in their molecules, and the hydrogen is bonded to a strongly electronegative element. Under these conditions, the electronegative atom has almost complete possession of the pair of electrons shared with the hydrogen atom. The molecule is therefore highly polar. This leaves the hydrogen atom with a strong partial positive charge. In fact, at the point of attachment of the hydrogen atom, there is a nearly bare hydrogen nucleus, or proton.

Consider the size of a proton compared to the size of the next largest ion with a 1+ charge, Li^+. The H^+ ion has a full positive charge in about one trillionth of the space. It simply will not exist near other particles without interacting with them. We will discuss this phenomenon again when we study the hydronium ion in Chapter 20.

In a molecule containing hydrogen bonded to a highly electronegative element, the proton is not completely bare. However, the partial charge on the hydrogen end of the molecule is much stronger than that at the positive end of an average dipole. Hydrogen is the only element to exhibit this property because all other positive ions have inner levels of electrons shielding their nuclei. In a substance

Hydrogen "bonds" have energies in the range of 2 to 9 kcal/mole.

Hydrogen bonded to a strongly electronegative element causes some substances to differ from predicted melting and boiling points.

A free proton does not ordinarily exist.

FIGURE 14-13. Compounds with polar molecules do not have the predicted boiling points.

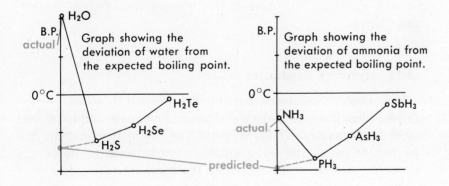

composed of polar molecules containing hydrogen, the hydrogen atom (positive portion) is attracted to the negative portion of other molecules. Since the hydrogen atom has been reduced to a proton with almost no electrons, the attractive force is strong. However, it is not nearly so strong as an actual chemical bond. The attractive

The hydrogen bond holds two molecules together electrostatically.

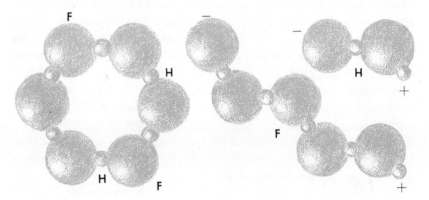

FIGURE 14-14. Hydrogen bonding is important in hydrogen fluoride polymers.

force in such substances is called the *hydrogen bond*. The result of the hydrogen bond is that the hydrogen atom tends to hold the two molecules, the one of which it is a part and the one to which it is attracted, firmly to each other.

Because of its special properties, the hydrogen bond has a greater effect than some other dipole with the same electronegativity difference. Hydrogen bonding is really just a subdivision of the large class of interactions called weak forces or dipole attractions. However, it is given a name and is considered apart from other dipole attractions because it has a greater effect on the properties of substances.

Nitrogen, oxygen, and fluorine have sufficient electronegativity to cause hydrogen bonding.

In general, the only elements electronegative enough to cause bonded hydrogen to behave in this manner are nitrogen, oxygen, and fluorine.

14:11 Hydrogen Bonding in Water

Hydrogen bonding accounts for the structure of ice.

The effects of hydrogen bonding can be seen in water. For example, when frozen, a molecule of water is hydrogen bonded to four other water molecules (Figure 14–16). The two hydrogen atoms that are part of the central water molecule are attracted to the oxygen atoms of two other water molecules. Hydrogen atoms from two other

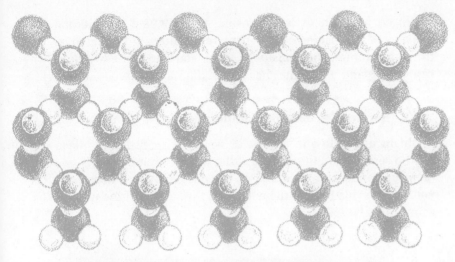

FIGURE 14-15. Hydrogen bonding causes water to expand as the temperature decreases below 3.98°C. An ice crystal is shown.

water molecules are attracted to the oxygen atom of the central water molecule. This type of crystalline structure is open and occupies a large amount of space.

As the molecules increase in kinetic energy, ice melts and many, but not all, of the hydrogen bonds are broken. As these bonds are broken, the lattice collapses. The water molecules actually move closer together and the same number of molecules occupy less space. Thus, water is more dense than ice. As water is heated above 0°C, more of the hydrogen bonds are broken, and the molecules continue to move closer together. Finally, at 3.98°C, many of the

Question: What would happen if ice were more dense than water?
Ans. Ice would be heavier than water and would sink to the bottom of oceans and lakes. They would freeze from the bottom up.

The energy due to hydrogen bonding in water is about 12 kcal per mole of water (or 6 kcal per mole of bonds since each water molecule forms 2 bonds).

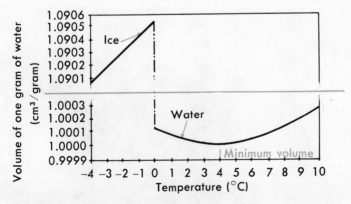

FIGURE 14-16. Note the sudden change in volume at 0°C. Water occupies a minimum volume at 3.98°C.

hydrogen bonds have been broken. Above 3.98°C, the normal expansion of a substance with increased temperature takes over. At this temperature, the density of water starts to decrease. Now, we can understand why water has its maximum density at 3.98°C.

Water is most dense at 3.98°C.

14:12   Surface Tension and Capillary Rise

Obtain a needle and a glass of water. With tweezers, place the needle carefully on the surface of the water. Be sure there is no soap on your hands, the tweezers, or the needle. With a little practice, you will be able to float the needle on the surface of the water. Why should this be so?

Surface tension of liquids is due to unbalanced forces on surface particles.

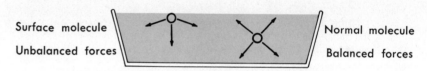

Surface molecule   Normal molecule
Unbalanced forces   Balanced forces

FIGURE 14-17. Notice that unbalanced forces are exerted on molecules at the surface of a liquid.

Surface tension causes the inverted meniscus of Hg and the almost spherical shape of liquid drops in a vacuum.

FIGURE 14-18. A needle floats on water (a) and a splashing liquid drop has a spherical shape (b) because of surface tension.

The particles at the surface have special properties because they are subjected to unbalanced forces (Figure 14–17). These unbalanced forces help explain the surface tension, or apparent *elasticity* (ih las TIS uht ee), of the surface.

a

W. Keith Turpie

b

Courtesy of Dow Corning Corporation

a

b

The net force not only accounts for the surface tension, but also helps explain why liquids form spheres when dropped. The net force acting on a surface particle is directed perpendicularly into the liquid. Thus, the body of the liquid is pulling the surface molecules inward. Since a sphere has the least surface area for any given bulk, liquids tend to assume a spherical shape when dropped.

The unbalanced force also accounts for capillary rise. If there is an attractive force between the liquid and the solid wall of the capillary tube, the liquid will rise in the tube. The attractive force relieves the unbalanced force on the surface molecules. Capillary rise is one method used for measuring surface tension. For example, water has a high surface tension at room temperature. It will rise

FIGURE 14-19. Because of unbalanced forces acting on the liquid surface, water (a) appears to climb the wall of a capillary tube, while mercury (b) is depressed in a capillary tube.

Surface tension causes drops of liquid to be spherical.

Capillary rise is a measure of surface tension.

FIGURE 14-20. Compare the meniscus of water (a) with the meniscus of mercury (b).

a

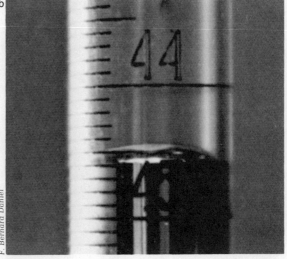

b

quite readily in a capillary tube. Mercury, on the other hand, is depressed in a capillary tube. It does not "wet" the glass of the tube. That is, there is not enough attractive force between the mercury and the glass to overcome the surface tension of mercury. Compare the meniscus of water and the meniscus of mercury in Figure 14–20 and see if you can think of an explanation for the difference in behavior.

14:13 Amorphous Materials

A number of solid-appearing substances do not have a crystalline form. Such substances are said to be *amorphous* (uh MOR fuhs), which means without shape. Glass is an excellent example of an amorphous material. When glass is heated, it does not reach a point at which it suddenly becomes liquid. Glass does not have a fixed melting point as ice has. Rather, as glass is heated, it softens more and more and melts gradually over a wide temperature range. The hotter it gets, the more easily the glass flows. The resistance of a liquid to such flow is called its *viscosity* (vis KAHS uh tee). Glass and

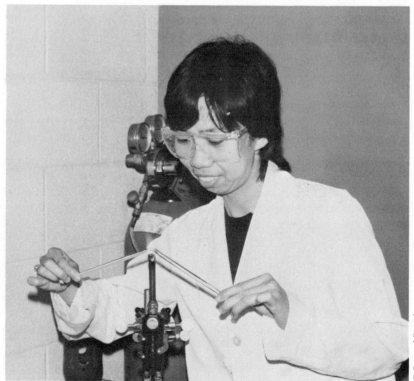

FIGURE 14-21. As glass is heated, it slowly softens and is easily bent.

F. Bernard Daniel

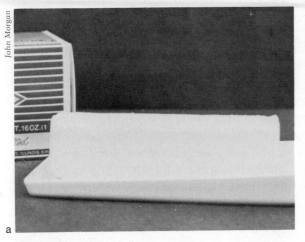

a

b

FIGURE 14-22. Butter (a) and molasses (b) are examples of amorphous materials.

cold molasses are good examples of viscous materials. Water and carbon tetrachloride are good examples of nonviscous liquids. Upon cooling, glass does not reach a specific temperature at which it turns into a solid. As it cools, it becomes more and more viscous and it flows more and more slowly. Most amorphous substances which appear to be solids are not really solids at all. They have characteristics similar to those of glass and are called *supercooled liquids*. Butter is another good example.

In order to distinguish between crystalline and amorphous substances in chemical equations, we must change the symbol (s). In the future, true crystalline solids will be shown by (c), and amorphous materials by (amor).

Amorphous substances are thought of as supercooled liquids.

New state symbols:
(c) = crystalline
(amor) = amorphous

FIGURE 14-23. Impact tests on eyeglass lenses are being done in a safety study. One type of lens (a) shatters when struck by a steel ball. The second type (b) bounces undamaged during the same test.

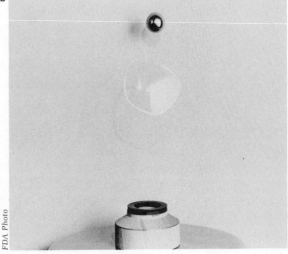

a

b

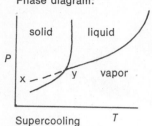

Supercooling occurs from x to y

Metastable amorphous substances do not change to crystalline forms over long periods of time.

One form of sulfur contains long chains. It is an amorphous form and is called plastic sulfur. A few hours after it is prepared, it changes back into the stable orthorhombic form. This change is characteristic of most amorphous substances. In these substances, the amorphous form is unstable. Many substances, such as glass, remain in the amorphous form for long periods instead of changing to a more stable crystalline form as sulfur does. Substances which can occur in a long-lasting amorphous form are said to be *metastable* (met uh STAY buhl). Although a metastable form is not the most stable form, a substance in this form is not likely to change unless subjected to some outside disturbance. Glass is a metastable substance. It normally occurs in the amorphous form, but even glass may be crystallized under the proper conditions.

SUMMARY

1. The melting point is the temperature at which the molecules of a solid move far enough apart to slip over one another. The freezing point is the temperature at which the molecules of a liquid can no longer slip past one another. At the melting or freezing point of any substance, the vapor pressure of the liquid and the vapor pressure of the solid are equal.
2. In a gas-liquid dynamic equilibrium, the number of molecules in both the liquid and gaseous phases remains constant.
3. The vapor pressure of a substance is the pressure exerted by the gaseous phase of the substance which is in equilibrium with the liquid or solid phase of the substance.
4. An equilibrium is often represented by arrows:

$$\text{ice} \overset{0°C}{\leftrightarrows} \text{water}$$

5. If stress is applied to a system at equilibrium, the system tends to readjust so that the stress is reduced (Le Chatelier's principle).
6. Sublimation is the change of state in which a substance passes directly from the solid to the gaseous state.
7. The boiling point of a liquid is the temperature at which the vapor pressure of the liquid is equal to the atmospheric pressure.

8. Evaporation is the process whereby molecules escape from the surface of a liquid or solid.

9. For every gas there is a critical temperature (T_c) above which no amount of pressure will result in liquefying the gas. The critical pressure (P_c) is the pressure which will produce liquefaction at T_c.

10. A low critical temperature indicates weak van der Waals forces between molecules.

11. A phase diagram is a graph showing the temperatures and pressures which result in an equilibrium between any two or three phases (solid, liquid, and gas) of a substance.

12. Compounds containing hydrogen bonded to fluorine, oxygen, or nitrogen have unusual properties because of the formation of hydrogen bonds.

13. Ice is less dense than water, which is most dense at 3.98°C. The expansion of ice upon freezing occurs because of the hydrogen bonding between the highly polar water molecules.

14. Unbalanced surface forces account for the surface tension of liquids. Capillary rise of liquids in small tubes is due to surface tension.

15. Solid-appearing substances which do not have a crystalline form are called amorphous substances.

16. Substances which occur in long-lasting amorphous form are called metastable substances.

17. The resistance to flow of a liquid is called its viscosity. The viscosity of substances usually decreases as the temperature increases.

PROBLEMS

1. What is critical temperature? What is critical pressure?
2. What is a triple point? Look at the phase diagram in Figure 14–12. Determine the triple point.
3. What is Le Chatelier's principle? How does pressing on a partially filled balloon demonstrate this?
4. Describe how a molecule could leave the surface of a solid. (How do solids evaporate?)
5. What is sublimation? List three practical examples of this.

— See Teacher's Guide.

See Teacher's Guide. ——————

6. Define boiling point and melting point in terms of vapor pressure.

7. Why would you expect the boiling point of HF to be higher than that of HBr?

8. Describe the mechanics of ice melting.

9. What is the difference between volatile and nonvolatile substances? Give a solid and a liquid example of each.

10. Name and describe briefly the various types of bonding that have been discussed.

11. A well stirred mixture of ice and water is at equilibrium. If a small amount of warm water or ice is added, the temperature doesn't change. Why?

12. Use the two phase diagrams shown in Figure 14–24. Determine the boiling point, melting point, triple point, and the critical temperature and pressure for substances x and y.

12.

	x	y
B.P.	243°K	430°K
M.P.	131°K	300°K
T.P.	124°K,	300°K,
	245 torr	0.6 atm
T_c	260°K	655°K
P_c	870 torr	8.1 atm

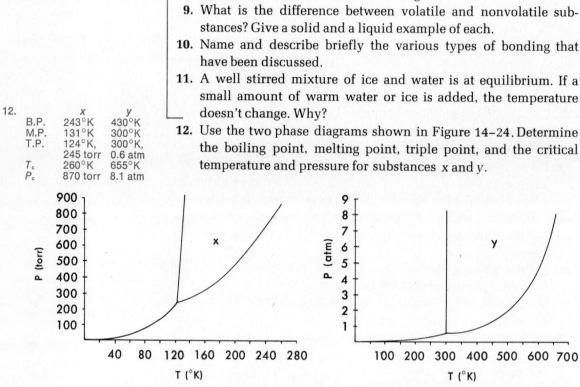

FIGURE 14-24. Phase diagrams.

See Teacher's Guide at the
front of this book.

ONE MORE STEP

1. A physics experiment uses a block of ice and two heavy weights at the ends of a thin wire. The ice is placed on a table and the wire is placed over the ice so that the weights hang over the edges of the table. Eventually the wire is under the ice but the block of ice is still whole. Explain.

2. Find out how Michael Faraday (1791–1867) liquefied chlorine.

3. Why does carbon dioxide "snow" form when a CO_2 fire extinguisher is used?

4. Look up the freezing points of the hydrogen compounds of the oxygen family. Of what significance are these?

5. There are substances other than water which expand on freezing. Find the names of some of them. Why do they behave as they do?

Suggested Readings for this chapter may be found in the Teacher's Guide at the front of this book.

Hot-air ballooning is a fascinating sport which is rapidly gaining wide-spread interest. When inflated, this balloon is about 21 meters high and about 17 meters in diameter. In order to inflate the balloon, cold air is blown into the balloon with a fan until the balloon is partially filled. The air inside the balloon is then heated. By controlling the temperature of the air in the balloon with a gas burner, the balloon can be made to rise. How can this phenomenon be explained?

Chapter 15 develops the ideal gas laws with the aid of the kinetic theory model.

You already know many of the characteristics of gases because air is made up of gases. When we speak of a cubic centimeter of a solid substance or a hundred milliliters of a liquid, we are referring to a definite amount of matter. Both solids and liquids expand and contract with temperature changes. However, the change is usually small enough to ignore. This statement is not true for gases. The kinetic theory, as well as common experience, shows that a given amount of gas will occupy the entire volume of its container. When gases are heated, the change in their volume is large. Most solids and liquids subjected to the same temperature change would change very little in comparison.

According to the kinetic theory, a gas is made up of particles which move about at random. Particles of gases are not held in a fixed position by the attraction of other particles as are those in a solid. These particles do not behave like those found in a liquid either. In a liquid, particles may change their relative position easily but their motion is restricted. This restriction occurs because particles of a liquid are held relatively close together by van der Waals forces.

The size of a gas molecule is insignificant when compared with the distance between molecules. Thus, we assume that the particles of gases have no effect on each other. They are called point masses since they are considered to have no volume or diameter.

A gas made up of such particles does not actually exist. This imaginary gas, composed of molecules with mass but with no diameter and no mutual attraction, is called an *ideal*, or *perfect*, *gas*.

GOAL: You will gain an understanding of the ideal gas laws based on the kinetic theory model and the actual behavior of real gases.

Under the same temperature change, gases change volume more than solids or liquids.

Gas particles move about at random.

An ideal gas is composed of point masses.

Molecules of an ideal gas are considered to be points with no attractive or repulsive force. Emphasize that this is not actually true of real gases.

STP = 760 torr and 0°C

The standard temperature for electrochemical and thermodynamic values is 25°C.

In the latter part of this chapter, you will study about *real gases*, and how they differ in behavior from ideal gases.

The number of gas particles in a volume of gas depends upon the pressure and temperature of the gas. Therefore, in discussing quantities of gas, it is necessary to specify not only the volume but also the pressure and the temperature. Scientists have agreed that gas volumes should be described as if the volume were measured at certain conditions of pressure and temperature. The standard pressure is 1 atm (760 torr) and the standard temperature is 0°C. We indicate that a gas has been measured under standard conditions by the capital letters STP (standard temperature and pressure).

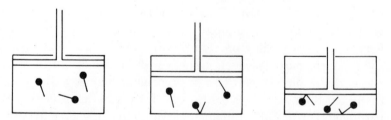

FIGURE 15-2. A gas volume must be measured under standard conditions or adjusted to standard conditions. The number of molecules remains the same but the volume changes.

Gas volumes are almost always reported in the scientific literature as so many liters or milliliters at STP. The system is convenient, but what can we do if we must actually measure a gas in the laboratory at a pressure of 740 torr and a temperature of 22°C? In the

Courtesy of Kodansha Ltd.

FIGURE 15-3. Tanks of gases under pressure are usually equipped with gauges to aid in regulating the flow of gas as it is directed into a system.

next several sections of this chapter, we will describe how a measured gas volume can be adjusted to correspond to the volume the gas would occupy at STP.

THE GAS LAWS

15:1 Boyle's Law

We will assume that a gas exerts pressure on the walls of its container because molecules of the gas collide with the walls. The pressure exerted by a gas will then depend on two factors: the number of molecules per unit of volume, and the average kinetic energy of the

Help students develop a mental picture of these relationships. Encourage them to reason through each gas law rather than to memorize a formula.

Don Parsisson

FIGURE 15-4. By increasing the pressure exerted on the inside walls of this molten glass bubble, this glassblower expands and shapes apparatus for scientific studies.

Pressure exerted by a gas
depends on:
  1. number of particles/
     unit volume
  2. average kinetic energy
     of particles

molecules. A change in either of these factors will change the pressure exerted by the gas. If the number of molecules in a constant volume increases, the pressure increases. If the number of molecules and the volume remain constant but the kinetic energy of the molecules increases, the pressure increases.

Consider a container of gas with a movable piston in the top, as shown in Figure 15–5a. Now imagine that the piston is lowered (without any change in the number of molecules present), and the temperature is kept exactly constant. If the piston is lowered until it is half the original distance from the bottom, there will be only half as much space as before (Figure 15–5b). The same number of molecules will occupy half the volume. The molecules will hit the walls of the container twice as often and with the same force per collision. The pressure will double.

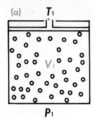

(a) T_1

V_1

P_1

V_2 contains twice as many
molecules per unit volume
as V_1 per unit volume

N = number of molecules

$N_1 = N_2$

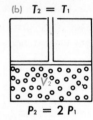

(b) $T_2 = T_1$

V_2

$P_2 = 2 P_1$

FIGURE 15-5. If the number of molecules in a container remains constant but the volume is decreased, the pressure increases inversely as the volume decreases ($P = \frac{k}{V}$).

The number of molecules was not increased but the volume was reduced. Since the same number of molecules in half the space is equivalent to twice as many molecules in the same space, the pressure is doubled. When the volume is halved, the pressure is doubled. We conclude that, at constant temperature, pressure varies inversely as volume, and the product of temperature and pressure is a constant.

The British chemist, Robert Boyle, arrived at this principle by experimentation 300 years ago. This relationship is called *Boyle's law*. Boyle's law states: If the temperature of a gas remains constant, the pressure exerted by the gas varies inversely as the volume. By putting the relationships into mathematical form, we can obtain the following relationship:

Boyle's law: At constant temperature, $PV = k$.

$$P = k'\frac{n}{V} \quad \text{and if} \quad k'n = k \text{ (}n\text{ is constant),}$$

$$\text{then} \quad P = \frac{k}{V}$$

where P is the pressure, V the volume, n is the number of molecules, and k is a constant which takes into account the number of molecules and the temperature. Thus, pressure varies directly as the number of molecules, and inversely as the volume.

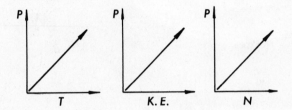

FIGURE 15-6. The graphs show the relationships between pressure, temperature, kinetic energy, and the number of molecules per unit volume.

15:2 Applying Boyle's Law

It usually is not convenient to experiment with gases under standard conditions. Experiments are often carried out at room temperature and pressure. Since the temperature and pressure vary from day to day, experimental results cannot be compared easily. It is desirable, therefore, to adjust all results mathematically to standard conditions. If P_1 = measured pressure and V_1 = measured volume, P_2 is standard pressure and V_2 is volume at standard pressure, then:

$$V_1 = \frac{k}{P_1}$$

and $\quad V_2 = \dfrac{k}{P_2}$ (n is constant)

In the first equation $k = V_1 P_1$. Since k is a constant, we may substitute $k = V_1 P_1$ into the second equation:

$$V_2 = \frac{V_1 P_1}{P_2} \quad \text{or} \quad V_2 = V_1\left(\frac{P_1}{P_2}\right)$$

Note that the original volume is simply multiplied by the ratio of the two pressures to find the new volume. We have derived this relationship by using Boyle's law.

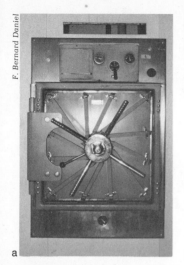

a

b

FIGURE 15-7. Increased pressure results from heating steam at constant volume. This results in a higher boiling point for water. Thus, steam and water can be superheated to sterilize medical instruments in an autoclave (a) and to fast-cook foods in a pressure cooker (b).

Use the pressure ratio which will provide the desired volume change.

$$V_2 = V_1 \left(\frac{P_1}{P_2} \right)$$

$$= 242 \text{ ml} \mid \frac{657 \text{ torr}}{760 \text{ torr}}$$

$$= 209 \text{ ml}$$

Visualize the change in volume and make the mathematics fit.

$$V_2 = \frac{V_1 \mid 120 \text{ torr}}{66 \text{ torr}}$$

$$= (1.8)V_1$$

EXAMPLE — PRESSURE CORRECTION

These problems can be solved by simply plugging values into the Boyle's law formula. However, students should be encouraged to reason their way to the solution.

Some gas is collected in a flask which has a volume of 242 ml. The pressure of the gas in the flask is measured and determined to be 657 torr. To what volume at standard pressure does this original volume correspond? (Assume that the temperature remains constant.)

Standard pressure is 760 torr. Thus, a change to standard pressure would compress the gas. Therefore, the gas would occupy a smaller volume. If the volume is to decrease, then the ratio of pressures by which the original volume is to be multiplied must be less than 1. The two possible ratios by which the original volume could be multiplied are 760 torr/657 torr and 657 torr/760 torr. The latter value is the proper one in this case because it is less than 1 and will decrease the volume. The corrected volume is (657 torr/760 torr) × 242 ml, or 209 ml.

The same process can be used to change the volume of a gas to correspond to a pressure other than standard. For instance, if we wish to compare the volume of a gas measured at 120 torr with another quantity measured at 66 torr, the mathematical operations would be as follows:

Correcting for a pressure change from 120 torr to 66 torr is equivalent to expanding the gas. The new volume would be greater, and the ratio of pressures must be greater than 1. The proper ratio is 120 torr/66 torr. Note that the two pressure measurements must be in the same units (for instance, you cannot divide atmospheres by torr). Do not fall into the habit of "plugging" numbers into equations.

Visualize the change to be made in the volume of the gas as it passes from one pressure to the other, and then multiply by the appropriate ratio.

PROBLEMS

1. Correct the following volumes of gas from the indicated pressures to standard pressure:
   a. 952 ml at 561 torr   ans.   703 ml
   b. 273 ml at 166 torr   ans.   59.6 ml
   c. 338 l at 6.30 atm   ans.   2130 liter
   d. 598 ml at 5.00 atm   ans.   2990 ml
   e. 77.0 l at 180 torr   ans.   18.2 liter
2. Correct the following volumes of gas from the indicated pressures to standard pressure:
   a. 930 ml at 697 torr 853 ml
   b. 50.0 liters at 413 torr 27.2 l
   c. 36.0 liters at 0.650 atm 23.4 l
   d. 329 ml at 1.65 atm 543 ml
   e. 231 ml at 605 torr 184 ml
3. Make the indicated corrections in the following volumes of gas:
   a. 0.600 liter at 669 torr to 0.870 atm   ans.   0.607 liter
   b. 380 ml at 772 torr to 804 torr   ans.   365 ml
   c. 0.338 liter at 364 torr to 0.589 atm   ans.   0.275 liter
   d. 459 ml at 4.32 atm to 9.40 atm   ans.   211 ml
   e. 0.123 liter at 0.832 atm to 865 torr   ans.   0.0899 liter
4. Make the indicated corrections in the following volumes of gas:
   a. 388 ml at 0.581 atm to 500 torr 343 ml
   b. 0.951 liter at 0.791 atm to 316 torr 1.75 l
   c. 31.5 ml at 142 torr to 122 torr 36.7 ml
   d. 524 ml at 166 torr to 910 torr 95.6 ml
   e. 171 ml at 332 torr to 0.877 atm 85.2 ml

15:3 Dalton's Law of Partial Pressure

How much pressure is exerted by a particular gas in a mixture of gases? John Dalton was the first to form a hypothesis about partial pressures. After experimenting with gases, he concluded that: The total pressure in a container is the sum of the pressures of the gases in the container. In other words, each gas exerts the same pressure it

Each gas in a mixture exerts its own pressure.

would if it alone were present at the same temperature. This statement is called *Dalton's law*. When a gas is one of a mixture, the pressure it exerts is called its *partial pressure*. Gases in a single container are all at the same temperature and have the same volume. Therefore, the difference in their partial pressures is due only to the difference in the numbers of molecules present.

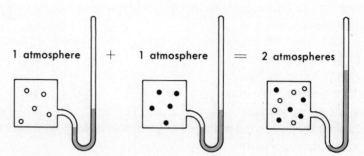

Doubling the number of particles (K.E. to remain constant) results in a doubling of the number of collisions. Therefore, the pressure doubles.

FIGURE 15-8. The total pressure is the sum of the partial pressures exerted by the various gases in the container.

For example, let one liter of O_2 and one liter of N_2, both of which are at room temperature and atmospheric pressure, be added together. The volume of the mixture is then adjusted to one liter with no change in temperature. The pressure exerted by this mixture will be 2 atmospheres. However, the pressure exerted by the oxygen will still be 1 atm (one-half the pressure), and the pressure exerted by the nitrogen will be 1 atm (one-half the pressure). Air is an example of such a mixture. The air contains nitrogen, oxygen, argon, carbon dioxide, and other gases in small amounts. The total pressure of the atmosphere at standard conditions is 760 torr. If 78% of the molecules present are nitrogen molecules, then 78% of the pressure is due to nitrogen. The partial pressure of nitrogen in the air at standard conditions is, then, 0.78×760, or 593 torr.

Chemists often obtain samples of gases by bubbling the gas through water, as shown in Figure 15–9. This procedure is known as *collecting a gas over water*. It is a useful system for collecting many gases, but the gas must be practically insoluble in water. Water vapor will be present in the gas sample. Thus, the measurement of the pressure in the container actually includes the sum of the partial pressures of the gas collected and the water vapor. We know that each of the gases exerts the same pressure it would if it alone were present in the container. Therefore, if we subtract the value for water vapor

The volume of a gas collected over water must be corrected for water vapor pressure.

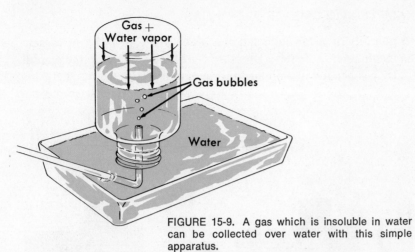

Gas +
Water vapor

Gas bubbles

Water

The assumption that the gas is saturated with water vapor is not always valid. The error, however, is very small, usually less than 1 torr.

FIGURE 15-9. A gas which is insoluble in water can be collected over water with this simple apparatus.

pressure from the total pressure, the result will be the pressure of the collected gas alone. The vapor pressure of water at various temperatures has been measured, and we need only to consult a table of these figures to determine the partial pressure of water (Table 15–1).

Pressure of dry gas = total pressure − water vapor pressure.

Table 15–1

Vapor Pressure of Water

These values represent the saturated or equilibrium pressure of water vapor.

Temperature (°C)	Pressure (torr)	Temperature (°C)	Pressure (torr)
0	4.58	26	25.2
5	6.54	27	26.7
8	8.05	28	28.4
10	9.21	29	30.0
12	10.5	30	31.8
14	12.0	35	42.2
16	13.6	40	55.3
18	15.5	50	92.5
20	17.5	60	149.4
21	18.7	70	233.8
22	19.8	80	355.3
23	21.1	90	525.9
24	22.4	100	760.0
25	23.8	200	11,664

EXAMPLE–VOLUME OF A DRY GAS

A quantity of gas is collected over water at 8°C in a 353 ml vessel. The manometer indicates a pressure of 634 torr. What volume would the dry gas occupy at standard pressure and 8°C?

FIGURE 15-10. The U-tube manometer shows the vapor pressure of ethyl alcohol at 0°C (a). Note the great increase in the vapor pressure as the alcohol is warmed to 30°C (b).

Courtesy of Kodansha Ltd.

FIRST. We must determine what part of the total pressure is due to water vapor. Table 15–1 indicates that at 8°C, water has a vapor pressure of 8 torr. To find the pressure of the collected gas:

$$P_{gas} = P_{total} - P_{water}$$
$$= 634 \text{ torr} - 8 \text{ torr}$$
$$= 626 \text{ torr}$$

SECOND. Since this pressure is less than standard, the gas would have to be compressed to change it to standard. The pressure ratio by which the volume is to be multiplied must be less than 1. The correct volume is:

$$\frac{353 \text{ ml} \mid 626 \text{ torr}}{760 \text{ torr}} = 291 \text{ ml}$$

Notice that according to the problem, the temperature remains constant.

$$V_2 = V_1 \left(\frac{P_1}{P_2}\right)$$
$$= \frac{353 \text{ ml} \mid 626 \text{ torr}}{760 \text{ torr}}$$
$$= 291 \text{ ml}$$

PROBLEMS

5. The following volumes of gases were collected over water under the indicated conditions. Correct each volume to the volume that the dry gas would occupy at standard pressure and the indicated temperature (T is constant):

Note that the temperature remains constant. See Table 15-1, page 325 for pressure corrections.

  a. 888 ml at 14°C and 700 torr   *ans.* 804 ml
  b. 30.0 ml at 16°C and 581 torr   *ans.* 22.4 ml
  c. 34.0 liter at 18°C and 618 torr   *ans.* 26.9 liter
  d. 384 ml at 12°C and 587 torr   *ans.* 291 ml
  e. 8.23 liter at 27°C and 655 torr   *ans.* 6.80 liter

6. The following volumes of gases were collected over water under the indicated conditions. Correct each volume to the volume that the dry gas would occupy at standard pressure and the indicated temperature (T is constant):

  a. 903 ml at 24°C and 715 torr   823 ml
  b. 317 ml at 25°C and 851 torr   345 ml
  c. 7.83 liters at 20°C and 1.08 atm   8.27 l
  d. 964 ml at 29°C and 836 torr   1020 ml
  e. 402 cm^3 at 30°C and 624 torr   313 cm^3

Robert Boyle

(1627–1691)

One of seven sons of the Earl of Cork, Ireland, Robert Boyle distinguished his family by entering Eton at the age of eight.

His chief contribution to science is his law concerning the behavior of a quantity of gas subjected to a change in pressure as the temperature remains constant.

Boyle also distinguished between a chemical element and a compound and was the first to define chemical reaction and analysis.

An intensely religious man, Boyle pursued studies and duties in this area. As a director of the East India Company, he worked for the propagation of Christianity in the East and circulated, at his own expense, translations of the Scriptures.

In the scientific arena, he helped found the Royal Society, membership in which became the ultimate honor for a British scientist.

15:4 Charles' Law

Jacques Charles, a French physicist, was the first to note a simple relationship between the volume of a gas and the temperature. He found that, starting at 0°C, the volume of any gas would double if the temperature were raised to 273°C while the pressure was held constant. For each Celsius degree increase in temperature, the volume of the gas increased by $\frac{1}{273}$ of its volume at 0°C. If the original volume (at 0°C) is expressed as $\frac{273}{273} = 1$, an increase in temperature of 273° will result in a new volume of $\frac{273+273}{273}$, or 2; an increase in temperature of 1C° will result in a new volume of $\frac{274}{273}$, or a $\frac{1}{273}$ increase in volume. Similarly, Charles found that a gas will decrease by $\frac{1}{273}$ of its 0°C volume for each Celsius degree decrease in temperature. This would suggest that at −273°C, a gas would have no volume, or would disappear. However, all gases become liquid before

For each 1C° change, a gas changes $\frac{1}{273}$ of its 0°C volume.

Be sure the students understand that the increase in volume per degree increase in temperature is 1/273 of the 0°C volume — not 1/273 of the gas volume at any temperature.

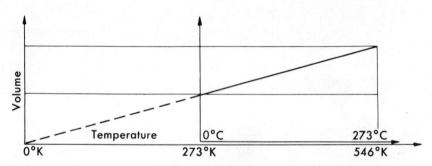

FIGURE 15-11. The volume of a gas at −273°C (0°K) is theoretically zero; that is, all gases would disappear at 0°K.

they are cooled to this low temperature, and Charles' relationship does not hold for liquids or solids.

This experimental information led to the formation of a new temperature scale called the *absolute* or *Kelvin* (K) temperature scale. 0°K is the temperature at which all gases theoretically have no volume, and 273.16°K is the triple point of water. The volume of a quantity of gas, held at a fixed pressure, varies directly with the absolute temperature. This relationship is called *Charles' law*.

Charles' law: At constant pressure, $V = k'T$

15:5 Applying Charles' Law

Charles' law states that volume varies directly as the absolute temperature: $V = k'T$. For any original volume, $V_1 = k'T_1$. A change in volume, with pressure constant, could be indicated as $V_2 = k'T_2$. Since $k' = \dfrac{V_1}{T_1}$, substituting would give:

$$\frac{V_1}{T_1} = \frac{V_2}{T_2} \quad \text{or} \quad V_2 = V_1\!\left(\frac{T_2}{T_1}\right)$$

To correct the volume for a change in temperature, you must, as in pressure correction, multiply the original volume by a ratio. For temperature changes, the ratio is of absolute (Kelvin) temperatures.

Use the absolute temperature ratio which will provide the desired volume change.

Patricia Hebda

FIGURE 15-12. A rotoevaporator can be used to distill a liquid at reduced pressure.

EXAMPLE – TEMPERATURE CORRECTION

A 225 ml volume of gas is collected at 57°C. What volume would this sample of gas occupy at standard temperature?

The temperature decreases and the pressure remains constant. Charles' law states that if the temperature of a gas decreases at constant pressure, the volume will decrease. Therefore, the original volume must be multiplied by a fraction less than 1. To determine what this fraction is, convert both the initial (57°C) and the final (0°C) temperatures to the Kelvin scale (330°K and 273°K). The two possible fractions are:

$57°C = 330°K$
$0°C = 273°K$

$$\frac{330°K}{273°K} \quad \text{and} \quad \frac{273°K}{330°K}$$

The correct fraction is $\dfrac{273°K}{330°K}$ because it is less than 1. The corrected gas volume is

$V_2 = \dfrac{225 \text{ ml} \mid 273°\cancel{K}}{\mid 330°\cancel{K}}$

$V_2 = 186 \text{ ml}$

$$\frac{225 \text{ ml} \mid 273°K}{\mid 330°K} \quad \text{or} \quad 186 \text{ ml}$$

PROBLEMS

7. Correct the following volumes of gases for a change from the temperature indicated to standard temperature (P is constant):
   a. 617 ml at 9°C   *ans.*   597 ml
   b. 609 ml at 83°C   *ans.*   467 ml
   c. 942 ml at 22°C   *ans.*   872 ml
   d. 7.16 l at 280°K   *ans.*   6.98 l
   e. 4.40 l at 7°C   *ans.*   4.29 l
8. Correct the following volumes of gases for a change from the temperature indicated to standard temperature (P is constant):
   a. 819 ml at 21°C 761 ml   d. 7.12 l at 988°K 1.97 l
   b. 5.80 l at 514°K 3.08 l   e. 213 l at 99°C 156 l
   c. 5.94 l at 79°C   4.61 l
9. Correct the following volumes of gases for the temperature changes indicated (P is constant):
   a. 2.90 l at 226°K to 23°C   *ans.*   3.80 l
   b. 608 ml at 158°K to 73°C   *ans.*   1330 ml
   c. 7.91 l at 52°C to 538°K   *ans.*   13.1 l
   d. 2.97 l at 72°C to 502°K   *ans.*   4.32 l
   e. 19.0 ml at 56.0°K to 53°C   *ans.*   111 ml
10. Correct the following volumes of gases for the temperature changes indicated (P is constant):
   a. 5.18 l at 76°C to 6°C 4.14 l   d. 880 ml at 563°K to 52°C 508 ml
   b. 994 ml at 27°C to 744°K—   e. 5.94 l at 44°C to 17°C 5.43 l
   c. 833 ml at 27°C to 84°C 991 ml   2470 ml

15:6   Combined Gas Laws

Laboratory experiments are almost always made at temperatures and pressures other than standard. It is sometimes necessary to correct the laboratory volumes of gases for both temperature and pressure. The correction is made by multiplying the original volume by two ratios, one for temperature and the other for pressure.

EXAMPLE – VOLUME TO STP

The volume of a gas measured at 567 torr pressure and 60°C is to be corrected to correspond to the volume it would occupy at STP. The measured volume of the gas is 10.0 ml.

The pressure must be increased from 567 torr to 760 torr. The volume must decrease. The correct pressure ratio is 567 torr/760 torr.

The temperature must be decreased from 333°K to 273°K. This would also decrease the volume; therefore, the correct temperature ratio is 273°K/333°K. The problem then reduces to

$$\frac{10.0 \text{ ml}}{} \left| \frac{567 \text{ torr}}{760 \text{ torr}} \right| \frac{273°K}{333°K} = 6.12 \text{ ml at STP.}$$

Introduce the combined gas laws as a two step procedure—the second step being a correction of the result of the first step.

A change in volume resulting from a change in both temperature and pressure can be found by combining the ratios.

The common sense approach used here simplifies use of gas laws in mass-volume problems at non-standard conditions.

FIGURE 15-13. This chemist regulates the gas flow and pressure in this system with a series of valves.

Lawrence Radiation Laboratory, Livermore

PROBLEMS

11. Correct the volumes of the following gases as indicated:
  a. 7.51 l at 5°C and 449 torr to STP   *ans.*   4.36 l
  b. 149 ml at 18°C and 710 torr to 68°C and 618 torr

                                                  ans.   201 ml
  c. 7.03 l at 31°C and 2.14 atm to STP   *ans.*   13.5 l
  d. 955 ml at 58°C and 3.12 atm to 76°C and 923 torr

                                                  ans.   2590 ml
  e. 960 ml at 71°C and 5.80 atm to 13°C and 445 torr

                                                  ans.   7910 ml

12. Correct the volumes of the following gases as indicated:
  a. 654 ml at 6°C and 490 torr to 4°C and 2.91 atm 144 ml
  b. 2.13 l at 95°C and 3.79 atm to STP 5.99 ml
  c. 4.76 l at 6°C and 934 torr to STP 5.72 l
  d. 61.4 ml at 67°C and 726 torr to STP 47.1 ml
  e. 164 ml at STP to 21°C and 735 torr 183 ml

The process by which gas molecules spread randomly throughout a space is called diffusion.

FIGURE 15-14. This series of photos shows the diffusion of bromine gas in a container after the drop of liquid bromine has just been added (a), after three minutes (b), and after twelve minutes (c).

15:7 Diffusion

One of the postulates of the kinetic theory is that the molecules of gases travel in straight lines. However, a molecule is always colliding with other molecules. Therefore, its actual path is a series of straight lines connected end to end in no particular pattern. If a bottle containing a substance with a strong odor is opened on one side of the room, its odor can later be detected on the other side of

a
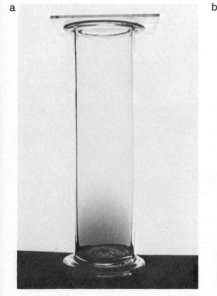
b
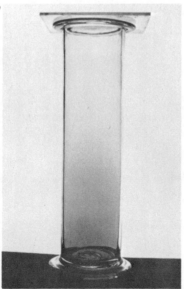
c
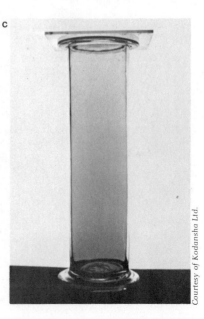

Courtesy of Kodansha Ltd.

the room. The molecules of the substance have traveled across the room by traveling in straight lines between collisions but they did not necessarily travel straight across the room. It took some time for them to reach the other side because they were colliding with air molecules. Some may even have been turned completely around. This random scattering of the gas molecules is called *diffusion*. As the gas molecules diffuse, they become more and more evenly distributed throughout the room.

Diffusion is random scattering of gas particles.

15:8   Graham's Law

All gases do *not* diffuse at the same rate. We will assume that the rate of diffusion varies directly as the velocity of the molecules. This assumption is supported by experimental evidence. Molecules of lower mass diffuse faster because they travel faster. They also will pass through a small hole (*effuse*) more rapidly than the molecules of higher mass.

Molecules of large mass diffuse more slowly than molecules of small mass.

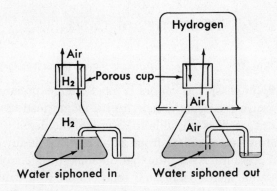

FIGURE 15-15. The relative rates of diffused gases vary inversely as the square roots of their molecular masses — Graham's law.

In Section 12–4 we derived the relationship of the velocities of substances. If the two substances are at the same temperature their kinetic energies must be the same. Thus,

$$m_1 v_1^2 = m_2 v_2^2 \quad \text{or} \quad \frac{v_1^2}{v_2^2} = \frac{m_2}{m_1}$$

which is equivalent to

$$\frac{v_1}{v_2} = \frac{\sqrt{m_2}}{\sqrt{m_1}}$$

Emphasize that the rate of diffusion of gases varies directly with the velocity of the molecules. In two samples of the same gas, the rate of diffusion will be higher for the one having a higher temperature because the velocity of the melocules will be higher.

Graham's law—The relative rates of diffusion of two gases under identical conditions vary inversely as the square roots of their molecular masses.

From this equation, we can see that the relative rates of diffusion of two gases vary inversely as the square roots of their molecular masses. This relationship is true only when the temperature is the same for each. This principle was first formulated by a Scottish chemist, Thomas Graham, and is known as *Graham's law*. Graham's law states: The relative rates at which two gases under identical conditions of temperature and pressure will pass through a small hole varies inversely as the square roots of the molecular masses of the gases.

PROBLEMS

13. Compute the relative rates of diffusion of helium and argon.

ans.   3.17 to 1

14. Compute the relative rates of diffusion of radon and argon.

2.36 to 1

PROPERTIES OF GASES

15:9   Gas Density   density = mass per unit volume

If the number of particles remains the same:
1. density increases as pressure increases
2. density decreases as temperature increases

The density of gases and vapors is most often expressed in grams per liter, because the usual density units, g/cm^3, lead to very small numbers for gases. It is possible to calculate the density of a gas at any temperature and pressure from data collected at any other temperature and pressure. Assuming that the mass (number of particles) remains the same, then a decrease in temperature would decrease the volume and increase the density. An increase of pressure would

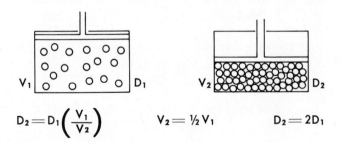

$$D_2 = D_1 \left(\frac{V_1}{V_2} \right) \qquad\qquad V_2 = \tfrac{1}{2} V_1 \qquad\qquad D_2 = 2D_1$$

FIGURE 15-16. If pressure is increased, the volume will decrease and the molecules will be forced closer together. The density will increase.

decrease the volume and increase the density. The following problem illustrates this procedure. (Remember 1 cm^3 equals 1 ml.)

EXAMPLE—DENSITY AT STP

It is found that 981 ml of a gas collected at 47°C and 736 torr has mass 3.40 g. What is its density at STP?

The temperature is decreased from 47°C (320°K) to 0°C (273°K). This decreases the volume and increases the density. Thus, use $\frac{320°K}{273°K}$. The pressure is increased from 736 torr to 760 torr. This decreases the volume and increases the density. Thus, use $\frac{760 \text{ torr}}{736 \text{ torr}}$. The solution, therefore, is

$$\frac{3.40 \text{ g}}{981 \text{ ml}} \left| \frac{1000 \text{ ml}}{1 \text{ l}} \right| \frac{320°K}{273°K} \left| \frac{760 \text{ torr}}{736 \text{ torr}} \right. = 4.20 \text{ g/l}$$

Original Density   T Correction   P Correction

Use a logical approach. Do not merely "plug" values into an equation.

PROBLEMS

15. Compute the gas density at STP of the following:

    a. 969 ml of gas at 64°C and 723 torr has mass 1.64 g

                                          ans.   2.20 g/l

    b. 4.98 l of gas at 31°C and 776 torr has mass 0.530 g

                                          ans.   0.116 g/l

    c. 833 ml of gas at 99°C and 2.60 atm has mass 8.30 g

                                          ans.   5.22 g/l

    d. 883 ml of gas at 37°C and 863 torr has mass 3.69 g

                                          ans.   4.18 g/l

    e. 4.75 l of gas at 26°C and 694 torr has mass 5.03 g

                                          ans.   1.27 g/l

16. Compute the gas density of the following at STP.

    a. 7.13 l of gas at 81°C and 3.95 atm has mass 6.40 g 0.295 g/l

    b. 5.61 l of gas at 54°C and 2.45 atm has mass 1.64 g 0.143 g/l

    c. 5.59 l of gas at 97°C and 501 torr has mass 6.57 g 2.42 g/l

    d. 513 ml of gas at 72°C and 765 torr has mass 0.0365 g 0.0893 g/l

    e. 158 ml of gas at 41°C and 746 torr has mass 0.0135 g 0.100 g/l

15:10 Deviations of Real Gases

In Sections 15:1 through 15:9, we assumed that (1) the gases under consideration were made of molecules that had no volume, and (2) that gas molecules had no attraction for each other. These assumptions are not really true. For many gases at low pressures, however, the molecules closely approach the behavior of ideal gas molecules.

Not all gases behave as ideal gases.

At low pressures, the molecules of both ideal and real gases are far apart. The volume occupied by the molecules is small when compared to the total gas volume. Most of the total volume is empty space. As the pressure is increased, the gas molecules are forced closer together. Ideal gas molecules still remain far apart but real gas molecules begin to occupy a significant portion of the total volume. Beyond a certain pressure, an increase in pressure does not always cause the predicted decrease in volume. If the pressure is increased still more, the molecules are forced close enough together for van der Waals forces to have an effect.

Roughly, you reduce only the space not occupied by gas molecules.

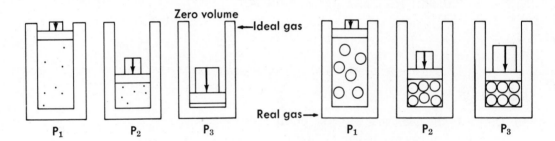

FIGURE 15-17. In an ideal gas, the molecules have no volume and there is always space around each molecule. An ideal gas can be compressed to zero volume. The molecules of a real gas have volume and compression of a real gas is limited by the volume occupied by the molecules.

For most common gases, the ideal gas law is accurate to 1% at the normal laboratory temperatures and pressures with which you will be working. It will be assumed, for convenience, that these gases have ideal gas properties. Generally, the lower the *critical temperature* of a gas (maximum temperature at which it liquefies) the more closely the gas obeys the ideal gas laws. Using this knowledge, we can estimate the degree to which the gases listed in Table 15–2 approach the ideal gas.

Gases with low critical temperatures approximate ideal gases.

Table 15–2

Critical Temperature

The ideal gas would have $T_c = 0°K$.

Gas	Critical Temperature (°K)
H_2	33.2
N_2	126.3
O_2	154.8
CO_2	304.2
SO_2	430.7
H_2O	647.4

There is an interesting property of real gases which depends upon the attractive forces which exist between molecules. If a highly compressed gas is allowed to escape through a small opening, its temperature decreases. This phenomenon is known as the Joule-Thomson effect, after the two scientists who first investigated it. In order to expand, the molecules of the gas must do some work in order to overcome the attractive forces between them. The energy used to do this work comes from their kinetic energy. As their kinetic energy decreases, the temperature falls. Consider the apparatus shown in Figure 15–18. The system shown is completely insulated so that no

Joule-Thomson effect: when a highly compressed gas effuses, its temperature decreases.

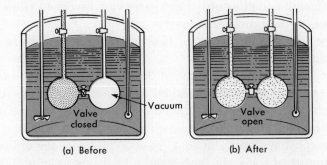

Valve closed   Vacuum   Valve open

(a) Before   (b) After

FIGURE 15-18. In this adiabatic system, the temperature of the gas in (a) is higher than its temperature will be in (b) after its expansion.

heat exchange can take place with the surroundings. Such a system is known as an adiabatic (ayd ee uh BAT ik) system. The temperature of the gas in (b) will be less than its temperature was in (a) before the expansion.

In an adiabatic system no heat exchange takes place with the surroundings.

SUMMARY

1. An ideal gas is an imaginary gas whose particles have no diameter and no mutual attraction.
2. The volume of a gas depends not only on the number of particles but also on temperature and pressure.
3. Standard temperature and pressure (STP) are 0°C and 1 atm. Gas volumes are usually reported in liters or milliliters at STP.
4. Gas pressure depends on the number of molecules per unit volume and the average kinetic energy of the molecules.
5. Boyle's law states that, at constant temperature, the volume of a gas varies inversely as its pressure $(V = k/P)$.
6. Dalton's law of partial pressures states that the total pressure in a container is the sum of the pressures of the individual gases in the container.
7. Charles' law states that, at constant pressure, the volume of a gas varies directly with the absolute temperature $(V = k'T)$.
8. Diffusion is the process by which gases spread to become evenly distributed throughout the entire space in which they are confined. All gases do not diffuse or effuse at the same rate.
9. Gas density varies directly as pressure and inversely as temperature. It is usually expressed in grams per liter (g/l).
10. Graham's law states that, under constant temperature and pressure, the relative velocities (and, therefore, the relative rates of diffusion and effusion) of two gases vary inversely as the square roots of their molecular masses.
11. The particles of real gases, as opposed to ideal gases, have both volume and mutual attraction. At high pressures, these two factors take effect: the volume of the gas particles becomes significant and hinders compression, and the van der Waals forces of attraction facilitate compression.
12. At normal laboratory temperatures and pressures, most common gases behave nearly as ideal gases. The lower the critical temperature of a gas, the more nearly it behaves as an ideal gas.

PROBLEMS

17. Find the volume of a dry gas at STP if it measures 928 ml at 27°C and 800 torr. 889 ml
18. At STP, a gas measures 325 ml. What will it measure at 20°C and 700 torr? 379 ml

19. The density of a gas is 2.97 g/l at STP. What would its density be at 27°C and 750 torr? 2.67 g/l

20. At 325°K and 800 torr, a gas has a density of 5.01 g/l. What would be its density at STP? 5.67 g/l

21. A chemist collects 96.0 l of gas over water at 27°C and 914 torr. What volume would the dry gas occupy at 70°C and 952 torr? 102 ml

22. A chemist collects 372 ml of gas over water at 90°C and 832 torr. What volume would the dry gas occupy at 2°C and 735 torr? 117 ml

23. A chemist collects 5.08 ml of gas at 3°C and 727 torr over water. What volume would the dry gas occupy at 44°C and 882 torr? 4.77 l

24. 30.0 ml of a gas are collected over water at 20°C and 700 torr. What volume would the dry gas occupy at STP? 25.1 ml

25. A chemist collects 8.00 ml of gas over water at STP. What volume would the dry gas occupy at STP? 7.95 ml

ONE MORE STEP See Teacher's Guide at the front of this book.

1. Using a bicycle tire pump or a football inflating pump and an air pressure gauge such as is used on auto tires, see if you can demonstrate Boyle's law. Don't forget that the air in the pump is already at 1 atm pressure before you depress the plunger.

2. There are a number of approximate equations which deal with the behavior of real gases. Using one of these equations, calculate the percent deviation from ideal of nitrogen gas at 0°C and 400 atm pressure. Suggested Readings for this chapter may be found in the Teacher's Guide at the front of this book.

Joseph Priestley discovered oxygen in 1774 while performing experiments in a laboratory much like this one. Further experiments with plants growing in large glass containers like those on the table in front of the window showed that green plants give off oxygen during photosynthesis. We know that a given amount of gas will completely fill any container in which it is placed. What system have chemists developed to express standard amounts of gaseous substances?

Gases and the Mole ——————————— 16

Chapter 16 continues the study of gases begun in Chapter 15 by comparing the ideal gas laws with experimental results obtained from real gases.

In Chapter 15, we examined the effect of temperature and pressure on the volume of a constant mass of gas. The principles applied to any gas exhibiting ideal behavior. Different gases, however, have molecules and atoms of different masses. In this chapter, we will look at the effect of the number of particles on the other gas variables, particularly volume. We will also find out how to obtain mass measurements of gases at various temperatures and pressures.

GOAL: You will gain an understanding of the molar volume of a gas and its use in solving gas reaction problems.

MOLAR VOLUME OF A GAS

16:1 Developing Avogadro's Principle

Suppose we place two different gases at exactly the same temperature and pressure in separate containers of exactly the same volume. At a given temperature, all gas molecules will have the same average kinetic energy regardless of size or mass. Massive molecules will travel slowly, less massive molecules will travel more rapidly: but average K.E. ($\frac{1}{2}mv^2$) will be the same for all. If the kinetic energies are equal, any difference in pressure exerted by the gases is determined solely by the number of molecules of each gas. Since we have already said that the two gases are at the same pressure, there must be an equal number of molecules in the two containers. The formal statement of the principle derived here is: At equal temperatures and equal pressures, equal volumes of gases contain the same number of molecules. This statement is called *Avogadro's principle*, after Amadeo Avogadro, the Italian chemist. At the time he proposed the principle, in 1811, the kinetic theory had not been developed.

The number of gas molecules in a container determines the pressure at a given temperature.

Avogadro's principle states that under similar conditions, equal volumes of gases contain the same number of molecules.

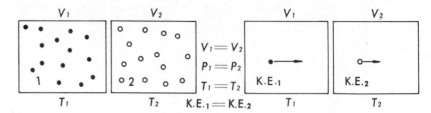

FIGURE 16-1. At equal temperatures and equal pressures, equal volumes of gases contain the same number of molecules. Box 1 and Box 2 contain the same number of molecules.

As we read in Section 6:5, Avogadro developed his hypothesis to explain some striking observations made by Gay-Lussac. Gay-Lussac had observed that two gases always react in such a way that the combining volumes can be expressed in small whole numbers.

Proust had previously stated his law of definite proportions. Avogadro concluded that if one molecule of chlorine always unites with one molecule of hydrogen to form two molecules of hydrogen chloride, equal volumes of gases *must* contain equal numbers of molecules. Avogadro's principle has been verified so often that it is sometimes called a law. We will use this principle often. One consequence of Avogadro's principle is that, since equal volumes of gases contain the same number of molecules, the value of the constant k, in $V = \dfrac{k}{P}$, is the same for all gases. Similarly, the value of the constant in $V = kT$ does not change. It is the same for all gases.

The values of the constants in the gas laws are the same for all gases.

16:2   Molar Volume

The molar volume of a gas is the volume of 1 mole of the gas at STP.

Let n represent the number of moles of a gas, and let V represent the volume. Then, for two gases under similar conditions, Avogadro's principle states: if $V_1 = V_2$, then $n_1 = n_2$. Conversely, if the

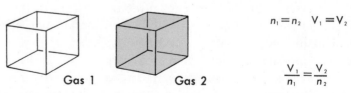

$$n_1 = n_2 \quad V_1 = V_2$$

$$\frac{V_1}{n_1} = \frac{V_2}{n_2}$$

FIGURE 16-2. Under standard conditions, one mole of any gas will occupy the same volume.

number of moles of two gases under similar conditions are equal, then their volumes are equal. From this we conclude that 1 mole of any gas at STP will occupy the same volume as 1 mole of any other gas at STP. For example, 1 mole of oxygen has mass 32.0 g and 1.00 liter of oxygen has mass 1.43 g. Therefore, a mole of oxygen will occupy:

$$\frac{32.0 \text{ g}}{1 \text{ mole}} \bigg| \frac{1.00 \text{ l}}{1.43 \text{ g}} = 22.4 \text{ l/mole}$$

One mole of hydrogen gas has mass 2.016 g and 1.00 liter of hydrogen has mass 0.0899 g. We again find that 1.00 l mole of hydrogen occupies:

$$\frac{2.016 \text{ g}}{1 \text{ mole}} \bigg| \frac{1.00 \text{ l}}{0.0899 \text{ g}} = 22.4 \text{ l/mole}$$

This volume, 22.4 l, the volume occupied by 1 mole of any gas under standard conditions, is called the *gram-molecular volume*, or *molar volume*, of the gas.

One mole of a gas at STP occupies 22.4 l.

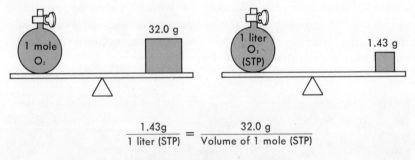

$$\frac{1.43 \text{g}}{1 \text{ liter (STP)}} = \frac{32.0 \text{ g}}{\text{Volume of 1 mole (STP)}}$$

Molar volume of O_2 = 22.4 l (STP)

FIGURE 16-3. One mole of a gas occupies 22.4 liters under standard conditions.

16:3 Ideal Gas Equation

We are now in a position to combine, in one equation, all four variables concerned with the physical characteristics of gases: *pressure, volume, temperature,* and *number of particles.* Charles' law states that volume varies directly as the absolute temperature, and Boyle's law states that volume varies inversely as the pressure. We have combined the two as:

Note: The capital N_A is a constant (Avogadro's number or 1 mole of molecules). The lower case n is a variable (the number of moles in a specific sample).

$$V = k''\left(\frac{T}{P}\right), \quad \text{or} \quad PV = k''T$$

The constant, k'', depends upon the number of particles present. Therefore, it will change if we add or take away molecules (if n is increased or decreased). We can write the equation using two constants, n and R, to replace the k''.

$$k'' = nR$$

therefore,

$$PV = nRT$$

The ideal gas equation is
$PV = nRT$.

The equation $PV = nRT$ is called the *ideal gas equation*. The value of the new constant, R, can be obtained by substituting into the equation a set of known values of n, P, V, and T. We know that the standard pressure (P) is 1 atm (760 torr), molar volume (V) is 22.4 l, standard temperature (T) is 273°K, and the number of moles (n) is 1. If we solve for R, we obtain the value 0.0821 l-atm/mole-°K. This value for R is constant, and can always be used if the units of the other quantities are not changed. We can determine the number of moles of a quantity of a substance by dividing the mass (in grams) of the substance being used by the gram-molecular mass of the substance. Any problem that can be solved by this equation can also be solved by direct application of the gas laws.

$R = 0.0821$ l-atm/mole-°K

Suggestion: Encourage the students to solve problems by using the individual gas laws. Do not emphasize the memorization and use of the ideal gas equation.

Battelle Memorial Institute, Columbus, Ohio

FIGURE 16-4. These flexible metal bellows are tested by flexing them alternately with high pressure and in a vacuum.

PROBLEMS

1. What pressure will be exerted by 0.300 mole of gas contained in an 8.00-liter vessel at 18°C? 0.896 atm
2. How many moles of gas will a 486-ml flask hold at 10°C and 500 torr pressure? 0.0138 mole

MOLECULAR MASS DETERMINATION

16:4   Molecular Mass from Gas Density

Many types of problems can be solved by using the ideal gas equation. One type, which we will illustrate here, is the calculation of molecular mass from gas density measurements. Such calculations are of importance to the chemist in determining the formulas and structures of unknown compounds.

Molecular mass of a gas can be found from gas density.

EXAMPLE—MOLECULAR MASS FROM GAS DENSITY

Suppose we measure the mass of the vapor form of an unknown compound contained in a 273-ml gas bulb, and find that the bulb contains 0.750 g of gas under the following conditions: pressure, 729 torr; temperature, 60°C. What is the density of the gas?

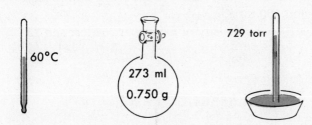

FIGURE 16-5. Molecular mass can be determined from gas density.

The number of moles (n) of a substance is equal to mass (m) divided by the molecular mass (M); therefore, the ideal gas equation may be written:

$$PV = \frac{mRT}{M}, \text{ or } M = \frac{mRT}{PV}$$

Substituting the known values, we get:

$$M = \frac{0.750 \text{ g}(0.0821 \text{ l-atm/mole-°K})(60°C)}{729 \text{ torr } (273 \text{ ml})}$$

Note that this simple procedure includes an application of:
Boyle's law
Charles' law
Avogadro's hypothesis
The kinetic-molecular theory and—if the gas is collected over water—Dalton's law.

Converting °C to °K, torr to atm, and ml to l:

$$M = \frac{0.750 \text{ g}(0.0821 \text{ l-atm/mole-}°K)(333°K)}{(729/760 \text{ atm})(0.273 \text{ l})}$$

$$= \frac{20.5 \text{ g(l-atm)/mole}}{0.262 \text{ l-atm}}$$

$$= 78.4 \text{ g/mole}$$

The solution is, therefore, 78.4 g/mole. Note that all other units in the problem divide out. The units remaining at the end of the problem serve as a check on the answer itself. In this problem, an answer with units of °C/torr, or any other except g/mole, would be wrong. If we solve a problem and the units of our answer are not the units of the quantity which we set out to determine, we have made an error. The wrong units can often serve as a starting point in locating an error.

$PV = \dfrac{mRT}{M}$

This modified form of the ideal gas equation, $PV = \dfrac{mRT}{M}$, may be used in many other types of problems.   This equation should be memorized.

PROBLEMS

3. What is the molecular mass of a gas if 372 ml has mass 0.800 g at 100°C and 800 torr? 62.6 g/mole

4. What will be the density of oxygen at 754 torr and 23°C? 1.31 g/l

GAS REACTION CALCULATIONS

16:5 Mass–Gas Volume Relationships

In Section 5:8, we discussed a method of finding the mass of product produced by a specific mass of reactant. One example involved the mass of chlorine gas needed to completely react with 10.0 g of sodium. It is usually not as easy to measure the mass of a gas as it is to measure the volume under existing conditions and convert the measured volume to the volume under standard conditions. One mole of gas molecules occupies 22.4 l (STP). This knowledge enables us to determine the volume of gas formed in a reaction by using the balanced equation for the reaction.

EXAMPLE – MASS–GAS VOLUME

How many liters of hydrogen at STP can be produced from the reaction of 6.54 of zinc with hydrochloric acid?

FIRST.   Write a balanced equation.

$$2HCl(aq) + Zn(c) \rightarrow H_2(g) + ZnCl_2(aq)$$

SECOND.   Express the mass (6.54 g) of zinc in moles.

(a) $\dfrac{\text{mass of sample}}{\text{molecular mass}} = \dfrac{6.54 \text{ g Zn}}{65.4 \text{ g Zn/mole}} = 0.100 \text{ mole Zn}$

Note that 1 mole of zinc yields 1 mole of hydrogen gas.

(b) $2HCl(aq) + Zn(c) \rightarrow H_2(g) + ZnCl_2(aq)$

        1 mole $\rightarrow$ 1 mole

Amadeo Avogadro

(1776–1856)

The theories of Italian Amadeo Avogadro were overlooked due to the short-sightedness of his compatriots. He is best known for his hypothesis that equal volumes of gases, under identical conditions of pressure and temperature, contain the same number of molecules. However, this hypothesis was discounted by the scientific community until very late in his lifetime. He also carried out investigations in other areas of science. Avogadro was particularly interested in electricity and heat, and he investigated the effects of varying amounts of heat on the temperature of a substance. These experiments led him to measure the expansion of substances when heated and the pressure of the vapor of mercury at various temperatures.

Find the moles of hydrogen produced.

(c) (1) $\times$ (0.100 mole) = 0.100 mole H_2

THIRD. Express 0.100 mole of hydrogen in terms of liters of hydrogen. Since 1 mole of hydrogen occupies 22.4 l, 0.100 mole of hydrogen will occupy:

(0.100 mole) $\times$ (22.4 l/mole) = 2.24 l H_2

We conclude that 2.24 l of hydrogen will be produced when 6.54 g of zinc reacts completely to produce hydrogen. All mass-gas volume problems in this book can be solved in a manner similar to that shown in the example.

Try to keep in mind the following three steps.

FIRST. Write a balanced equation.

SECOND. Find the number of moles of reactant and product involved.

THIRD. Express moles of gas in terms of liters of gas.

Remember that 1 mole of gas occupies 22.4 l (STP). To find the liters of gas formed, multiply the number of moles of gas by 22.4.

$$\frac{x \text{ moles}}{1} \left| \frac{22.4 \text{ l}}{\text{mole}} \right. = (22.4)(x) \text{ l gas}$$

16:6   Gas Volume–Mass Relationships

EXAMPLE – GAS VOLUME–MASS

How many grams of NaCl can be produced by the reaction of 112 l of chlorine at STP with an excess of sodium?

FIRST. $2Na(c) + Cl_2(g) \rightarrow 2NaCl(c)$

SECOND. $\dfrac{112 \text{ l } Cl_2}{} \left| \dfrac{1 \text{ mole } Cl_2}{22.4 \text{ l } Cl_2} \right. = 5.00 \text{ moles } Cl_2$

$2 Na(c) + Cl_2(g) \rightarrow 2 NaCl(c)$
1 mole $\rightarrow$ 2 moles
(2) $\times$ (5.00 moles) = 10.0 moles NaCl

THIRD. Convert 10.0 moles of NaCl to grams of NaCl (a solid, not a gas).

$$1 \text{ mole of NaCl has mass: Na } 1(23.0 \text{ g}) = 23.0 \text{ g}$$
$$\text{Cl } 1(35.5 \text{ g}) = 35.5 \text{ g}$$
$$\text{one gram formula mass of NaCl} = 58.5 \text{ g}$$

Ten moles of NaCl have mass $(10.0 \text{ mole})\left(\dfrac{58.5 \text{ g}}{1 \text{ mole}}\right) = 585$ g. We conclude that 112 l of Cl_2, plus enough sodium to completely react with the Cl_2, will yield 585 g of NaCl.

Check by the factor-label method:

$$\frac{112 \text{ l } Cl_2 \text{ (STP)}}{} \left| \frac{1 \text{ mole } Cl_2}{22.4 \text{ l } Cl_2 \text{ (STP)}} \right| \frac{2 \text{ moles NaCl}}{1 \text{ mole } Cl_2} \left| \frac{58.5 \text{ g NaCl}}{1 \text{ mole NaCl}} \right.$$

$$= 585 \text{ g NaCl}$$

Note that the second and third steps varied from the steps given in our mass-gas volume procedure. We began with gas volume and found the mass of solid produced. We previously started with the mass of solid and found the volume of gas produced. However, we are still concerned with the mole relationships. The new procedure would be:

FIRST. Write a balanced equation.

SECOND. (a) Change liters of gas to moles of gas. (b) Determine how many moles of product are formed by 1 mole of reactant. (c) Find the number of moles of product formed (a × b).

THIRD. Express moles of solid product as grams of solid product. After you have worked enough problems to become familiar with these procedures, you should be able to vary your approach to suit the problem.

PROBLEMS

5. An excess of hydrogen will react with 14.0 g of nitrogen to produce how many liters of ammonia at STP?   ans.   22.4 l

6. How many liters of hydrogen at STP will be produced from 28.0 grams of zinc with an excess of sulfuric acid? 9.59 l

7. Bromine will react with 5.60 l of hydrogen to yield how many grams of hydrogen bromide at STP?   ans.   40.5 g

8. How many grams of antimony(III) chloride can be produced from 6.72 l of chlorine at STP reacting with an excess of antimony? 45.6 g

You may wish to give the students the equations so that they can concentrate on the stoichiometry.

FIGURE 16-6. Natural gas,
which is burned in many gas
stoves, is mostly methane.

16:7 Gas Volume–Gas Volume Relationships

The equation for the complete burning of methane is

$$CH_4(g) + 2O_2(g) \rightarrow CO_2(g) + 2H_2O(g)$$

Notice that all reactants and all products are gases. Since gas is more easily measured by volume than by mass, we will solve problems involving gases by converting moles to liters, instead of converting moles to grams.

EXAMPLE — VOLUME–VOLUME

How many liters of oxygen are required to burn 10.0 l of methane? (All of these substances are gases measured at the same temperature and pressure.)

FIRST. Write a balanced equation.

$$CH_4(g) + 2O_2(g) \rightarrow CO_2(g) + 2H_2O(g)$$

Students should be reminded that this applies only to gases.

SECOND. Change 10.0 l to moles.

(a) 22.4 l = 1 mole

$$10.0 \text{ l} = \frac{10.0 \text{ l}}{22.4 \text{ l/mole}} = 0.446 \text{ mole } CH_4$$

(b) $CH_4 + 2O_2 \rightarrow$ (———) + (———)

1 mole + 2 moles

(c) $(2) \times (0.446 \text{ mole}) = 0.892 \text{ mole } O_2$

350

THIRD.   Change 0.892 mole to liters.

$$\frac{22.4 \text{ l}}{\text{mole}} \Bigg| \frac{0.892 \text{ mole}}{} = 20.0 \text{ l } O_2$$

We conclude that 10.0 l of methane will be completely burned by 20.0 l of O_2. This is no different from the gas volume-mass problems we discussed in the previous section, except that we start and end with volume.

    There is an easier way to solve volume–volume problems. The mass of one mole of a solid may be larger or smaller than the mass of 1 mole of a different solid. Also, most solids do not have the same molecular mass. One mole of any gas, however, occupies the same volume, 22.4 l, regardless of the molecular mass. It is, therefore, possible to eliminate the second and third steps of our procedure. We can find the ratio of moles of reactant to moles of product by inspecting the balanced equation.

In volume-volume problems, the coefficients of the balanced equation may be used.

EXAMPLE – VOLUME–VOLUME

    We will solve the preceding example by a different method.

FIRST.   Write a balanced equation.

$$CH_4(g) + 2O_2(g) \rightarrow CO_2(g) + 2H_2O(g)$$

Note that 1 mole of CH_4 reacts with 2 moles of O_2. Therefore,

$$(10.0 \text{ l } CH_4)\left(\frac{2(22.4) \text{ l } O_2}{1(22.4) \text{ l } CH_4}\right) = 20.0 \text{ l } O_2$$

One mole of CH_4 unites with 2 moles of O_2, or 22.4 l of CH_4 unites with 44.8 l of O_2, or 1 l of CH_4 unites with 2 l of O_2. Note that the ratio of CH_4 to O_2 is 1/2, or of O_2 to CH_4 is 2/1. Both 2 and 1 are whole numbers. This is reasonable because a fractional coefficient would indicate a fractional atom or molecule, and fractional atoms and molecules do not exist.

Gases combine by volume in ratios of small whole numbers.

    In 1809, Joseph Louis Gay-Lussac discovered this experimentally and formulated a law. *Gay-Lussac's law* of combining volumes of gases states: The combining volumes of reacting gases and the volumes of gaseous products can be related by small whole number ratios.

Gay-Lussac's law states that combining volumes of reacting gases and the volumes of gaseous products can be related by small whole number ratios.

Gay-Lussac's law holds only when all gases involved are measured at the same temperature and pressure or when all of the gases are converted to standard conditions.

EXAMPLE—GAY–LUSSAC'S LAW

$$CH_4(g) + 2O_2(g) \rightarrow CO_2(g) + 2H_2O(g)$$

$$\frac{CH_4}{O_2} = \frac{1}{2}, \quad \frac{O_2}{CO_2} = \frac{2}{1}, \quad \frac{CO_2}{H_2O} = \frac{1}{2}$$

$$2C_2H_6(g) + 7O_2(g) \rightarrow 4CO_2(g) + 6H_2O(g)$$

$$\frac{C_2H_6}{O_2} = \frac{2}{7}, \quad \frac{O_2}{CO_2} = \frac{7}{4}, \quad \frac{CO_2}{H_2O} = \frac{4}{6} = \frac{2}{3}$$

The ratio of the combining volumes is the same as the ratio of the combining gram-molecular masses. Thus, you can make use of the coefficients of the balanced equation as the ratios of the combining volumes.

EXAMPLE—VOLUME–VOLUME

How many liters of CO_2 will be produced by burning completely 5.00 l of ethane? (The formula for ethane is C_2H_6.) (All of these substances are gases measured at the same temperature and pressure.)

FIRST. Write a balanced equation.

$$2C_2H_6(g) + 7O_2(g) \rightarrow 4CO_2(g) + 6H_2O(g)$$

Note that 1 mole or 1 l of ethane yields 2 moles or 2 l of CO_2. Therefore,

$$(5.00 \text{ l } C_2H_6)\left(\frac{4(22.4) \text{ l } CO_2}{2(22.4) \text{ l } C_2H_6}\right) = 10.0 \text{ l } CO_2$$

We conclude that 5.00 l of ethane will yield 10.0 l of CO_2.

Point out that this is the usual case for reactions in the laboratory.

16:8 Limiting Reactants: 1 to 1 Mole Ratio

Suppose four liters of hydrogen and one liter of oxygen are placed in a container and ignited by means of a spark. An explosion occurs and water is formed. But we know that two volumes of hydrogen are all that can combine with one volume of oxygen, so two liters of hydrogen must be left unreacted. To take another example, let us drop nine moles of sodium into a vessel containing four moles of chlorine. If we warm the container slightly, the sodium will burn with a bright yellow flame, and crystals of sodium chloride will be formed. We know that one mole of Cl_2 will react completely with two moles of Na, so it is clear that one mole of sodium will remain un-reacted. We say that the hydrogen and sodium are in "excess" and that the oxygen and chlorine are "limiting reactants." In a chemical reaction, the *limiting reactant* is the one which is completely reacted. It is not present in sufficient quantity to react with all of the other reactant(s). The reactants which are left are said to be in excess.

A "limiting reactant" is completely used in a reaction.

Emphasize that the number of moles is the basis on which judgment is made.

EXAMPLE – LIMITING REACTANTS

How many grams of CO_2 are formed if 10.0 grams of carbon are burned in 20.0 l of oxygen? (Assume STP.)

FIRST.   Write a balanced equation.

$$C(c) + O_2(g) \rightarrow CO_2(g)$$

SECOND.   (a) $\dfrac{10.0 \text{ g C} \mid 1 \text{ mole C}}{12.0 \text{ g C}} = 0.833 \text{ mole C}$

$\dfrac{20.0 \text{ l } O_2 \mid 1 \text{ mole } O_2}{22.4 \text{ l } O_2} = 0.893 \text{ mole } O_2$

(b) 1 mole C + 1 mole O_2 → 1 mole CO_2

Because there are fewer moles of carbon, the carbon limits the reaction. Some oxygen (0.060 mole) is left unreacted. We call carbon the *limiting reactant*.

(c) (1) × (0.833 mole of carbon) = 0.833 mole CO_2

THIRD.   Express 0.833 mole of CO_2 in grams.

$$\dfrac{(0.833 \text{ mole } CO_2) \mid [12.0 + 2(16)]\text{g}}{\text{mole } CO_2} = (0.833 \times 44.0)\text{g}$$
$$= 36.7 \text{ g } CO_2$$

We conclude that 10.0 g of carbon will react with excess O_2 to form 36.7 g of CO_2.

EXAMPLE—LIMITING REACTANTS

Let 7.00 grams of iron and 8.00 g of sulfur react to produce iron(II) sulfide. What reactant is in excess, and which is the limiting reactant? (Assume STP.)

FIRST. $Fe(c) + S(c) \rightarrow FeS(c)$

SECOND.   (a) $\dfrac{7.00 \text{ g Fe}}{} \bigg| \dfrac{1 \text{ mole Fe}}{55.8 \text{ g Fe}} = 0.125 \text{ mole Fe}$

$\dfrac{8.00 \text{ g S}}{} \bigg| \dfrac{1 \text{ mole S}}{32.1 \text{ g S}} = 0.249 \text{ mole S}$

(b) 1 mole Fe + 1 mole S $\rightarrow$ 1 mole FeS

Iron is the limiting reactant, and sulfur is in excess.

16:9   Limiting Reactants: Non 1 to 1 Mole Ratio

Notice that in the previous two examples, all coefficients are 1. When coefficients other than 1 are introduced, as in the following problem, an additional calculation is necessary.

EXAMPLE—LIMITING REACTANTS

FIGURE 16-7. The iron and sulfur (a) combine when heated to form iron(II) sulfide (b).

How many grams of aluminum sulfide are formed if 9.00 grams of aluminum react with 8.00 grams of sulfur? (Assume STP.)

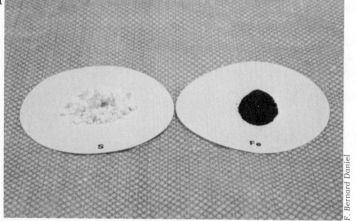

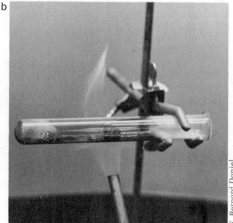

F. Bernard Daniel

FIRST. $2 Al(c) + 3S(c) \rightarrow Al_2S_3(c)$

SECOND.   *Aluminum*

(a) $\dfrac{9.00 \text{ g Al}}{} \bigg| \dfrac{1 \text{ mole Al}}{27.0 \text{ g Al}} = 0.333 \text{ mole Al}$

(b) 1 mole Al yields 0.500 mole Al_2S_3

(c) $(0.333 \times 0.500 \text{ mole}) = 0.166 \text{ mole } Al_2S_3$

Sulfur

(a) $\dfrac{8.00 \text{ g S}}{} \bigg| \dfrac{1 \text{ mole S}}{32.1 \text{ g S}} = 0.249 \text{ mole S}$

(b) 1 mole S yields 0.333 mole Al_2S_3

(c) $(0.249 \times 0.333 \text{ mole}) = 0.0829 \text{ mole } Al_2S_3$

THIRD.   0.0829 mole of Al_2S_3 is less than 0.166 mole of Al_2S_3. Since using all of the sulfur would produce less product than using all of the aluminum, sulfur is the limiting reactant and 0.084 mole of aluminum is in excess.

Therefore, using sulfur as the limiting reactant, 0.0829 times the molecular mass of aluminum sulfide will give the mass of aluminum sulfide produced.

$$0.0829 \text{ mole} \times [2(27.0) + 3(32.1)] \text{ g/mole}$$
$$= 0.0829 \text{ mole} \times 150 \text{ g/mole}$$
$$= 12.4 \text{ g } Al_2S_3$$

12.4 g of Al_2S_3 will be produced from 8.00 g of sulfur and an excess of aluminum.

An alternate method for solving this problem is as follows:

FIRST. $2Al(c) + 3S(c) \rightarrow Al_2S_3(c)$

SECOND.   According to the equation,

(a) 2 moles Al require 3 moles S
    1 mole Al requires 1.5 moles S

(b) $\dfrac{9.00 \text{ g}}{27.0 \text{ g/mole}} = 0.333 \text{ mole Al requires } 0.500 \text{ mole S}$

(c) Since we have only $\dfrac{8.00 \text{ g}}{(32.1 \text{ g/mole})} = 0.249 \text{ mole S}$, sulfur is the limiting reactant. If we had more than 0.500 mole of sulfur, aluminum would have been the limiting reactant.

Another way of solving this problem is as follows:

$$\frac{1}{3} \times \frac{3}{2} = \frac{1}{2} \text{ mole}$$

⅓ mole of Al requires ½ mole of S. Since only ¼ mole of S is available, S is the limiting reactant.

PROBLEMS

9. What volume of oxygen is required to burn completely 401 ml of butane, C_4H_{10}? (All substances are gases measured at the same temperature and pressure.) 2.61 l O_2

10. What volume of bromine gas is evolved if 75.2 ml of Cl_2 react with excess HBr? (All substances are gases measured at the same temperature and pressure.) 75.2 ml Br_2

$$Cl_2(g) + 2HBr(g) \rightarrow Br_2(g) + 2HCl(g)$$

11. $2NaBr(aq) + 2H_2SO_4(aq) + MnO_2(c) \rightarrow Br_2(l) + MnSO_4(aq) + 2H_2O(l) + Na_2SO_4(aq)$. What mass of bromine could be produced from 2.10 g of NaBr and 9.42 g of H_2SO_4? 1.63 g Br_2

12. $2Ca_3(PO_4)_2(c) + 6SiO_2(c) + 10C(c) \rightarrow P_4(g) + 6CaSiO_3(c) + 10CO(g)$. What volume of carbon monoxide gas is produced from 4.14 g $Ca_3(PO_4)_2$ and 1.20 g SiO_2? (Assume STP.) 0.747 l CO

13. What volume of O_2 is required to oxidize 0.500 liter of NO to NO_2? (Assume STP.) 0.250 l O_2

14. $C_6H_{14}(g) \rightarrow C_6H_6(g) + 4H_2(g)$. What volume of hydrogen is produced when 941 m^3 of C_6H_6 are produced? (All substances are gases measured at the same temperature and pressure.) 3760 ml H_2

15. $H_2S(g) + I_2(aq) \rightarrow 2HI(aq) + S(c)$. What mass of sulfur is produced by 4.11 g of I_2 and 317 ml of H_2S at STP? 0.456 g S

16. $2Cl_2(g) + HgO(c) \rightarrow HgCl_2(c) + Cl_2O(g)$. What volume of Cl_2O can be produced from 116 ml of Cl_2 at STP and 7.62 g HgO? 58.0 ml Cl_2O

16:10 Non-Standard Conditions

Problems must be reviewed for conditions other than STP.

Students need to be reminded that corrections are not needed if the mass of the gas is used instead of the volume.

It is important to keep in mind when working problems of the type described in Sections 16:5 through 16:8 that pressure and temperature affect the volume of a gas. Thus, the equality 22.4 liters = 1 mole is true only at STP. If a problem involves a gas under conditions other than standard conditions, it is necessary, before changing gas volume to moles of gas, to calculate the gas volume under standard conditions. The secret to success in these problems is to remember that the central step (moles of given to moles of requested) must take place at STP. Thus, if you are given a volume of gas at other than STP, you must convert to STP before performing the moles to moles step. On the other hand, if you are requested to find the volume of a gas at conditions other than STP, you must convert the volume after the moles to moles step. Let us look at some examples.

EXAMPLE—MASS–GAS VOLUME (NON-STANDARD)

What volume of chlorine gas at 24°C and 744 torr would be required to react with 2.51 g of silver according to the equation $2Ag(c) + Cl_2(g) \rightarrow 2AgCl(c)$?

In order to solve this problem, we calculate the volume needed at STP, then we convert to the conditions stated. The solution is

$$(2.51 \text{ g Ag})\left(\frac{1 \text{ mole Ag}}{108 \text{ g Ag}}\right)\left(\frac{1 \text{ mole Cl}_2}{2 \text{ moles Ag}}\right)\left(\frac{22.4 \text{ l Cl}_2}{1 \text{ mole Cl}_2}\right)\left(\frac{297°K}{273°K}\right)\left(\frac{760 \text{ torr}}{744 \text{ torr}}\right)$$
$$= 0.289 \text{ l Cl}_2$$

Must be at STP if a gas is involved in a mass-volume problem.

EXAMPLE—GAS VOLUME–MASS (NON-STANDARD)

What mass of mercury(II) chloride will react with 0.567 liters of ammonia at 27°C and 770 torr according to the equation $HgCl_2(aq) + 2NH_3(aq) \rightarrow Hg(NH_2)Cl(c) + NH_4Cl(aq)$?

In this problem, we must change the volume of ammonia to standard conditions before converting it to moles. The solution is

$$(0.567 \text{ l NH}_3)\left(\frac{273°K}{300°K}\right)\left(\frac{770 \text{ torr}}{760 \text{ torr}}\right)\left(\frac{1 \text{ mole NH}_3}{22.4 \text{ l NH}_3}\right)\left(\frac{1 \text{ mole HgCl}_2}{2 \text{ moles NH}_3}\right)$$

Must be at STP if a gas is involved in a mass-volume problem.

$$\left(\frac{271 \text{ g HgCl}_2}{1 \text{ mole HgCl}_2}\right) = 3.16 \text{ g HgCl}_2$$

The same procedure can be used to solve limiting reactant problems. If one of the given materials is a gas at other than STP, its volume must be converted to STP before computing the number of moles in the sample. If the answer to the problem is the volume of a gas at other than STP, the volume must be computed at STP and then converted to the required conditions.

In solving volume–volume problems, the situation is altered slightly. If both original and final gas volumes are measured at the same temperature and pressure, we would first correct the volumes to STP and then convert back to the original conditions. The corrections would all divide out. Thus, as long as the temperature and pressure remain the same, a volume-volume problem need not be worked at STP.

This is because we do not convert to moles.

EXAMPLE—VOLUME–VOLUME (CONSTANT CONDITIONS)

How much oxygen at 100°C and 800 torr is required to burn 684 liters of methane at the same temperature and pressure according to the equation $CH_4(g) + 2O_2(g) \rightarrow CO_2(g) + 2H_2O(g)$?

$$(684 \text{ l CH}_4)\left(\frac{2 \text{ l O}_2}{1 \text{ l CH}_4}\right) = 1370 \text{ l O}_2$$

Under constant conditions, a volume-volume problem can be solved without first converting gas volume to STP.

If the given material in a volume-volume problem is at a different temperature and pressure than the required material, the volume of the given material must be changed to correspond to the conditions of the required material. Then the problem may be solved as a regular volume-volume problem.

EXAMPLE – VOLUME–VOLUME (NON-CONSTANT CONDITIONS)

What volume of oxygen at 26°C and 765 torr is required to burn 684 liters of methane at 100°C and 800 torr?

$$(684 \text{ l CH}_4)\left(\frac{299°\text{K}}{373°\text{K}}\right)\left(\frac{800 \text{ torr}}{765 \text{ torr}}\right)\left(\frac{2 \text{ l O}_2}{1 \text{ l CH}_4}\right) = 1150 \text{ l O}_2$$

SUMMARY

1. Avogadro's principle states that, at equal temperatures and pressures, equal volumes of all gases contain equal numbers of molecules.
2. The molar volume of a gas is the volume occupied by 1 mole of the gas at STP; its value is 22.4 l for all gases.
3. The ideal gas equation is $PV = nRT$, where P = pressure, V = volume, n = number of moles, R = a constant, and T = absolute temperature.
4. The molecular mass of a gas may be determined by the gas density and the equation

$$M = \frac{mRT}{PV}$$

5. Gay-Lussac's law of combining volumes of gases states that the ratio of the volumes of reacting gases and of their gaseous products can be expressed in ratios of small whole numbers. These small whole numbers are the coefficients of the balanced equation.
6. A limiting reactant is a reactant which is completely "used up" in a reaction. The remaining reactants are said to be in excess.
7. In solving problems involving gas volumes, consideration must be given to the change of gas volume with change in pressure and temperature. One mole of gas occupies 22.4 liters only at STP.

PROBLEMS

17. What pressure will be exerted by 0.400 mole of a gas in a 10.0 liter vessel at 27°C? 0.985 atm

18. What is the molecular mass of a gas if 500 ml weigh 10.0 g at −23°C and 380 torr? 821 g/mole

19. The burning of ethane (C_2H_6) produces CO_2 and water vapor as the only products. 10.0 liters of ethane would produce how many liters of CO_2? (All substances are gases measured at the same temperature and pressure.)   *ans.*   20.0 l

20. How many liters of O_2 would be required for the completion of the reaction described in Problem 19? 35.0 l O_2

21. Carbon disulfide will burn to produce CO_2 and SO_2. How many liters of SO_2 at STP can be produced from 7.00 l of CS_2 vapor?

   ans.   14.0 l

22. How many moles of CO_2 would be produced in the preceding reaction? 0.313 mole CO_2

23. How many grams of nickel(II) sulfide can be produced by the reaction of 10.0 g of nickel with 4.00 g of sulfur?   *ans.*   11.4 g

24. 7.00 grams of CaO react with 2.00 g of water. How many grams of calcium hydroxide will be formed? 8.23 g $Ca(OH)_2$

25. How many grams of sodium chloride could be produced from the reaction of 23.0 g of sodium with 22.4 l of chlorine?

   ans.   58.5 g

26. Using the equation $Fe_2O_3(c) + 3CO(g) \rightarrow 2Fe(c) + 3CO_2(g)$, determine how many liters of CO_2 at STP can be produced from 16.0 g of Fe_2O_3 and 10.0 l of CO. 6.72 l CO_2

27. In Problem 26, if the gas were collected at 27°C and 800 torr pressure, what volume would it occupy? 7.02 l CO_2

28. What would be the density of the CO_2 gas collected under the experimental conditions stated in Problem 27? 1.88 g/l

29. Show how Gay-Lussac's law can be used with Avogadro's law to explain the fact that some gases are diatomic. Use the equation:

$$N_2(g) + 3H_2(g) \rightarrow 2NH_3(g)$$

1 volume N_2 produces 2 volumes of ammonia. Each molecule of ammonia must contain at least one atom of nitrogen. Since equal volumes of gases contain equal numbers of molecules under similar conditions, each molecule of nitrogen must contain 2 atoms.

ONE MORE STEP See Teacher's Guide at the front of this book.

1. Investigate the part played by Cannizzaro in gaining acceptance for Avogadro's principle.

2. Molecular masses of materials are often found today by using a mass spectrograph, which we have already discussed (Chapter 6). Find out how a "time-of-flight" spectrometer works.

3. How would knowledge of chemistry help an iron foundry?

Suggested Readings for this chapter may be found in the Teacher's Guide at the front of this book.

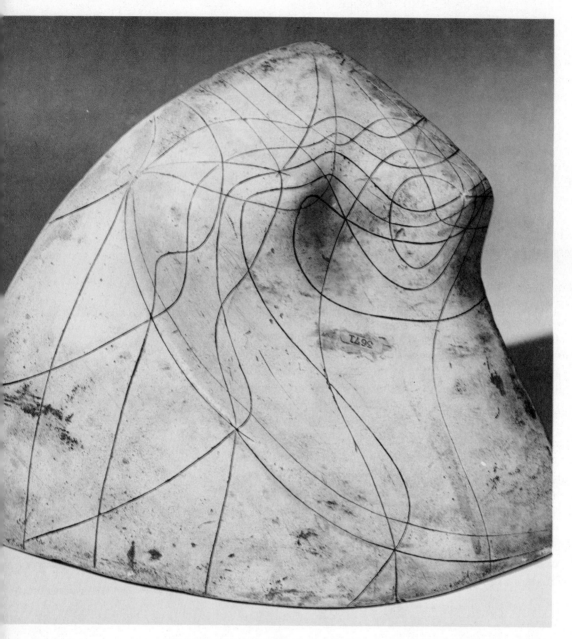

We have seen how chemical reactions can be represented by symbols. Such reactions can also be shown geometrically as in this Gibbs' Surface. By plotting three reaction variables on the x,y, and z axes, one can construct a three-dimensional surface of the extent of the reaction. What are the variables in a reaction?

Chapter 17 introduces the student to thermodynamics through a study of state functions.

In the last several chapters, we have been studying macroscopic amounts of matter. We have been interested in physical properties and physical changes. Where chemical reactions were involved, it was simply stated that they occurred. Now, we will consider what makes reactions occur.

We have noted that reactions which are exothermic generally take place spontaneously (without help). On the other hand, those that are endothermic are generally not spontaneous. In everyday life, we can see that changes in nature are usually "downhill." That is, nature tends to go from a state of higher energy to one of lower energy. Likewise, natural processes tend to go from an orderly state to a disorderly one. However, there are some exceptions.

How is it possible, then, for processes involving reverse tendencies to take place? In this chapter we will find the answer to such questions. However, keep in mind that we will be concerned principally with reactions taking place at constant temperature and pressure. Such processes taking place at a constant temperature are called _isothermal_ processes. The processes that take place at constant pressure are called _isobaric_.

GOAL: You will gain an understanding of the relationship of enthalpy, entropy, and free energy to chemical reactions.

Natural processes:
high energy → low energy
order → disorder

Isothermal: constant temperature
Isobaric: constant pressure

SPONTANEOUS CHANGE

17:1 Enthalpy

Remind students that $\triangle H$ values are relative: The free elements are taken to have $\triangle H_f^\circ = 0$.

In Chapter 5, the term enthalpy was defined as heat content. Chemists often work with the change in the enthalpy of a system. The change in enthalpy or heat content is given the symbol ΔH.

Change in enthalpy $= \Delta H$

FIGURE 17-1. Just as this wagon rolls downhill, nature tends to go from a state of higher energy to one of lower energy.

Exothermic: $\Delta H < 0$
Endothermic: $\Delta H > 0$

In an exothermic reaction, the products have less heat content than the reactants. ΔH is therefore negative. In an endothermic reaction, ΔH is positive.

17:2 Entropy

Highly exothermic reactions tend to take place spontaneously. However, weakly exothermic and endothermic reactions also can occur spontaneously. However, sometimes they need stronger reaction conditions. For example, they can proceed if the temperature is raised.

Consider the reaction of steam on very hot carbon to form carbon monoxide and hydrogen:

$$C(c) + H_2O(g) + energy \rightarrow H_2(g) + CO(g)$$

A simple demonstration of a change where energy is absorbed can be done by pouring 25 ml of water into a 150 ml beaker half full of NH_4NO_3.

Most spontaneous reactions:
$$\Delta H < 0$$

The products have a higher heat content than the reactants. Therefore, since heat energy is used up in this process, ΔH is positive. It has been determined experimentally that if 1 mole of carbon reacts with 1 mole of steam then, $\Delta H = 31,400$ cal (as in the above reaction). We have observed in previous sections that most spontaneous reactions seem to have negative ΔH. Since in this reaction ΔH is positive, some additional factor must be at work.

Entropy (S) is a measure of disorder in a system.

This additional factor is entropy, or disorder. We have seen, in Chapter 13, that there is a very orderly arrangement of atoms in crystalline solids. In liquids, there is somewhat less order. In gases, there is a great lack of orderly arrangement. The degree of disorder is given the name *entropy*. It is represented by the symbol S.

Increase in disorder:
$$\Delta S > 0$$
Increase in order:
$$\Delta S < 0$$

Change in entropy is symbolized by ΔS. A positive value for ΔS means a decrease in the degree of orderly arrangement. That is to

You may also wish to present the concept of entropy in terms of probability.

362

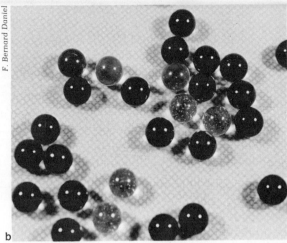

a   b

say, disorder increases. Such a change (positive ΔS) occurs when a solid is converted to a liquid or a gas. When the opposite reaction occurs (liquid or gas is converted to a solid), ΔS is negative.

FIGURE 17-2. Natural processes tend to go from an ordered state to a disordered state as represented by the marbles in (a) and (b).

17:3 Free Energy

The combined effect of ΔH and ΔS is called free energy. It is represented by G, and ΔG represents the change in free energy. ΔG is defined by the following relationship:

Change in free energy$=\Delta G$

$$\Delta G = \Delta H - T\Delta S$$

The term $\triangle G$ is often called Gibbs free energy. Josiah Gibbs (see page 364) was the first to suggest that any reaction which can do useful work at constant temperature and pressure is spontaneous.

where T is the temperature in degrees Kelvin (absolute temperature).

It can be shown, both by theory and by experiment, that in a spontaneous change, ΔG is always negative. If a reaction takes place at low temperatures and involves little change in entropy, then the term $T\Delta S$ will be negligible. In such a reaction then ΔG is largely a function of ΔH, the change in enthalpy. Thus, most reactions occurring at room temperature have a negative ΔH.

Spontaneous reaction:
$\Delta G < 0$

Highly endothermic reactions (high positive value for ΔH) can occur only if $T\Delta S$ is large. This means that either the temperature is high, or there is a large increase in entropy. In the example of the endothermic reaction of carbon with steam, both of these conditions occur. ΔS is positive because the orderly arrangement of carbon in the solid is converted to the disorderly arrangement in CO gas. T is high because the reaction only takes place at red heat (600–900°C) or higher. If the temperature decreases, the reaction stops and, in fact, goes into reverse.

Endothermic reactions occur when $T\Delta S$ is large.

If ΔH and ΔS have the same sign, there will be some temperature at which ΔH and $T\Delta S$ will be numerically equal, and ΔG will be exactly zero. This is the thermodynamic definition of a system in *equilibrium*. At equilibrium (Section 14:2), the value of the free energy (not the value of ΔG) is at a minimum for the particular system.

At equilibrium: $\Delta G = 0$

All spontaneous processes proceed toward equilibrium. For example, a ball rolls down a hill and not up. The bottom of the hill is where the ball has the least potential energy. Chemical potential energy, technically called free energy, is least when a system is at equilibrium.

Specifically, the "chemical potential" of a species is its partial molar free energy.

An interesting result of the entropy contribution to the free energy equation is that molecules like H_2, O_2, and N_2, which are stable on earth, do not exist on the sun and stars. To see why this is true, consider the case of N_2. In order to decompose one mole of N_2 molecules, much energy must be supplied:

$$N_2 + energy \rightarrow 2N \qquad energy = \Delta H = +225,000 \text{ cal}$$

Since ΔH has such a large positive value, at ordinary temperatures N_2 is a very stable molecule. This is a direct result of $T\Delta S$ being very small in comparison to the large positive ΔH (which makes ΔG posi-

Josiah Willard Gibbs

(1839–1903)

One of the great native American theorists, J. Willard Gibbs was born and raised in New Haven, Connecticut. In 1871 he became professor of mathematical physics at Yale, where he remained until his death.

Gibbs' principal contribution to science was his thermodynamic theory. In this work, among other things, he related the behavior of systems in equilibrium to the volume, energy, and degree of order present. He extended his theory to heterogeneous systems undergoing reaction, to which no previous theory applied.

Although recognized as the work of a genius in America, his theories were not really appreciated either here or (except for the greatest minds) in Europe.

Gibbs also made contributions in mathematics and electromagnetic theory.

FIGURE 17-3. As a result of very high temperatures, matter exists in atomic forms rather than in molecular forms near stars.

tive). A gas composed of separate nitrogen atoms has a greater entropy than one made up of N_2 molecules. The pairing of the nitrogen atoms is a kind of order. Therefore, the decomposition of these molecules represents an increase in entropy or a positive ΔS. If N_2 molecules are exposed to higher temperatures (like those near the sun), the value of $T\Delta S$ is greater than 225,000 calories and thus ΔG is negative. As a result, nitrogen exists near the sun only as discrete atoms.

CALCULATIONS ON FREE ENERGY

17:4 Standard States

You may wish to introduce the concept of "state functions" here.

All three quantities (enthalpy, entropy, and free energy) depend on temperature. Thus, chemists have had to agree on a standard set of conditions for measuring these quantities. The conditions chosen are 298°K and 760 torr. The pressure is specified because the quantities also depend on pressure in some reactions.

Standard thermodynamic measurement conditions: 298°K and 760 torr

17:5 Calculations

In Appendix A-8 are listed the standard free energies, enthalpies, and entropies of some substances. We already know (Section 5:14) that the enthalpy change for a reaction is found by:

More extensive tables are available in many reference books, e.g. *The Handbook of Chemistry and Physics.*

$$\Delta H^\circ_{(reaction)} = \Delta H^\circ_{(products)} - \Delta H^\circ_{(reactants)}$$

In a like manner, we may compute the free energy and entropy changes for a reaction:

$$\Delta G^\circ_{(reaction)} = \Delta G^\circ_{(products)} - \Delta G^\circ_{(reactants)}$$

$$\Delta S^\circ_{(reaction)} = \Delta S^\circ_{(products)} - \Delta S^\circ_{(reactants)}$$

EXAMPLE — ENTROPY CHANGE

What is the change in entropy for the reaction between methane and oxygen:

$$CH_4(g) + 2O_2(g) \rightarrow CO_2(g) + 2H_2O(g)$$

under standard measurement conditions? Use $\Delta G = \Delta H - T\Delta S$.

Value (per mole)	CH_4	O_2	CO_2	H_2O
ΔG_f° (cal)	−12,130	0	−94,258	−56,688
ΔH_f° (cal)	−17,880	0	−94,051	−68,315
S° (cal/K°)	44.492	48.996	51.06	16.71

To find ΔG°:

$$\Delta G^\circ = [(-94,258 \text{ cal}) + 2(-56,688 \text{ cal})] - [2(0) + (-12,130 \text{ cal})]$$
$$= -195,504 \text{ cal}$$

To find ΔH°:

$$\Delta H^\circ = [(-94,051 \text{ cal}) + 2(-68,315 \text{ cal})] - [2(0) + (-17,880 \text{ cal})]$$
$$= -212,801 \text{ cal}$$

To find ΔS°:

$$\Delta S^\circ = -\frac{(\Delta G^\circ - \Delta H^\circ)}{T} \quad \text{and} \quad T = 25°C + 273 = 298°K$$

$$\Delta S^\circ = -\left[\frac{(-195,504 \text{ cal}) - (-212,801 \text{ cal})}{298°K}\right]$$

$$= -58.0 \text{ cal/K}°$$

We can check the entropy change by using the standard entropies. Use $\Delta S^\circ_{(reaction)} = S^\circ_{(products)} - S^\circ_{(reactants)}$.

$$\Delta S^\circ = [(51.06 \text{ cal/K}°) + 2(16.71 \text{ cal/K}°)] -$$
$$[(44.492 \text{ cal/K}°) + 2(48.996 \text{ cal/K}°)]$$
$$= -58.004 \text{ cal/K}°$$

These thermodynamic equations allow us to determine a great deal about the possible direction of a reacting system.

EXAMPLE—ONE MISSING PROPERTY

What is the standard entropy of bismuth(III) sulfide? Use the equations: $2Bi(c) + 3S(c) \rightarrow Bi_2S_3(c)$ and $\Delta G = \Delta H - T\Delta S$.

Value (per mole)	Bi	S	Bi_2S_3
ΔG_f° (cal)	0	0	−33,600
ΔH_f° (cal)	0	0	−34,200
S° (cal/K°)	13.56	7.60	?

To find ΔG°:

$$\Delta G^\circ = (-33,600 \text{ cal}) - [2(0) + 3(0)]$$
$$= -33,600 \text{ cal}$$

To find ΔH°:

$$\Delta H^\circ = (-34,200 \text{ cal}) - [2(0) + 3(0)]$$
$$= -34,200 \text{ cal}$$

To find ΔS°:

$$\Delta S^\circ = -\frac{(\Delta G^\circ - \Delta H^\circ)}{T} \quad \text{where T} = 298°\text{K}$$

$$\Delta S^\circ = \frac{(-33,600 \text{ cal/K}°) - (-34,200 \text{ cal/K}°)}{298°\text{K}}$$

$$= -2.01 \text{ cal/K}°$$

To find $S^\circ_{Bi_2S_3}$:

$$\Delta S^\circ = S^\circ_{Bi_2S_3} - [2(S^\circ_{Bi}) + 3(S^\circ_S)]$$
$$S^\circ_{Bi_2S_3} = \Delta S^\circ + 2(S^\circ_{Bi}) + 3(S^\circ_S)$$
$$= (-2.01 \text{ cal/K}°) + [2(13.56) + 3(7.60)] \text{ cal/K}°$$
$$= 47.92 \text{ cal/K}°$$

By checking with Appendix A-8, we can verify that the answer is correct.

ENERGY AND WORK

17:6   Energy

You may wish to introduce the concept of "unavailable" energy at this point.

We have learned (Section 1:6) that energy can be changed from one form to another. For example, under the proper conditions, energy may be converted to work. We know from the law of conservation of energy, that the total amount of energy in an isolated system (such as the universe) remains constant except for nuclear changes.

The total amount of energy in an isolated system is constant.

Work can also be converted into energy. For instance, work is done in moving a book from the floor to a table. The book's energy is increased by an amount equal to the work done on it. It has a greater potential energy on the table than on the floor.

FIGURE 17-4. As this book is raised from the floor to the table, it gains potential energy.

If a system undergoes a change, its internal energy changes according to the equation:

Emphasize q <u>from</u> surroundings and w <u>on</u> surroundings.

$$\Delta E = q - w$$

Heat received *from* the surroundings $= q$

Work performed *on* the surroundings $= w$

In this equation, q is defined as the heat received *from* the surroundings, and w is the work performed *by* the system *on* the surroundings. ΔE is the internal energy change. In changing, a system is said to go from one state to another state. Usually, there is more than one path from state 1 to state 2.

For example, consider the change of a definite quantity of water from the liquid state at 100°C to steam at 104°C. One way of accomplishing such a change is to heat the water at constant pressure so that it boils at 100°C and then continue heating until the steam reaches 104°C. An alternate path is to increase the pressure on the water to 875 torr and heat. At that pressure, water boils at 104°C. Thus, the liquid water is heated to 104°C and then vaporized to steam. The pressure is then reduced to 760 torr.

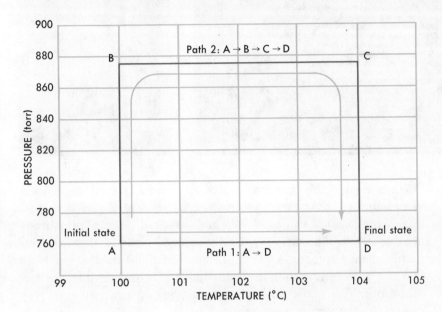

FIGURE 17-5. The overall change in internal energy is the same whether a given amount of water is heated from 100°C to steam at 104°C at constant pressure or is heated at increased pressure to 104°C before the water is converted to steam.

Notice that the final states, in both cases, were the same. One of the basic laws of science is that the change in the internal energy of a system is independent of the path taken in going from state to state. ΔE depends only on the conditions of the two states not the path followed between them. Thus, in the preceding example, ΔE is the same in both cases since the final states are equivalent.

ΔE is independent of the path in going from A to B.

An isolated system is a special case. In an isolated system there can be no interchange with the surroundings. Therefore, both q and w must be zero. As a result, ΔE is also equal to zero and we see that the law of conservation of energy is demonstrated mathematically for an isolated system. This is an adiabatic system.

17:7 Relation to Chemical Systems

How is the internal energy related to the other thermodynamic quantities we have studied? The strict definition of enthalpy is:

$$H = E + PV \quad \text{or} \quad \Delta H = \Delta E + \Delta(PV)$$

Note that $\Delta(PV)$ represents work done by the system.

where P = pressure, and V = volume.

a

b

FIGURE 17-6. Coils of an air conditioning unit (a) are designed to absorb heat from the surroundings. A thermos bottle (b) is designed to prevent exchange of heat with its surroundings.

Under normal laboratory conditions, ΔH equals the heat absorbed from the surroundings.

Since most of the changes observed by chemists are done in open vessels in the laboratory, the pressure is constant (equal to atmospheric pressure). It can be shown mathematically that if pressure is held constant, then $\Delta H = q$. Under such conditions, then, the enthalpy change is just the heat absorbed from the surroundings. Note that if q is negative, then heat must have been given up to the surroundings. This is the same thing as saying that a negative ΔH represents an exothermic reaction.

SUMMARY

1. Enthalpy is the change of heat content in a system.
2. Entropy is the change in the degree of disorder of a system.
3. Spontaneous changes generally have negative enthalpy changes and positive entropy changes.
4. When the enthalpy change and entropy change differ, the net effect is found from the equation $\Delta G = \Delta H - T\Delta S$, where G is free energy, H is enthalpy, T is the absolute temperature, and S is the entropy.
5. When ΔG is zero, the system is at equilibrium.
6. The change in a thermodynamic quantity (ΔH, ΔG, or ΔS) accompanying a reaction is found by subtracting the sum of the quantities of the reactants from the sum of the quantities of the products.
7. The change in the internal energy of a system is equal to the difference between the heat absorbed from the surroundings and the work done on the surroundings.

8. All the thermodynamic quantities discussed in this chapter are "state" quantities. That is, a change in one of these quantities depends only on the conditions in one state compared to another. The change is independent of the path chosen in going from one state to another.

9. The change in enthalpy is related to the internal energy by the relation: $\Delta H = \Delta E + \Delta(PV)$.

10. For a constant pressure process, $\Delta H = q$.

PROBLEMS

1. Using Appendix A-8, decide whether the following reactions should occur spontaneously or not. That is, will ΔG be negative?

   a. $PbBr_2 + Cl_2 \rightarrow PbCl_2 + Br_2$ reaction spontaneous

   b. $H_2O_{(l)} \rightarrow H_2O_{(g)}$ reaction not spontaneous

   c. $2C_4H_{10} + 13O_2 \rightarrow 8CO_2 + 10H_2O$ reaction spontaneous

   d. $Cu_2S + S \rightarrow 2CuS$ reaction spontaneous

   e. $CuS + 2O_2 \rightarrow CuSO_4$ reaction spontaneous

2. Using Appendix A-8, compute the one thermodynamic quantity missing from the tables for the following substances:

   a. $Hg_2Cl_2 + Cl_2 \rightarrow 2HgCl_2$ $S°(HgCl_2) = 28.5$ cal/K°

   b. $3Be + N_2 \rightarrow Be_3N_2$ $S°(Be_3N_2) = 3.45$ cal/K°

   c. $CoCO_3 \rightarrow CoO + CO_2$ $S°(CoCO_3) = 23.5$ cal/K°

   d. $2H_2O_2 \rightarrow 2H_2O + O_2$ $\Delta H_f°(H_2O_2) = -44{,}881$ cal

   e. $2NO + O_2 \rightarrow 2NO_2$ $\Delta G_f°(NO) = 20{,}685$ cal

ONE MORE STEP   See Teacher's Guide at the front of this book.

1. Prepare a report for the class on the difference between heat capacity and heat content.

2. What is meant by the thermodynamic quantity "work function"?

Suggested Readings for this chapter may be found in the Teacher's Guide at the front of this book.

The separation of some solutions is one concern of environmentalists. Here, a method of removing dissolved organic material from wastewater is tested. Activated carbon is being used to adsorb the contaminants (solute) from the water (solvent). Why are solutions difficult to separate? How does a solution such as saltwater differ from a suspension such as muddy water, and from a colloid such as homogenized milk?

Solutions _____ 18

Chapter 18 classifies mixtures of homogeneous aggregates into nine groups of solutions. The properties of the nine groups are predicted and these properties are discussed along with a study of colloids.

What do we mean by solution? In Chapter 3, we referred to heterogeneous matter and homogeneous matter. Homogeneous matter is the same throughout. It is often made up of only one substance—a compound or an element. Homogeneous matter may also be made up of a mixture of several substances. Such a homogeneous mixture is called a solution. Most, but not nearly all, solutions consist of a solid dissolved in a liquid. The particles in a true solution are molecules, atoms, or ions which will pass easily through the pores of filter paper. Solutions cannot be separated into their components by filtration. Other fluid mixtures of solids and liquids which are heterogeneous can be separated into their components by filtration.

The substance which occurs to the greater extent in a solution is said to do the dissolving and is usually called the solvent. The less abundant substance is said to be dissolved and is called the solute.

GOAL: You will gain an understanding of the various types of solutions and their properties as well as the properties of colloids.

A solution is a homogeneous mixture.

The more abundant substance in a solution is called the solvent.

THE DISSOLVING PROCESS

18:1 The Solvent

The most common solvent is water. Using water as a typical solvent, let us look at the mechanism of solvent action. Water molecules are very polar. They have a large dipole moment. Because of their large dipole moment, they are attracted to other polar molecules and to ions. Table salt (NaCl) is an ionic compound

Polar water molecules are attracted to ions and other polar molecules.

FIGURE 18-1. Water molecules are typical polar molecules. Water is an excellent solvent.

This is called solvation, or, in the case of water, hydration.

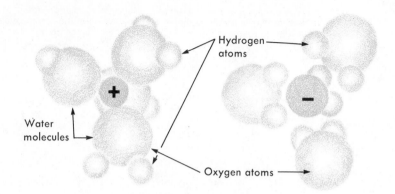

made up of sodium and chloride ions. If a salt crystal is put in water, the polar water molecules are attracted to ions in the crystal face and gradually surround and isolate the surface ions. Thus, the ions become hydrated (Figures 18–1 and 18–2). The attraction between the hydrated sodium and chloride ions and the remaining crystal ions becomes so small that the hydrated ions are no longer held by the crystal. They gradually move away from the crystal into solution. This separation of ions from each other is called *dissociation*.

Dissociation is the separation of ions from each other.

18:2 Solvent-Solute Combinations

There are four basic solution situations with polar and nonpolar substances.

Four simple solution situations can be considered: polar solvent-polar solute, polar solvent-nonpolar solute, nonpolar solvent-polar solute, and nonpolar solvent-nonpolar solute. Not all possible combinations of substances will fit into these four rigid categories. However, we will now consider these four as sample cases for studying solutions.

polar solvent-polar solute

FIRST CASE (polar solvent-polar solute). The mechanism of solution involving a polar solvent and a polar solute is the one we

Table 18–1

Solvent-Solute Combinations

Solvent Type	Solute Type	Is Solution Likely?
Polar	Polar	yes
Polar	Nonpolar	no
Nonpolar	Polar	no
Nonpolar	Nonpolar	yes

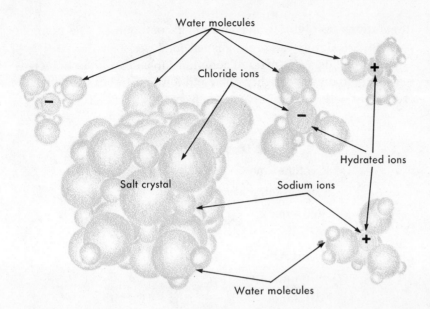

FIGURE 18-2. Table salt is an ionic compound. It dissolves readily in water because the polar water molecules are strongly attracted to the charged sodium and chloride ions.

described for salt and water. The polar solvent particles *solvate* the polar solute particles. They attach themselves due to the polar attraction, and reduce the intracrystalline forces so much that the surface particles are carried away by the solvent particles. In water, this process is called *hydration*.

Chemical reaction between solute and solvent is called solvolysis. If water is involved, the reaction is called hydrolysis. Be careful not to confuse the terms solvolysis and hydrolysis, which imply chemical reactions, with solvation and hydration, which imply no chemical change.

SECOND CASE (polar solvent-nonpolar solute). Because these solvent particles are polar, they are attracted to each other. However, the solute particles in this case are nonpolar and have little attraction for particles of the solvent. Thus, solution to any extent is unlikely.

polar solvent-nonpolar solute

THIRD CASE (nonpolar solvent-polar solute). Reasoning similar to that of the second case applies here. The solvent particles are nonpolar and thus have little attraction for the solute particles. In addition, the solute particles in this case are polar and are attracted to each other. Again, solution to any extent is unlikely.

nonpolar solvent-polar solute

FOURTH CASE (nonpolar solvent-nonpolar solute). There are only van der Waals forces among the nonpolar solvent particles. The same is true for the nonpolar solute particles. Thus, all of the particles in the solution are subject only to van der Waals forces, and solution can occur. Random motion of solute molecules will cause some of them to leave the surface of the solute. There can be solvation in such cases, but the forces involved are far weaker than those

nonpolar solvent-nonpolar solute

dispersion forces only

in solutions involving water and polar compounds. The nonpolar particles are simply randomly dispersed.

Table 18–2 lists a number of common solvents in order of increasing ability to dissolve highly polar and ionic materials. Compare the order here with that in Table 11–1, page 241.

Table 18–2

Ionic Dissolving Ability

Cyclohexane	C_6H_{12}
Carbon tetrachloride	CCl_4
Benzene	C_6H_6
Toluene	C_7H_8
Ethoxyethane	$C_4H_{10}O$
Ethyl acetate	$C_4H_8O_2$
1-Butanol	$C_4H_{10}O$
l-Propanol	C_3H_8O
Propanone	C_3H_6O
Ethanol	C_2H_6O
Methanol	CH_4O
Water	H_2O

(increasing ↓)

18:3 Solids, Liquids, and Gases in Solution

There are nine possible combinations of solvent-solute pairs.

Since there are three common physical states of matter (solid, liquid, and gas), there are nine possible combinations of physical state (solvent-solute pairs). These combinations are given below.

Table 18–3

Possible Solution Combinations

Solvent	Solute	Common Example
gas	gas	oxygen-helium (deep-sea diver's gas)
gas	liquid	air-water (humidity)
gas	solid	air-naphthalene (mothballs)
liquid	gas	water-carbon dioxide (carbonated beverage)
liquid	liquid	acetic acid-water (vinegar)
liquid	solid	water-salt (seawater)
solid	gas	palladium-hydrogen (gas stove lighter)
solid	liquid	silver-mercury (dental amalgam)
solid	solid	gold-silver (ring)

a   b

FIGURE 18-3. Water and alcohol are miscible liquids (a). Vinegar and oil are immiscible liquids (b).

The property of mutual solubility of two liquids is called *miscibility*. If two liquids are mutually soluble in all proportions, they are said to be *completely miscible*. Ethylene glycol (the usual "permanent" automobile antifreeze) and water are two such liquids. Water and carbon tetrachloride, however, do not appreciably dissolve in each other and are, therefore, *immiscible*. Two liquids such as ethyl ether ($C_4H_{10}O$) and water, which dissolve in each other to some extent but not completely, are referred to as *partially miscible*.

Miscible: mutually soluble

Immiscible liquids separate into layers on standing.

A number of metals (such as gold and silver) are mutually soluble and can form solid-solid solutions. Such solid metal-metal solutions constitute one type of *alloy*.

Some alloys are solid metal-metal solutions.

18:4 Solution Equilibrium

When crystals are first placed in a solvent, many particles may leave the surface and go into solution. As the number of particles of solute in solution increases, some of the dissolved particles begin to return to the surface of the crystal. Eventually, a point is reached where the number of particles leaving the crystal surface is equal to the number of particles returning to the surface. This point is called *solution equilibrium*.

At solution equilibrium, particles leaving the solute surface equal the particles returning.

At a specific temperature, there is a limit to the amount of solute that will dissolve in a unit quantity of solvent. For instance, at 20°C, a maximum of 64.2 g of nickel chloride will dissolve in 100 ml of water. This quantity is called the *solubility* of the substance at 20°C. This solubility can be changed by altering the temperature. A solution in which undissolved substance is in equilibrium with the dissolved substance is called a *saturated* solution. A solution containing less than the saturated amount of solute for that temperature is an *unsaturated* solution.

Solubility of a solute depends on the temperature.

Recall the use of saturated in discussion of vapor pressure equilibrium.

Larger amounts of solute can usually be dissolved in a solvent at a temperature higher than room temperature. If the solution is

FIGURE 18-4. Rock candy (a) is simply sugar crystals. It can be prepared by allowing sugar to crystallize from a supersaturated solution onto a string suspended in the solution (b).

A supersaturated solution contains more solute than a saturated solution at a given temperature.

A solution which is 3*M* or stronger is considered to be a concentrated solution.

"Concentrated" and "dilute" are inexact terms.

Solution rate is affected by
1. surface area exposed to solvent
2. kinetic energy of particles

then cooled, an unstable solution containing more solute than a saturated solution can normally hold is formed. This solution is called a *supersaturated solution*. A supersaturated solution is possible because solids will not crystallize unless there is a special surface upon which to start crystallization. A container which has a smooth interior and which contains a dust-free solution has no such surfaces. However, a supersaturated solution will crystallize almost instantly if a crystal of the solute is introduced. How could you find out if a solution is saturated, unsaturated, or supersaturated?

Introduce a crystal of the solute, or a substance with a similar crystal lattice. If it dissolves, the solution is unsaturated; if it does not dissolve, it is saturated; if it crystallizes, it is supersaturated. Dust or glass scratches may also cause

18:5 Solution Proportions crystallization in a supersaturated solution.

Solutions may also be classified on the basis of the relative amounts of solvent and solute present. If a relatively large amount of solute is present per unit volume, the solution is a *concentrated solution*. If only a relatively small amount of the solute is present per unit volume, the solution is a *dilute solution*. This terminology is less exact than indicating the degree of saturation or the ratio of solute to solvent.

18:6 Solution Rate The solution rate decreases as more solute dissolves because undissolved solute concentration decreases and dissolved solute concentration increases.

Solution rate is affected by the surface area of the crystal which is exposed to fresh solvent. When the area of exposed surface is increased, more particles of the solute are subjected to solvation. The surface area can be increased by breaking the crystal to be dissolved into very small particles. This exposure may also be done by stirring the mixture as the solute is dissolving. In this way, the solvent which is saturated with solute is moved away from the surface of the solid solute, and fresh solvent is brought into contact with the solid surface.

a   b   c

FIGURE 18-5. Solution rate can be increased by stirring the mixture (a), increasing the surface area of the solute (b), and by heating the mixture (c).

Solution rate is also a function of the kinetic energy of both the solute and solvent particles. The faster the solvent particles are moving, the more rapidly they will circulate among the crystal particles. This motion has the effect of increasing the surface area. Also, if a solute particle's kinetic energy is increased, once it is solvated it will move away from the solid material more rapidly. This motion exposes fresh surface, thus increasing solution rate. Finally, with increased kinetic energy, particles are more easily removed from the crystal, and solvation and removal from the surface are accomplished more rapidly. The kinetic energy can be increased by heating the mixture.

An increase in temperature may decrease the overall solubility while increasing rate if ΔH is negative.

18:7 Heat of Solution You may wish to review the discussion of ΔH, ΔG, and ΔS in Chapter 17.

The reaction involving the solution of most solids in water is endothermic (ΔH positive). Recall from Chapter 17 that the free energy difference (ΔG) for a change is negative if the reaction proceeds spontaneously. For ΔG to be negative in $\Delta G = \Delta H - T\Delta S$, ΔS must be positive if ΔH is positive. The solid has a high degree of order in the crystalline form. When dissolved, the particles are randomly distributed throughout the solution. The random distribution represents less order than the crystal. We see, then, that ΔS is positive, as predicted.

When gases dissolve in water, the hydrated molecules represent a higher degree of order than the random distribution in the gas. ΔS for the dissolving of a gas is, therefore, negative. Soluble gases, then, must have a negative ΔH. Experiment shows that the dissolving of gases is, in fact, an exothermic process. The same facts are true of some few solids in which the degree of hydration is so high that more order exists in the solution than in the separate solid and liquid.

FIGURE 18-6. The heat of reaction can be determined experimentally by performing the reaction in an insulated container.

Demonstration: Add a large amount of ammonium nitrate to some water in a beaker and pass the container around the class while the solution process is occurring. The container becomes strikingly cool. The opposite effect is observed during the solution of sodium hydroxide. (Take care to warn the students to handle this solution carefully. It becomes quite hot!)

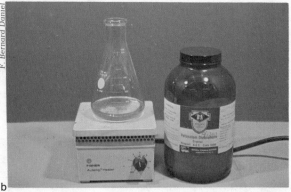

a

b

FIGURE 18-7. A gas is more soluble in a cold liquid than in a warm liquid (a). Solids tend to be more soluble in a warm liquid than in a cold liquid (b).

Generally solids are more soluble in hot water; gases in cold.

Using our knowledge of the change of enthalpy in solutions, we can predict the effect of temperature on solubility. Most solids, having positive heats of solution ($\Delta H > 0$), are more soluble in hot water than in cold. However, most gases, with negative heats of solution, ($\Delta H < 0$) are more soluble in cold water.

18:8 Effects of Pressure

More gas will dissolve at high pressure than at low pressure.

Pressure has little effect on solutions unless the solute is a gas. The amount of gas which dissolves in a given amount of solvent is greater at high pressure than it is at low pressure. The mass of a gas which will dissolve in a liquid at a given temperature varies directly with the partial pressure of that gas. This is *Henry's Law*, named in honor of William Henry, the English chemist who first discovered this relationship.

CONCENTRATION UNITS

You may wish to review the introduction of Avogadro's number and the mole before starting concentration and standard solutions. If so, see pages 78-81.

18:9 Molar and Formal Solutions

A 1 molar (1M) solution contains one mole of solute per liter of solution.

Thus far in our discussion of solutions, all the methods we have used to describe the relationship of solute to solvent (saturated-unsaturated and concentrated-dilute) have been relatively inexact. It is often important to know precisely how much solute is present for a given amount of solvent or solution at a specific temperature. An example of a precise concentration unit is molarity. A *one-molar* (1M) solution contains 1 mole of solute in 1 liter of solution. If 1 mole (58.5 g) of sodium chloride is dissolved in sufficient water to make a total of 1 liter of solution, the solution is called a 1-molar solution of sodium chloride. Sodium chloride is in the form of dissociated ions in solution. Therefore, the solution can also be said to be 1-molar in sodium ions and 1-molar in chloride ions. Sometimes, the preceding solution of sodium chloride is called *one-formal* (1F), since a mole of sodium chloride is one gram-formula mass. Some references reserve the term molar for solutions of substances which actually occur as molecules (for instance, sugar). We will use the term *molar* to refer to any solution containing 1 mole of solute per liter of solution. We will not use the term formal.

Whenever the concentration of solute in a solution is known with some degree of precision, the solution is called a *standard solution*.

The concentration of a standard solution is known with some precision.

EXAMPLE—MOLARITY

If 15.3 g of magnesium iodide are dissolved in enough water to make 500 ml of solution, what is the molarity of the solution?

Molar mass of MgI_2 = 24.3 g + 2(127 g) = 278 g

$$\frac{15.3 \text{ g } MgI_2}{500 \text{ ml of solution}} \left| \frac{1 \text{ mole } MgI_2}{278 \text{ g } MgI_2} \right| \frac{1000 \text{ ml of solution}}{1 \text{ l of solution}} = 0.110M$$

Since the concentration of solute is precisely known, this is a standard solution. This same solution is also a 0.110M solution of Mg^{2+} ions and a 0.220M solution of iodide ions (I^-), since each MgI_2 unit from the crystal produces one magnesium ion and two iodide ions.

$$MgI_2(c) \xrightarrow{H_2O} Mg^{2+}(aq) + 2I^-(aq)$$

18:10 Molal Solutions *Molal solutions are useful in studying colligative properties.*

Sometimes, it is convenient to express concentration in terms of moles of solute per kilogram of solvent. A solution which contains 1 mole of solute in each 1000 g of solvent is called a *one-molal* (1m) solution. This differs from a 1-molar (1M) solution, which contains 1 mole of solute in 1 liter of solution.

A 1 molal (1m) solution contains one mole of solute in 1000 g of solvent.

EXAMPLE—MOLALITY

If 52.0 g of K_2CO_3 are dissolved in 518 g of H_2O, what is the molality of the solution?

Molar mass of K_2CO_3 = 2(39.1 g) + 12.0 g + 3(16.0 g) = 138 g

$$\frac{52.0 \text{ g } K_2CO_3}{518 \text{ g } H_2O} \left| \frac{1 \text{ mole } K_2CO_3}{138 \text{ g } K_2CO_3} \right| \frac{1000 \text{ g } H_2O}{1 \text{ kg } H_2O} = 0.726m$$

18:11   Mole Fraction The mole fraction is most commonly used by organic chemists in fractional distillation calculations.

The mole fraction is a comparison of moles of solute to the total number of moles of solution.

Another method of describing concentration is used frequently in organic chemistry. This is the *mole fraction*: the comparison of moles of solute to moles of solution.

EXAMPLE – MOLE FRACTION

What is the mole fraction of alcohol in a solution made up of 2 moles of ethyl alcohol and 8 moles of water?

The total number of moles is $(8 + 2) = 10$ moles. The mole fraction of alcohol is 2/10 or 0.2. A solution, by definition, is homogeneous. Thus, any size sample of this solution will have an alcohol mole fraction of 0.2. Note that the sum of the mole fractions of all components of a solution must equal 1.

PROBLEMS

1. Calculate the molarity of the following solutions:
    a. 316 g $MgBr_2$ in 859 ml solution 2.00M
    b. 8.28 g $Ca(C_5H_9O_2)_2$ in 414 ml solution 0.0826M
    c. 31.1 g $Al_2(SO_4)_3$ in 756 ml solution 0.120M
    d. 59.5 g $CaCl_2$ in 100 ml solution 5.36M
    e. 313.5 g $LiClO_3$ in 250 ml solution 13.9M
2. Calculate the molality of the following solutions:
    a. 199 g $NiBr_2$ in 500 g water 1.82m
    b. 92.3 g KF in 1000 g water 1.59m
    c. 98.0 g RbBr in 824 g water 0.721m
    d. 85.2 g $SnBr_2$ in 140 g water 2.18m
    e. 10.0 g $AgClO_3$ in 201 g water 0.260m
3. Calculate the mole fraction for each component in the following solutions:
    a. 12.3 g of C_4H_4O in 100 g of C_2H_6O
    b. 56.3 g of $C_{12}H_{22}O_{11}$ in 300 g H_2O
    c. 54.3 g of $C_{10}H_8$ in 600 g $C_4H_{10}O$
    d. 67.4 g of C_9H_7N in 200 g C_2H_6O
    e. 5.48 g of $C_5H_{10}O_5$ and 3.15 g of CH_6ON_4 in 21.2 g H_2O

3. a. 0.0770 C_4H_4O; 0.923 C_2H_6O
   b. 0.00976 $C_{12}H_{22}O_{11}$;
      0.988 H_2O
   c. 0.0497 $C_{10}H_8$; 0.951 $C_4H_{10}O$
   d. 0.107 C_9H_7N; 0.893 C_2H_6O
   e. 0.0292 $C_5H_{10}O_5$;
      0.0280 CH_6ON_4; 0.944 H_2O

COLLIGATIVE PROPERTIES

18:12   Raoult's Law

Colligative properties depend on the number of particles in solution.

Colligative properties are those properties which are determined by the number of particles in solution rather than by the type of particle in solution. When a solute is dissolved in a liquid solvent, some of the solute particles take up space on the surface of the liquid normally occupied by solvent particles. These solute particles decrease the opportunity for solvent particles to escape (evaporate) from the liquid surface. Thus, if the solute is nonvolatile, the vapor pressure of a solution is always less than that of the pure solvent at the same temperature. The lowering of the vapor pressure of the solvent is proportional to the mole fraction of dissolved solute. One mole of any nonvolatile solute will lower the vapor pressure of a given quantity of a liquid solvent by an amount characteristic of that solvent. The characteristics of the solute are not involved. Thus, to determine the vapor pressure of a solution, we must correct the vapor pressure of the pure solvent for the presence of the solute. The equation used for correcting the vapor pressure is:

> This is a statistical consideration.

> Assuming a nonvolatile solute.

$$\underset{\text{(solution)}}{\text{vapor pressure}} = \underset{\text{(solvent)}}{\text{vapor pressure}} \times \underset{\text{(solvent)}}{\text{mole fraction}}$$

This expression is a mathematical statement of *Raoult's law*. Francis Raoult, a French chemist, first stated the principle that the vapor pressure of a solution is proportional to the mole fraction of solvent present.

> Raoult's Law states that the vapor pressure of a solution is proportional to the mole fraction of solvent present.

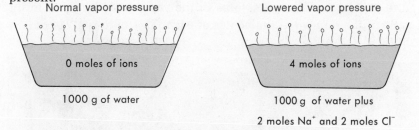

(4 moles)(1.86C°/mole)=7.44C° Lowering of freezing point

FIGURE 18-8. The vapor pressure of a solution is proportional to the mole fraction of solvent present.

Raoult's law holds in an ideal solution. Let us define an ideal solution as one in which all intermolecular attractions are the same. In other words, solute-solute, solvent-solvent, and solute-solvent attractions are all essentially the same.

In the case of a volatile solute, Raoult's law is often inadequate to predict the behavior of the solution. However, there are many solutions whose behavior approaches the ideal closely enough to be treated as such. Each volatile component of an ideal solution has a vapor pressure which can be determined by Raoult's law.

EXAMPLE—RAOULT'S LAW

Consider a solution composed of 1 mole of benzene (C_6H_6) and 1 mole of toluene ($CH_3C_6H_5$). The mole fraction of each component is 0.5. Thus, the number of molecules of benzene is equal to that of toluene. At 25°C, benzene has a vapor pressure of 94 torr, and toluene has a vapor pressure of 28 torr. What is the vapor pressure of the resulting solution?

For our solution, the vapor pressure is the sum of the individual pressure of benzene and toluene. The vapor pressure of benzene in the solution is

$$(0.5)(94 \text{ torr}) = 47 \text{ torr}$$

The vapor pressure of toluene in the solution is

$$(0.5)(28 \text{ torr}) = 14 \text{ torr}$$

Thus, the vapor pressure of the resulting solution is 61 torr.

Note that the vapor phase is much richer in the more volatile component (benzene) than was the liquid phase. Since the vapors of the two substances are in the same volume and at the same temperature, the ratio of their pressures in the vapor must be equal to the ratio of the number of molecules of each. This ratio is 47/14 or 3.36 to 1.

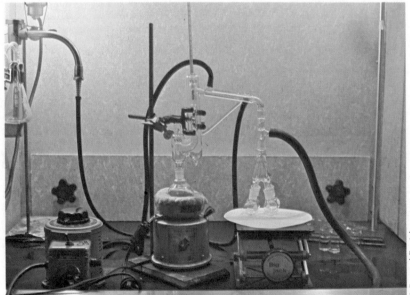

FIGURE 18-9. Some mixtures of liquids such as a benzene-toluene mixture can be separated by fractional distillation.

F. Bernard Daniel

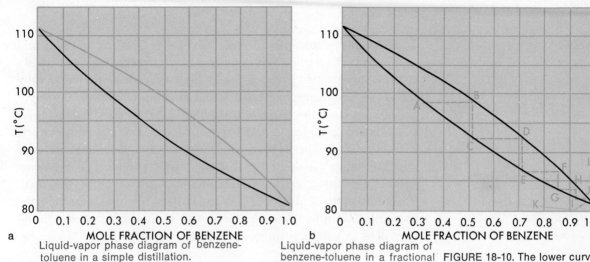

a MOLE FRACTION OF BENZENE
Liquid-vapor phase diagram of benzene-toluene in a simple distillation.

b MOLE FRACTION OF BENZENE
Liquid-vapor phase diagram of benzene-toluene in a fractional distillation.

FIGURE 18-10. The lower curve in (a) represents the composition of benzene-toluene mixtures of varying concentrations at their boiling points. The upper line represents the concentrations of the corresponding vapor. The stepwise line in (b) indicates how a benzene-toluene mixture can be separated into its components by fractional distillation.

18:13 Fractional Distillation

We take advantage of this difference in vapor pressure in the process of fractional distillation. If we plot the boiling point of mixtures of benzene and toluene, we obtain a graph as shown in Figure 18–10a. The boiling point of each mixture is, of course, the temperature at which the sum of the two vapor pressures equals 760 torr. At each of these points, however, the vapor phase would be richer in the more volatile component. Let us calculate the composition of the vapor in equilibrium with the liquid at each of these points, and plot the data on the same graph.

Fractional distillation depends upon vapor pressure difference.

Look at Figure 18–10b. Consider the boiling of a solution of benzene and toluene in which the mole fraction of benzene is 0.3. It will boil at the temperature represented by point A. The vapor obtained will have the composition represented by point B. If we condense this vapor, the condensate will boil at point C. It will produce a vapor of composition D. This process can be continued until nearly pure benzene is obtained as vapor, and almost pure toluene remains behind. It is possible to construct a distillation apparatus in which separate distillations for each step are not necessary. The structure of the apparatus is such that each step takes place in a separate section of the equipment. In the laboratory, a *fractional distillation* apparatus is often used in separating volatile liquids. In industry, a *fractionating tower* is used for the same purpose on a commercial scale.

A fractionating tower works on the principle of condensing and revaporizing the already vaporized substance many times as it flows through the tower.

18:14 Boiling Point and Freezing Point

The presence of nonvolatile solute particles at the surface causes the boiling point of a solution to be raised. The *boiling point* of a

The boiling point of a liquid is the temperature at which the vapor pressure of the liquid equals the atmospheric pressure.

liquid is the temperature at which the vapor pressure of the liquid equals the atmospheric pressure. Vapor pressure varies directly as the concentration of particles in the vapor phase (gaseous state) above the liquid. Because particles of the liquid escape to the vapor phase only from the surface of the liquid, fewer surface molecules mean fewer particles in the vapor phase at a given temperature. A higher temperature is then needed to put enough solvent particles into the vapor phase to equal atmospheric pressure. The boiling point of a solution is, therefore, higher than that of the pure solvent.

The boiling point (B.P.) of a solution is higher than the B.P. of the pure solvent.

How does the addition of a nonvolatile solute affect the freezing point of a solution? The kinetic energy of the particles of a liquid decreases as the liquid is cooled. As the speed of the particles decreases, the attractive forces between particles become more effective, until the slower moving particles remain together and begin to crystallize.

The freezing point of a liquid is the temperature at which the vapor pressures of the solid and liquid are equal.

The *freezing point* is the temperature at which the vapor pressure of the solid and liquid are equal. Since addition of solute particles lowers the vapor pressure, the vapor pressures of the solid and liquid will be equal at a lower temperature. Solutions, then, will freeze at a lower temperature than the pure solvent alone.

The freezing point (F.P.) of a solution is lower than the F.P. of the pure solvent.

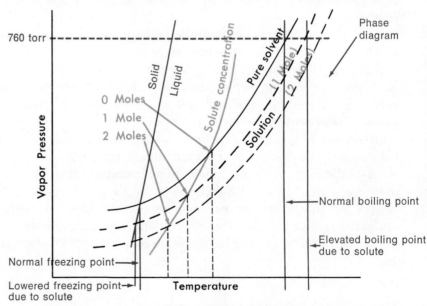

FIGURE 18-11. The addition of solute particles lowers the vapor pressure and causes the solution to freeze at a lower temperature than the pure solvent.

In summary, the addition of nonvolatile solute particles to a pure liquid causes both a boiling point elevation and a freezing point depression. Both boiling point elevation and freezing point depression occur because the vapor pressure of the solvent is lowered by the solute particles. These changes depend only on the concentration of the solute particles, and not upon the nature of the solute. We will now consider some general quantitative statements which can be made about these changes.

B.P. elevation and F.P. depression depend on concentration of solution.

18:15   Calculating Freezing and Boiling Points

It has been found experimentally that 1 mole of nonvolatile solute particles will raise the boiling temperature of 1000 g of water 0.512C°, and will lower the freezing point of 1000 g of water 1.86C°. These two figures are the *molal boiling point constant* and *molal freezing point constant* for water. The corresponding constants for some other common solvents are given in Table A–6 of the Appendix. A 1m solution of sugar in water contains 1 mole of solute particles per 1000 g of water. However, a 1m solution of salt contains 2 moles of solute particles (1 mole of Na^+ ions and 1 mole of Cl^- ions). Furthermore, a 1m solution of calcium chloride contains 3 moles of solute particles per 1000 g of water (1 mole of Ca^{2+} and 2 moles of Cl^- ions). The 1m sugar solution freezes 1.86C° below the freezing point of pure water. However, the 1m salt solution freezes about 2(1.86C°) below the freezing point of pure water, and the 1m solution of calcium chloride freezes approximately 3(1.86C°) below the freezing point of pure water. The multiple lowering of the freezing point and elevation of the boiling point by ionic substances gives support to the theory of ionization.

Molal F.P. depression for $H_2O = 1.86°C$.

Molal B.P. elevation for $H_2O = 0.512°C$.

Students should not be required to memorize these constants.

Actual B.P. or F. P. depends greatly on ionization.

EXAMPLE – FREEZING POINT DEPRESSION AND BOILING POINT ELEVATION

If 85.0 g of sugar are dissolved in 392 g of water, what will be the boiling point and freezing point of the resulting solution?

The molecular formula of sugar is $C_{12}H_{22}O_{11}$. The solution contains 85.0 g of sugar.

FIRST. Determine the molality of the solution. The mass of one mole of $C_{12}H_{22}O_{11}$ equals:

$$12(12 \text{ g}) + 22(1 \text{ g}) + 11(16 \text{ g}) = 342 \text{ g}$$

Since there are 85.0 g of sugar present, the moles of sugar in 392 g of water is:

$$\frac{85.0 \text{ g of sugar}}{342 \text{ g/mole}} = 0.248 \text{ moles of sugar}$$

Converting this to moles/1000 g of water gives:

$$\frac{0.248 \text{ mole sugar}}{392 \text{ g water}} \quad \frac{1000 \text{ g water}}{1 \text{ kg water}} = 0.633 m \text{ solution}$$

Molality can also be determined directly:

$$\frac{85.0 \text{ g C}_{12}\text{H}_{22}\text{O}_{11}}{392 \text{ g H}_2\text{O}} \quad \frac{1 \text{ mole}}{342 \text{ g C}_{12}\text{H}_{22}\text{O}_{11}} \quad \frac{1000 \text{ g H}_2\text{O}}{1 \text{ kg H}_2\text{O}} = 0.633 m \text{ solution}$$

SECOND. Determine the boiling point elevation. The boiling point is raised 0.512C° for each mole of sugar added to 1000 g of water. Therefore the boiling point is:

$$100°\text{C} + (0.633)(0.512\text{C}°) = (100 + 0.324)°\text{C}$$
$$= 100.324°\text{C}$$

Boiling point can also be determined directly:

$$\frac{85.0 \text{ g sugar}}{392 \text{ g H}_2\text{O}} \quad \frac{1000 \text{ g H}_2\text{O}}{1 \text{ kg H}_2\text{O}} \quad \frac{1 \text{ mole sugar}}{342 \text{ g sugar}} \quad \frac{0.512\text{C}°}{1 \text{ mole sugar/1 kg H}_2\text{O}}$$

$$= 0.324\text{C}°$$

$$\text{Boiling point} = (100 + 0.324)°\text{C}$$

THIRD. Determine the freezing point depression. The freezing point is lowered 1.86C° for each mole of sugar added to 1000 g of water. Therefore, the freezing point is:

$$0°\text{C} - (0.633)(1.86\text{C}°) = (0 - 1.18)°\text{C}$$
$$= -1.18°\text{C}$$

Freezing point can also be determined directly:

$$\frac{85.0 \text{ g sugar}}{392 \text{ g } H_2O} \left| \frac{1000 \text{ g } H_2O}{1 \text{ kg } H_2O} \right| \frac{1 \text{ mole sugar}}{342 \text{ g sugar}} \left| \frac{1.86C°}{1 \text{ mole sugar/1 kg } H_2O} \right.$$

$$= 1.18C°$$

$$\text{Freezing point} = (0 - 1.18)°C$$
$$= -1.18°C$$

EXAMPLE—FREEZING POINT DEPRESSION AND BOILING
POINT ELEVATION

If 26.4 g of nickel(II) bromide are dissolved in 224 g of water, what
will be the boiling point and freezing point of the resulting solution?
(Assume 100% dissociation and no interaction between ions.)

FIRST. Determine the molality of the solution. The formula mass of
one mole of $NiBr_2$ is 58.7 g + 2(79.9 g) = 219 g.

The number of moles of $NiBr_2$:

$$= \frac{26.4 \text{ g of } NiBr_2}{219 \text{ g/mole}}$$
$$= 0.121 \text{ moles of } NiBr_2$$

Since the mass of water is 224 g, the molality equals:

$$\frac{0.121 \text{ mole}}{224 \text{ g water}} \left| \frac{1000 \text{ g water}}{1 \text{ kg water}} \right. = 0.539m \text{ } NiBr_2$$

But the molality in total particles is three times this number or 1.62m
because:

$$NiBr_2(c) \rightarrow Ni^{2+}(aq) + 2Br^-(aq)$$

SECOND. Determine the boiling point.

$$\text{Boiling point} = 100°C + (1.62)(0.512C°)$$
$$= 100.828°C$$

Or directly, boiling point $= 100°C + 3 \times$

$$\left[\frac{26.4 \text{ g NiBr}_2}{224 \text{ g H}_2\text{O}} \middle| \frac{1000 \text{ g H}_2\text{O}}{1 \text{ kg H}_2\text{O}} \middle| \frac{1 \text{ mole NiBr}_2}{219 \text{ g NiBr}_2} \middle| \frac{1.86\text{C}°}{1 \text{ mole NiBr}_2/\text{kg H}_2\text{O}}\right]$$

$$= 100.828°C$$

THIRD. Determine the freezing point.

$$\text{Freezing point} = 0°C - (1.62)(1.86\text{C}°)$$
$$= -3.01°C$$

Or directly, freezing point $= 0°C - 3 \times$

$$\left[\frac{26.4 \text{ g NiBr}_2}{224 \text{ g H}_2\text{O}} \middle| \frac{1000 \text{ g H}_2\text{O}}{1 \text{ kg H}_2\text{O}} \middle| \frac{1 \text{ mole NiBr}_2}{219 \text{ g NiBr}_2} \middle| \frac{1.86\text{C}°}{1 \text{ mole NiBr}_2/\text{kg H}_2\text{O}}\right]$$

$$= -3.01°C$$

18:16 Experimental Determination of Molecular Mass

Molecular mass can be determined by the change in F.P. or B.P.

The molecular mass of a solute may be determined by adding a known mass of the solute to a known mass of a solvent and measuring the resulting shift in the boiling or freezing point.

EXAMPLE – MOLECULAR MASS DETERMINATION

In actual practice in organic chemistry, camphor is often used as the solvent in molecular mass determination because it has a freezing point constant of 39.7°C (for water, this is 1.86°C). The temperature change is therefore easier to observe accurately than the temperature change in water.

If 99.0 g of nonionizing solute are dissolved in 669 g of water, and the freezing point of the resulting solution is $-0.96°C$, what is the molecular mass of the solute?

Solution lowers the freezing point 0.96C°.
A 1m solution would lower the freezing point 1.86C°.

$$\text{Molality of solution} = \left(\frac{0.96\text{C}°}{1.86\text{C}°}\right)\left(\frac{1 \text{ mole}}{1 \text{ kg}}\right) = \frac{0.516 \text{ mole}}{\text{kg}} = 0.516m$$

$$\text{Molecular mass} = \left(\frac{99 \text{ g of solute}}{669 \text{ g of water}}\right)\left(\frac{1000 \text{ g of water}}{0.516 \text{ mole of solute}}\right)$$

$$= 287 \text{ g/mole}$$

PROBLEM

4. Calculate the molecular mass of the nonionic solutes:

   a. 6.70 g of solute in 983 g of water lower the freezing point to −0.430°C. 29.5 g/mole

   b. 42.6 g of solute in 189 g of water raise the boiling point to 100.680°C. 169 g/mole

   c. 17.2 g of solute in 128 g of acetic acid lower the freezing point to 13.5°C. 169 g/mole

   d. 15.9 g of solute in 164 g of phenol lower the freezing point to 36.3°C. 153 g/mole

   e. 3.54 g of solute in 63.5 g of nitrobenzene lower the freezing point to 3.40°C. 169 g/mole

18:17 Ion Activity

Although the present view is that all ionic compounds are completely dissociated in solution, certain phenomena associated with their solutions seem to contradict this view. For instance, since 1 mole of sodium chloride would produce 1 mole of each kind of particle (see Section 5–8), you would expect that a 2m solution of NaCl would lower the freezing point of the water by 4 × 1.86C°, or 7.44C°. Such a solution is ideal. Salt actually lowers the freezing point only about three-quarters of this amount. This difference between theoretical prediction and experimental results could be explained by assuming that the solute is not completely dissociated into ions. It is believed, however, that the salt *is* completely dissociated into ions. However, these ions interact and thus the salt does not appear to be completely dissociated. A more detailed explanation of ion interaction in solution is given by the Debye-Hückel theory.

The actual effectiveness of the ions in such phenomena as freezing point lowering and boiling point elevation is known as the activity of the ions. In dealing with a nonideal solution, one should use activities in place of concentrations. As the solution becomes more concentrated, each ion individually becomes less effective through interaction with its neighboring ions. For many purposes, our solutions are dilute enough that we can assume, without serious error, that the ion activity is equal to the concentration.

Non-ideal activity is due to ion interaction.

It is necessary to know the ion activity because, in solutions with appreciable concentrations of solvent, the electrostatic interaction between oppositely charged ions reduces their effect upon the colligative properties.

When ions interact in solution, their effective concentration is reduced.

This is assumed in all calculations in the remainder of this text.

COLLOIDS

18:18 Colloids and Phases

Over one hundred years ago, Thomas Graham, an English chemist, conducted an experiment involving the passage of different substances through a parchment membrane. He found that one group of substances passed readily through the membrane, and another group did not pass through it at all. He called the first group *crystalloids* and the second group *colloids*. The name colloid means gluelike, and glue was one of the substances which did not pass readily through the membrane. Graham thought the ability or inability to pass through the membrane was due to particle size. It was later discovered that any substance could be used to produce a colloid, including some of those substances Graham had classified as crystalloids. *Colloids* are now defined as mixtures composed of two phases of matter, the *dispersed phase* and the *continuous phase*. They are intermediate between suspensions and solutions. Colloid particles are larger than the single atoms, ions, or molecules of solutions. They are smaller than the particles of suspensions, which can be seen through a microscope and which settle out of suspension on standing.

Some extremely large molecules may be dispersed colloidally, for example proteins and polymers.

Colloids are mixtures of two phases of matter.
1. dispersed phase
2. continuous phase

Colloidal particles are intermediate in size between solutions and suspensions.

18:19 Colloidal Size

Colloidal particles are too small to be seen with a microscope. In 1912, Richard Zsigmondy, a German professor of chemistry, designed the ultramicroscope. With the ultramicroscope, it is possible to "see" colloidal particles. Let us see how large these particles are.

If a finely ground substance is placed in water, one of three things will happen. First, it may form a true solution. A true solution is simply a dispersion of atoms, molecules, or ions of the substance into a solvent. The limit of the size of particles in a true solution is about one nanometer.

Second, the particles may remain larger than 100 nm. These particles are large enough to be seen with a microscope. They are strongly affected by gravity and gradually fall to the bottom of the container. Since the particles are temporarily suspended and settle out upon standing, this mixture is called a *suspension*.

What happens, though, if the particles are of the size from 1 to 100 nm? These particles usually remain dispersed throughout the medium. Such a mixture is called a *colloid*. Colloids are neither homogeneous nor heterogeneous. They represent a transition be-

FIGURE 18-12. Emulsions are colloids composed of two immiscible liquids and a protective substance. This technician is measuring the density of the emulsion on photographic film.

USDA Photo

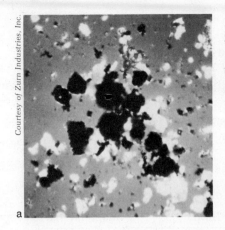

a

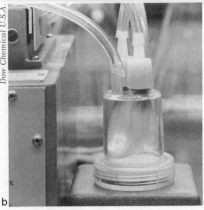

b

FIGURE 18-13. Smoke is a colloid of air and tiny solid particles such as those greatly magnified in (a). Hollow fiber membranes have been developed for use in separating some colloids (b).

tween homogeneous solutions and heterogeneous suspensions. However, they are generally considered heterogeneous (with the medium as one phase and the dispersed substance as a separate phase).

Table 18–4

Comparison of Solution, Suspension, and Colloid

Name	Particle Size	Permanence
Solution	< 1 nm	Permanent
Suspension	> 100 nm	Settle out
Colloid	< 100 nm but > 1 nm	Permanent

Particle size in solutions ≤ 1 nm.

Particle size in suspensions ≥ 100 nm.

Particle size in colloids ≥ 1 nm and ≤ 100 nm.

Actually, it is not enough to refer to colloids as being composed of particles in the above size range. Experiments have shown that substances show unusual properties even when only one of the three dimensions of their particles is brought into the colloidal range.

FIGURE 18-14. A solution such as that of sugar in water (a) is homogeneous. Milk (b) is a colloid and, unlike a solution, can be separated into layers by spinning it in a centrifuge.

a

b

This includes thin sheets as well as minute particles. Thus, *colloid chemistry* could be defined as the study of the properties of matter whose particles are in the colloidal size range in at least one dimension.

Note! ⎯

Table 18–5 compares the properties of solutions, colloids, and suspensions.

Table 18–5

Properties of Solutions, Colloids, and Suspensions

Solutions	*Colloids*	*Suspensions*
Do not settle out	Do not settle out	Settle out on standing
Pass unchanged through ordinary filter paper	Pass unchanged through ordinary filter paper	Separated by ordinary filter paper
Pass unchanged through membrane	Separated by a membrane	Separated by a membrane
Do not scatter light	Scatter light	Scatter light
Affect colligative properties	Do not affect colligative properties	Do not affect colligative properties

The table may be used to derive experimental methods of differentiating the three kinds of mixtures.

FIGURE 18-15. Notice how the beam from this searchlight is scattered by the water droplets in the night air.

Official U.S. Coast Guard Photograph

18:20 Properties of Colloids

If a beam of light is allowed to pass through a true solution, some of the light will be absorbed, and some will be transmitted. The particles in solution are not large enough to scatter the light. However, if light is passed through a colloid, the light is scattered by the larger, colloidal particles and the beam becomes visible from the side.

This effect, called the *Tyndall effect,* is used in Zsigmondy's ultramicroscope. You may be familiar with this effect as the beam of a searchlight in the night air (suspended water droplets in air). You may also have observed it as the sunbeam coming through a hole in the blinds (suspended dust particles in air).

Colloids have another interesting property. If you could look through an ultramicroscope, you would notice that the colloidal

Courtesy of Kodansha Ltd.

Courtesy of Kodansha Ltd.

a

b

particles are in continuous motion. This motion is called *Brownian
motion*. Brownian motion is a random motion of the particles. This
motion is caused by their constant bombardment by the smaller
molecules of the medium. The motion is the result of the collision
of many molecules with the particle. It is as if a large crust of bread
were being constantly nibbled by tiny, invisible fish. The bread is
moved back and forth as first one fish and then another hits the bread
from opposite sides. Brownian motion is named in honor of Robert
Brown, a biologist. Brown first noticed it while observing the motion
of particles in a suspension of pollen grains in water.

Brownian motion is the constant random movement of
colloidal particles.

As noted in Chapter 14, particles on the surface of a liquid are
subject to unbalanced forces. Atoms, ions, or molecules at the surface of solids are also subject to unbalanced forces. As a result, solid
and liquid surfaces tend to attract and hold substances with which
they come into contact. This phenomenon is called *adsorption*.
Colloidal particles, because of their small size, have an extremely
large ratio of surface to mass. A cube with a volume of 1 cm^3 has a
surface area of 6 cm^2. If that cube is cut into 1000 smaller cubes of
equal size, the surface area of that same amount of matter is now
60 cm^2. If we subdivide the same matter until we have cubes measuring 10 nm on edge, the surface area has risen to 6,000,000,000 cm^2!
Consequently, colloidal particles are excellent adsorbing materials,
or *adsorbents*. Dispersed particles have the property of adsorbing
charge on their surface.

Brownian movement can be
demonstrated by allowing a CS$_2$
solution of sulfur to evaporate.
(Caution: CS$_2$ is dangerous to
use.) The tiny sulfur crystals as
they first form show a
Brownian-like motion. If a
microscope is available, place
some powder and a drop of
water on a slide and shine a
light on top of the slide.

Colloidal particles are excellent adsorbing materials.

If a colloid is subjected to an electrical field, a migration of the
particles can be observed. The positive particles are attracted to the
cathode. The negative particles are attracted to the anode. This
migration is called *electrophoresis* and is evidence that colloid
particles are charged.

Electrophoresis is the migration of charged colloidal
particles within an electrical
field.

Suggestion: The electrophoretic separation of amino acids is a good
demonstration of a practical application of electrophoresis. See Teacher's Guide
and Chapter 11, page 257, One More Step, question 2.

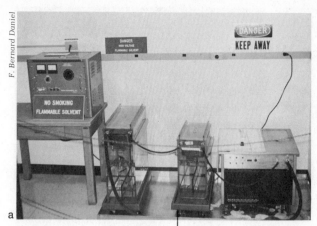

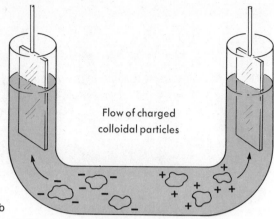

Flow of charged
colloidal particles

F. Bernard Daniel

FIGURE 18-17. An electrophoresis apparatus (a) can be used to separate colloids. The principle of electrophoresis is illustrated in (b).

Speed of migration can be increased by using high voltages as illustrated in this paper electrophoresis apparatus.

18:21 Importance of Colloids

Colloids make up some of our most useful products, and produce some of our biggest problems.

Much of the human body is composed of colloidal matter.

Our bodies are composed primarily of matter in the colloidal state. The study of colloids aids in the study of living cells and cell division. In medicine, many antibiotics, such as penicillin, form colloids rather than true solutions. Many foods are colloidal. Milk, for example, is a colloid of butterfat in water. Salad dressing, gelatin desserts, fruit jellies, and whipped cream are other examples.

Some foods and medicines are colloids.

Paint, plastics, cellulose, and many of the man-made fibers are colloids. Rubber is precipitated from latex, which is a colloidal dispersion of rubber particles.

One of the great problems facing an industrial nation is the elimination of smoke and dust. These particles, along with smog and fog, create hazards to navigation, traffic, health, and personal well-being.

FIGURE 18-18. Gelatin dessert and fruit jelly are colloidal foods (a). Paint is a useful commercial colloid (b).

John Morgan

FIGURE 18-19. Smog from automobile exhausts (a) and smoke from a variety of sources (b) are unpleasant colloids. They are potential hazards which scientists seek to lessen or eliminate.

Most air pollutants are colloids.

These are all colloids of one kind or another. Steps must be taken to prevent and eliminate these unpleasant colloids.

Much remains to be done in the field of colloid chemistry. There is much to learn, perhaps even the secret of life.

Agnes Pockels

(1862–1935)

Agnes Pockels was born in 1862, the daughter of an Austrian army officer. Although she attended high school for some time, she was largely self-taught. In her late teens, she made her first observations on the changes in surface tension of water contaminated by oil. Her first paper was printed under the sponsorship of Lord Rayleigh nearly ten years later when she was 29.

Most of her experimentation was done at home with homemade apparatus. Among other makeshift devices, she developed the Pockels' trough which was used to measure surface tension of liquids.

At 69 she won the Laura-Leonard prize for her work in the properties of surface layers and films. One year later she received her first degree, an honorary doctorate. An extension of her work in surface chemistry led to the Nobel Prize for Irving Langmuir in 1932.

SUMMARY

1. A homogeneous mixture is called a solution.
2. The solvent is usually the substance which occurs to the greater extent in a solution. The dissolved substance in a solution is called the solute.
3. Water is a good solvent because strong dipole bonds form between the molecules of water and the solute molecules or ions for a large number of solutes.
4. There are four basic solvent-solute combinations:
   (a) polar solvent-polar solute (solution)
   (b) polar solvent-nonpolar solute (no appreciable solution)
   (c) nonpolar solvent-polar solute (no appreciable solution)
   (d) nonpolar solvent-nonpolar solute (solution)
5. There are nine possible combinations of the three physical states in solution. For a list of these possibilities, see Table 18-3.
6. Two liquids which are mutually soluble in all proportions are said to be completely miscible. If they are not appreciably soluble in each other, they are said to be immiscible.
7. A solution is said to reach solution equilibrium when the rates of particles leaving and returning to the solution are equal.
8. At a given temperature, a definite amount of dissolved solute will be in equilibrium with undissolved solute in a unit quantity of solvent. This is called the solubility of the solute.
9. A saturated solution contains undissolved material in equilibrium with the undissolved material. A solution containing less than the saturated amount of solute for that temperature is an unsaturated solution. A solution containing more solute than the saturated amount of solute for that temperature is called a supersaturated solution and is unstable.
10. If a relatively large amount of solute is present per unit volume, the solution is a concentrated solution.
11. The rate of solution is affected by the surface area of crystal exposed and the kinetic energy of solute and solvent.
12. Heat of solution is the enthalpy change which occurs when one substance is dissolved in another. Most solids have positive heats of solution. Gases have negative heats of solution.
13. Henry's law: The mass of a gas which will dissolve in a liquid at a given temperature varies directly with the partial pressure of that gas.

14. A one molar (M) solution is any solution which contains 1 mole of solute per liter of solution. The concentration of solution expressed in moles per liter is called the molarity of the solution.

15. A standard solution is a solution whose concentration is known with some degree of precision.

16. A one-molal (m) solution contains 1 mole of solute in 1000 g of solvent. The strength of solution in moles per 1000 g of solvent is called the molality of the solution.

17. The mole fraction of a solute or solvent is the ratio of moles of solute (or solvent) to moles of solution. Moles of solution = moles of solute(s) + moles solvent.

18. Raoult's law states that the vapor pressure of a solvent varies directly with the mole fraction of solvent present in solution.

19. Many substances can be separated by taking advantage of the differences in their vapor pressures. The process is called fractional distillation.

20. The boiling point of a solution increases as nonvolatile solute is added.

21. The freezing point of a solution is lowered as nonvolatile solute is added.

22. The molal freezing point constant for water is $1.86C°$ per mole of solute per kg of water. The molal boiling point constant for water is $0.512C°$ per mole of solute per kg of water.

23. The molecular mass of a solute may be determined by adding a known mass of a solute to a known mass of a solvent and measuring the resulting change in boiling point or freezing point.

24. In concentrated solutions, the effect of ionized particles on the freezing point and boiling point is altered by interionic attraction.

25. Colloids are intermediate between homogeneous mixtures (solutions) and heterogeneous mixtures (suspensions).

26. Colloid particles range between 1 and 100 nm in at least one dimension.

27. A colloid is composed of two phases: the dispersed phase and the continuous phase.

28. Colloid particles, unlike solution particles, are large enough to reflect light. If light is passed through a colloid, the light is scattered and the beam becomes visible from the side. This phenomenon is called the Tyndall effect.

29. Colloid particles are constantly bombarded by the ions, molecules, or atoms of the dispersing (continuous) phase. This bombardment results in a constant random motion called Brownian motion.

30. Surface ions, atoms, or molecules attract substances they contact. This attraction is called adsorption. The unbalanced forces of the surface atoms, ions, or molecules cause adsorption.

31. Because of the small dimensions of colloid particles, the dispersed phase has a large reactive surface.

32. Migration of colloid particles in response to an electric field is called electrophoresis. Colloid particles can adsorb electrical charges.

33. Colloids are found in blood and protoplasm and are used in medicines, paint, plastic, and rubber.

34. Some colloids must be eliminated or avoided. Examples of undesirable colloids are smoke, fog, and smog.

PROBLEMS

5. a. not soluble
   b. not soluble
   c. miscible
   d. not soluble
   e. not soluble

5. Predict the solubility of the first substance in the second:

   a. RbF in ethyl alcohol   **d.** NCl_3 in C_6H_6

   b. CuS in water   **e.** Gasoline in water

   c. Ethyl alcohol in water

6. Predict the solubility of the following in water:

   a. CuF_2 slightly soluble   **d.** ThS_2 not soluble

   b. $ScCl_3$ soluble   **e.** CsI soluble

   c. Rb_2S soluble

7. Compute the masses of solute needed to make the solutions listed below:

   a. 1000 ml of 0.780M $Sc(NO_3)_3$ 180 g $Sc(NO_3)_3$

   b. 200 ml of 0.301M $Er_2(SO_4)_3$ 37.4 g $Er_2(SO_4)_3$

   c. 100 ml of 0.626M VBr_3 18.2 g VBr_3

   d. 250 ml of 0.0965M $DyCl_3$ 6.49 g $DyCl_3$

   e. 500 ml of 0.0978M $IrCl_4$ 16.1 g $IrCl_4$

8. a. 320 g $Fe_2(C_2O_4)_3$
   b. 164 g $VOBr_3$
   c. 1170 g $C_7H_4O_2Br_2$
   d. 1630 g $C_{14}H_{16}N_2$
   e. 77.4 g $LiMnO_4$

8. Compute the mass of solute needed to add to the given amounts of solvent:

   a. $Fe_2(C_2O_4)_3$ to be added to 1000 g of water for a 0.851m solution

   b. $VOBr_3$ to be added to 1000 g water for a 0.534m solution

   c. $C_7H_4O_2Br_2$ to be added to 200 g of C_2H_6O so that the mole fraction of the solvent is 0.510

   d. $C_{14}H_{16}N_2$ to be added to 1000 g of $C_4H_{10}O$ so that the mole fraction of the solute is 0.363

   e. $LiMnO_4$ to be added to 1000 g of water for a 0.614m solution

9. Compute the masses of solute needed to make the solutions listed below:
    a. 1000 ml of 0.0130M YBr$_3$ 4.28 g YBr$_3$
    b. 100 ml of 0.528M Li$_2$SO$_4$ 5.81 g Li$_2$SO$_4$
    c. 200 ml of 0.0469M KHC$_2$O$_4$ 1.20 g KHC$_2$O$_4$
    d. 250 ml of 0.274M UO$_2$(NO$_3$)$_2$·6H$_2$O 34.4 g UO$_2$(NO$_3$)$_2$·6H$_2$O
    e. 500 ml of 0.512M HSO$_3$F 25.6 g HSO$_3$F

10. Calculate the boiling point and the freezing point of the following solutions of molecular substances.
    a. 97.5 g of C$_{12}$H$_{22}$O$_{11}$ in 185 g water 100.788°C, −2.86°C
    b. 14.0 g of C$_{10}$H$_8$ in 25.0 g C$_6$H$_6$ 91.2°C, −16.0°C
    c. 500 g of C$_{20}$H$_{27}$NO$_{11}$·3H$_2$O in 500 g of water 101.00°C, −3.65°C
    d. 250 g of C$_7$H$_4$BrNO$_4$ in 500 g C$_6$H$_6$ 85.2°C, −4.47°C
    e. 60.0 g of C$_9$H$_{18}$ in 1000 g of acetic acid 119.0°C, 14.7°C

11. How is used motor oil an illustration of a colloid? carries away dirt and carbon by dispersion

12. What is the Tyndall effect? scattering of light by colloidal particles

ONE MORE STEP See Teacher's Guide at the front of this book.

1. Obtain an unknown substance from your instructor and attempt to identify it experimentally by determining its solubility curve.

2. Try to make a supersaturated solution of Na$_2$S$_2$O$_3$.

3. Try to separate a solution of two liquids by distillation, with and without a fractionating column. See your instructor about technique and possible mixtures.

4. Measure the heat of solution of anhydrous sodium phosphate at several different concentrations. See if you can determine how the molar heat of solution varies with temperature.

5. An ultracentrifuge can be used to separate colloids. Prepare a report to the class on the use of this apparatus in characterizing colloids.

6. Find out what methods are now being used industrially to remove dust from stack gases and thus to reduce air pollution.

7. Measurement of Brownian motion may be used in determining Avogadro's number. Investigate this procedure.

8. Find three examples of *protective* colloids.

9. Look through an extremely thin sheet of gold leaf. Why does everything appear green?

10. Describe the structure of protoplasm in terms of solutions and colloids. Suggested Readings for this chapter may be found in the Teacher's Guide at the front of this book.

Just as the speed of a motorcycle can be measured, so can the speed of a chemical reaction. The units of a motorcycle's speed are km/hr. What units are used to measure the speed of a reaction? Road conditions and the wind are factors that affect a motorcycle's speed. What factors determine reaction rate?

Reaction Rate and Chemical Equilibrium 19

Chapter 19 introduces the quantitative study of equilibrium.

In studying the properties of matter, chemists wish to find out both the physical and the chemical characteristics of a substance. They wish to be able to describe the behavior of a given substance with many other substances. Does it react? We have found that the change in free energy for a reaction can be used to answer the question. Of great importance, especially to the industrial chemist, is the answer to the question: how fast does it react?

Josiah Willard Gibbs discovered the relationship between entropy and enthalpy called the free energy. The amount of free energy after a spontaneous reaction is less than before the reaction.

As we have seen, a negative free energy change (ΔG is negative) indicates a reaction will proceed spontaneously. However, some spontaneous reactions take place so slowly that it takes hundreds of years for any perceptible change to occur. For example, the ΔG for combustion of glucose, a common sugar, is $-686,000$ cal/mole.

$$C_6H_{12}O_6(s) + 6O_2(g) \rightarrow 6CO_2(g) + 6H_2O(l) \quad \Delta G = -686,000 \text{ cal/mole}$$

But, at room temperature, the reaction proceeds so slowly that sugar is stable. Therefore, to predict whether a given spontaneous reaction will be useful, we must know the rate at which the reaction occurs as well as at what point equilibrium is established.

Consider what happens when we add an ice cube to a beaker of water. The temperature of the water drops. Heat is absorbed as the ice cube gets smaller and solid ice is converted into liquid water. We may represent this process by an equation:

$$\text{solid} + \text{heat} \rightarrow \text{liquid}$$

GOAL: You will gain an understanding of the factors which affect reaction rate and the relationship of these factors to quantitative chemical equilibrium.

The free energy change is the maximum work that can be obtained from a system.

A reaction proceeds spontaneously if $\Delta G < 0$.

The free energy decreases in a spontaneous reaction because the system is changing to a more stable state.

FIGURE 19-1. As ice cubes absorb heat from warm water (a), they melt. When a piece of metal at −20°C is lowered into a thermos containing an ice cube and water in equilibrium at 0°C (b), the ice cube increases in size.

If we use a thermos bottle instead of a beaker and our ice cube is large enough, the temperature of the water will drop to 0°C. After the temperature reaches 0°C, we observe no further melting of the ice. If we now add a piece of metal which has been chilled to −20°C, we may be surprised to find that the ice cube grows larger! Evidently the process can go either way. At 0°C an equilibrium exists:

$$\text{solid} + \text{heat} \rightleftarrows \text{liquid}$$

The relative amounts of solid and liquid can be changed by adding or taking away a small amount of heat without changing the temperature. We say that the water-ice mixture is in equilibrium.

At 0°C, an ice-water mixture is in equilibrium.

REACTION RATE

19:1 Reversible Reactions

A chemist studies the composition of matter and the transformations that occur in matter. These transformations are known as chemical reactions. Actually, the study of chemical reactions is the study of the breaking and forming of chemical bonds. The formation of chemical bonds is a complex subject. So far we have discussed only the simplest chemical reactions, those which go to completion. A reaction goes to completion when all of one of the reactants is used up and the reaction stops. Reactions of this kind go from

Not all reactions go to completion.

reactants to products. Not all reactions go to completion. Consider the following reaction:

$$H_2(g) + I_2(g) \rightarrow 2HI(g) \quad \text{(left to right)}$$

The arrow means the reaction is read from left to right, but this equation is only partially true. The bond between the hydrogen and iodine in the hydrogen iodide molecule is a weak bond, and hydrogen iodide breaks easily into hydrogen gas and iodine vapor. The following equation represents this reaction:

$$H_2(g) + I_2(g) \leftarrow 2HI(g) \quad \text{(right to left)}$$

Note: This can just as accurately be written:
$$2HI(g) \rightarrow H_2(g) + I_2(g)$$

Notice the direction in which the arrow points. This reaction is read from right to left. We now combine the two equations:

$$H_2(g) + I_2(g) \rightleftarrows 2HI(g) \quad \text{(reversible reaction)}$$

A reversible reaction may eventually reach equilibrium.

The first reaction is said to go from left to right. The second reaction is said to go from right to left. The combined equation represents *a reversible reaction.*

19:2 Definition

If the product of a reversible reaction decomposes more rapidly than the reactants form the product, there will always be more reactant than product. Here is an example. If the HI decomposes to H_2 and I_2 more rapidly than H_2 unites with I_2 to form HI, there will always be more hydrogen and iodine than hydrogen iodide. If a flask contains hydrogen, iodine, and hydrogen iodide, and if the hydrogen iodide is decomposing rapidly, it is possible that the hydrogen iodide is disappearing more rapidly than H_2 and I_2 can combine to produce it. The rate of disappearance of hydrogen iodide is defined to be the reaction rate:

Remind students that chemical equations are algebraic and that algebraic equations can be derived from chemical equations by replacing the formulas with molecular masses or volumes. Algebraic equations derived in this manner are subject to the same laws as other algebraic equations.

$$H_2(g) + I_2(g) \leftarrow 2HI(g) \quad \text{(rate of disappearance of HI)}$$

(Notice this is the reaction from right to left.) The rate of appearance of hydrogen iodide is defined as the rate of the reaction from left to right:

$$H_2(g) + I_2(g) \rightarrow 2HI(g) \quad \text{(rate of appearance of HI)}$$

Reaction rate is the rate of disappearance of reactant or rate of appearance of product.

Reaction rate is defined in terms of the rate of disappearance of one of the reactants, or in terms of the rate of appearance of one of the products. If we know the reaction rates from left to right and from right to left, we can predict whether product or reactant will be in the higher concentration at equilibrium. We will now consider some factors which affect reaction rates.

19:3   Nature of Reactants

The chemical properties of a substance determine its nature.

Reaction rate depends upon the nature of the reactants.

The nature of the reactants involved in a reaction will determine the kind of reaction that occurs. Reactions in which bonds are rearranged or electrons are transferred may take longer than reactions where no bond rearrangement or electron transfer occurs. Ionic reactions (such as double displacement and neutralization reactions) occur almost instantaneously. This is because ions of one charge are attracted by those of opposite charge and oppositely charged ions collide frequently.

Ionic reactions involve no electron transfer.

In an ionic reaction, no electron transfer is involved. Reactions between neutral molecules may be much slower than ionic reactions because electron transfer and bond rearrangement must occur. As pointed out in Chapter 12, most molecular collisions are elastic. The molecules simply rebound and move away unchanged. However, some collisions do have enough energy to cause changes in the electron clouds of the colliding molecules. When the change occurs, the colliding molecules may form the activated complex. The energy required to form the activated complex is known as the activation energy. If the activation energy is high, few of the collisions have enough energy to form the activated complex. As a result, the reaction may be so slow that it cannot be detected.

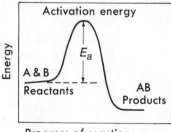

FIGURE 19-2. Activation energy is the energy that must be added to a reaction to cause the formation of an activated complex.

For example, hydrogen and oxygen can be kept in the same container at room temperature for ages without reacting. Although the molecules collide, the activation energy will not be reached. If, however, the mixture is heated to 800°C, or a flame or spark is introduced into the container, the hydrogen and oxygen will react violently. The heat, flame, or spark furnishes the activation energy. Most reactions occur in a series of steps. Each step normally involves the collision of only two particles. Steps involving three or more particles are unlikely because of the low chance of three or more particles colliding with the proper position and energy to cause a reaction.

If a reaction consists of several steps, for example,

$$A \rightarrow B$$
$$B \rightarrow C$$
$$C \rightarrow product$$

one of the steps will be the slowest one. This step is called the rate determining step. The other faster steps will not affect the rate. The series of reaction steps that must occur for a reaction to go to completion is called the *reaction mechanism*.

19:4   Concentration

Concentration refers to the quantity of matter that exists in a unit volume. For instance, in Chapter 15 we discussed the concentration in moles per liter of solution. We referred to this concentration as the molarity of the solution. For a particular reaction at a given temperature, concentration has the greatest effect on the reaction rate. For a reaction to take place, the molecules must collide. If the number of molecules per unit volume is increased, the chance of their colliding is also increased. Reconsider the reaction:

$$H_2(g) + I_2(g) \rightarrow 2HI(g)$$

Keep the concentration of the hydrogen molecules the same. We would expect then that doubling the concentration of iodine would double the number of collisions between iodine and hydrogen molecules. This, in turn, would double the reaction rate. Actual experiment confirms that the rate of reaction varies directly as the concentration of iodine. We write this in equation form:

$$rate_1 = k_1[I_2]$$

where the brackets around the I_2 ([   ]) mean "moles per liter."

Emphasize that most reactions occur in a series of steps. The series of steps involved in the overall reaction is called the reaction mechanism. Often several different mechanisms are possible for the same overall reaction. Where a catalyst is involved, the mechanism for the catalyzed reaction is always different from the mechanism for the uncatalyzed one.

The reaction mechanism is the series of steps that occur during a reaction.

Reaction rate depends upon concentration of the reactants.

Suggestion: Concentration has been discussed on pages 380–382. Review these discussions and spend extra time on the discussion of concentration in this chapter. It is important that students have a good grasp of the concept of concentration before proceeding further.

What if the concentration of iodine remains constant, and the concentration of hydrogen is allowed to vary? We can say that the number of collisions and, therefore, the reaction rate, varies directly as the concentration of hydrogen molecules. We write this:

$$\text{rate}_2 = k_2[\text{H}_2]$$

If we allow the concentration of both iodine and hydrogen to vary, what will happen? For instance, if we double the concentration of hydrogen and also double the concentration of iodine, we know that there will be four times as many molecules. What will the reaction rate be? There will be four times as many molecules per unit volume and four times as many collisions. The reaction rate is found to be quadrupled. We conclude, then, that the reaction rate varies directly as the concentration of hydrogen times the concentration of iodine. We write this:

$$\text{rate} = k[\text{H}_2][\text{I}_2]$$

In this case, the constant, k, depends upon the size, speed, and kind of molecule involved in the reaction. Each reaction has only

Henry Louis Le Chatelier

(1850–1936)

Henry Le Chatelier began his professional career as a mining engineer before turning to the teaching of chemistry. It was his experience as an engineer, however, that dictated his scientific investigations.

His greatest contribution to science was the equilibrium principle. Commonly known as the Le Chatelier Principle, it states that if a system in stable equilibrium is subjected to stress, then the equilibrium will shift to relieve the stress.

In other fields, he developed the platinum-rhodium thermocouple for measuring high temperatures, designed a special microscope to study metals, and developed new abrasives to polish the surface of the metal to be examined.

one value of k for a given temperature; this k is called the *specific rate constant of the reaction*. It should be pointed out here that the actual mechanism of this reaction involves the breaking of the I-I bond before collision. However, it can be demonstrated mathematically that the same rate expression results.

Specific rate constant: k

19:5   Temperature

It would seem that reaction rate should be determined by the frequency of collision between molecules. Thus, the reaction rate should increase as the frequency of collision increases.

The dependence of the rate on the increased number of particles in the activation energy range is given by the Arrhenius equation:

$$k = Ae^{-E_a/RT}$$

where k = specific rate constant
A = a constant for a particular reaction
e = base of natural logarithms
E_a = activation energy
R = gas constant
T = absolute temperature
The slope of a plot of ln k vs. $1/T$ is used to determine E_a.

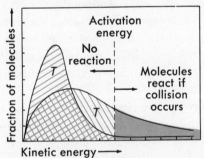

Area under T_1 is equal to area under T_2.

Area under curves represents number of molecules

FIGURE 19-3. A ten degree increase in temperature will double or triple the number of molecules that attain activation energy.

According to the kinetic theory, the speed (kinetic energy) of molecules increases as the temperature increases. Increased kinetic energy means that more collisions will occur and the reaction rate will increase. However, the increase in reaction rate depends not so much on the increase in the number of collisions as it does on the increase in the number of molecules which have reached activation energy. Note that the graph in Figure 19–3 indicates that molecules must collide with a kinetic energy sufficient to react, or collision will not lead to reaction. At temperature T_1 (the area under the curve indicates the number of molecules present), few molecules have attained activation energy. At temperature T_2, $(T_2 > T_1)$ many times as many molecules have reached activation energy. The same number of molecules are present at this higher temperature. However,

Reaction rate depends upon the temperature of the reactants.

Increased temperature in-
creases the number of activated complexes formed.

Figure 19-4 is a simplified
diagram. The graph of a multi-
step reaction would have
several valleys and peaks. The
"controlling" step in such a
reaction is the one with the
highest peak.

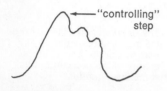

"controlling"
step

When molecules collide very
energetically, they form an
activated complex.

the fraction of molecules that have attained activation energy
is greater at the higher temperature (T_2).

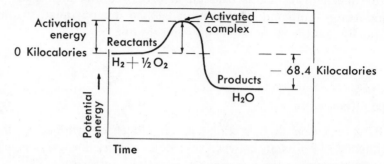

FIGURE 19-4. The energy changes involved in the formation
of water.

Figure 19–4 is a graph which shows the energy changes involved
in the reaction of hydrogen with oxygen. This graph can be thought
of as a map of the *potential* energy possessed by the atoms and molecules taking part in a reaction. The gases, H_2 and O_2, are considered
to have no potential energy (0 kcal). As two molecules approach, the
kinetic energy of motion is transformed into the potential energy of
repulsion. As more and more kinetic energy is transformed into
potential energy, the line of the graph, which represents potential
energy, rises. If the molecules have enough kinetic energy to cause
them to approach close enough to react chemically, they are said to
be *activated*, and an *activated complex* is formed. From here, the
reaction *must* go downhill. The activated complex may fall back
on the left side and break into H_2 and O_2 molecules, or it may react
(fall down on the right side). The chance of falling either way is
equal. If the activated complex does react, heat will be released and
a molecule of water will be formed. The effect of raising the temperature is to produce more activated complexes through collision. Thus,
with the increase in number of activated complexes, the number that
will react will also increase.

An increase in temperature will increase the rate of any reaction.
More activated complexes are formed because the number of
collisions increases as the temperature increases.

19:6 Pressure of Gases

An increase in pressure results in a decrease in the volume
occupied by the molecules. Since there are more molecules per unit
volume, the number of collisions per unit time increases. The re-

action rate also increases. In general, if the temperature remains constant, increasing the pressure speeds up the reaction rate. This rate increase occurs because a pressure increase causes a corresponding increase in concentration.

19:7 State of Subdivision

This factor is important in chemical reactions which take place on the surface of reactants which involve two or more phases. Reactions involving two or more phases are called *heterogeneous* reactions. An example of a heterogeneous reaction is zinc (a solid) dissolving in sulfuric acid (a liquid). The reaction takes place on the surface. If more surface is exposed, the reaction will take place more rapidly. Because of the unusual properties of surface molecules, their bonds are more easily broken, and they react more readily than molecules not on the surface. Increasing the surface area increases the number of surface molecules and tends to increase the speed of a reaction.

FIGURE 19-5. The reaction of solid zinc with aqueous sulfuric acid is an example of a surface reaction. The rate of this reaction is affected by the surface area of the solid zinc.

19:8 Catalysis

Catalysis (kah TAL uh suhs) is the process of changing the rates of reaction by the presence of a substance that remains (apparently) chemically unaffected throughout the reaction. The substance which causes this change in a reaction rate without being permanently changed is called a *catalyst* (KAT uhl ihst). The catalyst alters the reaction mechanism in such a way that the activation energy required is less than in the uncatalyzed reaction. We will discuss two kinds of catalyst: the heterogeneous (or contact) catalyst, and the homogeneous catalyst.

The reaction of sulfur dioxide gas with oxygen gas:

$$2SO_2(g) + O_2(g) \rightarrow 2SO_3(g)$$

is extremely slow at room temperature. If these two gases are brought into contact in the presence of *solid* vanadium pentoxide (V_2O_5), the reaction is rapid. Vanadium pentoxide is called the catalyst in this reaction. Notice that vanadium pentoxide is a solid and the reactants are gases.

A reaction in which the reactants and catalysts are not in the same phase (state) is a *heterogeneous reaction*. The catalyst is called a *heterogeneous catalyst*. This kind of catalyst usually produces a surface on which the substances can react, and is sometimes called a *contact catalyst*. Platinum and other finely divided metals and metallic oxides are common examples of this kind of catalyst. Most heterogeneous catalysts work by adsorbing one of the reactants. It might be correct to think of the contact catalyst as taking part in the reaction. Adsorption is the adherence of one substance to the surface of another. In the process of adsorbing a molecule, such as O_2, the catalytic surface attracts the O_2 molecule. This attraction weakens the O—O bond to the point where the other reactant can break the O—O bond. The reaction then proceeds.

A contact catalyst is a heterogeneous catalyst.

A heterogeneous catalyst works by absorbing one of the reactants.

Adsorption is the adherence of one substance to the surface of another.

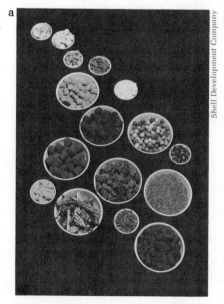

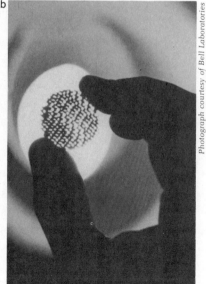

Shell Development Company

Photograph courtesy of Bell Laboratories

FIGURE 19-6. A few of the many catalysts available today are shown in (a). The catalytic device in (b) consists of a honeycomb ceramic support coated with a catalyst.

A *homogeneous catalyst* exists in the same phase (state) as the reactants. This kind of catalyst does enter into the reaction, but is returned unchanged in a final step of the reaction. It forms an intermediate compound or compounds which react more readily (require less activation energy) than the uncatalyzed reactants. As an example of homogeneous catalysis, consider the hydrolysis of sucrose (cane sugar). The reaction is:

$$C_{12}H_{22}O_{11}(aq) + H_2O(l) \rightarrow C_6H_{12}O_6(aq) + C_6H_{12}O_6(aq)$$
$$\text{Sucrose} \qquad\qquad\qquad \text{Glucose} \qquad \text{Fructose}$$

A homogeneous catalyst may enter into the reaction.

Again, the reaction is very slow. If, however, the solution is made acidic, the presence of the acid causes the reaction to proceed readily. In the reaction, all substances are in aqueous solution (the same phase), so the reaction is a homogeneous one, and the acid is a homogeneous catalyst.

Catalysts are used a great deal in industry, as well as in the chemical laboratory. Other substances called *inhibitors* are also used to affect reaction rates. These substances do not "slow up" a reaction. Rather they "tie up" a reactant or catalytic substance in a complex, so that it will not react. Preservatives used in foods and additives to medical preparations included to avoid spoilage are examples of inhibitors.

Inhibitors slow up reaction rates by tying up a reactant.

John Morgan

FIGURE 19-7. Preservatives have been added to each of these foods to preserve flavor and freshness.

19:9   Reaction Mechanisms

We have seen that, at a given temperature, the rate of a chemical reaction varies directly as the product of the concentrations of the reactants in the slowest step. For the reaction $H_2(g) + I_2(g) \rightarrow 2HI(g)$, the rate expression was: rate $= k[H_2][I_2]$. For the general reaction $A + B \rightarrow C$, the rate expression would be: rate $= k[A][B]$. Hydrogen iodide decomposes into hydrogen and iodine: $2HI(g) \rightarrow H_2(g) + I_2(g)$. This reaction might be written: $HI + HI \rightarrow H_2 + I_2$. The rate expression (if it is a one-step reaction) would be: rate $= k[HI][HI]$, or rate $= k[HI]^2$. Note that the coefficient in the equation became the exponent in the rate expression. For the equation $mA + nB \rightarrow C$, the rate expression takes the form: rate $= k[A]^m[B]^n$, where m and n are coefficients (also exponents) and A and B are reactants. The exponents of the concentration factors are spoken of as the *order* of the expression. Remember, this generalization is true only for single-step reactions, or the slowest step in a sequence.

For the reaction

$mA + nB \rightarrow C$,

the rate $= k[A]^m[B]^n$.

Reaction steps can be determined experimentally.

How do we know if a reaction is single-step? The *only* way to obtain accurate rate information is experimentally. As a result, the observation of rates of reaction has given scientists an insight into the mechanisms of reactions. For example, the reaction $C_2H_4Br_2(l) + 3I^-(aq) \rightarrow C_2H_4(l) + 2Br^-(aq) + I_3^-(aq)$ has been shown by experiment to obey the rate expression: rate $= k[C_2H_4Br_2][I^-]$. Thus, the reaction is first order with respect to $C_2H_4Br_2$, and first order with respect to I^-.

Overall, then, the reaction is second order. However, the reaction should be third order in I^- if it is a single step reaction. This would mean that four particles (1 $C_2H_4Br_2$ and $3I^-$) would have to collide all at once in the right orientation to react. This is very unlikely. Therefore, the rate data tells us that we need to consider multiple step mechanisms. The slowest step, according to the rate data, involves only one I^- with the $C_2H_4Br_2$. There are a large number of possible mechanisms which would agree with the observed rate law. Consider just one:

Reaction rate depends on the slowest step.

$$C_2H_4Br_2 + I^- \rightarrow C_2H_4Br^- + IBr \quad \text{(slow)}$$
$$C_2H_4Br^- \rightarrow C_2H_4 + Br^- \quad \text{(fast)}$$
$$IBr + I^- \rightarrow Br^- + I_2 \quad \text{(fast)}$$
$$I_2 + I^- \rightarrow I_3^- \quad \text{(fast)}$$

See if you can devise other mechanisms for this reaction which will agree with the rate data.

PROBLEMS

1. Assume that $NO(g)$ and $H_2(g)$ react according to the rate law: rate $= k[NO]^2[H_2]$. How does the rate change if:

a. The concentration of H_2 is doubled? doubled

b. The volume of the enclosing vessel is suddenly halved? eight times faster

c. The temperature is decreased? slows down

2. For the reaction $H_2(g) + I_2(g) \rightarrow 2HI(g)$, the following data were obtained:

Experiment	Initial $[H_2]$	Initial $[I_2]$	Initial Rate of Formation of HI
1	1.0 M	1.0 M	0.20 mole/liter/sec
2	1.0 M	2.0 M	0.40 mole/liter/sec
3	2.0 M	2.0 M	0.80 mole/liter/sec

(a) Write the rate law for this reaction, and calculate the value of the rate constant. **(b)** What would be the initial rate of formation of HI if the initial concentrations of H_2 and I_2 were each of 0.50 M?

2. a. Rate $= k[H_2][I_2]$
　　k = 0.2 l²/mole-sec
　b. 0.05 moles/sec

CHEMICAL EQUILIBRIUM

19:10　Equilibrium Constant

The reaction of H_2 and I_2 to form HI is an equilibrium reaction. As the reaction proceeds, the reaction rate of the hydrogen and iodine reaction decreases because fewer collisions between H_2 and I_2 molecules occur per unit time. The reverse reaction, the collision of two HI molecules to form H_2 and I_2, does not occur initially because the concentration of HI is zero.

However, as the concentration of HI increases, the reverse reaction, the decomposition of hydrogen iodide, steadily increases. Equilibrium is attained when the rates of the two opposing reactions are equal.

Emphasize that k forward must equal k reverse when the reaction attains equilibrium.

If
$H_2(g) + I_2(g)$　　$2HI(g)$
then
$k_f = k_r$

The rates of the forward and reverse reactions of the hydrogen iodide reaction are written:

$$\text{rate of forward reaction} = k_f[I_2][H_2]$$

$$\text{rate of reverse reaction} = k_r[HI]^2$$

At equilibrium, opposing reaction rates are equal.

At equilibrium, the two rates are equal, and:

$$k_f[I_2][H_2] = k_r[HI]^2$$

Dividing both sides by $k_r[I_2][H_2]$

$$\frac{k_f[I_2][H_2]}{k_r[I_2][H_2]} = \frac{k_r[HI]^2}{k_r[I_2][H_2]}$$

We obtain:

$$\frac{k_f}{k_r} = \frac{[HI]^2}{[I_2][H_2]}$$

The ratio of two constants is a constant.

An equilibrium constant is the ratio of the rate expression of the reverse reaction to the rate expression of the forward reaction:
$$K_{eq} = \frac{k_f}{k_r}.$$

Since both k_f and k_r are constants, the ratio $\frac{k_f}{k_r}$ is a constant. This new constant is called the *equilibrium constant*:

$$K_{eq} = \frac{[HI]^2}{[I_2][H_2]}$$

(Note that the equilibrium constant, K_{eq}, is capitalized to distinguish it from the specific rate constant, k.)

Does this mean that we must know the rate expressions for the forward and reverse reactions for every equilibrium condition? Guldberg and Waage, two Norwegian chemists, determined experimentally in 1867 that the numerator of the equilibrium expression contained the products, and the denominator contained the reactants. They also found that the exponents in the equilibrium expression were the same as coefficients from the chemical equation. Thus, it is possible to determine the equilibrium constant without knowing the reaction mechanism. This principle is known as the *law of mass action*.

The law of mass action states that the exponents in the equilibrium constant are the coefficients from the chemical equation.

For the general equation $mA + nB \rightarrow sP + rQ$, the equilibrium constant is:

$$K_{eq} = \frac{[P]^s[Q]^r}{[A]^m[B]^n}$$

This K_{eq} (equilibrium constant) establishes a relationship between the concentrations of the reactants and products of a reaction. If K_{eq} is less than 1, $\frac{[P]^s[Q]^r}{[A]^m[B]^n}$ is less than 1. This condition would indicate that, at equilibrium, the product of concentration of reactants is greater than the product of concentration of products. Therefore, if K_{eq} is very small (much less than 1), equilibrium will be established before much product is formed. If product is desired, the reaction will be of little value.

If $K_{eq} < 1$, reactants are favored at equilibrium.

If K_{eq} is greater than 1, $\dfrac{[P]^s[Q]^r}{[A]^m[B]^n}$ is greater than 1, and the product of concentration of products is greater than the product of concentration of reactants. If K_{eq} is large (much greater than 1), the reaction will approach completion. If product is desired, the reaction will be useful. For any reaction, K_{eq} remains constant only if the temperature remains constant. Thus, each reaction has a unique K_{eq} for any temperature.

If $K_{eq} > 1$, products are favored at equilibrium.

The K_{eq} is unique for any reaction at a given temperature.

If K_{eq} is 1, the product of concentrations of the product and reactant at equilibrium will be equal.

If $K_{eq} = 1$, neither reactants nor products are favored.

For example, a K_{eq} of 1×10^{-8} would mean that equilibrium will be established before much product is formed. A K_{eq} of 10^8 would mean that equilibrium is established only after a great deal of product is formed. Consider the following example:

$$CO_2(g) + H_2(g) \rightleftarrows CO(g) + H_2O(g).$$

A measurement of a vessel containing the four gases at equilibrium at 1120°C shows that the concentration of each is 0.01 M except H_2O, which is 0.02 M. Substitution of the observed concentrations into the equilibrium expression results in a calculation of $K_{eq} = 2$. Thus the products are favored. On the other hand, consider the reaction: $PCl_5(g) \rightleftarrows PCl_3(g) + Cl_2(g)$. Measurement of its equilibrium constant at 200°C indicates a K_{eq} of 0.457. In this case, the reactant is favored.

PROBLEMS

3. At a given temperature, the K_{eq} for the gas phase reaction:

$$2HI(g) \rightleftarrows H_2(g) + I_2(g)$$

is 1.4×10^{-2}. If the concentrations of both H_2 and I_2 at equilibrium are 2×10^{-4}, find [HI]. $1.69 \times 10^{-3}M$

4. At a given temperature the reaction (all gases):

$$CO(g) + H_2O(g) \rightleftarrows H_2(g) + CO_2(g)$$

produces the following concentrations: [CO] = 0.2M; [H_2O] = 0.5M; [H_2] = 0.32M; [CO_2] = 0.42M. Find the K_{eq} at that temperature.   1.3

5. If the temperature in the reaction in Problem 4 is changed, the K_{eq} becomes 2.4. If all concentrations except CO are then adjusted to the values given in Problem 4, what is the new CO concentration? 0.11M

6. Hydrogen sulfide decomposes according to the equation:

$$2H_2 S (g) \rightleftarrows 2H_2(g) + S_2(g)$$

At 1065°C, measurement of an equilibrium mixture of these three gases shows the following concentrations: $H_2S = 7.06 \times 10^{-3}$ M, $H_2 = 2.22 \times 10^{-3}$ M, and $S_2 = 1.11 \times 10^{-3}$ M. What is the value of K_{eq} for this reaction? 1.10 $\times$ 10^{-4}

7. At 60.2°C, the equilibrium constant for the reaction (all gases):

$$N_2O_4 \rightleftarrows 2NO_2$$

is 8.75×10^{-2}. If at equilibrium at this temperature, a vessel contains N_2O_4 at a concentration of 1.72×10^{-2} M, what concentration of NO_2 does it contain? 3.88 $\times$ 10^{-2}M

19:11   Le Chatelier's Principle

If a system is in stable equilibrium and one of the conditions (temperature, pressure, or concentrations of either reactants or products) is changed, then the equilibrium will shift toward restoration of the original conditions. This statement is called Le Chatelier's principle, in honor of the French chemist who first described the effect of stress (change of conditions) upon systems at equilibrium. If stress is put on a reversible reaction at equilibrium, the equilibrium will shift in such a way that the stress is lessened. We have mentioned this many times. Let us see how it applies here.

For example, the reaction for the preparation of ammonia by the Haber process is:

$$N_2(g) + 3H_2(g) \rightleftarrows 2NH_3(g) + heat$$

Let us consider the effect of concentration, pressure, and temperature on the equilibrium.

If the concentration of either of the reactants is increased, the number of collisions between reactant particles will increase. The result is an increase of the rate of the reaction toward the right. As the amount of NH_3 increases, the rate of the reverse reaction will also increase. However, the net result to the system as a whole is to shift the equilibrium toward the right. That is, more product is produced.

If the pressure is increased, the same effect is noted. That is, more product is formed. Consider the situation if the pressure is doubled.

Le Chatelier's principle states that a closed system will shift to relieve stress.

Increasing the concentration of reactant will produce a greater concentration of product.

Increased pressure on a reaction system with a gas phase has the same effect as increased concentration.

The concentration of the nitrogen is doubled, the concentration of the hydrogen is doubled, and the concentration of the ammonia is doubled. In the equilibrium expression

$$K_{eq} = [NH_3]^2/[N_2][H_2]^3$$

the concentration of ammonia is squared. The reverse reaction must then speed up by a factor of 4. On the other hand, the concentration of hydrogen is cubed. Further, it is multiplied by the concentration of nitrogen. Doubling the pressure then should increase the rate of the forward reaction by $2^3 \times 2$, or 16 times! The net result is clearly an increase in product.

In the reaction $H_2(g) + Cl_2(g) \rightleftarrows 2HCl(g)$, again all substances are gases, pressure would not shift the equilibrium, as the rate in each direction would be affected the same way. Pressure, of course, has an effect only on the gases in a reaction. A reaction taking place in solution would be unaffected by pressure.

Both the forward and the reverse reactions in an equilibrium are speeded up by an increase in temperature. However, they are increased by different amounts. Also, the value of the equilibrium constant itself is changed by a change in temperature. One easy way to predict the shift in an equilibrium subjected to a temperature change is to consider the heat term as a reactant or product.

In the Haber process:

$$N_2(g) + 3H_2(g) \rightleftarrows 2NH_3(g) + heat$$

heat is produced when hydrogen and nitrogen react. If heat is considered to be a product, the addition of heat (a product) will increase the concentration of the product and cause the equilibrium to shift to the left. In the Haber process, the reverse reaction (the decomposition of ammonia) is favored by the addition of heat.

$$K_{eq} = \frac{[NH_3]^2}{[N_2][H_2]^3}$$

As the $[H_2]$ is increased, the $[N_2]$ decreases and the $[NH_3]$ increases. Thus the value of the equilibrium constant K_{eq} remains the same.

This observation applies only to ideal gases.

Pressure changes concentration, not K_{eq}.

Temperature change causes a change in K_{eq}.

Heat can be treated as a reactant or product in a reaction.

The relationship for short temperature ranges (assuming $\Delta H°$ constant for the short range) is:

$$\ln \frac{K_{T_2}}{K_{T_1}} = \frac{\Delta H°}{R}\left(\frac{1}{T_2} - \frac{1}{T_1}\right)$$

where K_{T_2} and K_{T_1} are the values of the equilibrium constant at the second and first temperatures respectively.

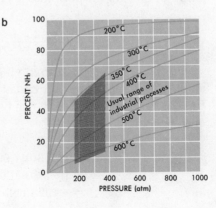

FIGURE 19-8. In the Haber process (a), nitrogen and hydrogen are chemically combined to form ammonia. As indicated in (b), an increase in pressure and a decrease in temperature will result in a larger yield of ammonia.

In industry, a desired chemical (such as ammonia) can sometimes be obtained by a reversible reaction, but equilibrium is often attained before enough product is produced to make the process economical. In such circumstances, the equilibrium can be shifted to give a higher yield of product. The chemist determines what conditions will tend to produce the highest yield. The conditions which produce the highest yield are called the *optimum* conditions.

Optimum conditions are those which produce the highest yield of product.

In the Haber process, there are five optimum conditions. First, a high concentration of hydrogen and nitrogen should be maintained. Second, ammonia should be removed. Third, a temperature should be maintained that is high enough to maintain a reasonable reaction rate but low enough not to favor the reverse reaction. Fourth, a contact catalyst should be used. Fifth, a high pressure should be maintained throughout. Why should each of these be needed?————

The optimum conditions for the Haber process are
1. *high concentration of H_2 and N_2*
2. *removal of NH_3*
3. *precise temperature control*
4. *use of a contact catalyst*
5. *high pressure*

Each increases the yield through a shift of equilibrium to favor the products.

19:12 Free Energy and Equilibrium

We saw in Chapter 17 that reactions with ΔG less than zero would occur spontaneously, and those with ΔG greater than zero would not occur. In this chapter, we have seen that reactions with very small K_{eq} do not occur to an appreciable extent, while those with very large K_{eq} go virtually to completion. As you might expect, there is a connection between free energy and the equilibrium constant. We will not derive the relationship here, as it involves complex mathematics. Simply stated, free energy and equilibria are connected by the expression: $\Delta G = -RT(\ln K_{eq})$. In the expression, R is the universal gas constant, T is the absolute temperature, and ln is the base of natural logarithms. Expressed in terms of common logarithms, the equation becomes $\Delta G = -2.30RT(\log K_{eq})$. Since ΔG is expressed in calories per mole, we need a value for R which will result in these units. Using the appropriate conversion factors, the value of R is found to be 1.99 cal per mole-K°.

$\Delta G = -RT(\ln K_{eq})$

$\Delta G = -2.30RT(\log K_{eq})$

EXAMPLE—FREE ENERGY CHANGE

Return to the problem involving CO_2 and H_2 reacting to form CO and H_2O. The equilibrium constant at 1120°C was 2. What is the free energy change for this reaction? Using $\Delta G = -2.30RT(\log K_{eq})$ and log tables, we find:

$$\Delta G = (-2.30)(1.99)(1393)(\log 2)$$
$$= [(-2.30)(1.99)(1393)(0.301)]$$
$$= -1920 \text{ cal}$$

For the decomposition of PCl_5 at 200°C, the equilibrium constant was 0.457. What is the free energy change for this reaction?

$$\Delta G = (-2.30)(1.99)(473)(\log 0.457)$$
$$= [(-2.30)(1.99)(473)(-0.340)]$$
$$= 736 \text{ cal}$$

EXAMPLE—EQUILIBRIUM CONSTANT

In Chapter 17, we found that the free energy change for the reaction:

$$CH_4(g) + 2O_2(g) \rightarrow CO_2(g) + 2H_2O(g)$$

was −195,504 cal at 25°C. What is the equilibrium constant for this reaction? Solving the equation relating free energy to equilibrium for K_{eq}, we find that $\log K_{eq} = \dfrac{\Delta G}{-2.30 \, RT}$

$$\log K_{eq} = \frac{-195,504}{(-2.30)(1.99)(298)}$$
$$= 143.337 \text{ and using log tables, this converts to}$$
$$K_{eq} = 2.17 \times 10^{143}$$

The equilibrium constant is such a large number we can safely assume that *all* the reactant is converted to product.

SUMMARY

1. A reversible reaction is a reaction which does not go to completion.
2. Reaction rate is the rate of disappearance of one of the reactants of a reaction or the rate of appearance of one of the products.
3. Six factors influence reaction rate: nature of reactants, concentration, temperature, pressure, state of subdivision, and catalysis.
4. More reactive materials require less activation energy. Therefore, they react more rapidly.
5. Most reactions take place in a series of steps called the reaction mechanism.
6. Concentration is the quantity of matter present in a unit volume. The symbol [ ] means concentration in units of moles per liter.

7. Increasing the concentration of a reactant increases the rate of reaction by increasing the number of collisions.

8. Increasing the temperature increases the rate of reaction. There are more frequent collisions and more of the collisions involve sufficient energy to form the activated complex.

9. Increasing the pressure on a gaseous reactant increases the rate of reaction by increasing the concentration of gas molecules.

10. In heterogeneous reactions, the amount of surface area of one reactant exposed to another reactant will affect the rate of reaction.

11. A catalyst is a substance which causes an increase in reaction rate without being permanently changed.

12. A reaction in which the reactants and catalysts are not in the same phase is a heterogeneous reaction. The catalyst used is called a heterogeneous catalyst.

13. A homogeneous catalyst is one which is in the same phase as the reactants.

14. Analysis of rate data can give chemists an insight into reaction mechanisms.

15. At a given temperature, the rate of a one-step chemical reaction varies directly as the product of the concentrations of the reactants. For the equation:

$$mA + nB \rightarrow C$$
$$\text{rate} = k[A]^m[B]^n$$

16. The equilibrium constant, K_{eq}, is the ratio of the rate of the forward reaction divided by the rate of the reverse reaction. For the equation:

$$mA + nB \rightarrow sP + rQ$$
$$K_{eq} = \frac{[P]^s[Q]^r}{[A]^m[B]^n}$$

This is the law of mass action.

17. Le Chatelier's principle applies to a system in chemical equilibrium. It states that if such a system is subjected to stress (such as change in concentration, pressure, temperature), then the equilibrium will shift to relieve the stress.

18. The free energy change for a reaction is related to the equilibrium constant for that reaction by the expression $\Delta G = -2.30RT$ $(\log K_{eq})$

PROBLEMS

8. Given $2NH_3(g) + H_2SO_4(g) \rightleftarrows (NH_4)_2SO_4(g)$: $\quad K_{eq} = \dfrac{[(NH_4)_2SO_4]}{[NH_3]^2[H_2SO_4]}$

   a. What is the equilibrium expression?

   b. If the concentrations in moles per liter after reaction of NH_3, H_2SO_4, and $(NH_4)_2SO_4$ are 2, 3, and 4, respectively, what is K_{eq}? 0.3

   c. If $[NH_3]$ is increased, what happens to $[(NH_4)_2SO_4]$? increases

   d. If pressure is added, what happens to the equilibrium? shifts to right

   e. If heat is added, what happens to K_{eq}? changes

9. Which of the following reactions would you expect to have the faster rate? (Assume the mechanism to be the same.)

$$\boxed{H_2(g) + Cl_2(g) \rightarrow 2HCl(g)} \quad \text{or} \quad H_2(g) + Br_2(g) \rightarrow 2HBr(g)$$

10. The following reaction goes to completion. What effect would an increase in temperature have on its rate? Rate increases.

$$2NO(g) + H_2(g) \rightarrow N_2O(g) + H_2O(g) + 87{,}030 \text{ cal}$$

11. Why must a fire in a fireplace be started with paper and kindling? Why not light the logs directly? See Teacher's Guide.

12. On the same set of axes, plot an energy diagram of a reaction, both catalyzed and uncatalyzed. See Figure 19-4, page 410.

13. Assuming the reaction of Problem 10 to be a single step reaction, what would be the effect on the reaction rate if the hydrogen gas concentration were doubled? Rate is doubled.

14. How would an increase in pressure affect the rate of a reaction in which the products occupied less volume than the reactants?   14. Rate increases.

ONE MORE STEP   See Teacher's Guide at the front of this book.

1. If K_{eq} for $2A + B \rightarrow 2C$ is 8, set up the expression used to calculate the concentration of C at equilibrium, if the starting conditions were one-half mole each of A and B in a ten liter container.

2. Thermodynamic quantities ΔH, ΔS, and ΔG apply to the activated complex as well as the products and reactants. Investigate the relationship between the energy of activation and these thermodynamic quantities.

3. Prepare a class report on the step-by-step mechanism of a multistep reaction. Be sure to include information on the slowest step.   Suggested Readings for this chapter may be found in the Teacher's Guide at the front of this book.

This ornate column, once beautiful, is rapidly becoming a victim of air pollution. The burning of coal and fuel oil with a high sulfur content produces sulfur oxides. These oxides are a major component of smog. They also combine with moisture in the air and rainwater to form sulfur-containing acids. These acids rapidly attack stone and concrete and can cause severe damage. What can be done to prevent this type of air pollution and its resulting damage?

Chapter 20 begins with a definition of acids, bases, and salts, and an introduction to three acid-base theories. It also includes a discussion of the general properties of acids, bases, and salts.

The sense of taste is actually more complex than this. It is quite variable. What tastes sour to one person may taste bitter to another. One particular substance divides people into two groups, those to whom it tastes bitter and those who can detect no taste when the substance is placed on their tongues.

Most foods have distinctive tastes. Some are bitter. Other foods are sour or salty. It is now known that a lemon or a grapefruit has a sour taste because it contains a compound called an _acid_. Soaps that contain lye, a _base_, taste bitter. Salty foods taste salty because they contain a _salt_, sodium chloride. The presence of these compounds, called acids, bases, and salts, gives many of our foods their distinctive flavors.

GOAL: You wil gain an understanding of the acid-base theories; the general properties of acids, bases, and salts; and the procedures for naming them.

It was discovered long ago that these substances, when dissolved in water, conduct an electric current. Because they conduct a current, they are called _electrolytes_. What are these three classes of electrolytes? Why do they conduct an electric current? Their definitions have undergone several modifications in the history of chemistry. As knowledge about our physical world expanded, definitions of these words were also expanded to cover larger and larger groups of compounds. We will devote the first part of this chapter to tracing the limits that have been imposed through various periods of chemical history on two of these classes of compounds: acids and bases.

Electrolytes conduct a current.

The three classes of electrolytes are acids, bases, and salts. They conduct an electric current because they dissolve to form ions in solution.

ACID-BASE THEORIES

20:1 The Arrhenius Theory

In 1887, a Swedish chemist, Svante Arrhenius, published a paper concerning acids and bases. He knew that solutions containing acids or bases conducted an electric current. Arrhenius tried to explain why. He concluded that these substances released charged particles

Arrhenius theory: an acid produces H⁺ in water solution; a base produces OH⁻ in water solution.

The Arrhenius theory is the traditional approach. However, it still is adequate for most introductory chemistry.

Brönsted-Lowry theory: an acid is a proton donor; a base is a proton acceptor.

The Brönsted-Lowry theory is the most prevalent of the three theories in inorganic chemistry.

when dissolved. He called these charged particles *ions* (wanderers). He concluded that acids were substances which separated (ionized) in water solution to produce hydrogen ions (H⁺, or free protons) and that bases were substances which ionized to produce hydroxide ions (OH⁻) in water solution.

20:2 The Brönsted-Lowry Theory

As chemistry developed, knowledge of catalysts and nonaqueous solutions increased. It became necessary to redefine the terms acid and base. In 1923, an English scientist, T. M. Lowry, and a Danish scientist, J. N. Brönsted, independently proposed that in a chemical reaction, any substance which donates a proton is an acid and any substance which accepts a proton is a base. When hydrogen chloride gas is dissolved in water, ions are formed:

$$HCl(g) + H_2O(l) \rightarrow H_3O^+(aq) + Cl^-(aq)$$

In this reaction, hydrogen chloride is an acid, and water is a base. Notice that the hydrogen ion (H⁺) has combined with a water molecule to form the polyatomic ion H_3O^+. There is strong evidence that

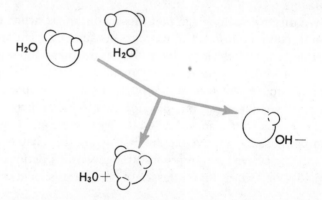

FIGURE 20-1. Formation of hydronium ion, H_3O^+. The hydronium ion is a Brönsted-Lowry acid and the hydroxide ion is a base.

Free protons are hydrated by water molecules to form H_3O^+, the hydronium ion.

the hydrogen ion is never found free as H⁺. The bare proton is so strongly attracted by the electrons of surrounding water molecules that H_3O^+ forms immediately. Consider the opposite reaction:

$$H_3O^+(aq) + Cl^-(aq) \rightarrow HCl(g) + H_2O(l)$$

In this reaction, the H_3O^+ ion, which is called the *hydronium* (hi DROH nee uhm) *ion*, is considered an acid because it donates a proton to the chloride ion, which is considered a base. Hydronium ion is said to be the conjugate acid of the base, water; and chloride ion is called the conjugate base of the acid, hydrochloric acid. In general, any acid-base reaction is described as:

H_3O^+ is the hydronium ion.

$$acid + base \rightarrow conjugate\ base + conjugate\ acid$$

The *conjugate base* of an acid is the remainder of the acid after the proton has been released by the acid. The *conjugate acid* of a base is formed when the base acquires a proton from the acid. Table 20-1 contains a list of some anions and their conjugate acids.

Bases have conjugate acids.
Acids have conjugate bases.

Table 20-1

Anions and Their Conjugate Acids

Anion	Name	Conjugate Acid
HSO_3^-	hydrogen sulfite	H_2SO_3
$HCrO_4^-$	hydrogen chromate	H_2CrO_4
$HCOO^-$	formate	$HCOOH$
BrO_3^-	bromate	$HBrO_3$
HTe^-	hydrogen telluride	H_2Te
CN^-	cyanide	HCN
CO_3^{2-}	carbonate	HCO_3^-
S^{2-}	sulfide	HS^-

The HSO_3^- ion can act as either an acid or a base.

Consider what happens when ammonia gas is added to water:

$$NH_3(g) + H_2O(l) \rightarrow NH_4^+(aq) + OH^-(aq)$$
$$base\ +\ acid\ \rightarrow\ conjugate\ +\ conjugate$$
$$acid\qquad base$$

In this reaction, water acts as an acid because it donates a proton to the ammonia molecule. The ammonium ion is the conjugate acid of ammonia, a base, which receives a proton from water. Hydroxide ion is the conjugate base.

The Lewis theory is the most prevalent of the three theories in organic chemistry.

Lewis theory: an acid is an electron-pair acceptor; a base is an electron-pair donor.

20:3 The Lewis Theory

In 1923, the same year that Brönsted and Lowry proposed their theories, Gilbert Newton Lewis, an American chemist, proposed an even broader definition of acids and bases. The same type of reasoning as Brönsted's and Lowry's led to his proposals, but Lewis focused on electron transfer instead of proton transfer. He defined an *acid* as an *electron-pair acceptor*, and a *base* as an *electron-pair donor*. This definition is more general than Brönsted's, and applies to solutions and reactions which do not even involve hydrogen or hydrogen ions. Consider the reaction between ammonia and boron trifluoride:

$$BF_3(g) + NH_3(g) \rightarrow F_3BNH_3(g)$$

The electronic structure of boron trifluoride and ammonia are:

$$\begin{matrix} & F & & H \\ F : & \ddot{B} & \text{and} & H : \ddot{N} : \\ & \ddot{F} & & H \end{matrix}$$

Note that boron has an empty orbital, and can accept two more electrons in its outer level. Since boron trifluoride can accept an electron pair, it is a Lewis acid. Now consider the structure of ammonia. Note that the nitrogen atom has an unshared electron pair, which can be donated to the boron. Ammonia is, therefore, a Lewis base because it can donate an electron pair. If we use dots to represent the electrons involved in the reaction, it can be written:

In the Lewis theory, as in the Brönsted-Lowry theory, many substances may act as acids or bases, for example:
base $NH_3 + H^+ \rightarrow NH_4^+$
acid $NH_3 \rightarrow H^+ + NH_2^-$
(amide)

$$\begin{array}{cccc} H_3N\!:\ + & BF_3 & \rightarrow & H_3N\!:\!BF_3 \\ \text{Lewis} & \text{Lewis} & & \text{Adduct} \\ \text{base} & \text{acid} & & \text{(Addition Product)} \end{array}$$

Consider again the reaction of ammonia gas and water:

$$\begin{array}{ccc} \begin{matrix} H \\ H : \ddot{N} : \\ \ddot{H} \end{matrix} + H\!-\!O\!-\!H \rightarrow & \left[\begin{matrix} H \\ H : \ddot{N} : H \\ \ddot{H} \end{matrix}\right]^+ & + \ OH^- \\ \text{Lewis} \quad\quad \text{Lewis} & & \\ \text{base} \quad\quad\ \ \text{acid} & & \end{array}$$

The ammonia donates an electron pair and is the Lewis base. The hydrogen atom attached to the oxygen of the water molecule acts as the Lewis acid. Notice that ammonia is a base in all three theories.

Table 20–2

Summary of Acid-Base Theories

Theory	Acid Definition	Base Definition
Arrhenius Theory	Any substance which releases H$^+$ ion in water solution.	Any substance which releases OH$^-$ ions in water solution.
Brönsted-Lowry Theory	Any substance which donates a proton.	Any substance which accepts a proton.
Lewis Theory	Any substance which can accept an electron pair.	Any substance which can donate an electron pair.

H$^+$, for example

A substance that is an acid or base under the Arrhenius theory is also an acid or base under the Lewis and the Brönsted-Lowry theories.

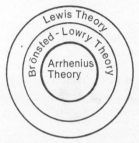

Each succeeding theory is more inclusive.

20:4   Naming Binary Acids

Binary acids are acids containing only two elements. If you look at Table 20–3, you will notice that the prefix is always *hydro-* and the suffix is always *-ic*.

The names of binary acids begin with hydro- and end in -ic.

Table 20–3

Naming Binary Acids

Binary Compound + Water	Prefix	Stem	Suffix	Name
Hydrogen chloride gas dissolved in water	Hydro-	-chlor-	-ic	Hydrochloric acid
Hydrogen iodide gas dissolved in water	Hydro-	-iod-	-ic	Hydriodic acid
Hydrogen sulfide gas dissolved in water	Hydro-	-sulfur-	-ic	Hydrosulfuric acid

To name a binary acid, we determine what stem to use by finding what element is combined with hydrogen. For instance, chlorine will have the stem *-chlor-*, and fluorine the stem *-fluor-*. To this stem, the prefix *hydro-* and the suffix *-ic* are added. There are a few exceptions to the rule that binary acids begin with *hydro-* and end with *-ic*. One example is hydrocyanic acid, HCN, which really is ternary. These exceptions must be learned separately, but HCN is the only one we will mention.

20:5 Naming Ternary Acids and Bases

Ternary acids are acids which contain three elements. Because almost all of the ternary acids we will be working with have oxygen as the third element, these are the only ones we will consider. We find the stem by determining what element is combined with oxygen and hydrogen in the acid molecule. We determine the prefix (if there is one) and the suffix by the number of oxygen atoms in each molecule.

Generally, the most common form of the acid is given the suffix *-ic*. No prefix is used. Examples of common ternary acids are sulfuric (H_2SO_4), chloric ($HClO_3$), phosphoric (H_3PO_4), and nitric (HNO_3).

If a second acid is formed containing the same three elements, but having less oxygen, this acid is given the suffix *-ous*. There is no prefix. Examples of these acids are sulfurous (H_2SO_3), chlorous ($HClO_2$), phosphorous (H_3PO_3), and nitrous (HNO_2).

If a third acid containing still less oxygen is formed, it is given the prefix *hypo-* and the suffix *-ous*. An example is hypochlorous acid ($HClO$).

Acids containing more oxygen than the common form are named by adding the prefix *per-* to the common name. For example, perchloric acid ($HClO_4$). See Table 20-4.

The stem for naming ternary acids is derived from the element that is combined with hydrogen and oxygen in the acid molecule.

The name of a ternary acid indicates the number of oxygen atoms in each molecule.

ic - most common
per - ic - more oxygen
ous - less oxygen
hypo - ous - still less
          oxygen

You may wish to mention peroxy-acids and condensed acids at this point.

Suggestion: Emphasize that the number of oxygen atoms in the -ic acid must be memorized. This number cannot be predicted. However, once the -ic acid is known, the others may be predicted although they may not exist.

Table 20-4

Naming Ternary Acids

Compound	Number of Oxygen Atoms	Prefix	Stem	Suffix	Name of Acid
H_2SO_4	4	no prefix	sulfur-	-ic	sulfuric
H_2SO_3	3	no prefix	sulfur-	-ous	sulfurous
$HClO_4$	4	per-	-chlor-	-ic	perchloric
$HClO_3$	3	no prefix	chlor-	-ic	chloric
$HClO_2$	2	no prefix	chlor-	-ous	chlorous
$HClO$	1	hypo-	-chlor-	-ous	hypochlorous

It is not possible, without previous knowledge, to know which form of an acid is most common. If the name of one form is known, the other ternary acids containing the same elements can be named. Bromine forms only two acids with hydrogen and oxygen: $HBrO$ and $HBrO_3$. Instead of being named bromous and bromic acids, they are named hypobromous and bromic acids, because they contain the same number of oxygen atoms as hypochlorous and chloric acids. The same pattern is followed in naming the ternary acids of the other halogens.

Arrhenius bases are composed of metallic, or positively charged, ions and the negatively charged hydroxide ion. Bases are named by adding the word *hydroxide* to the name of the positive ion. Examples are sodium hydroxide ($NaOH$) and ammonium hydroxide (NH_4OH).

FIGURE 20-2. Sulfur dioxide, an acid anhydride, readily absorbs water, and is sometime used in the preparation of dried fruits.

Bases are named by using the name of the metallic ion and the word hydroxide.

20:6   Acid Anhydrides and Basic Anhydrides

When sulfur dioxide is dissolved in water, sulfurous acid is formed. Any oxygen-containing substance which will produce an acid when dissolved in water is called an *acid anhydride* (an HI drid). If sodium oxide is added to water, sodium hydroxide, a base, is formed. Any oxygen-containing substance which will produce a base when dissolved in water is called a *basic anhydride*. The equations for the reactions just mentioned are:

An acid anhydride will form an acid with water. A basic anhydride will form a base with water.

$$SO_2(g) + H_2O(l) \rightarrow H_2SO_3(aq)$$
$$\text{acid} \quad + \quad \text{water} \quad \rightarrow \quad \text{acid}$$
$$\text{anhydride}$$

Note that an acid anhydride reacts with a basic anhydride to produce a salt. This is a neutralization reaction but no water is produced.

$$Na_2O(c) + H_2O(l) \rightarrow 2NaOH(aq)$$
$$\text{basic} \quad + \quad \text{water} \quad \rightarrow \quad \text{base}$$
$$\text{anhydride}$$

Anhydride means without water, so anhydrides may be classified as acids or bases without water.

20:7   Acid-Base Behavior

Consider a compound of the formula HOX. If the element X is highly electronegative, it will have a strong attraction for the electrons it is sharing with the oxygen. As these electrons are pulled toward X, the oxygen, in turn, will pull more strongly on the electrons it is sharing with the hydrogen. The hydrogen ion, or proton, would then be easily lost. In this case, HOX is behaving as an acid.

If the element X has a low electronegativity, the oxygen will tend to pull the shared electrons away from X, and the hydrogen will remain joined to the oxygen. Since in this case the formation of hydroxide ion is likely, HOX is behaving as a base.

We know that nonmetals have high electronegativities and metals low electronegativities. We can conclude, then, that nonmetals will tend to form acids, and metals will tend to form bases.

Metals tend to form bases; nonmetals tend to form acids.

SALTS

acid - nonmetallic ions (-) + (H⁺)
+
base - metallic ions (+) + (OH⁻)
↓
salt - nonmetallic ion (-) of acid
+ metallic ion (+) of base

20:8 Definition of Salt

Review the various kinds of neutralization reaction now discussed:
acid + base
acid + basic anhydride
acid anhydride + base
acid anhydride + basic
anhydride

An acid-base neutralization reaction produces a salt.

A salt is a crystalline substance which is neither an acid nor a base.

Acids react with bases to form a salt and water. The water is formed by the union of hydrogen ion from the acid and hydroxide ion from the base. An acid is composed of positive hydrogen ion(s) combined with negative nonmetallic ion(s). Metallic bases are composed of negative hydroxide ion(s) combined with positive metallic ion(s). If the water formed when the hydrogen and hydroxide ions unite is evaporated, the negative ions of the acid will unite with the positive ions of the base to form a new compound. This ionic compound is called a *salt*. It would appear that such a reaction should result in removal of all hydrogen and hydroxide ions from solution. The resulting solution should be neither an acid nor a base. We could say that the solution is *neutral* (neither acidic nor basic). The reaction of an acid and a base is called a *neutralization reaction*. A *salt* is a crystalline compound composed of the negative ion of an acid and the positive ion of a base. For example, if equivalent amounts of chloric acid and sodium hydroxide react, sodium chlorate and water are formed:

$$HClO_3(aq) + NaOH(aq) \rightarrow H_2O(l) + NaClO_3(aq)$$

Salts may also result from the reactions of acid or basic anhydrides with a corresponding base, acid, or anhydride.

Although the process by which a salt is formed from an acid and a base is called neutralization, solutions of salts in water are not necessarily *neutral*. It is also possible to obtain acidic and basic salts. For example, if sodium hydroxide reacts with sulfuric acid:

$$H_2SO_4(aq) + NaO\bar{H}(aq) \rightarrow H_2O(l) + NaHSO_4(aq)$$

the product, sodium hydrogen sulfate, is called an acidic salt because it still contains an ionizable hydrogen atom. In a similar manner, partially neutralized bases form basic salts.

Acidic or basic salts do not produce neutral solutions. Normal salts, even though formed by neutralizing an acid with a base, may give water solutions which are not neutral. In such a case, a reaction has occurred between the salt formed and the water. Such a reaction is called a *hydrolysis* (hi DROL ih sihs) reaction (Section 20:18).

> Salts are not necessarily neutral.

ACID-BASE EQUILIBRIA

20:9 Strengths of Acids and Bases

Not all acids and bases are completely ionized in water solution. An acid (such as hydrochloric) which is considered to ionize completely into positive and negative ions is called a *strong acid*. A base (such as sodium hydroxide) which is completely dissociated into positive and negative ions is called a *strong base*.

> Strong acids and bases are completely dissociated in water solution.

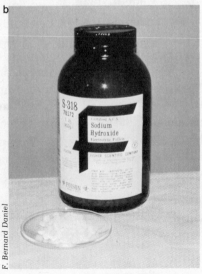

FIGURE 20-3. Hydrochloric acid (a) is a strong acid; sodium hydroxide (b) is a strong base.

Strong acids and bases ionize completely. Weak acids and bases ionize only slightly. Fortunately, there are few acids or bases which ionize almost completely or in some other partial way. This makes it possible for us to group acids and bases as either strong or weak with no intermediate groups.

Exception: Orthophosphoric acid is an example of an acid which is intermediate between strong and weak acids. It is much weaker than strong acids like HCl, H₂SO₄, etc., but much stronger than acetic acid.

Table 20–5

Relative Strengths of Some Acids and Bases

Compound	Formula	Relative Strength
Perchloric acid	$HClO_4$	strong acid
Iodic acid	HIO_3	
Periodic acid	HIO_4	
Arsenic acid	H_3AsO_4	
Hydrofluoric acid	HF	
Carbonic acid	H_2CO_3	
Hydrosulfuric acid	H_2S	
Hypobromous acid	$HBrO$	
Silicic acid	H_4SiO_4	
		neutral solution
l-Aminoindane	$C_9H_{11}N$	
Quinine	$C_{20}H_{24}N_2O_2$	
Hydroxylamine	NH_2OH	
N,N-Diethylaniline	$C_{10}H_{15}N$	
Hydrazine	N_2H_4	
Ammonia	NH_3	
Lead hydroxide	$Pb(OH)_2$	
Calcium hydroxide	$Ca(OH)_2$	
2-Methylpyrazine	$C_5H_6N_2$	
Acetamide	C_2H_5NO	
Sodium hydroxide	$NaOH$	strong base

(left margin arrow: increasing basicity, decreasing acidity)

(right margin arrow: decreasing basicity, increasing acidity)

In weak electrolytes, the K_{eq} is less than 1.

Weak acids and bases ionize only slightly in water solution.

Some acids and bases ionize only slightly in solution. The most important base of this kind is ammonia. In water solution, this base ionizes only partially into NH_4^+ and OH^-. The major portion of the ammonia molecules remain unreacted. Such a base is called a weak base. Acetic acid ionizes only slightly in water solution. It is called a weak acid. A *weak acid* or a *weak base* is one which ionizes only slightly in solution.

20:10 Ionization Constant

The equation of the ionization of acetic acid at equilibrium is:

$$CH_3COOH(l) + H_2O(l) \rightleftarrows CH_3COO^-(aq) + H_3O^+(aq)$$

The equilibrium constant for this reaction is:

$$K_{eq} = \frac{[CH_3COO^-][H_3O^+]}{[CH_3COOH][H_2O]}$$

Make it clear to students that the ionization constant is simply a special case of the equilibrium constant.

Acetic acid is a weak acid and ionizes only slightly. This means that the CH_3COO^- and H_3O^+ ion concentrations are small, and the concentration of CH_3COOH is almost unaffected by the ionization. When acetic acid ionizes, hydrogen ions attach to a water molecule and form the hydronium ion (H_3O^+). However, because acetic acid is a weak acid and ionizes only slightly, few hydrogen ions are formed, and the concentration of water remains nearly constant (55.6 moles per liter—Section 20:15). Thus, we can multiply the concentration of water by the equilibrium constant and obtain the equation:

Ionization constant:
$K_{eq}[H_2O] = 55.6 K_{eq}$

$$K_{eq}[H_2O] = \frac{[CH_3COO^-][H_3O^+]}{[CH_3COOH]}$$

Because $[H_2O]$ is constant, the product of the equilibrium constant and the concentration of water ($K_{eq}[H_2O]$) produces a new constant. This new constant is called the *ionization constant*, and is given the symbol K_a. For any weak acid ($HA + H_2O \rightarrow H_3O^+ + A^-$), the ionization constant is:

Ionization constant (K_a) is a special case of an equilibrium constant.

$$K_a = \frac{[H_3O^+][A^-]}{[HA]}$$

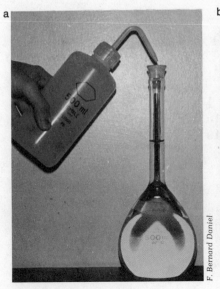

F. Bernard Daniel

FIGURE 20-4. A standard solution is prepared by placing a known amount of the standard in a volumetric flask and adding water (a) until the meniscus reaches the calibration mark. (b)

20:11   Percent of Ionization

When a weak acid (or base) is dissolved in water, it ionizes only slightly. It is often desirable in such cases to know just how much of a substance is ionized. This amount is usually expressed in terms of percent, and is called the *percent of ionization*. For example, at room temperature, we find the ionization constant of 0.100M formic acid (HCOOH) is 1.77×10^{-4}. We know that

$$\frac{[H_3O^+][HCOO^-]}{[HCOOH]}$$

Thus, we can find the percent ionization of formic acid by dividing either $[H_3O^+]$ or $[HCOO^-]$ by $[HCOOH]$. Either $[H_3O^+]$ or $[HCOO^-]$ will show the correct ratio of dissociated ions because the two concentrations are equal. If we let $x = [H_3O^+]$ or $[HCOO^-]$, then the concentration of formic acid $[HCOOH]$ is $(0.100 - x)$. Because x is so small when compared with the concentration of formic acid, $(0.100 - x)$ is approximately equal to 0.100M.

Percent ionization can be calculated from the ratio obtained by comparing the concentration of the ions in solution to the concentration of the solute before it dissolved.

Note: If the x in $(0.1 - x)$ is considered, and the resulting quadratic equation is solved, the answer is 4.5% instead of 4.6%. A good "rule-of-thumb" is to neglect x when it is added to or subtracted from a number differing from the K by three orders of magnitude or more.

EXAMPLE—PERCENT OF IONIZATION

Find the percent of ionization of a 0.100M solution of formic acid if the ionization constant for formic acid is 1.77×10^{-4}.

Solution: $HCOOH(l) + H_2O(l) \rightarrow H_3O^+(aq) + HCOO^-(aq)$

$$K_a = \frac{[H_3O^+][HCOO^-]}{[HCOOH]} = 1.77 \times 10^{-4}$$

Let x represent $[H_3O^+]$ and $[HCOO^-]$. (The balanced equation shows that $[H_3O^+]$ is equal to $[HCOO^-]$ in this example.)

Therefore, $1.77 \times 10^{-4} = \dfrac{x^2}{0.100}$

$$\begin{aligned} \text{and } x^2 &= 0.100 \times 1.77 \times 10^{-4} \\ &= 1.77 \times 10^{-5} = 17.7 \times 10^{-6} \\ x &= 4.21 \times 10^{-3}M \end{aligned}$$

% ionization

$= \dfrac{[x]}{\text{electrolyte}} \times 100$

Percent of ionization $= \dfrac{[x]}{[\text{original acid}]} \times 100$

$$= \frac{4.21 \times 10^{-3}}{0.100} \times 100$$

$$= 4.21\%$$

PROBLEMS

1. The ionization constant of acetic acid (CH_3COOH) is 1.76×10^{-5}. Find the percent of ionization of 0.100 M acetic acid. *ans.* 1.33%
2. A solution of 1.00M HA in water ionizes 2.00%. Find K_a. 4.1×10^{-4}

20:12 Common Ion Effect

Acetic acid ionizes in a water solution to form acetate and hydronium ions. What will happen if we add some sodium acetate to the solution?

An increase in acetate ion concentration will cause a decrease in hydrogen ion concentration.

Sodium acetate dissociates into acetate (CH_3COO^-) and sodium ions:

$$NaC_2H_3O_2(c) \rightarrow Na^+(aq) + CH_3COO^-(aq)$$

Acetic acid ionizes into acetate and hydronium ions:

$$H_2O(l) + CH_3COOH(l) \rightleftarrows H_3O^+(aq) + CH_3COO^-(aq)$$

K_a for acetic acid is:

$$\frac{[CH_3COO^-][H_3O^+]}{[CH_3COOH]} = 1.76 \times 10^{-5}$$

K_a is a constant, and does not change unless the temperature changes. If sodium acetate is added to an acetic acid solution, acetate ion concentration is increased and a shift in the equilibrium occurs. Because there are more particles of CH_3COO^-, there will be more collisions between CH_3COO^- and H_3O^+. Thus, the rate of reaction will increase toward acetic acid. Some of the excess acetate ions unite with hydronium ions to form un-ionized acetic acid and water. This results in the removal of hydronium ions from solution (thus decreasing hydronium ion concentration), and acetic acid concentration increases slightly. A new equilibrium is established, with more acetate ions and fewer hydronium ions. K_a remains unchanged.

A common ion causes equilibrium to shift toward reactants.

The acetate ion is common to both acetic acid and sodium acetate. The effect of the acetate ion on the acetic acid solution is called the *common ion effect*. A common ion, by increasing the concentration of one of the products of the ionization, causes the equilibrium to shift toward the reactants.

The common ion effect is a good example of Le Chatelier's principle.

The K_a remains the same if a common ion is added.

20:13 Polyprotic Acids

Polyprotic acids have more than one ionizable hydrogen atom.

It is possible for an acid to contain more than one ionizable hydrogen atom. Such an acid (example, sulfuric acid) is called a *polyprotic acid*. In sulfuric acid, the hydrogen atoms leave the molecule in steps. Sulfuric acid is a strong acid because the first hydrogen atom ionizes readily. The hydrogen sulfate ion ionizes only slightly, and is considered a weak acid. The reaction can be represented by the following equations:

$$H_2SO_4(l) + H_2O(l) \rightarrow H_3O^+(aq) + HSO_4^-(aq) \qquad \text{Ionizes readily (strong acid)}$$

$$HSO_4^-(aq) + H_2O(l) \rightarrow H_3O^+(aq) + SO_4^{2-}(aq) \qquad \text{Ionizes slightly (weak acid)}$$

The second ionization of a polyprotic acid contributes few hydrogen ions.

Each successive ionization of a polyprotic acid increases the negative charge of the remaining ion and, therefore, increases the attraction of the ion for hydrogen. Because of this, each successive ionization is more difficult, and occurs to a lesser extent. Phosphoric acid is a *triprotic acid* (an acid containing three ionizable hydrogen atoms); it ionizes as follows:

See problem 31, page 460.

$$H_3PO_4(c) \quad + H_2O(l) \rightarrow H_3O^+(aq) + H_2PO_4^-(aq)$$
$$H_2PO_4^-(aq) + H_2O(l) \rightarrow H_3O^+(aq) + HPO_4^{2-}(aq)$$
$$HPO_4^{2-}(aq) + H_2O(l) \rightarrow H_3O^+(aq) + PO_4^{3-}(aq)$$

Calculations involving polyprotic acids are more complex because we have three unknown quantities: hydronium ion, protonated anion, and anion. Since there is such a large difference between the extent of first and second (and subsequent) ionizations, it is usually possible to ignore the hydronium ion contributed by the second and subsequent ionizations.

SALTS AND WATER

20:14 Solubility Product Constant

Silver bromide is an ionic compound that is only slightly soluble in water. When an ionic compound (such as silver bromide) is in a solution so concentrated that the solid (AgBr) is in equilibrium with its ions (Ag^+, Br^-), the solution is saturated. The equilibrium equation for a saturated solution of silver bromide is

$$AgBr(c) \rightleftarrows Ag^+(aq) + Br^-(aq)$$

The equilibrium constant (K_{eq}) is

$$K_{eq} = \frac{[Ag^+][Br^-]}{[AgBr]}$$

However, because we are dealing with a solid substance, the [AgBr] is constant. Both sides of the equation can be multiplied by [AgBr]. This gives a new expression:

$$K_{eq}[AgBr] = \frac{[Ag^+][Br^-][AgBr]}{[AgBr]}$$

$$K_{sp} = K_{eq}[AgBr] = [Ag^+][Br^-]$$

$$K_{sp} = [Ag^+][Br^-]$$

The ions in a saturated solution are in equilibrium with the undissolved ionic solid.

K_{sp} = product of concentrations of the ions at equilibrium

The concentration of a solid such as AgBr is a constant because the equilibrium between the solid and liquid is established at the surface of the solid. The number of ions per square centimeter of solid surface is dependent on the crystal structure which does not vary.

The concentration of a pure solid is constant.

The solubility product is derived from a special case of equilibrium.

Svante August Arrhenius

(1859–1927)

In the beginning, the brilliant ideas of Svante August Arrhenius were rejected by his colleagues. His theory of electrolytic dissociation or ionization nearly caused his dismissal as a student at the University of Stockholm. Arrhenius was barely allowed to receive his doctorate degree. The significance of his work, his advisors contended, was not important.

However, through perseverance and help, he was finally able to promote his ideas. Ironically, Arrhenius was granted the Nobel Prize for the same theory that had once been viewed as an unsatisfactory doctoral thesis.

Throughout his life, Arrhenius continued to investigate and publish his results on the electrolytic behavior of solutions. He was, however, interested in other phases of science; namely, astronomy and biochemistry.

This new constant, K_{sp}, is called the *solubility product constant*. At room temperature, K_{sp} of silver bromide is 7.7×10^{-13}. If some silver bromide is dissolved in water and allowed to stand until the solution is in equilibrium, the product of the silver and bromide ion concentrations will be 7.7×10^{-13}.

$$[Ag^+][Br^-] = 7.7 \times 10^{-13}$$

However, since $AgBr(c) \rightleftarrows Ag^+(aq) + Br^-(aq)$

$$[Ag^+] = [Br^-]$$

or $\qquad\qquad\qquad [Ag^+][Ag^+] = 7.7 \times 10^{-13}$

therefore, $\qquad\qquad [Ag^+]^2 = 7.7 \times 10^{-13}$

$$[Ag^+] = 8.8 \times 10^{-7} M$$

In a saturated solution containing only silver bromide and water, the concentration of silver ions is 8.8×10^{-7} moles per liter, and the concentration of bromide ions is 8.8×10^{-7} moles per liter.

Suppose, however, that some potassium bromide solution is added. KBr dissociates to K^+ and Br^- ions. What will happen? If potassium bromide is added to a silver bromide solution which is in equilibrium, the increased number of bromide ions collide more frequently with silver ions, and the equilibrium is shifted toward the solid silver bromide. When equilibrium is again established, the concentration of silver ion, $[Ag^+]$, has decreased, and the concentration of bromide ion, $[Br^-]$, has increased. Solid silver bromide has precipitated out, and K_{sp}, 7.7×10^{-13}, has been re-established. This is an example of the common ion effect. The addition of a common ion (bromide ion in this example) removes silver ion from solution, and causes the equilibrium to shift toward the solid silver bromide. We could also say the addition of a common ion decreases the solubility of a substance in solution.

The solubility product constant is the product of the concentrations of the ions in a saturated solution.

Silver bromide will precipitate out. See next paragraph.

The addition of a common ion to a saturated solution causes precipitation of the solute.

The solubility of a substance is decreased by the addition of a common ion.

The result is predicted by the application of Le Chatelier's principle.

EXAMPLE—SOLUBILITY PRODUCT CONSTANT

Suppose 500 ml of 0.0200M NaCl are added to 500 ml of 0.0100M $AgNO_3$. If K_{sp} of AgCl is 1.56×10^{-10}, will any precipitate be formed?

The total volume of solution will be 1000 ml since 500 ml of each solution is used. Therefore, the concentrations of both the NaCl solution and the $AgNO_3$ solution will be halved:

$$[NaCl] = \frac{1}{2} \times 0.0200M = 0.0100M$$

$$[AgNO_3] = \frac{1}{2} \times 0.0100M = 0.00500M$$

Since both NaCl and $AgNO_3$ dissociate completely:

$$\begin{aligned} K_{sp} &= [Ag^+][Cl^-] \\ &= (0.00500)(0.0100) = 0.0000500 \\ &= 5.00 \times 10^{-5} \end{aligned}$$

However, K_{sp} cannot exceed 1.56×10^{-10}. Therefore, AgCl will precipitate out of solution until the $[Ag^+] \times [Cl^-] = 1.56 \times 10^{-10}$.

Students often need a little review on comparing $(>, <)$ numbers expressed in scientific notation.

PROBLEMS

3. The solubility product constant of silver iodide is 1.5×10^{-16}. What is $[Ag^+]$ in a solution at equilibrium?   *ans.* $1.2 \times 10^{-8}M$
4. If $[D^+]$ is $2.00 \times 10^{-5}M$ at equilibrium, what is K_{sp} for D_2A? 4.00×10^{-15}
5. At equilibrium, the concentration in moles per liter of H^+ is 0.200, the concentration of $CHCl_2COO^-$ is 0.200, and the concentration of $CHCl_2COOH$ is 1.20. What is the K_{eq} for the reaction
   $$CHCl_2COOH \rightleftarrows CHCl_2COO^- + H^+ \qquad 3.33 \times 10^{-2}$$
6. In the reaction in Problem 5, what is the percent ionization? 14.3%
7. If enough $CHCl_2COO^-$ were added as a common ion to make the concentration of $CHCl_2COO^-$ exactly $0.400M$, what would be the concentration of $CHCl_2COOH$? $1.29M$

20:15   Ionization of Water

Conductivity experiments have shown that water ionizes:

$$H_2O(l) + H_2O(l) \rightleftarrows H_3O^+ (aq) + OH^-(aq)$$

Even though it does conduct a current, pure water is a poor conductor. An electric current is carried in a solution by the ions in the solution. Since pure water is a poor conductor of electricity, it must contain few ions. Thus, pure water must ionize only slightly. In pure water, the concentration of H_3O^+ ion is equal to the concentration of OH^- ion because each molecule of H_2O that ionizes produces one ion each of H_3O^+ and OH^-.

Since water ionizes, it should be possible to find an equilibrium constant for this reaction:

$$K_{eq} = \frac{[H_3O^+][OH^-]}{[H_2O][H_2O]}$$

Conductivity experiments have indicated that pure water contains $1 . \times 10^{-7}$ mole (gram-ions) of H_3O^+ (and the same amount of OH^-) per liter. Therefore:

$$K_{eq} = \frac{(10^{-7})(10^{-7})}{[H_2O]^2}$$

We can find K_{eq} if we can arrive at some value for $[H_2O]$. Since water ionizes so slightly, we can approximate $[H_2O]$ in pure water by assuming that no ionization occurs. We assume that pure water contains only un-ionized H_2O molecules.

One mole of water has mass 18.0 g (16.0 + 2.0). One liter of pure water has mass 1000 g. We can find the concentration of water in pure water:

$$[H_2O] = \frac{1 \text{ mole}}{18.0 \text{ g}} \left| \frac{1000 \text{ g}}{1.00l} \right.$$

$$= 55.6 \text{ mole/l}$$

We can now find K_{eq} for water:

$$K_{eq} = \frac{(10^{-7})(10^{-7})}{(55.6)^2}$$

Because the value 55.6 moles per liter is so constant (water ionizes only slightly), we can multiply both sides of the equation by $(55.6)^2$ and get a new constant:

$$K_{eq}(55.6)^2 = [H_3O^+][OH^-] = 10^{-14}$$

We will call this new constant $K_{eq}(55.6)^2$ the *ion product constant of water*, K_w.

K_w is the ion product constant of water.

$$K_w = [H_3O^+][OH^-] = 10^{-14}$$

K_w is a constant for all dilute aqueous solutions. This indicates that, although the concentration of H_3O^+ and OH^- may change when acids or bases are added to water, the product of $[H_3O^+]$ and $[OH^-]$ remains the same:

$$[H_3O^+][OH^-] = 10^{-14}$$

In any water solution, $[H_3O^+] \times [OH^-]$ always equals 10^{-14}.

EXAMPLE—CONCENTRATION OF ACID IN WATER

If an acid (HA) is added to water,

$$HA + H_2O \rightarrow H^+ + A^- + H_2O$$
$$H^+ + H_2O \rightarrow H_3O^+$$

an excess of hydronium ion is produced. Collisions between H_3O^+ and OH^- also increase:

$$H_3O^+ + OH^- \rightarrow H_2O + H_2O$$

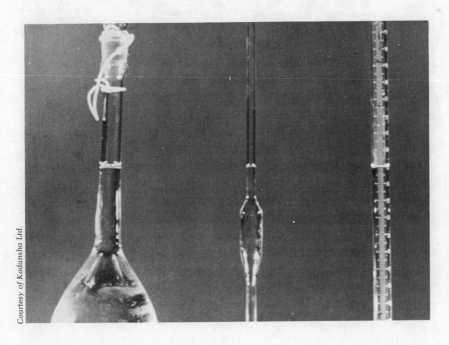

Courtesy of Kodansha Ltd.

FIGURE 20-5. Standard solutions are usually prepared in a volumetric flask (left) and can be delivered in measured amounts with a pipet (center) or a buret (right).

If an acid is added to an aqueous solution, $[H_3O^+]$ increases and $[OH^-]$ decreases.

As the $[H_3O^+]$ increases, the $[OH^-]$ decreases, and K_w remains 10^{-14}. For instance, the $[H_3O^+]$ in a neutral solution is 10^{-7}. If the $[H_3O^+]$ is increased to 10^{-5} by the addition of acids, the $[OH^-]$ must decrease to 10^{-9}:

$$[H_3O^+][OH^-] = 10^{-14}$$

Also $[H_3O^+] = \dfrac{10^{-14}}{[OH^-]}$ and $[OH^-] = \dfrac{10^{-14}}{[H_3O^+]}$

$$[OH^-] = \frac{10^{-14}}{10^{-5}}$$

$$[OH^-] = 10^{-9}$$

If a base is added to an aqueous solution $[OH^-]$ increases and $[H_3O^+]$ decreases.

If a base is added to water, the equilibrium shifts in the opposite direction, and the solution becomes more basic:

$$OH^-(aq) + H_3O^+(aq) \rightarrow H_2O(l) + H_2O(l)$$

H_3O^+ is removed from solution, and the ion product constant remains 10^{-14}.

FIGURE 20-6. Water containing dissolved carbon dioxide reacts slowly with limestone and gradually dissolves it. In this way, caverns may be formed over a long period of time.

Courtesy of Ohio Caverns

20:16   The pH Scale

The ionization of water is so slight that it is almost never considered in the actual production or use of acids and bases. Why, then, was it introduced? Knowledge of the ion product constant for water has enabled chemists to develop a simple scale, called the

The pH scale is a simplified way of stating the concentration of hydrogen ions in solution. In pure water, there are 10^{-7} moles of hydrogen ion per liter.

Table 20–6

pH of Some Common Substances

Substance	pH	Substance	pH
0.1M HCl	1	Urine	6.6
Stomach contents	2	Bile	6.9
Vinegar	2.9	Saliva	7
Soda pop	3	Blood	7.4
Beer	4.5	Intestinal contents	7.5
Pumpkin pulp	5	0.1M NH₄OH	11.1
Bread	5.5	0.1M NaOH	13

pH scale, which can be used to indicate the acidity or basicity of any water solution. The *pH* scale is a measure of *hydrogen ion concentration.*

Hydrogen ion concentration is measured by pH.

The concentration of H_3O^+ is expressed as powers of 10, from 10^{-13} to 10^{-1}. This is a convenient way to indicate the $[H_3O^+]$. We could simplify this even further by writing only the exponent. For instance, 10^{-7} would be written as -7. However, the negative sign is undesirable. If $[H_3O^+] = 10^{-7}$, the log of $[H_3O^+] = -7$. If, however, we take the negative log of $[H_3O^+]$, we get the desired $+7$. The negative log of $[H_3O^+]$ is the pH.

$pH = -\log[H_3O^+]$

EXAMPLE – pH DETERMINATION

The hydrogen ion concentration of a solution is $1 \times 10^{-7}M$. Find the pH of the solution.

$$pH = -\log [H_3O^+]$$

$$[H_3O^+] = 1 \times 10^{-7}$$

Therefore: $pH = -\log (1 \times 10^{-7}) = -\log 10^{-7}$

$$pH = -(-7) = 7$$

Note that a pH of 7 indicates a neutral solution ($[H_3O^+] = [OH^-]$).

The pH of a neutral solution equals 7.

EXAMPLE—pH DETERMINATION

One-tenth mole of HCl is added to enough water to make 1000 ml of solution. What is the pH of the solution? (Assume that the HCl is 100% ionized.)

$$[H_3O^+] = 10^{-1} \text{ mole per liter}$$

$$pH = -\log [H_3O^+] = -\log (10^{-1})$$

$$pH = -(-1)$$

$$pH = 1$$

Acidic solution: pH < 7 but ≥ 0
Basic solution: pH ≤ 14 but > 7

Note that as the hydronium ion concentration increases and a neutral solution is made more acidic, the pH goes from 7 toward 0. If the pH of a solution falls between 7 and 14, the solution is basic. Table 20–6 indicates the pH of several common solutions. Note that many of these are vital to life.

If we take the logarithm of both sides of the ion product of water, we get

$$\log ([H_3O^+][OH^-]) = \log 10^{-14}$$

$$\log [H_3O^+] + \log [OH^-] = -14$$

Multiplying both sides of the equation by −1:

$$-\log [H_3O^+] + (-\log [OH^-]) = 14$$

If we now designate −log [OH⁻] as pOH, and substitute:

$$pH + pOH = 14$$

Students should form the habit of deciding whether the solution will be acidic or basic before they work the problem. Then they should check to see whether their answer is in the correct range (>7 or <7).

The sum of pH and pOH is 14.

This relationship is often useful. For instance, if you wished to know the pH of a solution which was basic or about which you had information concerning only the hydroxide ion, you could calculate the pOH and subtract the pOH from 14 to obtain the pH.

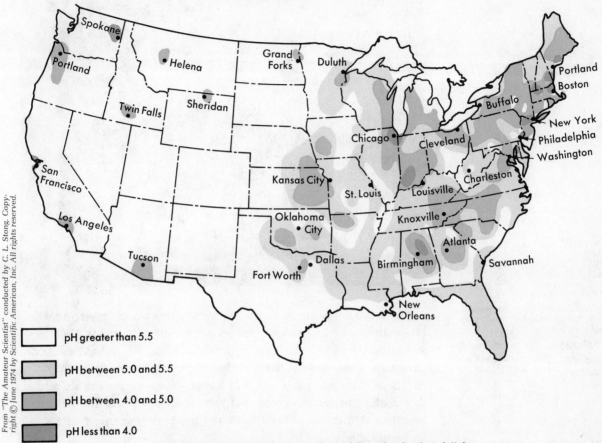

pH greater than 5.5

pH between 5.0 and 5.5

pH between 4.0 and 5.0

pH less than 4.0

FIGURE 20-7. This map shows the acidity of rain that fell in the United States during a two-week period in March, 1973. What reasons can you give for the variation in pH from place to place as indicated on this map?

20:17 Indicators

In the laboratory, how does the chemist know whether he is using an acidic, basic, or neutral solution? He could taste the solution to determine whether it was bitter or sour. However, this method is inexact. It is also dangerous because most solutions are poisonous or corrosive. He could experiment to determine what reactions his solution undergoes, but this would take too much time. The modern chemist uses a *pH meter* to determine the degree of acidity in a solution. This electronic device indicates the pH of a solution directly when its electrodes are immersed in the solution. We will investigate the operation of the pH meter in Chapter 22.

As pH meters become more
common, the use of indicators
will decline.

Indicators are used to determine pH through color
change.

The ability of the human eye
to distinguish color changes is
the limiting factor in precision
measurement of pH with
indicators.

Indicators are useful only
over narrow ranges of pH.

The broad range of litmus is a
detriment when used for
titrations. For titration,
bromothymol blue is better.

There are many times in the laboratory when a pH meter may not
be available, or its use may not be convenient. Chemists, therefore,
sometimes employ the use of substances called *indicators*. Indicators are weak organic bases and acids whose colors differ from the
colors of their conjugate acids or bases. When indicators are added
to a test solution, the color that results is related to the pH of the
solution. A number of indicators and their color changes are shown
in Figure 20–9.

There are, however, limitations to the use of indicators. Solutions
in which they are to be successfully used must be colorless; otherwise, the color of the solution may mask the color changes of the
indicator. Another important limitation is the ability of the human
eye to distinguish a slight color change. For any given indicator, we
can notice a color change over only a very narrow range of the pH
scale. To test for pH over a wide range of the pH scale, many indicators
must be used. However, given a definite pH, any change in $[H_3O^+]$ or
$[OH^-]$ can be detected by the use of one properly chosen indicator.

20:18 Hydrolysis

We would expect that a salt, which is composed of positive ions
from a base and negative ions from an acid, would dissolve in water

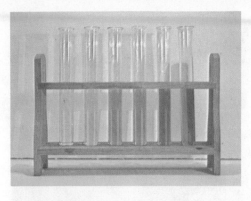

The color change of methyl violet over the range of pH 0.0, 0.5, 1.0, 1.5, 2.0, and 2.5.

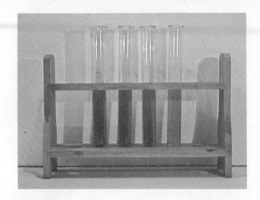

The color change of Congo red over the range of pH 3.5, 4.0, 4.5, and 5.0.

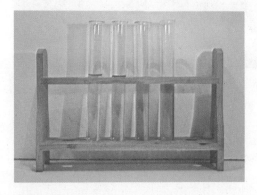

The color change of bromothymol blue over the range of pH 6.0, 6.5, 7.0, and 7.5.

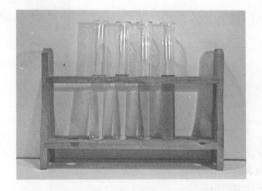

The color change of phenol red over the range of pH 6.5, 7.0, 7.5, and 8.0.

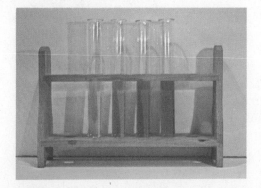

Robert C. Smoot

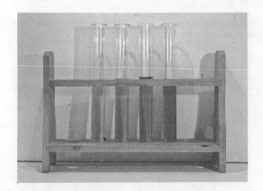

The color change of phenolphthalein over the range of pH 8.0, 8.5, 9.0, and 9.5.

The color change of alizarin over the range of pH 10.0, 10.5, 11.0, and 11.5.

FIGURE 20-9. Indicators commonly used in acid-base titrations are pictured here. Each indicator changes color over a very narrow pH range. With proper selection of indicators, pH can be determined over the entire pH scale.

449

FIGURE 20-10. Special indicator paper can be used to determine the approximate pH of a solution.

Bruce Charlton

Hydrolysis is the reaction of a salt with water to produce an acidic or basic solution.

The salt produced from a strong acid and a strong base is neutral.

In hydrolysis, the H_3O^+ and OH^- ions are produced in solution and do not actually come from the dissolved salt but from ionized water molecules which form as the salt dissolves and upsets the equilibrium between the water ions.

The salt produced from a strong acid and a weak base is acidic.

to release an equal number of positive and negative ions, and that a solution of a salt would be neither acidic nor basic. Some salts do form a neutral solution, but others react with water (hydrolyze) to form acidic or basic solutions. We will discuss four kinds of salt solutions.

If potassium chloride, a salt, is dissolved in water, a neutral solution results. Each of the ions from the salt, K^+ and Cl^-, is hydrated with no apparent reaction (except hydration). Water ionizes very slightly to form H_3O^+ and OH^- ions. The solution will, therefore, contain ions from the salt and ions from the water. In solution, the positive potassium ion could unite with the negative chloride ion or the negative hydroxide ion. However, potassium chloride is a salt which ionizes completely in water, and potassium hydroxide is a strong base which also ionizes completely. The same reasoning applies to Cl^- and H_3O^+. No reaction occurs. The four ions remain in solution as ions, and the solution is neutral. The ions produced by the salt of a strong acid and strong base do not react with water, and the $[H_3O^+]$ remains equal to the $[OH^-]$. Such a solution has a pH of 7. No hydrolysis occurs.

If an indicator is added to a solution of aluminum chloride, a salt, we will find that the solution is acidic, not neutral as expected. With the exception of the metals of Groups IA and IIA, metallic hydroxides are all weak bases and in fact have low solubilities. The positive ions of such metals are strongly hydrated and give up a proton readily

450

from the associated water molecule. In a water solution of $AlCl_3$, the reaction is:

$$Al(H_2O)_6^{3+}(aq) + H_2O(l) \rightarrow Al(OH)(H_2O)_5^{2+}(aq) + H_3O^+(aq)$$

Since HCl is a strong acid, the H_3O^+ ions do not combine with the Cl^- ions, and the solution is acidic.

If an appropriate indicator is added to a water solution of sodium carbonate, a salt, the indicator will show the solution to be basic:

$$CO_3^{2-}(aq) + H_2O(l) \rightarrow HCO_3^-(aq) + OH^-(aq)$$

This reaction goes almost to completion and produces a large excess of hydroxide ions. Hydrogen carbonate ion (HCO_3^-) is an exceedingly weak acid, so that the reverse reaction proceeds only to a very slight extent:

$$HCO_3^-(aq) + H_2O(l) \rightarrow H_3O^+(aq) + CO_3^{2-}(aq)$$

Since more OH^- ions than H_3O^+ ions form, the solution becomes basic.

If the salt, ammonium acetate, is dissolved in water, ammonium hydroxide and acetic acid are formed. Ammonium hydroxide is a weak, slightly ionized base. Acetic acid is a weak, slightly ionized acid. Both H_3O^+ and OH^- ions are removed from solution. This results in a neutral or nearly neutral solution because acetic acid and ammonium hydroxide are of approximately the same degree of weakness. For other salts composed of two weak ions, it is necessary to know their relative degrees of weakness in order to predict the character of the solution. For example, a solution of NH_4CN would be basic. The acid, HCN, is far weaker than the base, NH_4OH. On the other hand, a solution of NH_4IO_3 would be acidic since HIO_3 is stronger as an acid than NH_4OH is as a base.

The salt produced from a weak acid and a strong base is basic.

A mixture of a weak acid and a weak base does not always produce a neutral solution. A neutral solution occurs only when both ions hydrolyze to approximately the same degree. This problem does not arise with a solution of strong acid and base because both ionize completely.

The salt produced from a weak acid and a weak base will probably be neutral.

20:19   Summary of Hydrolysis

Some dissolved salts react with water to form acidic or basic solutions. The action of a salt with water to form an acidic or basic solution is called *hydrolysis*. Salts are formed as products of acid-base reactions. The kinds of acid and base (strong or weak) that react to form a salt determine the kind of solution the salt will produce (acidic or basic) in water.

Table 20–7

Hydrolysis

| | | Possible Solution Types | | | Example |
Acid	Base	(Acidic)	(Neutral)	(Basic)	(Acid + Base)
strong acid	strong base		×		$HCl(aq) + NaOH(aq)$
strong acid	weak base	×			$HCl(aq) + NH_3(aq)$ $H_2SO_4(aq) + NaHCO_3(aq)$
weak acid	strong base			×	$H_2CO_3(aq) + NaOH(aq)$
weak acid	weak base	× ←	× variable	→ ×	$HC_2H_3O_2(aq) + NH_3(g)$ $+ H_2O(l)$

20:20 Buffers

Many of the fluids in your body must be maintained within a very narrow pH range if you are to remain healthy. There are also many instances in laboratory and industrial chemistry when the maintenance of a certain pH is important. In both cases, the end is accomplished in the same way: the creation of a *buffer system*. A buffer system is a solution which can absorb fairly large amounts of acid or base without changing its pH by a significant amount.

Consider the reaction of ammonia in water:

$$NH_3(g) + H_2O(l) \rightleftarrows NH_4^+(aq) + OH^-(aq)$$

If we look at the reverse reaction in this equilibrium, we can see that ammonium ions will react with a base. What happens when we dissolve ammonium ions (from ammonium chloride, for example) in water? $NH_4^+(aq) + H_2O(l) \rightleftarrows NH_3(aq) + H_3O^+(aq)$. From this reverse reaction, we can see that ammonia molecules will react with acid. If we had a solution with a large amount of each of these substances, we would have our desired buffer solution. The ammonia molecules would react with any added acid, and the ammonium ions would react with any added base. Buffer solutions are prepared by using a weak acid or a weak base (in our present case, ammonia) and one of its salts (in our case, ammonium chloride).

Buffers can absorb acids or bases without significant change in pH.

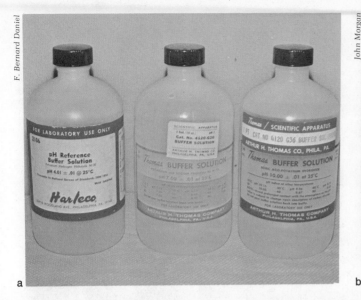

a   b

FIGURE 20-11. Standard buffers used in the laboratory are shown in (a). Buffered products commonly found in the home are shown in (b).

Stated in general terms, the reactions would appear as follows:

FOR A WEAK ACID: $HA \rightleftarrows H^+ + A^-$

The weak acid, HA, will react with added base. The negative ion from the salt, A^-, will react with added acid.

FOR A WEAK BASE: $MOH \rightleftarrows M^+ + OH^-$

The weak base, MOH, will react with added acid. The positive ion from the salt, M^+, will react with added base.

Buffers are most efficient at neutralizing added acids or bases when the concentrations of weak acid (or base) and salt are equal. By choosing the correct weak acid (or base) we can prepare a buffer solution of almost any pH value we wish.

Buffer solutions are formed from a weak acid or base and one of its salts.

20:21   Titration

Titration is the use of a standard solution to determine the concentration of another solution. A titration usually involves the use of a standard solution, burets, and an indicator (or a pH meter). (A *standard solution* is one for which the concentration is known.)

If an acid is added to a base, a neutralization reaction occurs. The acid unites with the base to form a salt and water:

Titration is a quantitative process which may be used to determine the molarity of an acid or a base.

$$\text{acid} + \text{base} \xrightarrow[\text{reaction}]{\text{neutralization}} \text{salt} + \text{water}$$

By adding an indicator, we can see at exactly what point complete neutralization occurs.

Bruce Charlton

To carry out a titration, a buret is filled with a standard solution. A small amount of indicator is added to a measured amount of the solution of unknown concentration to be titrated. The buret is opened and the standard solution is allowed to flow (with stirring) into the solution to be titrated until a color change occurs. The color change indicates that neutralization has occurred and that an equivalent amount of standard solution has been added to the solution titrated. The moles of standard solution can be calculated by multiplying the volume of standard solution used by the molarity of the standard solution:

Titration is a form of volumetric analysis.

Standard solutions can be used to determine the concentration of other solutions through titration.

$$\text{moles}_{\text{standard solution}} = \text{volume}_{\text{standard solution}} \times \text{molarity}_{\text{standard solution}}$$

The moles in the titrated solution of unknown concentration are then found by using the coefficients in the balanced equation. Then, dividing the moles of the titrated solution by the volume of that solution gives us the concentration of the titrated solution:

$$\text{molarity } (M)_{\text{titrated solution}} = \frac{\text{moles}_{\text{titrated solution}}}{\text{volume}_{\text{titrated solution}}}$$

Let us use an example to show how titration works. Suppose you wanted to find the molarity of vinegar. Such a solution is acidic because vinegar is dilute acetic acid derived from the fermentation of fruit juice. Let us use a standard NaOH solution that we know to be 0.500M. (This you could prepare quite easily.) The indicator we will use because of the reactants will be phenolphthalein.

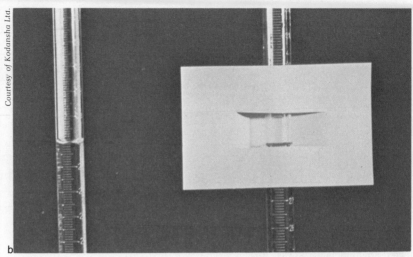

FIGURE 20-13. Flow of liquid from the buret is regulated with this special ground glass stopper (a). The amount of liquid delivered can be read directly from the graduations on the buret (b).

Fill two burets, including the nozzle, with solution, one with acid and one with base, and record the initial volumes. (Watch the meniscus.) Allow 20–25 milliliters of the vinegar solution to run into a beaker which contains a few drops of phenolphthalein. What color is phenolphthalein in acid solution? Colorless

While stirring constantly, allow the basic solution to run slowly into the beaker. You will be able to tell when the acid is exactly neutralized. How? This is called the endpoint of the titration. One drop of first one (NaOH) and then the other (vinegar solution) should alternately change the color. Record the volume of each used.

Solution turns pink

EXAMPLE—MOLARITY

Suppose that we had used 15.0 ml of 0.500M NaOH and 25.0 ml of vinegar solution of unknown concentration. What is the molarity of the vinegar solution?

$$\text{moles of base} = (0.015 \text{ liter})(0.500 \text{ moles/liter})$$
$$= 0.00750 \text{ moles of base}$$

The balanced equation is:

$$NaOH(aq) + CH_3COOH(aq) \rightarrow CH_3COONa(aq) + H_2O(l)$$

Since the coefficients are all 1's, 0.0075 moles of base will react with 0.0075 moles of acid. The concentration of acid (vinegar) is:

$$\text{molarity of acid} = (0.0075 \text{ mole})/(0.025 \text{ liter})$$
$$= 0.3M$$

EXAMPLE–NEUTRALIZATION

How many ml of 0.0200M KOH will exactly neutralize 15.0 ml of 0.400M H_2SO_4? The equation is:

$$2KOH(aq) + H_2SO_4(aq) \rightarrow K_2SO_4(aq) + 2H_2O(l)$$

$$\text{moles of acid} = (0.015 \text{ liter})(0.400 \text{ moles/liter})$$
$$= 0.00600 \text{ moles of acid}$$

Since 2 moles of base are required for 1 mole of acid, 0.0120 moles of KOH will be required. Therefore:

$$(0.0120 \text{ moles})/(0.0200 \text{ moles/liter}) = 0.600 \text{ liters base}$$
$$= 600 \text{ ml base}$$

To check the answer:

$$\frac{0.00600 \text{ mole acid}}{} \left| \frac{2 \text{ mole base}}{1 \text{ mole acid}} \right| \frac{1000 \text{ ml base}}{0.0200 \text{ mole base}} = 600 \text{ ml base}$$

FIGURE 20-14. This chemist is using an automatic titrator to test for impurities in dyes.

SUMMARY

1. There are three common acid-base theories: the Arrhenius theory, the Brönsted-Lowry theory, and the Lewis theory.
2. The Arrhenius definitions are: A base is a substance which produces hydroxide ions in water solution, and an acid is a substance which produces hydrogen ions in water solution. However, we assume the existence of H_3O^+ instead of H^+.
3. The Brönsted definitions are: An acid is a proton donor; a base is a proton acceptor. A Brönsted acid-base reaction can be written:

$$\text{acid} + \text{base} \rightarrow \text{conjugate base} + \text{conjugate acid}$$

4. The Lewis definitions are: An acid is an electron pair acceptor; a base is an electron pair donor.
5. To name a binary acid, determine what stem to use by finding what element is combined with hydrogen. To this stem add the prefix *hydro-* and the suffix *-ic*.

6. To name ternary acids which contain oxygen, find the stem by determining what element is combined with oxygen and hydrogen. The suffix and prefix are determined by the number of oxygen atoms in a molecule:

per- stem -*ic*	more oxygen
stem -*ic*	most common form
stem -*ous*	less oxygen
hypo- stem -*ous*	still less oxygen

7. To name bases, add the word hydroxide to the name of the metallic or positive ion.
8. Any oxygen-containing substance which produces a base when dissolved in water is called a basic anhydride.
9. Any oxygen-containing substance which produces an acid when dissolved in water is called an acid anhydride.
10. Metallic elements tend to form basic anhydrides, while nonmetallic elements tend to form acidic anhydrides.
11. A salt is a crystalline compound composed of the negative ion of an acid and the positive ion of a base.
12. A strong acid ionizes completely in a water solution. A weak acid ionizes only slightly in a water solution.
13. The ionization constant, K_a, for any weak acid is:

$$K_a = \frac{[H_3O^+][A^-]}{[HA]}$$

14. Percent ionization is the ratio of concentration of ions to concentration of original reactant:

$$\% \text{ ionization} = \frac{[A^+] \times 100}{[AB]}$$

15. If the concentration of a product ion is increased by adding similar ions, the equilibrium shifts toward the reactants. This shift is called the common ion effect.
16. Polyprotic acids contain more than one ionizable hydrogen atom.
17. The solubility product constant, K_{sp}, can be used to predict precipitation. For the equation

$$AB \leftrightarrows A^+ + B^-$$

$K_{sp} = [A^+][B^-]$, if AB dissolves only slightly.

18. Water ionizes slightly to form H_3O^+ and OH^- ions:

$$H_2O(l) + H_2O(l) \rightarrow H_3O^+(aq) + OH^-(aq)$$

19. K_w (ion product constant for water) is:

$$[H_3O^+][OH^-] = 10^{-14}$$

20. The pH of a solution is equal to $-\log [H_3O^+]$. A pH of 7 is neutral, less than 7 is acidic, and more than 7 is basic. The pH can range from 0 to 14.

21. Indicators are chemicals used to measure the pH of a solution. Their most important characteristic is a color change which occurs within a limited pH range.

22. Hydrolysis is the action of a salt on water to form an acidic or basic solution.

23. Buffer solutions are prepared from a weak acid or base and a corresponding salt. They are capable of absorbing moderate amounts of acid and/or base without a significant change in their pH value.

24. Acids and bases react with each other to form a salt and water. This type of reaction is called a neutralization reaction.

25. Titration is a laboratory process used to find the concentration of a substance in solution.

26. The volume of a solution in liters (or milliliters) multiplied by its molarity is equal to the number of moles (or millimoles) of solute in that volume.

PROBLEMS

8. From each of the following reactions, select the substance which is the conjugate acid and the substance which is the conjugate base:

a. $NH_3(g) + H_3O^+(aq) \rightarrow NH_4^+(aq) + H_2O(l)$
b. $CH_3OH(l) + NH_2^-(aq) \rightarrow CH_3O^-(aq) + NH_3(g)$
c. $OH^-(aq) + H_3O^+(aq) \rightarrow H_2O(l) + H_2O(l)$
d. $NH_2^-(aq) + H_2O(l) \rightarrow NH_3(g) + OH^-(aq)$
e. $H_2O(l) + HClO_4(aq) \rightarrow H_3O^+(aq) + ClO_4^-(aq)$

9. Draw electron-dot formulas for each of the following substances and decide whether the substance would be a Lewis acid or a Lewis base:

a. $AlCl_3$ c. PH_3 e. Zn^{2+}
b. SO_3 d. Xe

8.   Conjugate
    acid   base
a. NH_4^+ H_2O
b. NH_3 CH_3O^-
c. H_2O H_2O
d. NH_3 OH^-
e. H_3O^+ ClO_4^-

9. a. $: \overset{..}{\underset{..}{Cl}} : \overset{..}{\underset{..}{Al}} : \overset{..}{\underset{..}{Cl}} :$ acid
        $\overset{.. }{\underset{..}{Cl}}$

b. $: \overset{..}{\underset{..}{O}} : \overset{..}{\underset{..}{S}} :: \overset{..}{O}$ acid

c. $H : \overset{..}{P} : H$ base
        H

d. $: \overset{..}{\underset{..}{Xe}} :$ base

e. Zn^{2+} acid

10. Name the following acids: selenious
  a. HBr(aq)   hydrobromic   **d.** H_2SeO_3 (H_2SO_3 is sulfurous acid)
  b. H_2Se(aq) hydroselenic   **e.** $H_2N_2O_2$ (HNO_3 is nitric acid and
  c. HIO_3(aq) iodic   hyponitrous HNO_2 is nitrous acid)

11. Give the name and formula of the salts obtained from complete neutralization reactions between the acid-base pairs indicated:
  a. sodium hydroxide and phosphoric acid   sodium phosphate, Na_3PO_4
  b. potassium hydroxide and boric acid (H_3BO_3) potassium borate, K_3BO_3
  c. chromium(III) hydroxide and perchloric acid chromium perchlorate, $Cr(ClO_4)_3$
  d. cadmium hydroxide and hydrobromic acid   cadmium bromide, $CdBr_2$
  e. lithium hydroxide and silicic acid (H_4SiO_4)   lithium silicate, Li_4SiO_4

12. If 86.2 ml of 0.765M sodium hydroxide are needed to neutralize 30.0 ml of hydrochloric acid solution, what is the concentration of the acid? 2.20M

13. If 40.8 ml of 0.106M sulfuric acid are needed to neutralize 61.8 ml of potassium hydroxide solution, what is the concentration of the base? 0.140M

14. The K_{sp} of magnesium hydroxide is 1.2×10^{-11}. What is the pH of a saturated solution at equilibrium? pH = 10.459

15. What is the pH of 0.0001M NaOH?   *ans.*   pH = 10

16. What is the pH of 0.005M H_2A, assuming 100% ionization? pH = 2

17. Indicate whether each of the following salts in solution would form an acidic, a basic, or a neutral solution. Write the ionic equation for each:
  a. NaCl   **c.** $AlBr_3$ **e.** $Ca(NO_3)_2$
  b. K_2CO_3 **d.** $HgCl_2$

17. a. neutral
    b. basic
       $CO_3^{2-} + H_2O \rightarrow HCO_3^- + OH^-$
    c. acid
       $Al^{3+} + H_2O \rightarrow AlOH^{2+} + H^+$
    d. acid
       $Hg^{2+} + H_2O \rightarrow HgOH^+ + H^+$
    e. neutral

18. What is the pH of a solution that is 0.100M in ammonium hydroxide and 0.100M in ammonium chloride? pH = 9.246

19. The solubility product of MnS is 1.4×10^{-15}. What concentration of sulfide ion is needed in a 0.100M solution of $Mn(NO_3)_2$ to just precipitate MnS? $[S^{2-}] = 1.4 \times 10^{-14}$

20. Name the following acids:
  a. HF(aq)   **c.** H_2Te(aq)   **e.** HIO_4
  b. HI(aq)   **d.** H_3AsO_4

20. a. hydrofluoric acid
    b. hydriodic acid
    c. hydrotelluric acid
    d. arsenic acid
    e. periodic acid

21. Name the following bases:
  a. $Sr(OH)_2$ **c.** $Cr(OH)_2$ **e.** $Cd(OH)_2$
  b. $Mg(OH)_2$ **d.** $Sm(OH)_3$

21. a. strontium hydroxide
    b. magnesium hydroxide
    c. chromium(II) hydroxide
    d. samarium hydroxide
    e. cadmium hydroxide

22. What is the hydronium ion concentration in a 0.100M solution of $KHSO_4$? (See Appendix A for K_a value.) $2.91 \times 10^{-2}M$

23. What is the percentage of ionization of the HSO_4^- ion in Problem 22? 29.1%

24. What is the pH of a 0.100M solution of H_2NOH? pH = 9.52
25. What is the percentage of ionization in Problem 24? 0.0332%
26. What is the benzoate ion concentration in a 0.0500M solution of benzoic acid (C_6H_5COOH)? $1.80 \times 10^{-3}M$
27. What is the pH of a 0.300M solution of HCN in which the CN^- concentration has been adjusted to 0.0100M? pH = 7.830
28. What pH is necessary in a solution to just precipitate FeS if the Fe^{2+} concentration is 0.167M? Assume the concentration of H_2S in the solution is 0.100M. pH = 1.63
29. What would be the hydronium ion concentration in a solution 0.100M in NaOH and 1.00M in NH_4OH? $10^{-13}M$
30. What would be the hydrogen ion concentration in a 0.200M solution of oxalic acid (HOOCCOOH)? $8.31 \times 10^{-2}M$
31. Calculate the ratio of the first ionization constant to the second ionization constant for each of the polyprotic acids listed in Appendix A . Do you see any pattern? See Teacher's Guide.

ONE MORE STEP

Lavoisier theory
Berthollet theory
Arrhenius theory
Brönsted-Lowry theory
Lewis theory

See Teacher's Guide at the front of this book.

1. Determine the names of five acid-base theories. Report on their similarities and differences.
2. What is meant by the "leveling effect" of water on very strong acids and very strong bases?
3. Find the names of the following acids, and why they are named as they are: H_2SO_5, $H_2S_2O_7$, $H_2S_2O_8$, HNCO, and HSCN.
4. Graph the pH of a solution (abscissa) versus the moles of base added (ordinate) for the titration of: a weak acid by a strong base, a weak acid by a weak base, a strong acid by a weak base, and a strong acid by a strong base.
5. What indicator would you use for each of these titrations:

5e. 1st proton—methyl red or 2,5-dinitrophenol; 2nd proton—litmus, phenol red, bromothymol blue; 3rd proton—thymolphthalein

    a. HCl(aq) + NaOH(aq) bromothymol blue, litmus, phenol red
    b. $HC_2H_3O_2$(aq) + NaOH(aq) thymol blue, phenolphthalein
    c. NH_4OH(aq) + HCl(aq) 2,5-dinitrophenol, methyl red
    d. NH_4OH(aq) + $HC_2H_3O_2$(aq) bromothymol blue, litmus, phenol red
    e. H_3PO_4(aq) + NaOH(aq) (use a different indicator for each successive proton transfer)

6. What is the pH of a 0.100M solution of sodium acetate? pH = 8.877

7. What is the concentration of hydroxide ion in a solution containing 1.00M NH_4Cl and 0.100M NH_4OH? $1.77 \times 10^{-6}M$

8. If NaCl is added slowly to a solution that is 1.00M in Ag^+ and 1.00M in Pb^{2+}, which salt will precipitate first? AgCl

9. In the preceding problem, what will be the concentration of the metal ion whose salt precipitates first when the second salt starts to precipitate? $3.8 \times 10^{-8}M$

10. Look up the structural formula for a particular indicator, and draw its structure in both the acidic and basic forms.

10. See Teacher's Guide at the front of this book.

Suggested Readings for this chapter may be found in the Teacher's Guide at the front of this book.

Corrosion is a serious economic problem. Chemists constantly seek new and effective ways to combat the problem. Some substances when added to metals help prevent corrosion. Coatings are also effective in preventing corrosion of some substances. This chemist is placing coated metal strips in an environmental chamber to test their ability to resist corrosion. Corrosion usually involves oxidation-reduction reactions. What is the nature of these reactions?

Chapter 21 presents the idea that redox reactions involve the transfer of electrons from one atom to another. Two ways to balance redox reactions are demonstrated and chemical equivalence is introduced.

There are basically two different types of chemical reactions: (1) Reactions in which ions or molecules react with no apparent change in the electronic structure of the particles; (2) Reactions in which ions or atoms undergo changes of electronic structure. In the second type of reaction, electrons may actually be transferred from one particle to another, or the sharing of the electrons may be somewhat changed. This latter type of reaction involving electron changes is called an *oxidation-reduction reaction*. It is these "redox" reactions which we will now discuss.

or molecules

GOAL: You will gain an understanding of oxidation-reduction reactions and the electron rearrangement that takes place during these reactions.

In oxidation-reduction reactions, electronic structures undergo change.

Oxidation-reduction reactions are known as "redox" reactions.

Table 21–1

Two Reaction Types

(1) *Double displacement*	(2) *Redox*
$BaCl_2(aq) + Na_2SO_4(aq) \rightarrow$ $BaSO_4(c) + 2NaCl(aq)$	$16H^+(aq) + 2MnO_4^-(aq) + 5C_2O_4^{2-}(aq) \rightarrow$ $2Mn^{2+}(aq) + 8H_2O(l) + 10CO(g)$
$Ba^{2+} \rightarrow Ba^{2+}$	$H^+ \rightarrow H_2O$
$Cl^- \rightarrow Cl^-$	$7+$ $MnO_4^- \rightarrow Mn^+$
$Na^+ \rightarrow Na^+$	$3+$ $C_2O_4^{2-} \rightarrow 2CO_2$ $4+$
$SO_4^{2-} \rightarrow SO_4^{2-}$	

Before we indicate what oxidation-reduction reactions are, we will briefly indicate what they are not.

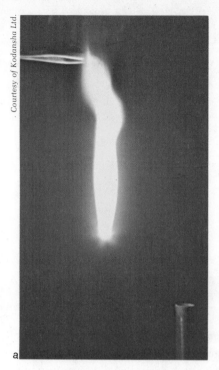

FIGURE 21-1. The burning of magnesium in air (a) and the rusting of iron (b) are examples of oxidation. In both examples, oxygen is one of the reactants.

a

b

In the $BaSO_4$ reaction in Table 21–1, the substances are all ionic. Since there is no change in the charge of these ions during reaction, there are no apparent electron changes. This is not an oxidation-reduction reaction. The production of a precipitate of this kind is nearly always a result of a non-redox reaction, as are also most acid-base reactions. Arrhenius acids and bases

Most double replacement reactions are not redox reactions.

Since nearly every other kind of reaction is an oxidation-reduction reaction, redox reactions are important in chemistry, and also in life processes and in industry.

a

b

FIGURE 21-2. The burning of antimony in chlorine (a) and the burning of a candle in bromine (b) are examples of oxidation. Oxygen is not a reactant in either example.

THE TRANSFER OF ELECTRONS

21:1 Oxidation

The term oxidation was originally applied to the combining of oxygen with other elements. There were many different known instances of this. Iron rusts and carbon burns. In rusting, oxygen combines slowly with iron to form Fe_2O_3; in burning, it unites rapidly with carbon to form CO_2. Observation of these reactions gave rise to the terms "slow" and "rapid" oxidation.

Chemists finally recognized, however, that other nonmetallic elements united with substances in the same manner that oxygen unites with these substances. Hydrogen, antimony, and sodium all burn in chlorine, and iron will burn in fluorine. Since these reactions (Table 21–2) were similar, chemists formed a more general definition of oxidation. Electrons were removed from each free element by the reactants O_2 or Cl_2. Thus, *oxidation* was defined as the process by which electrons are apparently removed from an atom or ion.

Oxidation was first defined as the union of oxygen with other substances.

Combustion is another name for rapid oxidation.

Oxidation is now defined as the process by which electrons are removed from atoms or ions.

This new definition of oxidation allows the term to be applied as a general term for a specific kind of reaction.

Table 21–2

Oxidation Reactions

Oxidation Reaction	Free Element	Oxidizing Agent	Electrons Transferred	Oxidized Material
$4Fe(c) + 3O_2(g) \rightarrow 2Fe_2O_3(c)$	Fe^0	O_2	$12e^-*$	Fe_2O_3
$C(c) + O_2(g) \rightarrow CO_2(g)$	C^0	O_2	$4e^-$	CO_2
$H_2(g) + Cl_2(g) \rightarrow 2HCl(g)$	H^0	Cl_2	$2e^-$	HCl
$2Sb(c) + 3Cl_2(g) \rightarrow 2SbCl_3(c)$	Sb^0	Cl_2	$6e^-$	$SbCl_3$
$2Na(c) + Cl_2(g) \rightarrow 2NaCl(c)$	Na^0	Cl_2	$2e^-$	$NaCl$

Here we introduce a zero superscript which is used to indicate the free element. This helps students to avoid overlooking some oxidation number changes.

* 12 moles of electrons are removed from 4 moles of Fe^0 to form 2 moles of Fe_2O_3 (Fe^{3+}).

21:2 Reduction

A reduction reaction was originally limited to the type of reaction in which ores were "reduced" from their oxides. Iron oxide was "reduced" to iron by carbon monoxide. Copper(II) oxide could be "reduced" to copper by hydrogen. In these reactions, oxygen is removed, and the uncombined form of the element, the free element, is produced. The free element can be produced in other ways. An iron nail dropped into a copper(II) sulfate solution causes a

Oxides are said to be "reduced" by the removal of oxygen.

All of these processes are reductions.

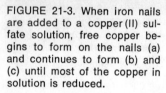
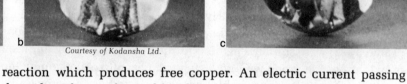

Courtesy of Kodansha Ltd.

FIGURE 21-3. When iron nails are added to a copper (II) sulfate solution, free copper begins to form on the nails (a) and continues to form (b) and (c) until most of the copper in solution is reduced.

reaction which produces free copper. An electric current passing through molten sodium chloride produces free sodium.

Table 21–3

Reduction Reactions

Reduction Reaction	Material Reduced	Reducing Agent	Electrons Transferred	Free Element
$Fe_2O_3(c) + 3CO(g) \rightarrow$ $2Fe(c) + 3CO_2(g)$	Fe^{3+}	CO	$6e^-$	Fe^0
$CuO(c) + H_2(g) \rightarrow$ $Cu(c) + H_2O(g)$	Cu^{2+}	H_2	$2e^-$	Cu^0
$2Na^+Cl^-(l) \xrightarrow[\text{current}]{\text{electric}}$ $2Na(c) + Cl_2(g)$	Na^+	e^-	$2e^-$	Na^0
$Cu^{2+}(aq) + SO_4^{2-}(aq) + Fe^0(c) \rightarrow$ $Fe^{3+}(aq) + SO_4^{2-}(aq) + Cu^0(c)$	Cu^{2+}	Fe^0	$2e^-$	Cu^0

Reduction is defined as the process by which electrons are added to atoms or ions.

The similarity between oxidation and reduction reactions led chemists to formulate a more generalized definition of reduction: *reduction* is the process by which electrons are apparently added to atoms or ions.

21:3 Oxidizing and Reducing Agents

Oxidation and reduction occur at the same time in a reaction.

In an oxidation-reduction reaction, electrons are transferred. All the electrons exchanged in an oxidation-reduction reaction must be accounted for. It seems reasonable, therefore, that both oxidation

466

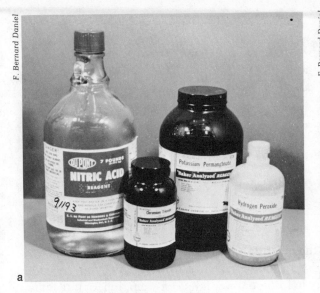

a

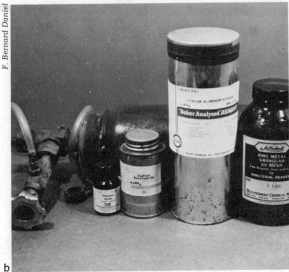

b

F. Bernard Daniel

F. Bernard Daniel

and reduction must occur simultaneously in a reaction: electrons are lost and gained at the same time. Otherwise, electrons (electricity) would be stored in the products. There is no evidence of electron storage.

The substance in the reaction which gives up electrons is called the *reducing agent*. The reducing agent contains the atoms which are oxidized (the atoms which lose electrons). The substance in the reaction which gains electrons is called the *oxidizing agent*. It contains the atoms which are reduced (the atoms which gain electrons).

If a substance gives up electrons readily, it is said to be a *strong reducing agent*. Its oxidized form, however, is normally a *poor oxidizing agent*. If a substance gains electrons readily, it is said to be a *strong oxidizing agent*. Its reduced form is a *weak reducing agent*.

FIGURE 21-4. Some common oxidizing agents (a) are nitric acid, chromium trioxide, potassium permanganate, and hydrogen peroxide. Some common reducing agents (b) are hydrogen, sodium borohydride, lithium aluminum hydride, zinc, and platinum oxide.

A reducing agent gives up electrons.

An oxidizing agent gains electrons.

Important

OXIDATION NUMBERS

21:4 Oxidation Number

How is it possible to determine whether an oxidation-reduction reaction has taken place? This can be done by determining whether any electron shifts have taken place during the reaction. To indicate electron changes, we can use the *oxidation number* of the atoms in the reaction. The *oxidation number* is the charge an atom appears to have when we assign a certain number of electrons to given atoms or ions. Any change of oxidation numbers in the course of a reaction indicates an oxidation-reduction reaction has taken place.

For example, suppose iron, as part of a reactant in a reaction, has an oxidation number of 2+. If iron appears as part of a product with

Sometimes a distinction is made between oxidation state and oxidation number. For instance, in MnO_2, O is in the 2 − oxidation state but O_2 (O_2^{4-}) in the compound has an oxidation number of 4 −. However, this distinction is not always made. Instead, we may use the term oxidation number for a group of atoms meaning the algebraic sum of the oxidation numbers of the atoms in the group.

A change in oxidation number of an atom indicates a redox reaction.

an oxidation number other than 2+, say 3+ or 0, then a redox reaction has taken place.

This raises the question, how are oxidation numbers assigned?

It is helpful to review electron dot diagrams before studying this section.

21:5 Assigning Oxidation Numbers

Electron dot formulas are helpful in assigning oxidation numbers.

We have already seen in Chapters 4 and 8 how to predict *possible* oxidation numbers.

Oxidation numbers are assigned according to the apparent charge of the element. To determine the apparent charge, you may find it helpful to consult the electron dot structure for the substance. However, the electron dot structure you draw will not give you the complete answer; it only helps you to visualize an atom, ion, or molecule.

Suppose you want to know the oxidation number of the sodium atom. The electron dot symbol is Na·. This states that the atom is not charged, or that the number of electrons is equal to the number of protons. The apparent charge of the sodium atom is 0, and its oxidation number is 0.

The sodium ion, however, is indicated in this manner: Na^+. This means that there is one more proton than electron. Since its apparent charge is 1+, its oxidation number is 1+.

Consider free chlorine (Cl_2), whose electronic structure is $:\ddot{C}l:\ddot{C}l:$. Since each chlorine atom has the same electronegativity, the two chlorine atoms share the electrons equally. Thus, each is assigned seven electrons in the outer level, giving a net charge of 0 for each. Free chlorine (Cl_2), then, is assigned oxidation number 0.

Shared electrons are assigned to the more electronegative element.

Chlorine in hydrogen chloride $H:\ddot{C}l:$ has an oxidation number different from 0. The chlorine atom is more electronegative than the hydrogen atom, and all the electrons shared are arbitrarily assigned to the chlorine atom. This means that the chlorine atom will have 18 electrons and 17 protons, and a resulting apparent charge of 1−. Its oxidation number is 1−. Hydrogen has had its electron assigned to chlorine, and will have one less electron than proton. The hydrogen atom's apparent charge will be 1+ and its oxidation state will be 1+.

Explain that oxidation numbers are used as an aid in understanding atomic structure. Point out, however, that oxidation numbers do not necessarily indicate the actual relationships existing between atoms and electrons in compounds.

Consider a possible electronic structure for sulfuric acid, H_2SO_4:

$$
\begin{array}{c}
:\ddot{O}: \\
H:\ddot{O}:\ddot{S}:\ddot{O}:H \\
:\ddot{O}:
\end{array}
$$

It can be seen that the oxygen atoms share electrons with both sulfur and hydrogen atoms. Since oxygen is more electronegative than sulfur, the shared electrons are arbitrarily assigned to each oxygen atom. Thus, the sulfur atom is assigned six fewer electrons than it has protons. The sulfur atom, with a resulting apparent charge of 6+, is assigned an oxidation number of 6+. Each hydrogen atom, less electronegative than the oxygen atoms, will also have its electron assigned to oxygen. The hydrogen oxidation number in this compound is 1+. Each oxygen atom has assigned to it all the shared electrons from either the sulfur or hydrogen atoms, or both. This gives each oxygen atom a 2− oxidation state (10 electrons, 8 protons). The total of the oxidation numbers of all the atoms in a compound must be zero. In this case, we have one sulfur atom with oxidation number 6+, four oxygen atoms with oxidation number 2−, and two hydrogen atoms with 1+. The apparent charge of the compound is zero.

In sulfur dichloride (SCl_2), sulfur has a different oxidation state. Consider a possible electronic structure:

$$:\overset{..}{\underset{}{Cl}}:$$
$$:\overset{..}{\underset{..}{S}}:\overset{..}{\underset{..}{Cl}}:$$

The sulfur atom shares only four electrons with chlorine. Sulfur has an oxidation state of 2+ (14 electrons, 16 protons). Chlorine has an oxidation state of 1− (18 electrons, 17 protons).

Since the oxidation number of an atom may change from compound to compound, an electronic structure must be made for each new compound. The oxidation number can be determined from this electronic structure. Drawing electronic structures is tiring and takes time. Fortunately, there is an easier way.

It is sometimes necessary to draw the electronic structure. See problem 4, page 483.

21:6   Rules for Assigning Oxidation Numbers

The following general rules have been made to enable you to find the oxidation number more easily.

1. The oxidation number of any free element is 0. This is true for all atomic and molecular structures: monatomic, diatomic, or polyatomic.

2. The oxidation number of a monatomic ion (Na^+, Ca^{2+}, Al^{3+}, Cl^-) is equal to the charge on the ion. Some atoms have several different possible oxidation numbers. For example, iron can be either 2+ or 3+; tin, 2+ or 4+.

Important factors in assigning oxidation numbers:

1. The oxidation number of any free element equals 0.

2. The oxidation number of any monatomic ion equals the charge on the ion.

3. The oxidation number of each hydrogen atom in most compounds is 1+. There are some exceptions to this. For instance, hydrogen, being the more electronegative atom, in compounds such as lithium hydride (LiH) has an oxidation number of 1−.

4. The oxidation number of each oxygen atom in most compounds is 2−. In peroxides, each oxygen is assigned 1−.

5. The sum of the oxidation numbers of all the atoms in a particle must equal the apparent charge of that particle.

For example, in the compound Na_2SO_4, sodium has an oxidation number of 1+ and oxygen has an oxidation number of 2−. Because there are two sodium atoms, the positive total is 2+. The four oxygen atoms have a negative total of 8−. The apparent charge of the compound must be 0. Therefore, the sulfur atom must have an oxidation number of 6+.

The nitrate ion (NO_3^-) has an oxidation number of 1−. Since each oxygen atom has an apparent charge of 2−, the negative total is 6−. In order for the total of the oxidation numbers to be 1−, nitrogen must have an oxidation number of 5+.

PROBLEM

1. In the following groups, give the oxidation number for the indicated atoms:

  a. S in Na_2SO_3 4+
  b. Mn in $KMnO_4$ 7+
  c. N in $Ca(NO_3)_2$ 5+
  d. C in Na_2CO_3 4+
  e. N in NO_2 4+

  f. S in HSO_4^- 6+
  g. S in $H_2S_2O_7$ 6+
  h. S in Al_2S_3 2−
  i. Mn in $MnCl_2$ 2+
  j. C in $C_{12}H_{22}O_{11}$ 0

21:7 Identifying Oxidation-Reduction Reactions

Oxidation numbers can be used to determine whether oxidation and reduction (electron transfer) occur in a specific reaction. Even the simplest reaction may be a redox reaction. Let us see how it is possible to determine whether a reaction is actually a redox reaction.

The direct combination of sodium and chlorine to produce sodium chloride is a simple example:

$$2Na(c) + Cl_2(g) \rightarrow 2NaCl(c)$$

As a reactant, each sodium atom has an oxidation number of 0. In the product, the oxidation number of each sodium atom is 1+. Similarly, each chlorine atom as a reactant has an oxidation number of 0. As a product, each chlorine atom has an oxidation number of 1−. Since a change of oxidation number has occurred, an oxidation-reduction reaction has taken place:

$$2Na^0(c) + Cl_2^0(g) \rightarrow 2Na^+Cl^-(c)$$

The change in oxidation number can result only from a shift of electrons between atoms, either by transferring or sharing. This shift of electrons alters the apparent charge (the oxidation number).

An increase in electrons means the substance is reduced. It also means that the apparent charge is algebraically lowered, and the oxidation number is lowered. In contrast, a loss of electrons is oxidation. When an atom is oxidized, its oxidation number increases.

The equation for a reaction can be used to determine whether the reaction is a redox reaction and, if so, the substance oxidized, the substance reduced, and the oxidizing and reducing agents. Since the oxidation number of sodium in the equation

$$2Na(c) + Cl_2(g) \rightarrow 2NaCl(c)$$

changed from 0 to 1+, sodium is oxidized. Sodium is also the reducing agent. A reducing agent always loses electrons and is, therefore, always oxidized as it reduces the other substance.   Important

EXAMPLE – REDOX

Tell what is oxidized, what is reduced, and identify the oxidizing and reducing agents in the reaction:

$$16H^+(aq) + 2MnO_4^-(aq) + 5C_2O_4^{2-}(aq) \rightarrow$$
$$2Mn^{2+}(aq) + 8H_2O(l) + 10CO_2(g)$$

Manganese is reduced (7+ → 2+) and carbon is oxidized (3+ → 4+). The permanganate ion (MnO_4^-) is the oxidizing agent because it contains manganese, and manganese is reduced. The oxalate ion ($C_2O_4^{2-}$) is the reducing agent; it contains carbon, which is oxidized.

PROBLEMS

2. Some of the following unbalanced reactions are oxidation-reduction reactions, and some are not. In each case: (a) Is the reaction redox? (b) If yes, name the element reduced, the element oxidized, the oxidizing agent, and the reducing agent:

A good mnemonic device: Reduction reduces the oxidation number.

A decrease in oxidation number indicates reduction.

An increase in oxidation number indicates oxidation.

Oxidation number change can help determine:
1. whether a reaction is redox
2. reducing, oxidizing agents in the reaction
3. elements that are oxidized or reduced

reduced = X
oxidized = O

a. $BaCl_2(aq) + Na_2SO_4(aq) \rightarrow 2NaCl(aq) + BaSO_4(c)$

b. $3H_2(g) + N_2(g) \rightarrow 2NH_3(g)$

c. $C(c) + H_2O(g) \rightarrow CO(g) + H_2(g)$

d. $3AgNO_3(aq) + FeCl_3(aq) \rightarrow 3AgCl(c) + Fe(NO_3)_3(aq)$

e. $H_2CO_3(aq) \rightarrow H_2O(l) + CO_2(g)$

ans. a. not redox

b. redox; nitrogen reduced, hydrogen oxidized, nitrogen the oxidizing agent, hydrogen the reducing agent

c. redox; hydrogen reduced, carbon oxidized, water oxidizing agent, carbon reducing agent

d. not redox

e. not redox

3. redox = b, d, e, g, h, i, j
not redox = a, c, f

	reducing agent	oxidizing agent
2. b.	hydrogen	nitrogen
c.	carbon	H_2O
3. b.	PbS	H_2O_2
d.	H_3PO_3	HNO_3
e.	I_2	HNO_3
g.	Fe^{2+}	NO_3^-
h.	$FeBr_2$	Br_2
i.	$S_2O_3^{2-}$	I_2
j.	H_2O_2	MnO_4^-

3. For each of the following equations indicate whether the reaction is redox or non-redox; and if oxidation-reduction occurs tell what is oxidized and what is reduced, and indicate the oxidizing and reducing agents.

a. $MgSO_4(aq) + Ca(OH)_2(aq) \rightarrow Mg(OH)_2(aq) + CaSO_4(c)$

b. $H_2O_2(aq) + PbS(c) \rightarrow PbSO_4(c) + H_2O(l)$

c. $KCl(c) + H_2SO_4(aq) \rightarrow KHSO_4(aq) + HCl(g)$

d. $HNO_3(aq) + H_3PO_3(aq) \rightarrow NO(g) + H_3PO_4(aq) + H_2O(l)$

e. $HNO_3(aq) + I_2(c) \rightarrow HIO_3(aq) + NO_2(g) + H_2O(l)$

f. $Na_2S(aq) + AgNO_3(aq) \rightarrow Ag_2S(c) + NaNO_3(aq)$

g. $H^+(aq) + NO_3^-(aq) + Fe^{2+}(aq) \rightarrow H_2O(l) + NO(g) + Fe^{3+}(aq)$

h. $FeBr_2(aq) + Br_2(l) \rightarrow FeBr_3(aq)$

i. $S_2O_3^{2-}(aq) + I_2(c) \rightarrow S_4O_6^{2-}(aq) + I^-(aq)$

j. $H_2O_2(aq) + MnO_4^-(aq) \rightarrow O_2(g) + Mn^{2+}(aq)$

BALANCING REDOX EQUATIONS

The half-reaction method of balancing equations more closely approximates what actually happens in reactions which take place in solution.

Half-reactions can be used to balance redox reactions.

21:8 The Half-Reaction Method

Balancing some oxidation reduction equations is difficult and lengthy by the trial and error method. There are easier ways.

The half-reaction method of balancing redox equations involves extra equations called *half-reactions*. One of these half-reactions represents the oxidation that is taking place, and the other half-reaction represents the reduction. The number of electrons gained in the process of reduction must equal the number of electrons lost in oxidation. You may add half-reactions involving equal numbers of electrons and obtain a balanced redox equation. A most important fact must be kept in mind while writing half-reactions: Always write the formulas of molecules and ions as they actually occur. For instance, in the reaction involving nitric acid and phosphorous acid:

$$HNO_3(aq) + H_3PO_3(aq) \rightarrow NO(g) + H_3PO_4(aq) + H_2O(l)$$

there are no actual N^{5+}, N^{2+}, P^{3+}, or P^{5+} ions. The substances must be represented in the form in which they actually occur. In this reaction, the actual ions and molecules are NO_3^-, NO, H_3PO_3, and H_3PO_4.

Each half-reaction and redox reaction can be balanced three ways: by *electrons*, by *total charge*, and by *atoms*. Any two of these three ways are sufficient to give an equation with overall balance. The third method may be used as a check. In the following illustrations, we will balance by electrons and atoms to obtain the balanced equation, and will balance by charge as a check.

21:9   The Nitric Acid-Phosphorous Acid Reaction

Consider the nitric-phosphorous acid reaction:

$$HNO_3(aq) + H_3PO_3(aq) \rightarrow NO(g) + H_3PO_4(aq) + H_2O(l)$$

FIRST. Write the skeleton half-reaction for the reduction process:

$$NO_3^- \rightarrow NO$$

Nitrogen is reduced from oxidation number 5+ to 2+, and therefore, each nitrogen atom gains three electrons. Incorporating the electrons in the skeleton equation, we have balanced the half-reaction with respect to electrons:

$$NO_3^- + 3e^- \rightarrow NO$$

Now we must balance the half-reaction with respect to atoms. Note that one nitrogen atom appears on each side of the equation, and the equation is balanced with respect to nitrogen. For oxygen however, there are three atoms on the left and only one on the right. It is, therefore, necessary to add two oxygen atoms to the right side of the half-reaction. From the information about the reaction taking place, we know that no oxygen is generated. Here is a second important rule for balancing redox reactions: In aqueous solutions, either H^+ and H_2O or OH^- and H_2O are always available. The nature of the reactants determines which pair of substances is present. In

---

Important

Redox reactions are balanced by electrons, total charge, and atoms.

Write an equation for the reduction half-reaction.

1. Balance the reduction half-reaction.

a. Balance the total number of electrons.

In aqueous solutions, either H^+ and H_2O or OH^- and H_2O are available.

the reaction we are now considering, two acids are involved, and the available substances are H^+ and H_2O. (If a basic substance is present, the substances available are OH^- and H_2O.) The solution in the nitric-phosphorous acid reaction is acidic, and the two oxygen atoms to be added to the right-hand side of the reduction half-reaction must be present in the form of water. The equation becomes:

b. Balance the total number of atoms.

$$NO_3^- + 3e^- \rightarrow NO + 2H_2O$$

The half-reaction is now balanced with nitrogen and oxygen atoms, but with the introduction of hydrogen on the right side, four hydrogen atoms must be placed on the left. In the acidic solution, hydrogen is available in the form of hydrogen ions. Hydrogen must be added to the equation in ionic form:

c. Balance the total charge.

$$NO_3^- + 3e^- + 4H^+ \rightarrow NO + 2H_2O$$

The half-reaction is now balanced with respect to electrons and to atoms. Let us check the balance by total charge. On the left side, one nitrate ion with a 1− charge, three electrons each with a 1− charge, and four hydrogen ions with 1+ charges give a net left-hand charge of 0. On the right, nitrogen(II) oxide and water are both neutral molecules and the total charge is 0. The half-reaction is then balanced with respect to total charge.

Write an equation for the oxidation half-reaction.

SECOND. Repeat the same procedure with the oxidation half-reaction:

$$H_3PO_3 \rightarrow H_3PO_4$$

2. Balance the oxidation half-reaction.

We calculate that the phosphorus atom changes in oxidation state from 3+ in H_3PO_3 to 5+ in H_3PO_4 as a result of losing two electrons. The half-reaction balanced with respect to electrons is then:

a. Balance the number of electrons.

$$H_3PO_3 \rightarrow H_3PO_4 + 2e^-$$

The half-reaction is already balanced with respect to hydrogen and phosphorus, so adding one oxygen atom to the left side of the equation should balance it with respect to atoms. However, the oxygen must be added in the form of water, making the half-reaction:

b. Balance the number of atoms.

$$H_3PO_3 + H_2O \rightarrow H_3PO_4 + 2e^-$$

Now the hydrogen is out of balance, and two hydrogen atoms must be added to the right side in the available form, H^+:

$$H_3PO_3 + H_2O \rightarrow H_3PO_4 + 2e^- + 2H^+$$

c. Balance the charges.

In checking charges, we see that each side is neutral.

THIRD. The two half-reactions are now balanced, but we have shown three electrons accepted and only two electrons released. You know that the number of electrons lost must equal the number of electrons gained. Before adding the two half-reactions, it is necessary to have the same number of electrons in each half-reaction. In algebra, you have learned to find the least common multiple of two numbers. In balancing oxidation-reduction reactions, you must find the least common multiple of the number of electrons lost and gained. In the example with which we are working, the least common multiple of electrons is 3×2 or 6. The half-reactions must then be adjusted so that six electrons are gained by the substance being reduced, and six electrons are lost by the substance being oxidized.

Jane Haldimond Marcet
(1769–1845)

Although not a research chemist, Jane Marcet nonetheless had a profound effect on the chemists of her day and those that followed. Her book, *Conversations in Chemistry*, was first published early in the 1800's and was continually revised to reflect the new scientific breakthroughs through 16 editions. By the time of the American Civil War nearly 200,000 copies had been sold in England and the United States.

The book, written in dialogue form, provided experiments to illustrate chemical concepts and an approach that today would be labeled discovery. Mrs. Marcet's work provided the chemical foundation for a young bookbindery clerk named Michael Faraday. Later during his distinguished scientific career, Faraday was to refer to *Conversations* as an "anchor in chemical knowledge."

Balance the electrons in the two half-reactions and add.

By multiplying the reduction half-reaction by 2 and the oxidation half-reaction by 3, we get:

$$2NO_3^- + 6e^- + 8H^+ \rightarrow 2NO + 4H_2O$$
$$3H_3PO_3 + 3H_2O \rightarrow 3H_3PO_4 + 6e^- + 6H^+$$

3. Add the two equations and simplify.

Adding the two equations, we get:

$$2NO_3^- + 6e^- + 8H^+ + 3H_3PO_3 + 3H_3O \rightarrow$$
$$2NO + 4H_2O + 3H_3PO_4 + 6e^- + 6H^+$$

Note that electrons, hydrogen ions, and water molecules appear on both sides of the equation. By subtracting those quantities which appear on both sides of the equation, the equation may be simplified:

$$2NO_3^-(aq) + 2H^+(aq) + 3H_3PO_3(aq) \rightarrow 2NO(g) + H_2O(l) + 3H_3PO_4(aq)$$

If any electrons remain on either side, you have made a mistake. You will note that this equation is balanced with respect to electrons, atoms, and total charge.

21:10   The Silver-Nitric Acid Reaction

Silver will react with nitric acid to produce silver nitrate, nitrogen(II) oxide, and water. Write and balance the equation for this reaction:

$$Ag(c) + \overset{1+5+2-}{HNO_3}(aq) \rightarrow \overset{1+5+2-}{AgNO_3}(aq) + \overset{2+2-}{NO}(g) + \overset{1+2-}{H_2O}(l)$$

The reduction half-reaction equation is the same as in the last reaction:

Reduction half-reaction

$$NO_3^- + 3e^- + 4H^+ \rightarrow NO + 2H_2O$$

The oxidation half-reaction is:

Oxidation half-reaction

$$Ag \rightarrow Ag^+ + e^-$$

This equation is balanced with respect to electrons, atoms, and charge. The least common multiple of the electrons in both half-reactions is 3. So that $3e^-$ will appear on both sides of the equation, the oxidation half-reaction is multiplied by 3:

Balance the electrons.

$$3Ag \rightarrow 3Ag^+ + 3e^-$$

Add the two half-reactions and simplify:

$$NO_3^-(aq) + 4H^+(aq) + 3Ag(c) \rightarrow NO(g) + 2H_2O(l) + 3Ag^+(aq)$$

This equation is the complete redox equation. It is balanced with respect to electrons, atoms, and charge.

21:11   The Iodine-Hypochlorous Acid Reaction

Suppose one or more of the substances appears as two or more atoms per formula unit of reactant. What happens then? Consider the reaction:

$$I_2(c) + HClO(aq) + H_2O(l) \rightarrow HIO_3(aq) + HCl(aq) \text{ (acidic)}$$

The oxidation number of iodine changes from 0 to 5+, and the oxidation number of chlorine changes from 1+ to 1−. However, iodine is a diatomic molecule, so both atoms are oxidized. If one atom must lose five electrons to go from 0 to 5+, two atoms must lose ten electrons. Each chlorine is reduced from 1+ to 1− and must gain two electrons for each atom. The balancing of the oxidation half-reaction then proceeds as follows:

Oxidation half-reaction

Skeleton	$I_2 \rightarrow 2IO_3^-$
Electrons	$I_2 \rightarrow 2IO_3^- + 10e^-$
Oxygen	$I_2 + 6H_2O \rightarrow 2IO_3^- + 10e^-$
Hydrogen	$I_2 + 6H_2O \rightarrow 2IO_3^- + 10e^- + 12H^+$
Check charge	$0 = 0$

Examples of how redox equations are balanced.

The reduction half-reaction proceeds as follows:

Reduction half-reaction

Skeleton	$HClO \rightarrow Cl^-$
Electrons	$HClO + 2e^- \rightarrow Cl^-$
Oxygen	$HClO + 2e^- \rightarrow Cl^- + H_2O$
Hydrogen	$HClO + 2e^- + H^+ \rightarrow Cl^- + H_2O$
Check charge	$1- = 1-$

Encourage students to check the charge.

Balance electrons and add.

To obtain the overall redox equation, proceed as follows:

$$\text{Electron least common multiple} = 10$$

Half-reactions are adjusted to obtain the correct number of electrons:

$$I_2 + 6H_2O \rightarrow 2IO_3^- + 10e^- + 12H^+$$
$$5HClO + 10e^- + 5H^+ \rightarrow 5Cl^- + 5H_2O$$

Adding and simplifying:

The final reaction should be checked for both atomic balance and charge balance.

$$I_2(c) + 5HClO(aq) + H_2O(l) \rightarrow 2IO_3^-(aq) + 7H^+(aq) + 5Cl^-(aq)$$

21:12 Two Review Examples

FIRST. Consider the reduction of permanganate ion (MnO_4^-) to manganese(II) ion in acid solution. The reduction is accomplished with sulfur dioxide as the reducing agent, and sulfur is oxidized to sulfate ion. Balance the equation:

$$H^+(aq) + MnO_4^-(aq) + SO_2(g) \rightarrow Mn^{2+}(aq) + SO_4^{2-}(aq)$$

Reduction half-reaction

Taking the reduction half-reaction first, we obtain the following sequence of steps:

Skeleton	$MnO_4^- \rightarrow Mn^{2+}$
Electrons	$MnO_4^- + 5e^- \rightarrow Mn^{2+}$
Oxygen	$MnO_4^- + 5e^- \rightarrow Mn^{2+} + 4H_2O$
Hydrogen	$MnO_4^- + 5e^- + 8H^+ \rightarrow Mn^{2+} + 4H_2O$
Check charge	$2+ = 2+$

Oxidation half-reaction

For the oxidation half-reaction:

Skeleton	$SO_2 \rightarrow SO_4^{2-}$
Electrons	$SO_2 \rightarrow SO_4^{2-} + 2e^-$
Oxygen	$SO_2 + 2H_2O \rightarrow SO_4^{2-} + 2e^-$
Hydrogen	$SO_2 + 2H_2O \rightarrow SO_4^{2-} + 2e^- + 4H^+$
Check charge	$0 = 0$

For the complete equation:

$$\text{Least common multiple for electrons} = 10$$

Multiplying equations appropriately:

Balance electrons and add.

$$2MnO_4^- + 10e^- + 16H^+ \rightarrow 2Mn^{2+} + 8H_2O$$
$$5SO_2 + 10H_2O \rightarrow 5SO_4^{2-} + 10e^- + 20H^+$$

Adding and simplifying:

$$2MnO_4^-(aq) + 5SO_2(g) + 2H_2O(l) \rightarrow 2Mn^{2+}(aq) + 5SO_4^{2-}(aq) + 4H^+(aq)$$

SECOND. Consider the oxidation of chloride ion to chlorine by dichromate ion, which in turn is reduced to the chromium(III) ion. The reaction takes place in acidic solution. Balance the reaction:

$$H^+(aq) + Cr_2O_7^{2-}(aq) + Cl^-(aq) \rightarrow Cl_2(g) + Cr^{3+}(aq)$$

The reduction half-reaction:

Reduction half-reaction

Skeleton	$Cr_2O_7^{2-} \rightarrow 2Cr^{3+}$
Electrons	$Cr_2O_7^{2-} + 6e^- \rightarrow 2Cr^{3+}$
Oxygen	$Cr_2O_7^{2-} + 6e^- \rightarrow 2Cr^{3+} + 7H_2O$
Hydrogen	$Cr_2O_7^{2-} + 6e^- + 14H^+ \rightarrow 2Cr^{3+} + 7H_2O$
Check charge	$6+ = 6+$

The oxidation half-reaction:

Oxidation half-reaction

Skeleton	$2Cl^- \rightarrow Cl_2$
Electrons	$2Cl^- \rightarrow Cl_2 + 2e^-$

The half-reaction is balanced with respect to atoms.

$$\text{Check charge} \quad 2- = 2-$$

To find the overall redox reaction:

Find the least common multiple of electrons (6), multiply the chlorine half-reaction by 3:

Balance electrons and add.

$$Cr_2O_7^{2-} + 6e^- + 14H^+ \rightarrow 2Cr^{3+} + 7H_2O$$
$$6Cl^- \rightarrow 3Cl_2 + 6e^-$$

Add the half-reactions and simplify. The result is the overall redox reaction:

$$14H^+(aq) + Cr_2O_7^{2-}(aq) + 6Cl^-(aq) \rightarrow 3Cl_2(g) + 2Cr^{3+}(aq) + 7H_2O(l)$$

PROBLEM

4. Balance the following equations: See Teacher's Guide.

a. $H^+ + 2MnO_4^-(aq) + 5H_2SO_3(aq) \rightarrow$

$$2Mn^{2+}(aq) + 5HSO_4^-(aq) + H^+(aq) + 3H_2O(l)$$

b. $Cr_2O_7^{2-}(aq) + 14H^+(aq) + 6I^-(aq) \rightarrow 2Cr^{3+}(aq) + 3I_2(c) + 7H_2O(l)$

c. $4NH_3(g) + 5O_2(g) \rightarrow 4NO(g) + 6H_2O(g)$ (basic)

d. $3As_2O_3(c) + 4H^+(aq) + 4NO_3^-(aq) + 7H_2O(l) \rightarrow 6H_3AsO_4(aq) + 4NO(g)$

e. $I_2(c) + H_2SO_3(aq) + H_2O(l) \rightarrow 2I^-(aq) + HSO_4^-(aq) + 3H^+(aq)$

f. $H_3AsO_4(aq) + 8H^+(aq) + 4Zn(c) \rightarrow AsH_3(g) + 4H_2O(l) + 4Zn^{2+}(aq)$

g. $3MnO_4^{2-}(aq) + 4H^+(aq) \rightarrow 2MnO_4^-(aq) + MnO_2(c) + 2H_2O(l)$

h. $2MnO_4^-(aq) + 5SO_2(g) + 2H_2O(l) \rightarrow 2Mn^{2+}(aq) + 5SO_4^{2-}(aq) + 4H^+(aq)$

i. $2NO_2(g) + 2OH^-(aq) \rightarrow NO_2^-(aq) + NO_3^-(aq) + H_2O(l)$

j. $8H^+ + 3HgS(c) + 12Cl^-(aq) + 2NO_3^-(aq) \rightarrow$

$$3HgCl_4^{2-}(aq) + H^+(aq) + 3S(c) + 2NO(g) + 4H_2O(l)$$

21:13 Net Ionic Equations

Ions not involved in the reaction are not included in the equation.

For reactions taking place in water, it is customary for chemists to write equations in the ionic form. In this method, only those ions taking part in the reaction are written. Other ions present in the solution but not involved in the reaction are known as *spectator ions* and are not included in the equation.

In using the half-reaction method, dissolved substances have been handled in their net ionic form. We listed other substances as molecules or atoms. The rule for writing equations is: Substances occurring in a reaction in molecular form are written as molecules and those occurring as ions are written as ions.

In equations for redox reactions, some substances are considered as molecules; others, as ions.

Weak electrolytes are written in molecular form.

Weak acids and bases are written in molecular form. Below are listed some "thumb rules" for deciding whether to use ions or molecules in writing net ionic equations. These rules are not applicable in all cases but work well in most reactions. However, if your equation must be exact, you should look in a handbook to determine whether substances are to be written as ions or as molecules.

Strong electrolytes are written in ionic form.

1. Binary acids: HCl, HBr, and HI are strong; all others (including HCN) are weak. Strong acids are written in ionic form.

2. Ternary acids: If the number of oxygen atoms in the molecule exceeds the number of hydrogen atoms by two or more, the acid is strong.

Weak: HClO, H_3AsO_4, H_2CO_3, H_4SiO_4, HNO_2
Strong: $HClO_3$, $HClO_4$, H_2SO_4, HNO_3, H_2SeO_4

3. Polyprotic acids: In the second and subsequent ionizations the acids are always weak, whether or not the original acid is strong or weak.

> It is often convenient to consider both protons of sulfuric acid as strong.

4. Bases: Hydroxides of the Groups IA and IIA elements (except beryllium) are strong. All others including ammonia, hydroxylamine, and organic bases are weak.

5. Salts: Salts are written in ionic form if soluble, and in molecular form if insoluble.

> even though the undissolved crystal is probably ionic in structure

Ionic: $K^+ + Cl^-$, $Zn^{2+} + 2 NO_3^-$
Molecular: AgBr, $BaSO_4$

6. Oxides: Oxides are always written in molecular form.
7. Gases: Gases are always written in molecular form.

SUMMARY

1. An oxidation-reduction reaction is one which involves an apparent transfer of electrons from one particle to another.
2. Oxidation is the process by which electrons are apparently removed from an atom or group of atoms.
3. Reduction is the process by which electrons are apparently added to atoms or groups of atoms.
4. Any substance in a reaction which loses electrons is a reducing agent.
5. Any substance in a reaction which gains electrons is an oxidizing agent.
6. If a substance gives up electrons readily, it is a strong reducing agent. Its oxidized form is usually a poor oxidizing agent.
7. If a substance acquires electrons readily, it is a strong oxidizing agent. Its reduced form is usually a poor reducing agent.
8. Oxidation number is the number representing the charge an atom *appears* to have when we assign a certain number of electrons to a given atom.
9. Any change in oxidation number during a reaction indicates an oxidation-reduction reaction has taken place.

10. Five rules for assigning oxidation numbers:
    (a) The oxidation number of any free element is 0.
    (b) The oxidation number of any single-atom ion is equal to the charge on that ion.
    (c) The oxidation number of hydrogen is usually 1+.
    (d) The oxidation number of oxygen in most compounds is 2−.
    (e) The sum of the oxidation numbers of all the atoms in a particle must equal the apparent charge of that particle.
11. In all chemical reactions, charge, number and kind of atoms, and number of electrons are conserved. Knowing this, you can balance a redox equation.
12. The steps in balancing a redox reaction are:
    a. Determine what is oxidized and what is reduced. Write the oxidation and reduction half-reactions.
    b. Balance each half-reaction for electrons.
    c. Balance each half-reaction for atoms other than hydrogen and oxygen. The number of atoms of each element should be the same on both sides.
    d. Balance first the oxygen and then the hydrogen by adding H^+ and H_2O or OH^- and H_2O.
    e. Check each half-reaction to see that the charges balance.
    f. Do steps a–e for both half-reactions.
    g. Find the least common multiple of the electrons exchanged in both half-reactions.
    h. Multiply the two half-reactions by appropriate factors so that the number of electrons exchanged is the same in each half-reaction.
    i. Add the two half-reactions. Simplify to obtain the balanced overall reaction.
13. Oxidation-reduction reactions are normally written as net ionic equations. There are some simple rules of thumb used in determining the proper form in which to write the various molecules, atoms, ions, or polyatomic ions of reacting substances.

PROBLEMS

5. See Teacher's Guide at the front of this book.

5. Balance the following equations after putting them in net ionic form:
   a. $Cu(c) + HNO_3(aq) \rightarrow Cu(NO_3)_2(aq) + NO(g) + H_2O(l)$
   b. $Fe(NO_3)_2(aq) + HNO_3(aq) \rightarrow Fe(NO_3)_3(aq) + NO(g) + H_2O(l)$
   c. $Zn(c) + HNO_3(aq) \rightarrow Zn(NO_3)_2(aq) + NO_2(g) + H_2O(l)$
   d. $Sb(c) + H_2SO_4(aq) \rightarrow Sb_2(SO_4)_3(aq) + SO_2(g) + H_2O(l)$
   e. $H_2S(g) + H_2SO_3(aq) \rightarrow S(c) + H_2O(l)$

6. Balance the following equations after putting them in net ionic form:

   a. $HCl(aq) + HNO_3(aq) \rightarrow HClO(aq) + NO(g) + H_2O(l)$

   b. $Ag(c) + HClO_3(aq) + HCl(aq) \rightarrow AgCl(c) + H_3O(l)$

   c. $KI(aq) + O_2(g) \rightarrow KI_3(aq) + H_2O(l)$

   d. $HNO_3(aq) + H_2SO_4(aq) + Hg(l) \rightarrow Hg_2SO_4(c) + H_2O(l) + NO(g)$

   e. $CO(g) + I_2O_5(g) \rightarrow CO_2(g) + I_2(g)$

6. See Teacher's Guide at the front of this book.

7. In terms of this chapter, how do oxidation and reduction differ?

7. oxidation = e^- loss reduction = e^- gain

8. How many grams of K_2SO_3 can be oxidized to K_2SO_4 by 7.9 g of $KMnO_4$ which will be reduced to MnO_2? 11.9 g

9. How many milliliters of 0.2M $KClO_3$ will be required to react completely with 20 ml of 0.1M Cr_2O_3 to produce K_2CrO_4 and Cl^-? 10 ml

ONE MORE STEP   See Teacher's Guide at the front of this book.

1. Select an industrial chemical process and make a list of all oxidation-reduction reactions which take place in the process.

2. Assuming maximum appropriate values for oxidation numbers, assign formulas to hypothetical binary compounds of the following pairs of elements:

   a. Pr and O   **d.** Ca and P   **g.** Li and O   **i.** Sc and F

   b. Ba and N   **e.** Sr and H   **h.** Fe and S   **j.** Ti and Cl

   c. Cr and O   **f.** Fr and C

3. Make a list of three oxidation-reduction reactions that occur in nature and three oxidation-reduction reactions that occur during the preparation of a meal in a modern kitchen.

4. Draw the electron dot diagram for the thiosulfate ion and assign oxidation numbers to each atom. What is unusual about this ion?

5. Nitrogen exhibits nine oxidation numbers (including zero). Try to write a formula for a compound representing each state.

Suggested Readings for this chapter may be found in the Teacher's Guide at the front of this book.

Electricity is an important factor in modern life. It provides light, allowing us to extend work, travel, and recreation into early morning and late
evening hours. It provides energy for running our homes and industry.
However, usable electricity must be produced from some other form of
energy. What energy sources now provide us with electric power? What
others are being developed? How does electricity travel from its source
to a lightbulb the instant a switch is thrown?

Chapter 22 uses the topics discussed in Chapters 20 and 21 to develop the concept of the electrochemical cell.

You press the button of your pocket flashlight and light (a form of radiant energy) is produced. You know already that the light results from the passage of an electric current through the flashlight bulb. But where does the electricity come from? The obvious answer is the battery. What then is a flashlight battery? And how does it function?

If we plug the apparatus in Figure 22–1 into an electrical outlet, the bulb does not light because the circuit is not complete. Whenever we close the circuit with a conducting substance, the bulb does light. We now have an easy way of observing what substances are

GOAL: You will gain an understanding of the relationship of electrolytes, controlled redox reactions, and energy and electron changes in electrochemical reactions.

A battery produces electricity.

A battery is a cell in which a spontaneous redox reaction takes place. The battery produces a current because the electrons involved in the redox reaction are forced to travel through a wire or external circuit.

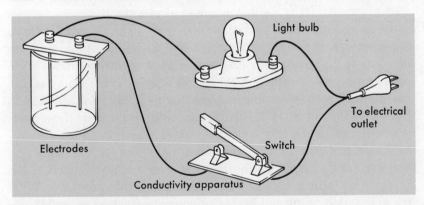

Light bulb

To electrical outlet

Electrodes

Switch

Conductivity apparatus

A 7½ or 15 watt bulb will keep the current low enough to avoid a serious shock. Use bare filament bulbs (unfrosted glass) and try several different sizes till you find the one that best suits your purposes.

FIGURE 22-1. If the electrodes are placed in a solution which conducts electricity, the bulb lights.

conductors of electricity. If we touch the two electrodes to a piece of copper or other metal, the bulb lights. Metals are conductors of electricity (copper is one of the best conductors; this is the reason for its use in electrical equipment). If we touch the electrodes to a piece of glass or to a sulfur crystal, the bulb does not light. Most nonmetallic solids, including salts, are nonconductors. If we immerse the electrodes in pure water, benzene, alcohol, or in a sugar solution, the bulb does not light. These liquids are all nonconductors. However, if we add a little sodium chloride or any other salt, a little hydrochloric acid, or some sodium hydroxide, the bulb lights. These

Metals conduct electricity.

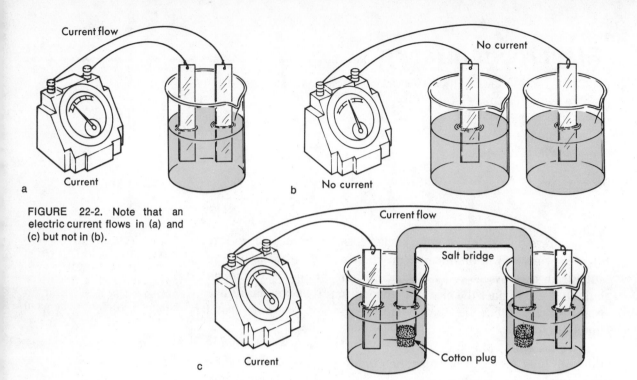

FIGURE 22-2. Note that an electric current flows in (a) and (c) but not in (b).

Ionic or ionizable materials and metals conduct electricity because these substances contain charged particles which are free to move in an electric field.

Current can be produced by two dissimilar metals immersed in a salt solution.

solutions are conductors of electricity. What kind of materials conduct electricity? Why do they conduct electricity?

Let us take pieces of two dissimilar metals and connect them to the terminals of a galvanometer (gal vuh NAHM uht uhr). A galvanometer is an instrument for measuring electrical current. If we plunge the two pieces of metal, while keeping them from making contact with each other, into a salt solution, the galvanometer needle registers a flow of current. How is the current produced? If we place the two metal plates into separate beakers containing salt solutions, as shown in Figure 22–2, no current flows. When we add to the system a salt bridge as shown in the figure, a current is produced. A salt bridge is an ionic substance in solution in a U-tube container. What is the function of the salt bridge? It connects the two separate solutions without mixing them. Can the solutions be mixed and still be used to produce a current? In this chapter we shall answer these and other related questions.

If the solutions are mixed, they will not conduct.

CHARGE MOVEMENT

22:1 Conductivity and Potential Difference

Metals, in general, are excellent conductors of electricity. This is true whether the metal is in the solid state or the liquid state. Mercury, the one metal which is liquid at room temperature, is often used in scientific apparatus because of its excellent electrical conductivity. In metallic crystals, the lattice positions are occupied by positive ions. The electrons which make the whole structure neutral are shared jointly by all of the ions in the crystal. These outer electrons are free to move. If the potential energy of the electrons in one part of the metal is raised, electrons will flow to a point where their potential energy is lower. The flow or movement of electrons through a conductor is an electric current.

Metallic conduction is by movement of delocalized electrons.

A difference in electrical potential can be brought about in a number of ways. One way is to use a generator. If we connect the two ends of a long wire to a generator, electrons are added at one end of the wire and taken away at the other end. When a potential difference is created at the ends of the wire, current flows. Energy is required to create a potential difference and work is done when a current of electrons is made to flow through a wire.

Work is done when electricity flows through a wire.

Metals are excellent conductors of electricity because their electrons are free to move when a small potential difference is created. In nonconducting substances, the outer electrons are tightly held either by the negative ions as in a salt crystal or by covalent bonds as in a sulfur crystal. Very large potential differences are required to move electrons in these substances which we call insulators. However, even the best insulators break down if the potential difference is high enough.

Even a small potential difference causes a current in metals.

Electrical potential difference is measured in units called *volts*. You will learn more about electrical units if you study physics. We

Electrical potential difference is measured in volts.

FIGURE 22-3. Electricity may be carried long distances through wires (a). Fuses (b) are special electrical conductors designed to protect some circuits from an overload.

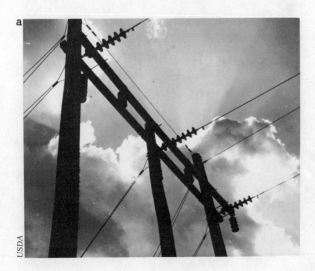

USDA

John Morgan

a

b

FIGURE 22-4. A lead storage battery such as a car battery (a) and smaller dry cell batteries such as those used in portable radios, flashlights, and some light meters (b) are voltage sources.

A battery is an "electron pump."

Resistance is measured in ohms.

will use only general definitions of electrical units. The voltage (potential difference) produced by a generator or battery can be thought of as electrical pressure. In fact, it is often easier to consider a generator or battery as an electron pump.

When a source of potential difference forces electrons through a wire, there is a resistance to the flow of current. Electrical resistance causes a voltage drop (lowering of electrical pressure). The electrical resistance is measured in units called *ohms*. The higher the resist-

Michael Faraday

(1791–1867)

The son of an English blacksmith, Michael Faraday early in life was apprenticed to a bookbinder and could only devote spare time to science. Largely self-educated, his real boost into the scientific world came through the sponsorship of Sir Humphrey Davy, English chemist and physicist.

Faraday's greatest work involved passing a current through different solutions and finding that it caused a reaction (electrolysis). The relationship between the amount of current used and the amount of product formed was expressed in the form of two laws now called Faraday's Laws. He also discovered that an electric current creates a magnetic field (electromagnetic induction).

In other areas, he discovered benzene and several organic chlorides and did research on the physics of polarized light and the diffusion and liquefication of gases.

ance of a conductor, the lower the number of electrons a particular voltage will be able to force through the conductor in a unit of time. The rate of flow of electrons, or the *current*, is measured in *amperes*. Electrical potential difference, resistance, and current are related by *Ohm's Law*. Georg Simon Ohm, after whom the unit of resistance was named, was a German physicist who discovered the mathematical relationship of electrical current, resistance, and potential difference. Ohm's Law may be expressed as

$$E = IR$$

where E is the potential difference in volts, I is the current in amperes, and R is the resistance in ohms. If the resistance remains constant, current varies directly as the voltage.

22:2 Electrolytic Conduction

Solid salts, solid bases, and solid acids (for example, oxalic acid) are nonconductors. When any of these substances are dissolved in water, however, the resulting solution is a conductor. Those substances which are conductors in solution are known as *electrolytes*. Any substance which produces ions in solution is an electrolyte. Salts are ionic even in the solid state; but when a salt dissolves, the ions are separated from each other and become free to move. (Conduction also occurs in a melted salt.) Acids and bases may be either ionic or molecular substances. However, when they dissolve in water, ions are formed. Electrolytic conduction is possible because ions move freely in the liquid state. If we connect the conductivity device to a direct current, one of the electrodes will be negative and the other electrode will be positive. It is customary to call the negative electrode the *cathode* (KATH ohd) and the positive electrode the *anode* (AN ohd). If we immerse the electrodes in an ionic solution, positive ions in the solution will be attracted to the negative electrode or cathode. For this reason, positive ions are called *cations* (KAT i uhns). Negative ions will be attracted toward the positive electrode or anode. Consequently, they are called *anions* (AN i uhns). Since ions are electrically charged particles, the movement of ions through a solution results in an electric current just as the movement of electrons through a metal results in a current.

Individual ions may move only a few hundred angstroms. It is the general trend of this motion which allows current to flow through a liquid.

22:3 Electrode Reactions

What happens to a moving ion when it reaches the electrode to which it is attracted? We will consider molten sodium chloride, a

It gains or loses electrons and becomes an atom or part of a molecule.

Current is measured in amperes.

$E = IR$

The current varies directly as the voltage if the resistance remains constant.

Electrolytes are substances whose solutions conduct electricity.

Molten salts and solutions of acids, bases, and salts will conduct electricity.

Anode: positive electrode
Cathode: negative electrode

Negative ions (anions) are attracted to the anode. Positive ions (cations) are attracted to the cathode.

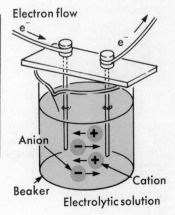

FIGURE 22-5. Anions are negatively charged ions and move toward the anode. Cations are positively charged ions and move toward the cathode.

Electron flow

Anion

Beaker

Cation

Electrolytic solution

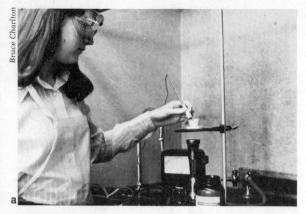

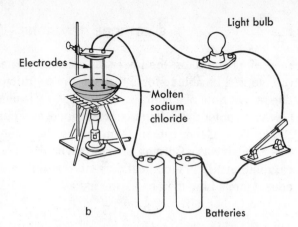

Light bulb

Electrodes

Molten
sodium
chloride

b

Batteries

FIGURE 22-6. Conductivity of a molten salt can be demonstrated with a voltmeter (a) or with a light bulb (b).

Note that there is also an entropy change which must be considered in accurate calculations.

At the cathode, positive ions are reduced by gaining electrons.

Chemical change at the cathode is reduction.

At the anode, negative ions are oxidized by losing electrons.

system which contains only two kinds of ions and no other particles. We will use electrodes which are inert, that is, electrodes which do not react chemically with sodium or chloride ions. The positive sodium ions, or cations, are attracted to the negative electrode, the cathode. The cathode is made negative by the action of a generator which, in effect, pumps electrons into it. The electrons in the cathode are in a state of high potential energy. The sodium ion has a positive charge. This means that it has an attraction for electrons and that an electron in a sodium atom would be in a state of lower potential energy than an electron on the cathode. Thus, we may expect electrons to move from the cathode where they have a high potential energy to sodium ions where they have a lower potential energy. At the cathode, the sodium ions will be converted into sodium atoms by addition of an electron. This is a chemical change and can be shown by an equation

$$Na^+ + e^- \rightarrow Na^0$$

Note that this chemical change represents a gain of electrons. We found in Chapter 21 that electron gain is called reduction. The chemical change which occurs at the cathode is always reduction. In this case, sodium ion is reduced to sodium metal.

Now consider what happens at the anode. The anode has a positive charge and negative ions are attracted to it. The anode is positive because the generator is, in effect, pumping electrons out of it. Thus, electrons in the anode may be said to exist in a state of low potential energy. Since the chloride ion has a negative charge, its outer electrons are in a state of higher potential. When chloride ions reach the anode they give up electrons to the electron-deficient anode. Electrons move from a state of higher potential energy to a state of lower potential energy. We can show the chemical change which occurs at the anode by another equation:

$$2Cl^- \rightarrow Cl_2 + 2e^-$$

Note that in this reaction chloride ions lose electrons to become chlorine atoms which then combine to form Cl_2 molecules. This reaction results in a loss of electrons. The name applied to a change in which electrons are lost is oxidation. The anode reaction is always oxidation.

Suggestion: It may be helpful to warn students now that reduction does not always take place at the positive or negative pole. In fact, it is probably desirable to avoid this means of labeling and to speak only of anode and cathode.

Chemical change at the anode is oxidation.

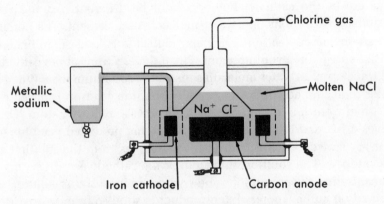

FIGURE 22-7. A Downs cell used in the production of sodium.

We have shown here the oxidation process and the reduction process by separate equations because they take place at different points. However, these processes do not occur independently. The generator does not produce the electrons; it moves the electrons from one place to another. The electrons which the generator adds to the cathode are taken from the anode. The reduction process cannot occur without the oxidation process going on at the same time. The role of the generator is to raise the potential energy of the electrons on the cathode.

These electrode reactions are called *half-reactions*. Since the anode reaction involves loss of electrons and the cathode reaction involves gain of electrons, the electrons balance when we add the two half-reactions. The overall reaction for the electrolysis of sodium chloride is:

In a cell, oxidation and reduction occur as separate half-reactions.

$$2Na^+(l) + 2Cl^-(l) \rightarrow 2Na(l) + Cl_2(g)$$

The process by which an electric current produces a chemical change is called *electrolysis*. Electrolysis of molten sodium chloride is the usual commercial process by which metallic sodium is produced. Chlorine gas is produced at the same time as a by-product.

22:4 Electrolysis of a Salt Solution

Another important commercial process involves the electrolysis of a concentrated sodium chloride solution. In this process the anode reaction is exactly the same as that which occurs when molten sodium chloride is used, and chlorine gas is produced at the anode. The situation at the cathode, however, will be different. Around the cathode, sodium ions and water molecules are present. The potential energy of an electron on a water molecule is lower than the potential energy on a sodium atom. Thus, the electrons at the cathode are transferred to water molecules instead of to sodium ions. When a water molecule acquires an extra electron, the electron is accepted by a hydrogen ion (a proton) which becomes a hydrogen atom. This leaves a hydroxide ion. The hydrogen atoms produced combine to form H_2 molecules, and hydrogen gas bubbles from the solution at the cathode. The solution surrounding the cathode acquires a high concentration of sodium ions and hydroxide ions. If this solution is drained off and evaporated, the product is solid sodium hydroxide. This is the most important process by which commercial sodium hydroxide is produced. Chlorine gas is also produced.

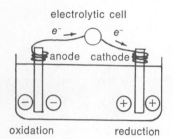

electrolytic cell

e^- e^-

anode   cathode

oxidation   reduction

The half-reactions are:

$$2Cl^- \rightarrow Cl_2 + 2e^-$$

$$2H_2O + 2e^- \rightarrow 2OH^- + H_2$$

The equation for the overall reaction may be written:

$$2NaCl(aq) + 2H_2O(l) \rightarrow 2NaOH(aq) + H_2(g) + Cl_2(g)$$

It should be noted that the sodium metal, chlorine gas, hydrogen gas, and sodium hydroxide are all produced from rock salt, a very cheap raw material. The costliest part of this operation is the electrical power required.

In the processes we have just described, two kinds of electrical conduction are involved. In the generator and the cables leading to the electrodes, conduction takes place by the movement of electrons through a metal. This is known as *electronic* or *metallic* conduction.

FIGURE 22-8. Sodium hydroxide and chlorine are prepared at this plant in Maine by electrolysis of solutions of this salt obtained from the evaporation of seawater.

Sobin Chemicals Inc.

The electrical path in electrolysis is completed through the liquid between the electrodes. This part of the conduction process takes place by the migration of ions and is called *electrolytic conduction*. Both kinds of conduction involve the movement of electrical charge. For electrolytic conduction it is necessary not only that ions be present, but that they be free to move as in a solution or a melted solid. Solid salts do not conduct electricity. Note that all electrolytic operations involve both oxidation and reduction.

Molten salts or electrolytic solutions conduct electricity.

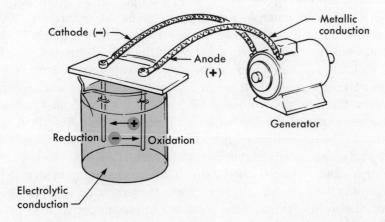

FIGURE 22-9. There are two kinds of electrical conduction: metallic and electrolytic.

You may wish to point out that in most electrolytic processes there are side reactions which take place because of contaminants which are present.

CELLS

22:5 Voltaic Cells Voltaic cells are often called galvanic cells.

The processes which we have described in the preceding sections are examples in which electrical energy is used to perform chemical work (produce a new chemical substance). When you use your pocket flashlight, however, you are using a chemical process to produce

493

FIGURE 22-10. A simple galvanic cell.

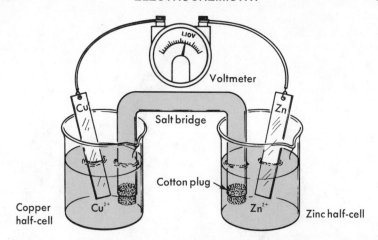

FIGURE 22-10. A simple galvanic cell.

A voltaic cell converts chemical energy into electrical energy.

Reactions take place at separate electrodes. Electrons travel through the external circuit.

When demonstrating a simple voltaic cell, use a vacuum tube voltmeter to measure voltage if possible. A vacuum tube voltmeter gives accurate readings with a minimum of current drain. Most meter movements are not so sensitive and require a fairly large current drain to cause the needle to register. This results in voltage readings considerably lower than the theoretically predicted reading. To obtain readings consistent with standard oxidation potential tables, use 1.0 M solutions. However, as long as the solutions involved are fairly concentrated and of equal strength, a variation from 1.0 M will not affect the voltage. Also, avoid completing the circuit for more than 10-12 seconds at a time. This is to avoid polarization around the electrodes.

In the zinc-copper cell, zinc metal is oxidized at the anode and copper ion is reduced at the cathode.

electricity. In other words, you are converting chemical potential energy into electrical energy. A device for doing this is known as a voltaic cell. An example of a simple kind of voltaic cell is shown in Figure 22–10. In this cell there are two compartments separated by a porous barrier which prevents the two solutions from mixing by diffusion, but permits the migration of ions from one side of the cell to the other. In the left hand compartment is a cathode which consists of a strip of copper immersed in a copper sulfate solution. Note that there is no external source of electrons (no generator). In the right hand compartment is an anode which consists of a strip of zinc immersed in a zinc sulfate solution. If the two electrodes are connected through a precision voltmeter, an electric current flows and the voltmeter reads 1.10 volts. The electrons flow from the zinc anode through the voltmeter to the copper cathode. Chemical changes occur at the electrodes. Zinc is commonly described as a more active metal than copper. This means that the outer electrons in zinc atoms have a higher potential energy than outer electrons in copper atoms. In other words, zinc has a greater tendency to give up electrons than copper. Electrons move from the zinc with its higher potential energy through the voltmeter to the copper with its lower potential energy. The anode half-reaction which occurs at the zinc electrode is:

$$Zn^0 \rightarrow Zn^{2+} + 2e^-$$

Since this change involves loss of electrons it is called oxidation. Zinc metal is oxidized at the anode (the zinc bar in the zinc half-cell, in Figure 22–10). The copper cathode in the copper half-cell (Figure 22–10) acquires an excess of electrons. It has a negative charge and copper ions move to it. The potential energy of electrons on the copper electrode is higher than the potential energy the electrons would have on the copper ions in the solution. The cathode transfers electrons to the copper ions and copper metal plates out on the cathode. The cathode reaction is:

Note that copper atoms are deposited on the surface of the zinc.

$$Cu^{2+} + 2e^- \rightarrow Cu^0$$

This reaction involves a gain of electrons and is called reduction. Note that the operation of the cell involves both oxidation and reduction, but the two changes do not take place at the same electrode. Rather, the electrons travel through the external circuit (in this case, the voltmeter) and do electrical work.

Note that these changes *can* take place without producing an electric current. If we place a piece of zinc directly in a copper sulfate solution, zinc metal (Zn^0) is converted into Zn^{2+} ions, and Cu^{2+} ions are converted into copper metal (Cu^0). Energy is also produced, but is released in the form of heat which is not available for practical use. No current is produced because the electrons are transferred directly from Zn^0 atoms to Cu^{2+} ions.

22:6   Structure of Voltaic Cells

A *voltaic cell* is a device for producing electrical energy from an oxidation-reduction reaction. The main feature of the voltaic cell is the porous barrier which separates the two solutions and keeps them from mixing freely. If this barrier is not porous and ions do not migrate through it, the cell will not operate. The anode compartment acquires an excess of zinc ions which are positive. In order to maintain neutrality, it must have negative ions to balance the positive zinc ions. At the same time, the cathode compartment uses up

FIGURE 22-11. Oxidation-reduction reactions can take place without producing electricity. As the reaction proceeds, heat is released and the copper sulfate solution becomes warm.

This experiment indicates that if we wish to produce a useful current, the two half-reactions must be separated.

For a voltaic cell to operate, free movement of ions between the anode and cathode compartments is necessary.

Note that the porous barrier completes the circuit. It also permits the free passage of ions. This prevents the accumulation of an excess of ions of one sign in a half-cell.

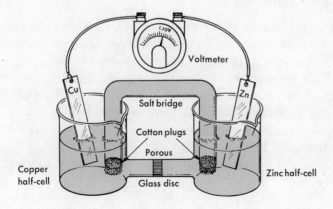

FIGURE 22-12. Two types of porous barriers are shown connecting the half-cells. Normally, only one is used.

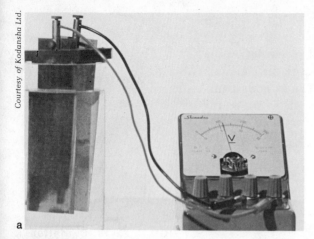

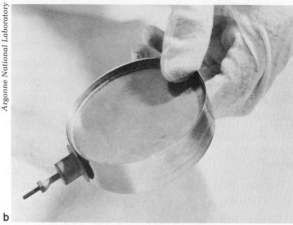

a

b

FIGURE 22-13. A simple voltaic cell made up of a zinc plate and a copper plate in dilute sulfuric acid is shown in (a). The lithium-sulfur storage cell (b) delivers ten times more energy than a conventional lead storage battery.

copper ions. In order to maintain neutrality, it must lose negative ions. Sulfate ions move through the porous barrier from the cathode compartment to the anode compartment and electrical neutrality is maintained in the two compartments. The cell continues to operate as long as there is a potential energy difference between the half-cells.

The two compartments in the voltaic cell are sometimes referred to as *half-cells* because the reactions which occur in them are half-reactions.

The two most commonly used types of voltaic cells are the dry cell and the lead storage cell. A flashlight battery is an example of a dry cell. An automobile battery is a lead storage cell.

POTENTIALS

22:7 Redox Potentials

There is no way in which the potential energy of a single half-cell can be measured. However, the difference in potential between two half-cells in a voltaic cell can be measured by means of a voltmeter. This difference of potential is a measure of the relative tendency of the two substances to take on electrons. If we arbitrarily assign a potential of zero to the copper half-cell, we will say the zinc half-cell has a potential of −1.10 volts. The negative sign indicates that zinc ions are less likely to take on electrons than the copper ions. On the other hand, if we assign a potential of zero to the zinc half-cell, we will say that the copper half-cell has a poten-

Note: The situation here is similar to measuring heat content as discussed on page 97, Section 5:12. The analogy used was "How high is a hill?" The height must be measured from some arbitrarily chosen point. See Fig. 5-4, page 97.

496

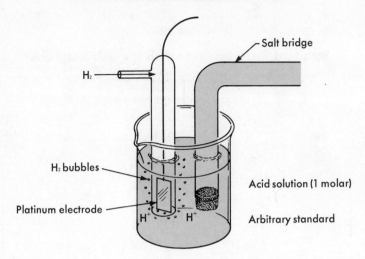

H₂ —

Salt bridge

H₂ bubbles

Platinum electrode

H⁺   H⁺

Acid solution (1 molar)

Arbitrary standard

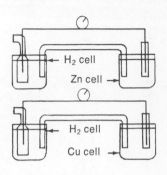

FIGURE 22-14. A standard hydrogen electrode has a potential of zero by definition.

tial of +1.10 volts. In principle, any half-cell could be used for the reference half-cell. That is, any half-cell could be the one assigned zero potential. In practice, the zero potential is assigned to the hydrogen half-cell. The half-reaction is:

The hydrogen half-cell is assigned zero potential.

$$H^+ + e^- \rightleftarrows \frac{1}{2}H_2$$

The hydrogen half-cell consists of a sheet of platinum whose surface has been specially treated. The platinum is immersed in a one molar (1M) solution of H^+ ions. Hydrogen gas, from a cylinder, is bubbled into the solution around the platinum at a pressure of 1 atmosphere. The H_2 molecules are adsorbed on the platinum surface and form the electrode. The hydrogen half-cell is an ideal which can only be approached in practice.

22:8   Standard Electrode Potentials

If we use the hydrogen half-cell with the zinc half-cell, our voltmeter reads −0.76 volts. We assign this potential to the zinc half-cell. If we use the hydrogen half-cell with the copper half-cell, the voltmeter reads +0.34 volts. This potential is assigned to the copper half-cell. In this way, potentials can be experimentally determined for almost all oxidation-reduction half-reactions. Some of these half-cell potentials are given in Table 22–1. Such potentials are dependent on temperature, pressure, and the concentration

The standard oxidation potential table is in Appendix A.

Potentials vary with temperature, pressure, and concentration.

Table 22–1

Standard Reduction Potentials for Half-Reactions*

(Ionic concentrations, 1M in water at 25°C)

	Half-Reaction	Volts	
Weak oxidizing agents	$Li^+ + e^- \rightarrow Li$	−3.02	*Strong reducing agents*
	$Rb^+ + e^- \rightarrow Rb$	−2.99	
	$\frac{1}{2}Mg^{2+} + e^- \rightarrow \frac{1}{2}Mg$	−2.37	
	$\frac{1}{2}Mn^{2+} + e^- \rightarrow \frac{1}{2}Mn$	−1.18	
	$\frac{1}{2}Zn^{2+} + e^- \rightarrow \frac{1}{2}Zn$	−0.76	
	$\frac{1}{3}Cr^{3+} + e^- \rightarrow \frac{1}{3}Cr$	−0.74	
	$\frac{1}{2}Ag_2S + e^- \rightarrow Ag + \frac{1}{2}S^{2-}$	−0.71	
	$\frac{1}{2}Fe^{2+} + e^- \rightarrow \frac{1}{2}Fe$	−0.44	
	$\frac{1}{2}Co^{2+} + e^- \rightarrow \frac{1}{2}Co$	−0.28	
	$\frac{1}{2}Ni^{2+} + e^- \rightarrow \frac{1}{2}Ni$	−0.24	
	$\frac{1}{2}Sn^{2+} + e^- \rightarrow \frac{1}{2}Sn$	−0.14	
	$\frac{1}{2}Pb^{2+} + e^- \rightarrow \frac{1}{2}Pb$	−0.13	
	$H^+ + e^- \rightarrow \frac{1}{2}H_2(g)$	0.00	
	$\frac{1}{2}S + H^+ + e^- \rightarrow \frac{1}{2}H_2S(g)$	0.14	
	$\frac{1}{2}Sn^{4+} + e^- \rightarrow \frac{1}{2}Sn^{2+}$	0.15	
	$Cu^{2+} + e^- \rightarrow Cu^+$	0.15	
	$\frac{1}{2}SO_4^{2-} + 2H^+ + e^- \rightarrow \frac{1}{2}SO_2(g) + H_2O$	0.20	
	$\frac{1}{2}Cu^{2+} + e^- \rightarrow \frac{1}{2}Cu$	0.34	
	$Cu^+ + e^- \rightarrow Cu$	0.52	
	$Fe^{3+} + e^- \rightarrow Fe^{2+}$	0.77	
	$\frac{1}{2}Hg_2^{2+} + e^- \rightarrow Hg(l)$	0.80	
	$Ag^+ + e^- \rightarrow Ag$	0.80	
	$\frac{1}{3}NO_3^- + \frac{4}{3}H^+ + e^- \rightarrow \frac{1}{3}NO(g) + \frac{2}{3}H_2O$	0.96	
	$\frac{1}{2}Br_2(l) + e^- \rightarrow Br^-$	1.07	
	$\frac{1}{2}Cl_2(g) + e^- \rightarrow Cl^-$	1.36	
	$\frac{1}{5}MnO_4^- + \frac{8}{5}H^+ + e^- \rightarrow \frac{1}{5}Mn^{2+} + \frac{4}{5}H_2O$	1.49	
	$\frac{1}{2}H_2O_2 + H^+ + e^- \rightarrow H_2O$	1.78	
Strong oxidizing agents	$\frac{1}{2}F_2(g) + e^- \rightarrow F^-$	2.87	*Weak reducing agents*

* For a more complete table, see Appendix A-9.

of the ions. The values given in the table assume a temperature of 25°C, a pressure of 1 atmosphere, and an ionic concentration of one mole per liter. A table of half-cell potentials is of great practical importance because it enables us to predict the direction in which a large number of chemical reactions will go. It also allows us to predict the maximum voltage that can be produced by a particular voltaic cell. A third use is in the prediction of the products of an electrolytic cell.

Half-cell potential tables are useful for predicting direction of chemical reactions.

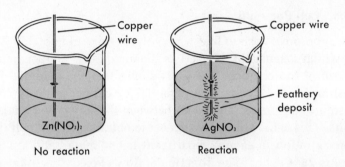

FIGURE 22-15. Copper atoms react with a silver nitrate solution (silver ions) but copper atoms do not react with a zinc sulfate solution (zinc ions).

In Table 22–1, the substance on the left side of the arrow in each case is an oxidizing agent. It is an electron acceptor. The oxidizing agent with the highest positive potential is the strongest oxidizing agent. The oxidizing agents in this table are arranged in the order of increasing strength from top to bottom. Think of this series of substances as a list arranged in order of ability to attract electrons in competition with other oxidizing agents. The substance on the right side of the arrow in each case is a reducing agent. The strongest reducing agent is at the top of the table and the strength of the reducing agents decreases toward the bottom of the table. Let us see how this table can be used to predict the course of a particular reaction. Remember that electrons must flow from an electron donor (reducing agent) to an electron acceptor (oxidizing agent).

— Emphasize!

Suggestion: Work with various combinations of half-reactions here so that use of the half-cell potential table becomes a habit.

Electrons flow from donor to acceptor.

As an example, consider what will happen if a coil of copper wire is immersed in a silver nitrate solution. A possible reaction could be written as:

$$Cu(c) + 2Ag^+(aq) \rightarrow 2Ag(c) + Cu^{2+}(aq)$$

If this reaction is to occur, copper must give up electrons to silver ions. A glance at the table shows that silver ions do have a greater attraction for electrons than copper ions. This reaction may be done in the laboratory by immersing a small coil of fine copper wire in a test tube containing silver nitrate solution. As a result of silver ions

Suggestion: Perform this experiment in the laboratory or as a demonstration.

being converted to silver atoms, a beautiful feathery deposit of metallic silver appears on the copper coil.

Suppose we immerse a strip of copper in a solution containing zinc ions. If a reaction is to occur, copper atoms must give up electrons to zinc ions. The table shows that copper has a greater attraction for electrons than zinc. Thus, we can predict that copper atoms cannot give electrons to zinc ions. No reaction will occur.

22:9 Cell Potential

Voltage of a cell is the algebraic difference of the half-cell potentials.

Suppose we wish to find what voltage we could obtain from a cell in which magnesium is used as the anode and copper ions are reduced at the cathode. The table shows that the potential for magnesium is −2.37 volts. The potential for copper is +0.34 volts. The absolute difference (algebraic) between these two potentials is 2.71 volts. This is the voltage we expect to obtain from this cell if the ion concentration in each compartment is one molar, and the temperature is 25° Celsius. The direction of flow of electrons in the external circuit can be determined from the fact that the magnesium ion is higher in the table (has less attraction for electrons). Magnesium (the anode) gives up electrons which flow through the external circuit to the copper electrode where the reduction reaction occurs. Would it be possible to construct a cell in which copper metal is used as the anode and magnesium ion is reduced at the cathode? No. If not, why not? Magnesium has a higher potential than copper.

The standard reduction potential indicates a tendency of the half-reaction to gain electrons. The greater the voltage, the greater the tendency to gain electrons. '

Look at the table of standard reduction potentials. Note that the potentials are expressed in volts. This voltage indicates how strong a tendency each half-reaction has to gain electrons. Lithium with a voltage of −3.02 has a weak tendency to gain an electron and fluorine at the bottom of the table has a strong tendency to gain an electron.

22:10 Products of Electrolysis

In Section 22:4 we saw that there could be competition for reaction at the electrodes in an electrolytic cell. In the case examined there, the competition was between sodium ions and water molecules.

Reduction tables can be used to predict electrolysis products.

In order to predict which of the possible reactions will actually occur at an electrode, we make use of the table of reduction potentials. The energy required to cause an electrode reaction to occur varies directly with the voltage of that reaction. The reaction which requires the least amount of energy will occur. Stated in another manner, the least amount of energy is associated with the least negative (most positive) voltage. Since most electrolysis reactions take place in water solution, we must have some idea of the voltage required to oxidize and reduce water. In investigating the voltages involved in these reactions, we must remember that water dissociates slightly into H^+ and OH^-. In a neutral solution both of these ions are found in a concentration of $10^{-7}M$. The reactions of interest to us then are:

Reduction of water: $2H_2O + 2e^- \rightleftarrows H_2 + 2OH^-$

-0.414 volts ($10^{-7}M$ OH^-)

Oxidation of water: $2H_2O \rightleftarrows 4e^- + 4H^+ + O_2$

$+0.815$ volts ($10^{-7}M$ H^+)

Let us assume we wish to predict the products of the electrolysis of a solution of potassium iodide in water. The possible reduction reactions are:

$$K^+ + e^- \rightarrow K \qquad\qquad -2.92 \text{ volts}$$
$$2H_2O + 2e^- \rightarrow H_2 + 2OH^- \quad -0.414 \text{ volts}$$

The least negative value is the reduction of water, so the product at the cathode is hydrogen gas. For the possible oxidations we get:

$$2I^- \rightarrow I_2 + 2e^- \qquad\qquad -0.54 \text{ volts}$$
$$2H_2O \rightarrow 4e^- + 4H^+ + O_2 \quad -0.815 \text{ volts}$$

The least negative value is the oxidation of iodide ion, so the product at the anode is iodine.

ELECTRICAL CELLS AND ENERGY

22:11 The Effect of Conditions

In the latter part of the nineteenth century, H. W. Nernst, a German chemist, worked out the relationship between the voltage of a cell and the conditions under which it was operating. The voltage of a cell under standard conditions is called $E°$. The values in Table 22–1 are $E°$ values for 1 molar solutions at 25°C and 1 atmosphere

The Nernst equation can be used to find the voltage at conditions other than standard.

pressure. If we now call the voltage of a cell at other than standard conditions E, we can use the relationship worked out by Nernst:

$$E = E° - \frac{RT}{nF} \ln \frac{\text{(concentration of products)}}{\text{(concentration of reactants)}}$$

Let us look at each of the factors in the equation. The value of R is the universal gas constant which we developed in the ideal gas equation (Section 16:3). However, in applying R to electrical measurements we wish to have it expressed in units different from the liter-atmospheres per mole-K° used in gas calculations. Conversion to calories per mole-K° gives a value of 1.99. The value of T is the absolute temperature in K°. The value of n is the number of electrons transferred in the balanced redox equation representing the change taking place in the cell. The value of F is a conversion factor from volts to calories per mole and is equal to 23,100. The symbol ln stands for the natural logarithm which we can replace with $(2.30 \log)$ to use common logarithms. If we combine $\frac{R}{F}$ 2.30, we obtain a value of 1.98×10^{-4}. If, in addition, we combine standard temperature, 298°K, with the previous value, we obtain 0.0592. We may then write the Nernst equation in two simpler forms:

$$E = E° - \frac{1.98 \times 10^{-4}\,T}{n} \log \frac{\text{(concentration of products)}}{\text{(concentration of reactants)}}$$

or,

$$E = E° - \frac{0.0592}{n} \log \frac{\text{(concentration of products)}}{\text{(concentration of reactants)}}$$

Let us now apply these to some sample problems.

EXAMPLE – DIFFERENT CONCENTRATIONS AT STANDARD TEMPERATURE

What would be the voltage of a cell using $Ni|Ni^{2+}(2.50M)$ for one half-cell and $Ag|Ag^+(0.100M)$ for the other half-cell if the pressure and temperature are at standard values?

$$Ni(c) + 2Ag^+(aq) \rightarrow Ni^{2+}(aq) + 2Ag(c)$$

$E° = 1.04$ volts

$E = 1.04 - \dfrac{0.0592}{2} \log \dfrac{(2.50)}{(0.100)(0.100)} = 1.04 - 0.0296 \log 250$

$E = 1.04 - 0.0296\,(2.40) = 1.04 - 0.07$

$E = 0.97$ volts

Note that the concentration of silver ion is squared in the expression. The concentrations of reactants and products are handled in the Nernst equation exactly as they were in an equilibrium expression.

EXAMPLE — DIFFERENT CONCENTRATIONS AT NONSTANDARD TEMPERATURE

What would be the voltage of a cell using $Zn|Zn^{2+}(2.00M)$ for one half-cell and $Cu|Cu^{2+}(0.500M)$ for the other half-cell at 45°C? The pressure is 1 atmosphere.

$$Zn(c) + Cu^{2+}(aq) \rightarrow Zn^{2+}(aq) + Cu(c)$$

$E° = 1.10$ volts (Section 22:8)

$E = 1.10 - \dfrac{0.000198(318)}{2} \log \dfrac{(2.00)}{(0.500)}$

(The solids, having a constant concentration, do not appear.)

$E = 1.10 - 0.0315 \log 4$

$E = 1.10 - 0.0315 \, (0.602) = 1.10 - 0.02 = 1.08$ volts

22:12   The pH Meter

The Nernst equation can be applied to half-cells as well as to an entire cell. Consider the hydrogen half-cell at standard temperature and pressure:

$$H^+ + e^- \rightarrow \frac{1}{2}H_2$$

$$E = E° - 0.0592 \log \frac{1}{[H^+]}$$

Using the relationship $\log \dfrac{1}{x} = -\log x$, we rearrange the above equation:

$$E = E° + 0.0592 \log [H^+]$$

We know that $E°$ for the hydrogen half-cell is 0.00 volts. We also know that $-\log [H^+] = pH$. Substituting these values we get:

$$E = -0.0592 pH$$

FIGURE 22-16. A pH meter is
a special voltmeter which is
calibrated to give a reading in
pH units rather than in volts.

F. Bernard Daniel

The pH meter makes use of
a hydrogen ion electrode.

Thus E is a linear function of pH. By combining a reference electrode
of known constant voltage with a hydrogen electrode, we can
measure the pH of a solution electrically. The reference electrode
usually chosen is the calomel electrode. The voltmeter measuring
the potential difference between the reference electrode and the
hydrogen ion electrode is usually calibrated to read directly in pH
units. This calibration then saves the chemist the trouble of converting from volts to pH units.

22:13 Energy and Electrical Cells

In Chapter 19 we saw that the free energy change for a reaction was
related to the equilibrium constant for the reaction. The relationship
was $\Delta G = -2.30RT \log K$. Perhaps you have already noticed the
similarity between this expression and the Nernst equation. The
Nernst equation may be written:

$$E = E° - \frac{2.30RT}{nF} \log K$$

At equilibrium, there is no net change, so E would equal zero.
Solving the equation for $(2.30RT) \log K$ and substituting 0 for E,
we obtain

$$2.30RT \log K = nFE°$$

Substituting the equivalent expression in the free energy equation
we get

$$\Delta G = -nFE°$$

These relationships are important to a chemist. Voltages of cells can be used to derive a great deal of other information, once they have been measured. If the voltage is known, the free energy change for the reaction may be calculated, and with other information, enthalpy and entropy changes can be found. Measurement of voltages may also be used to determine the equilibrium constant for reactions.

Voltages can be used to determine K_{eq}.

22:14 Quantitative Aspects of Electrochemistry

The equations for the electrode half-reactions can be balanced like any other chemical equation, and they have the same quantitative significance. The equation for the formation of sodium metal in the electrolysis of molten sodium chloride indicates that 1 mole of electrons is required to produce 1 mole of sodium atoms. However, other than in chemical reactions, electricity is not measured in moles. The more common unit of quantity of electricity is the coulomb. One *coulomb* (KOO lahm) is the quantity of electricity produced by a current of one ampere flowing for one second. 96,500 coulombs is the equivalent of 1 mole of electrons. This quantity is such a convenient unit for electrochemical calculations, that it is given the name of one *faraday* (FEHR uh day).

One faraday = 96,500 coulombs = 1 mole of electrons

1 mole of electrons
= 96,500 coulombs
= 1 faraday

One mole of sodium is 23 g. To produce 23 g of sodium by an electrolytic reaction, one faraday of electricity must be used. One faraday equals 96,500 coulombs. Since 1 coulomb is equal to the electricity produced by a current of one amp flowing for one second, 1 coulomb is equal to 1 amp-second. The number of coulombs used in a reaction can be obtained by multiplying the number of amperes times the number of seconds. We could produce 23 g of sodium by using a current of 10 amp for 9,650 sec. Any combination of amperes and seconds which gives a product of 96,500 amp-sec will yield 23 g of sodium (one mole).

In the anode reaction for the electrolysis of sodium chloride, the formation of one chlorine molecule requires the release of two electrons. Thus, one mole of chlorine gas will require two faradays of electricity.

The principles which we have just discussed are expressed in more concise form as Faraday's laws. They were discovered by the great British chemist and physicist Michael Faraday, and they are the basis for all electrochemical calculations.

Since the amount of electricity produced is equal to the current in amperes multiplied by the time in seconds, we may say:

1 coulomb = 1 amp-sec

$$\text{coulombs} = \text{amperes} \times \text{seconds}$$

Further, since 96,500 coulombs are equivalent to 1 faraday of electricity, we can write the expression:

$$\begin{array}{c}\text{faradays} \\ \text{(moles of} \\ \text{electrons)}\end{array} = \frac{\text{amp}}{}\left|\frac{\text{sec}}{}\right|\frac{1 \text{ coulomb}}{1 \text{ amp-sec}}\left|\frac{1 \text{ faraday}}{96{,}500 \text{ coulombs}}\right.$$

From a balanced equation representing an electrochemical change, we may obtain the relationship between the formula mass of a substance and the number of moles of electrons taking part in the change:

$$\frac{\text{mass of substance}}{\text{per mole of electrons}} = \frac{\text{formula mass of substance}}{\text{moles of electrons transferred}}$$

Combining the two expressions, we get the mathematical statement of Faraday's laws:

$$\text{mass of substance} = \frac{\text{faradays}}{}\left|\frac{1 \text{ mole } e^-}{1 \text{ faraday}}\right|\frac{\text{formula mass}}{\text{moles } e^-}$$

It should be noted that the formula mass of the substance in the equations above would have to be multiplied by the coefficient of the substance in the equation.

EXAMPLE – FARADAY'S LAW CALCULATION

What mass of copper will be deposited by a current of 7.89 amperes flowing for a period of 1200 seconds? The cathode reaction is:

$$Cu^{2+}(aq) + 2e^- \rightarrow Cu(c)$$

and therefore 2 faradays plate out 63.5 g Cu(c).

$$\text{mass of Cu(c)} = \frac{7.89\ \text{amp}}{} \left| \frac{1200\ \text{sec}}{} \right| \frac{1\ \text{coulomb}}{\text{amp-sec}} \left| \frac{1\ \text{faraday}}{96{,}500\ \text{coulombs}} \right|$$

$$\frac{1\ \text{mole}\ e^-}{1\ \text{faraday}} \left| \frac{1\ \text{mole Cu}}{2\ \text{moles}\ e^-} \right| \frac{63.5\ \text{g Cu}}{1\ \text{mole Cu}}$$

$$= 3.12\ \text{g Cu}$$

EXAMPLE—FARADAY'S LAW CALCULATION

What mass of Cr^{3+} ion is produced by a current of 0.713 ampere flowing for 12,800 seconds? The equation for the total reaction is:

$$14H_3O^+(aq) + 6Fe^{2+}(aq) + Cr_2O_7{}^{2-}(aq)$$
$$\rightarrow 6Fe^{3+}(aq) + 2Cr^{3+}(aq) + 21H_2O(l)$$

You must verify that the moles of electrons involved in the equation as written are equal to six $(Cr_2O_7{}^{2-} \rightarrow 2Cr^{3+})$. Then by substituting in the Faraday's Law equation:

$$\text{mass of Cr}^{3+} = \frac{0.713\ \text{amp}}{} \left| \frac{12{,}800\ \text{sec}}{} \right| \frac{1\ \text{coulomb}}{1\ \text{amp-sec}} \left| \frac{1\ \text{faraday}}{96{,}500\ \text{coulombs}} \right|$$

$$\frac{1\ \text{mole}\ e^-}{1\ \text{faraday}} \left| \frac{2\ \text{moles Cr}^{3+}}{6\ \text{moles}\ e^-} \right| \frac{52.0\ \text{g Cr}^{3+}}{1\ \text{mole Cr}^{3+}}$$

$$= 1.64\ \text{g Cr}^{3+}$$

PROBLEMS

1. What period of time was required if a current of 5.00 amps was passed through a salt (sodium chloride) solution and one mole of chlorine was produced? 10.7 hrs

2. What current must be used to plate 2.00 moles of copper on an electrode in 3.00 minutes? 2140 amps

3. A current of 1.00 amp flowing for 9,650 seconds will deposit how many grams of silver? 10.8 g Ag

4. A current of 5.00 amps flows through a cell for 10.0 minutes. How many grams of silver could be deposited during this time? Write the cathode reaction. 3.36 g Ag

5. How many minutes would be necessary to deposit 0.400 g of calcium from a cell with a current of 10.0 amps? 3.22 min

FIGURE 22-17. This chemist is
determining the amount of copper in a sample by electroanal-
ysis.

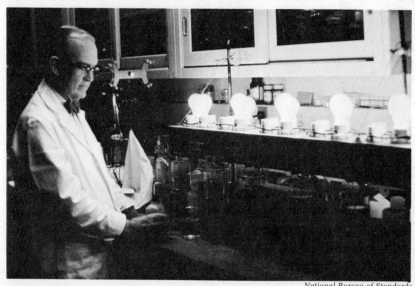

National Bureau of Standards

22:15   Electroanalysis

Electrolysis can be used for
quantitative analysis.

An immediate application of electrochemistry is its use in quantitative analysis. An example might serve to explain.

Suppose that it is necessary for you to determine the percentage
of copper in a given water soluble copper compound. A sample of
the compound of known mass could be dissolved in water and inert

Platinum is usually used. — electrodes inserted. The mass of the cathode should be measured
before the current is applied. As the current is passed through the
cell, metallic copper plates onto the electrode of known mass. When
the action is complete and current no longer flows, all the copper is
plated. The mass of the electrode is again measured and the difference in mass (due to the copper) is compared to the mass of the
sample to find the percentage of copper in the sample. Electro-
analysis is a useful tool of the chemist.

PROBLEM

6. A chemist must analyze for copper content a sample of brass
with mass 2.36 g. The alloy is dissolved in nitric acid, and the
tin present is precipitated as SnO_2. The solution is then treated
with sulfuric acid, precipitating the lead as $PbSO_4$. The resulting
solution is prepared for electrolysis to determine the copper
content. The mass of the cathode of the electrolysis apparatus is
measured and found to have a mass of 26.203 grams. The electrolysis is run, the cathode is dried, and its mass is again measured. Its new mass is 28.273 g. What is the percentage of copper in
the alloy?   87.7% Cu

SUMMARY

1. A conductor is a substance that will easily convey an electric current from one point to another. An insulator is a nonconductor.

2. An electric current is carried through a metal by the movement of electrons; through a solution or molten salt by the movement of positive and negative ions.

3. Metallic crystals are good conductors because their outer electrons are highly mobile.

4. When two points with a potential difference are connected by a conductor, an electric current will flow from the point of higher potential to the point of lower potential.

5. An electric current is the flow of electricity through a conductor.

6. Ohm's Law relates the potential difference (E), the current (I), and the resistance (R) in a circuit: $E = IR$.

7. Current is measured with an ammeter or galvanometer, and is expressed in amperes (amp).

8. Voltage is the measure of potential difference. Voltage is measured with a voltmeter, and is expressed in volts (V).

9. An electrolyte is a substance which dissolves in water to form a water solution which conducts electricity.

10. Electrolytes are electrically neutral, but contain ions which are free to move, as do molten ionic compounds.

11. A salt bridge is an electrolyte in solution in a U-tube.

12. When ions migrating through an electrolytic cell reach an electrode, they undergo an oxidation or reduction reaction.

13. The products of the electrolysis of molten sodium chloride are sodium metal and chlorine gas.

14. The gaseous products of the electrolysis of sodium chloride solution are hydrogen and chlorine. Sodium hydroxide remains behind in solution.

15. A voltaic cell is a cell which produces an electric current and is composed of two dissimilar metals and an electrolyte.

16. Any oxidation-reduction reaction can (theoretically) be set up in such a way that current will be produced.

17. In an electrochemical reaction, there is always an oxidation half-reaction and a reduction half-reaction.

18. An oxidation-reduction reaction is an equilibrium reaction. Therefore, any change in temperature, pressure, or concentration will affect the flow of electric current.

19. The reduction potential of an electrode reaction measures the relative strength of oxidizing and reducing agents.

20. The standard electrode potential series is a group of half-reactions arranged in order of their reduction potential.
21. The hydrogen half-cell is the standard reference cell, and is assigned a voltage of 0.00 V for convenience.
22. We can find the reduction potential of a half-reaction by making it half of a cell which has a standard hydrogen half-cell as the other half.
23. Standard conditions for determining reduction potential are 25°C (temperature), 1M (concentration), and 1 atm (pressure).
24. The table of standard electrode potentials indicates the direction of reaction, the electromotive force of cells, and the products of electrolysis.
25. A reaction for which the reducing agent has less attraction for electrons than the oxidizing agent will occur spontaneously.
26. An electrolytic cell is a cell in which the electrons are forced to flow in a direction opposite to their normal flow. This flow-reversing process is called electrolysis.
27. In both electrolytic and electrochemical cells, oxidation occurs at the anode and reduction occurs at the cathode.
28. Cations are positive ions; anions are negative ions.
29. The Nernst equation relates the voltage of a cell to the conditions under which the cell is operating: $E = E° - \dfrac{2.30RT}{nF} \log K$
30. The relationship between hydrogen ion concentration and the voltage of the hydrogen half-cell can be used as the basis for the electrical measurement of pH.
31. The relationship between the voltage generated by a cell and the free energy change associated with the reaction occurring in the cell is given by: $\Delta G = -nFE°$
32. One coulomb is the quantity of electricity produced by a current of 1 amp flowing for 1 sec.
33. One faraday = 96,500 coulombs = 1 mole of electrons.
34. The amount of matter reacting in an electrochemical cell is determined by the formula mass of the substance reacting and by the amount of electricity which passes through the cell.

PROBLEMS

7. Which of the following reactions will proceed spontaneously?
   a. $Na^0 + Cl_2^0 \rightarrow$?   yes
   b. $Fe^{2+} + Cu^0 \rightarrow$?   no
   c. $Cu^0 + H_2^0 \rightarrow$?   no
   d. $Cu^{2+} + Ag^+ \rightarrow$? no
   e. $Zn + Pb^{2+} \rightarrow$?   yes

8. Explain how to determine whether a given electrode is an anode or a cathode. Oxidation occurs at the anode, reduction at the cathode.

9. How long must a current of 20.0 amps be passed through a sodium chloride solution to produce 40.0 grams of NaOH? 1.34 hr (80 min)

10. A silver ion solution is subjected to a current of 5.00 amps for 2.00 hours. (a) Give the cathode reaction. (b) How much silver would be plated out? $Ag^+(aq) + e^- \rightarrow Ag(c)$ ———— 40.3 g Ag

11. How do electronic and electrolytic conduction differ? See Teacher's Guide.

12. What maximum voltage could you expect from a cell which consisted of Ca–Ca^{2+} and Ag–Ag$^+$ half-cells? Write the electrode reactions and the overall reaction.

12. $Ca(c) \rightarrow Ca^{2+} + 2e^-$
$2Ag^+ + 2e^- \rightarrow 2Ag(c)$
$Ca + 2Ag^+ \rightarrow Ca^{2+} + 2Ag(c)$
3.67 volts

13. What reaction would you expect at the electrodes of a Hooker cell (a device for the electrolysis of sodium chloride solution)?

13. $2NaCl(c) + 2H_2O(l) \rightarrow$
$2NaOH(aq) + H_2(g) + Cl_2(g)$

14. The electrolysis of 10.0 grams of water would produce what volume of O$_2$ at STP? Give the electrode reactions. See Teacher's Guide.

ONE MORE STEP   See Teacher's Guide at the front of this book.

1. Trace the development of man's search for an understanding of electricity from his first experience with static electricity to our present-day knowledge. You can find this information most easily in a history of science or in an encyclopedia.

2. Use the Nernst equation to compute the voltage of a cell in which one half-cell is made with Zn and 1.00M Zn^{2+}, and the other half-cell is Zn and 0.100M Zn^{2+}.

3. Compute the voltage of a cell in which one half-cell is the hydrogen half-cell with hydrogen at a pressure of 2.00 atm, and the other half-cell is Zn and Zn^{2+} at 1.00M.

Suggested Readings for this chapter may be found in the Teacher's Guide at the front of this book.

Controlled nuclear reactions provide energy which can be converted to electricity. The tiny fuel pellets shown, each with mass less than one gram, contain a uranium-plutonium oxide mixture. Each pellet can provide energy equal to 257 kilograms of coal. As the demand for the world's limited supply of fossil fuels increases, nuclear power offers an alternative source of needed energy. What are some advantages and disadvantages of nuclear reactors as a source of energy?

Nuclear Chemistry ——————————— 23

Chapter 23 introduces reactions which involve a nuclear change, radioactivity, or radioactive isotopes. Nuclear reactions (fission and fusion) are discussed in relation to their development and control.

In 1896, Henri Becquerel, a French physicist, found that matter containing uranium exposes photographic film. This led Becquerel and two of his assistants, Pierre and Marie Curie, to the discovery that rays are given off by the elements uranium and radium.

Uranium and radium can be found in nature in an ore called pitchblende. This ore is mined in Canada, Colorado, and Germany. Obtain some of this ore. Place it near, but not touching, a charged electroscope. What do you observe? How have the leaves become discharged? Substances which have the same effects as uranium and radium are called *radioactive* substances. The whole phenomenon is called *radioactivity*.

The air surrounding the radioactive source becomes ionized by the emitted rays. The air also becomes a conductor which discharges the electroscope leaves.

GOAL: You will gain an understanding of natural and artificial nuclear reactions and the instruments used by chemists to study, control, and utilize radioactive materials and nuclear processes.

RADIOACTIVITY

23:1 Nuclear Structure

The rays produced by radioactive materials are a mixture of several particles and quanta of energy. The particles and quanta are given off by the nuclei of radioactive atoms during spontaneous nuclear decay. We say the decay is spontaneous because we have no control over it. The amount of energy released in a nuclear change is very large. It is so large that it cannot be a result of an ordinary chemical change.

Albert Einstein was the first to explain the origin of this energy (Chapter 1). From his theory, we see that mass and energy are equivalent. This can be expressed in the equation:

$$E = mc^2$$

E is the energy (in ergs) released
m is the mass (in grams) of matter involved
c is a constant, the speed of light in centimeters per second

Radioactive materials produce particles and energy.

Nuclear decay is spontaneous.

Ordinary chemical reactions do not produce nearly as much energy as nuclear reactions produce.

Einstein's mass-energy relationship: $E = mc^2$.

Actually more accurately expressed: $\Delta E = \Delta mc^2$

Savannah River Laboratory Photo

Oak Ridge National Laboratory

a   b

FIGURE 23-1. Enough heat energy is released during nuclear change of cobalt-60 to boil the water in the beaker (a). The radioactive strontium power sources (b) glow with heat of radioactivity.

Ordinary forces do not account for nuclear energy.

Suggestion: Point out that mass-energy interconversion involves a nuclear reaction and that the popular term "atomic bomb" is inaccurate. Such a bomb should be called a nuclear bomb.

Mesons may hold the nucleus together.

Pions were predicted by Yukawa in 1935, 10 years before their discovery.

Nuclear forces holding neutrons and protons together act only over very short distances.

Nucleons exhibit a spin property.

Electrons can be emitted from the nucleus.

The predicted energy-mass change in normal chemical reactions is too small to be measured. However, we are all familiar with the nuclear changes which involve a mass-energy interconversion. The great amount of energy released by fission devices is measurable. It is given off when nuclei of uranium or plutonium atoms split.

The nucleus of the uranium-238 atom contains 92 protons and 146 neutrons. These particles are bound tightly in the nucleus. Acting alone, the electrostatic attraction involved in bonding and van der Waals forces should allow the uncharged neutrons to float away. Since protons all have the same positive charge, electrostatic forces should cause them to fly apart. Gravitational force, which keeps us at the surface of the earth and keeps the moon in orbit, is not strong enough to hold the nucleus together. What force, then, holds the nucleus together?

Today, protons and neutrons are thought to be made of simpler particles. One type is the *meson* (MAY sahn). There are several kinds of mesons. Some scientists think that mesons hold the nucleus together through "trading" or "sharing" among neutrons and protons. The meson hypothesis seems to fit the facts, but it has not yet been firmly established. Nuclear structure is a field of intense study. It will continue to be so for some time.

Hypotheses explaining nuclear structure differ, but scientists are agreed on certain facts. (1) The nuclear force which holds the protons and neutrons together is effective for very short distances only. This distance is about the same as the diameter of the nucleus. (2) Nucleons (protons and neutrons) have a property which corresponds to the spin of electrons. (3) Electrons do not exist in the nucleus, yet they can be emitted from the nucleus. How can these facts be explained?

23:2   Nuclear Magnetic Resonance

Let us consider one of these facts in more detail. We know that a charged particle in motion creates a magnetic field. A spinning proton, then, should have a magnetic field, but a spinning neutron should not. It can be shown that both particles have a magnetic field! Just as electrons pair in orbitals, nucleons also pair. A proton pairs with a proton, and a neutron pairs with a neutron. If two neutrons pair, their spins will be opposite and their magnetic fields will cancel each other. However, for nuclei with unpaired nucleons, the nucleus as a whole should possess a magnetic field.

> Nucleons of the same kind with opposing spins may pair.

If a nucleus with a magnetic field is placed in an external magnetic field, two energy states are possible for the nucleus. The two fields are either aligned or opposed. The opposed fields represent a higher energy state. The energy required to "flip" the nucleus from one of these states to the other is greatly affected by the other atoms surrounding the nucleus under study. This energy can be measured by a process called nuclear magnetic resonance (NMR) spectroscopy.

> NMR spectroscopy can be used to identify substances.

About two-thirds of the naturally occurring nuclei have magnetic fields. The hydrogen atom, with its single proton as a nucleus, has been by far the most widely studied through NMR spectroscopy. This analytical method has been very useful in studying the structures of organic molecules. An NMR spectrum of an organic molecule will show several energy peaks. These peaks correspond to

F. Bernard Daniel

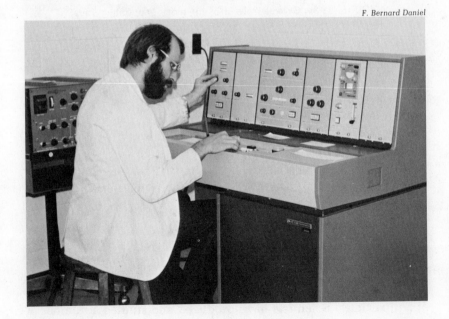

FIGURE 23-2. This chemist is studying the structure of an organic molecule with a NMR spectrometer.

hydrogen atoms (protons) in different locations in the molecule. Each hydrogen atom with a different kind and arrangement of the other atoms around it will give a separate peak.

23:3 Elementary Particles

Three types of radiation can originate from naturally radioactive nuclei. Two of these types are made up of particles. The third is made up of rays (or beams) of quanta. The particles are alpha (α) and beta (β) particles. The rays are gamma (γ) rays. An *alpha particle* is a helium nucleus ($^4_2$He). It consists of two protons and two neutrons. A *beta particle* is an electron (β^- or $_{-1}^0$e). Gamma rays are very high energy X rays. The symbol for gamma radiation is γ.

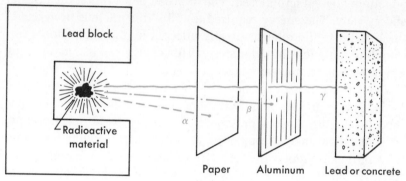

FIGURE 23-3. Gamma rays are the most penetrating rays; alpha rays are the least penetrating.

While studying nuclear phenomena, scientists have discovered many elementary particles. However, many of these particles are not as elementary as they were first thought to be. Many break up into even simpler particles. The neutron, for example, breaks up into even simpler particles under certain conditions. One of the earliest simple particles to be discovered was the positron (PAHZ uh trahn). The positron (β^+ or $_{+1}^0$e) has the same properties as the electron except that its charge is positive, not negative. Positrons are not common. They exist only until they collide with an electron. Such a collision is very likely in our world. When the collision occurs, both particles are annihilated (ah NI uh layt uhd) and two quanta of energy are produced. Other particles decay spontaneously. These particles have lifetimes of 10^{-6} to 10^{-20} seconds or even shorter.

A particle, such as the positron, which is a sort of mirror image of a normal particle is called an antiparticle. Antimatter is made up of antiparticles. Scientists have produced and studied a number of antiparticles. Most of these particles have been formed and observed

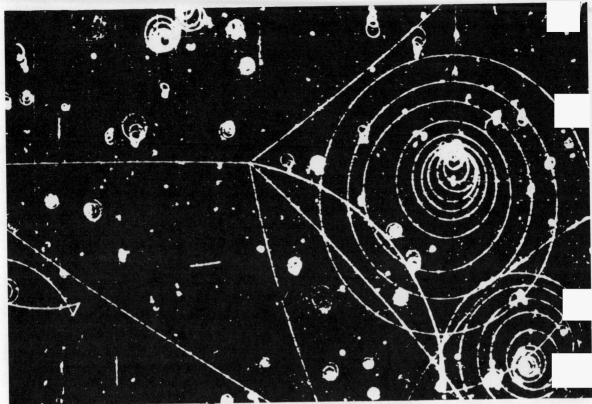

Lawrence Radiation Laboratory, Berkeley, California

during the bombardment of normal nuclei in particle accelerators. They may also be formed in other ways. The positron, for example, is emitted spontaneously from some artificially formed nuclides. Other artificially radioactive nuclides decay by capturing one of the two 1s electrons outside the nucleus. The first energy level ($n = 1$) is sometimes called the K level. For this reason, this radioactive process is called K-capture.

Theoretically, every natural particle should have an antiparticle. Actually, there is at least one particle which is its own antiparticle. This particle is the neutral pion.

FIGURE 23-4. This is a photograph of particle tracks in a particle detector. The large counterclockwise spiral is the path of a positron. The smaller clockwise spiral is the path of an electron.

K-capture is the process in which the nucleus captures an electron from the first energy level outside the nucleus.

Every particle either has an antiparticle or is its own antiparticle.

DETECTORS

23:4 Radiation Detectors

Radiation from radioactive materials ionizes atoms by knocking off electrons. This property is useful in identifying radiation. A radiation detector can be made from a tube, metal foil, and wire

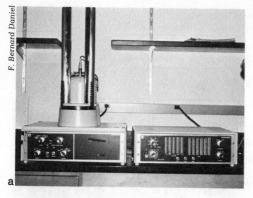

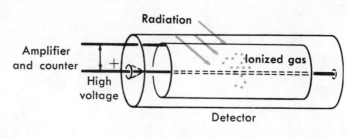

Radiation

Amplifier
and counter

High
voltage

Ionized gas

Detector

a

b

FIGURE 23-5. A Geiger counter (a) can be used to detect radiation. Radiation ionizes the gas in the tube detector (b) and is registered by the counter.

A photographic emulsion can also be used to detect radioactive particles.

(Figure 23–5b). A sheet of metal foil is wrapped around a tube containing a gas. A wire is run through the center of the tube. A voltage source and a light are connected in series to the tube. The light will not shine unless the circuit across the tube is complete. When a particle from a radioactive atom passes through the tube, it ionizes the gas. This completes the circuit and the light will shine. Radiation could also be detected with this device by connecting it to a buzzer or a meter instead of to a light. Using appropriate electronic attachments, a similar detector can be made which counts both the number and kinds of particles entering the tube.

The detecting devices used today are much more complex than the one we have just described. Many have attachments which not only count the number of particles passing through, but also determine the energy of the particles. Almost all of these devices depend upon the ionizing ability of radiation for the detection.

Some path-recording devices are the spark chamber, the cloud chamber and the bubble chamber.

FIGURE 23-6. Radiation is being monitored by this technician in the counting room in a nuclear center in Puerto Rico.

23:5 Path-Recording Devices

The spark chamber is a device which has the added advantage of showing the path of the particle. The particle passes through a chamber filled with gas, as in the Geiger tube. However, the chamber also contains a number of charged metal plates. When the particle ionizes the gas, a spark occurs between plates. The sparks expose photographic film and thus record the path of the particle.

Other path-recording devices are even better than the spark chamber. Examples are the cloud chamber and the bubble chamber. Both operate on a similar principle. In the cloud chamber, a gas is supersaturated with vapor. If an ionizing particle passes through the cloud chamber, it leaves a trail of ions. These ions act as points on which droplets condense. In the bubble chamber, a liquid, usually liquid hydrogen, is superheated. As an ionizing particle

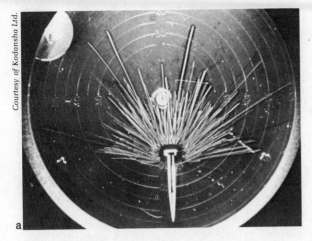

a

b

passes through the bubble chamber, it leaves behind many ions on which bubbles can form. The paths of particles in these chambers are then photographed as a trail of droplets or as a stream of tiny bubbles. If the chamber is surrounded by powerful magnetic and electrical fields, the paths of charged particles will be curved. Information on the masses of the particles involved can be obtained from the curvature of the paths.

FIGURE 23-7. Tracks of nuclear particles are shown in a bubble chamber (a). The electronic measuring device (b) can be used to plot the tracks and program the information for use on a computer.

23:6 Light-Detecting Devices

Some detection devices make use of the fact that radiation will cause some substances to emit light. The energy of the particle causes electrons to be excited to higher energy levels. When these electrons "fall back" to their normal levels, they emit light. This light can be detected by a special kind of electronic tube and the results displayed in a number of ways. Scintillation detectors use

Radiation causes some substances to scintillate (emit light).

FIGURE 23-8. This physicist is examining material (a) which is used in the construction of a scintillation counter (b).

a

b

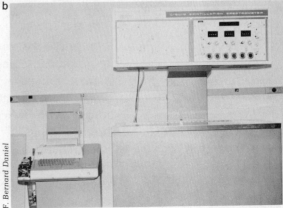

solid crystals which emit light, or scintillate (SINT uhl ayt), when exposed to radiation. When fast moving particles pass through some liquids, they cause light to be emitted at an angle to their path. The angle depends upon the velocity of the particle. This emission of light is called Cerenkov radiation. It is named after the Russian scientist who first explained it. By measuring the angle of Cerenkov radiation, the velocity of emitted particles may be obtained.

23:7   Tracers

Radioactive nuclides can be used as tracers.

Radioactive nuclides are used in the laboratory and in industry to trace the path of various reactions and products. Studies using these *tracers* have led to important discoveries in science and better products from industry.

FIGURE 23-9. Solutions of radioactive substances are being handled by remote control (a) during tracer studies. Blood tracer studies are being performed by these scientists (b).

Suppose we want to know what part of the human body utilizes a certain substance in our diets. We would prepare some of the substance, using a radioactive nuclide of one of the elements in the substance. (The radiation from the nuclide would have to be very low level if we were working with human beings.) After a subject eats or drinks the substance, we would examine the subject's body with radiation detectors. By finding the part of the body showing radioactivity of the type expected from the nuclide used in the preparation, we would know where the substance is concentrated in the body.

Some nonradioactive nuclides can also be used as tracers.

Argonne National Laboratory

FIGURE 23-10. Money, marked invisibly by atomic methods, may prove useful in solving some criminal cases.

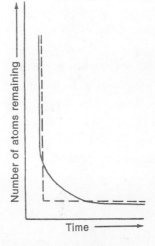

Plot of Radioactive Decay

23:8 Half-Life

It has been determined experimentally for large amounts of radio-active atoms that the number of atoms which disintegrate in a unit of time varies directly as the number of atoms present. The percent-age of atoms which disintegrate in any given period of time is constant for a given nuclide. In order to compare the activity of various radioactive species, the length of time it takes for one-half of the atoms to disintegrate has been chosen as a standard. This is called the *half-life*. For example, the half-life of ^{131}Ba is 12 days. If we start with a given number (n) of atoms of ^{131}Ba, then at the end of 12 days, $\frac{1}{2}n$ atoms will have disintegrated, and we will have $\frac{1}{2}n$ atoms left. At the end of the next 12 days, half of the remaining atoms will have disintegrated and we will have $\frac{1}{4}n$ atoms left. In 12 more days, half of these atoms will have disintegrated and $\frac{1}{8}n$ atoms of ^{131}Ba will remain. How many atoms will remain at the end of another 12 days?

Half-life is the length of time required for one-half of the atoms of a radioactive sample to disintegrate.

F. W. Hoffman, AEC Oak Ridge Operations Office

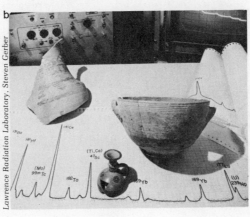

Lawrence Radiation Laboratory, Steven Gerber

FIGURE 23-11. Nature of marine sediments (a) and age of ancient pottery (b) can be studied on the basis of radionuclide content.

These half-life figures are determined experimentally for a large number of atoms of an individual nuclide. They are statistically determined and describe the behavior of large numbers of atoms. At present, it is not possible to predict the exact instant of an individual atom's disintegration.

23:9 Dating With Radionuclides

Knowledge of the half-life of a nuclide is useful in almost all calculations involving tracer nuclides. It also leads to an interesting use for naturally occurring nuclides—dating of ancient objects. In the upper atmosphere, ^{14}C is formed as a result of bombardment of ^{14}N in the upper atmosphere by cosmic rays. This radioactive carbon soon reacts with oxygen to form $^{14}CO_2$. Through mixing by winds, the distribution of $^{14}CO_2$ in the atmosphere remains virtually uniform. Carbon dioxide containing $^{14}CO_2$ is constantly being removed from the air by plants. We can assume that the percentage of $^{14}CO_2$ in the air has been approximately the same for several hundred millions of years. All living plants have a constant concentration of ^{14}C in their composition because they use the radioactive ^{14}C in photosynthesis. However, when the plant dies, no more $^{14}CO_2$ is replaced by photosynthesis. Now, only disintegration is occurring. The ^{14}C concentration in the plant begins to decrease. By measuring the ^{14}C level in the dead plant and comparing it with the ^{14}C level in a living plant, it is possible to tell how long a plant has been dead. If an archeologist unearths logs in an excavation of an ancient city, *radiocarbon dating* of the timbers will indicate approximately when the trees were cut down.

Half-life may be used to date objects.

Carbon-14 may be used to estimate the age of ancient objects that contain carbon.

Because of the low original concentration of ^{14}C, this method is sensitive only for about four half-lives (23,000 years).

FIGURE 23-12. The half-life of different radionuclides has been used in estimating the age of some fossils (a) and lunar rocks (b).

a

Meston Specialties

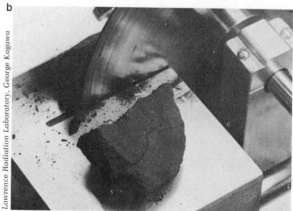

b

Lawrence Radiation Laboratory, George Kagawa

By employing various nuclides in a somewhat similar fashion, geologists have been able to date the formation of many ancient rocks and even to date roughly the formation of the earth and the moon. Table 23–1 lists the half-life times of some important nuclides.

Other radioactive nuclides may be used in estimating the age of some rocks.

Table 23–1

Half-Life of Selected Nuclides

Nuclide	Half-Life	Decay Mode	Nuclide	Half-Life	Decay Mode
^3_1H	12.3 years	β^-	$^{183}_{76}Os$	12 hours	K-capture and γ
$^{14}_6C$	5730 years	β^-	$^{212}_{82}Pb$	10.6 hours	β^- and γ
$^{19}_8O$	27 seconds	β^- and γ	$^{194}_{84}Po$	0.6 seconds	α
$^{20}_9F$	11.4 seconds	β^- and γ	$^{210}_{84}Po$	138 days	α
$^{39}_{17}Cl$	55.5 minutes	β^- and γ	$^{227}_{92}U$	1.3 minutes	α and γ
$^{49}_{21}Sc$	57.5 minutes	β^- and γ	$^{235}_{92}U$	7.1×10^8 years	α and γ
$^{71}_{30}Zn$	2.4 minutes	β^- and γ	$^{238}_{92}U$	4.51×10^9 years	α and γ
$^{87}_{37}Rb$	5×10^{10} years	β^-	$^{236}_{94}Pu$	2.85 years	α and γ
$^{100}_{46}Pd$	4 days	K-capture and γ	$^{242}_{94}Pu$	3.79×10^5 years	α
$^{129}_{55}Cs$	32.4 hours	K-capture and γ	$^{244}_{100}Fm$	0.0033 seconds	Spontaneous fission
$^{149}_{61}Pm$	53.1 hours	β^- and γ			

Suggestion: The facts given in this chart can be used for practice writing of nuclear equations.

23:10   Stability of Nuclides

Not all isotopes of an element are equally stable. It is possible to estimate which nuclides will be most stable by applying the three rules which follow.

First rule: The greater the binding energy (energy needed to separate the nucleus into individual protons and neutrons) per particle, the more stable the nucleus.

Consider the oxygen-16 nuclide. It contains eight protons, eight electrons, and eight neutrons. We can think of it as made from eight hydrogen atoms and eight neutrons. Each hydrogen atom has a mass of 1.007825 a.m.u. Each neutron has a mass of 1.008665 a.m.u. Thus, the total mass of an oxygen-16 atom should be 16.131920 a.m.u.

Stability of a nuclide depends upon:
1. the binding energy per particle
2. the neutron-proton ratio
3. an even number of both protons and neutrons

These are comparative rules, not absolute rules.

However, the actual mass of the oxygen-16 atom is 15.99491 a.m.u. The difference between the calculated mass and the actual mass is called the *mass defect*.

$$8 \text{ hydrogen atoms} + 8 \text{ neutrons} = 1 \text{ oxygen atom}$$

$$
\begin{array}{rl}
8(1.007825 \text{ a.m.u.}) = & 8.062600 \text{ a.m.u.} \\
+ \ 8(1.008665 \text{ a.m.u.}) = & \underline{8.069320} \text{ a.m.u.} \\
= & 16.131920 \text{ a.m.u.} \\
- \text{ actual } {}^{16}_{8}\text{O mass} = & \underline{15.99491} \ \text{ a.m.u.} \\
\text{mass defect} = & 0.13701 \ \text{ a.m.u.}
\end{array}
$$

For an oxygen-16 atom, the mass defect is 0.13701 a.m.u. This mass has been converted to energy and released in the formation of the nucleus. Thus, it is also the energy that must be put back into the nucleus to separate the nucleons.

We can convert this mass defect of 0.13701 a.m.u. into its energy equivalent by the formula

$$E = mc^2$$

$$E = \frac{0.13701 \text{ a.m.u.}}{} \times \frac{1.6605 \times 10^{-24} \text{ g}}{1 \text{ a.m.u.}} \times \frac{(2.9979 \times 10^{10} \text{ cm})^2}{(\text{sec})^2}$$

$$= 2.0447 \times 10^{-4} \ \frac{\text{g·cm}^2}{\text{sec}^2}$$

$$= 2.0447 \times 10^{-4} \text{ ergs}$$

Binding energy is the energy needed to separate the nucleus into individual particles.

This energy ($E = 2.0447 \times 10^{-4}$ ergs) is called the *binding energy*. If we divide the total binding energy by the total number of particles in the oxygen atom, we obtain the binding energy per particle:

$$8 \text{ protons} + 8 \text{ neutrons} = 16 \text{ particles} = 1.6 \times 10^1 \text{ particles}$$

$$\frac{2.0447 \times 10^{-4} \text{ ergs}}{1.6 \times 10^1 \text{ particles}} = 1.2779 \times 10^{-5} \ \frac{\text{ergs}}{\text{particle}}$$

The binding energy per particle is an indication of the stability of a nucleus.

The greater the binding energy per particle, the greater the stability of the nucleus. In Figure 23–13, the binding energy per particle is graphed against the mass number of known nuclides. Note that energy will be released in two reaction types involving the nucleus: when two small nuclei join to form a medium sized nucleus, and when one large nucleus splits to form two medium sized nuclei.

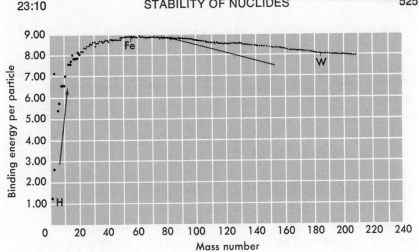

FIGURE 23-13. Binding energy per particle decreases as mass increases in the heavy elements and it also decreases as mass decreases in the lighter elements.

Note: Two kinds of nuclear change lead to greater binding energy: the break-up of large nuclei (fission) and combination of light nuclei (fusion).

Second rule: Nuclei of low atomic numbers with a 1:1 neutron-proton ratio are very stable. In Figure 23–14, the ratio of neutrons to protons is plotted for the known stable nuclei. For low atomic numbers, the ratio has a value very close to one. However, as the atomic number increases, the value of the neutron-proton ratio steadily increases. The closer the value of the neutron-proton ratio of a nuclide is to the shaded area in this figure, the more stable it is.

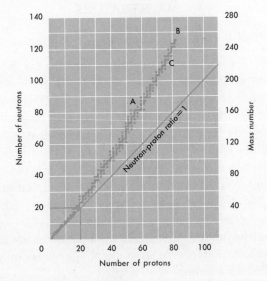

FIGURE 23-14. Stable nuclei are represented by the shaded area. The solid line represents a 1/1 neutron-proton ratio. Region A nuclei emit neutrons or beta particles. Region B nuclei emit alpha particles. Region C nuclei emit positrons or capture electrons.

Third rule: The most stable nuclei tend to contain an even number of both protons and neutrons. Of the known stable nuclei, 57.8% have an even number of protons and an even number of neutrons.

Those with an even number of one kind of nucleon but an odd number of the other are slightly less stable. Thus, 19.8% of stable nuclei have an even number of neutrons but an odd number of protons. 20.9% of stable nuclei have an even number of protons and an odd number of neutrons. Only 1.5% of stable nuclei have both an odd number of neutrons and an odd number of protons.

In Figure 23–14, nuclei falling within the regions A, B, and C are all unstable. Those lying in region A have excess neutrons and become more stable either by emitting neutrons or, more commonly, beta particles. Nuclei falling within the B region are too large for stability and are usually alpha emitters. A nucleus in the C region has excess protons and can become stable by positron emission or by K-electron capture. The loss of a positron (β^+) or the capture of an electron (β^-) results in a new atom with the same mass number but with an atomic number whose value is one unit lower. When a nucleus in the B region emits an alpha particle, its composition moves parallel to the 1:1 ratio line toward the A region. Note that in the heavy-element radioactivity series, several alpha emissions are always followed by beta emission which moves the nucleus back into the B region.

ACCELERATORS

23:11   Tools of the Nuclear Scientist

A number of very large and complex devices are used to investigate the structure of atomic nuclei. One of the earliest devices used was the Cockcroft-Walton accelerator. Like its more complex successors, this device was designed to accelerate charged particles to very high speeds (and thus to very high energies). When the high energy particles collide with a nucleus, interactions take place. The results of these interactions give clues to the structure of the nucleus. The Cockcroft-Walton accelerator used electronic circuitry to build up a very high voltage. This voltage, or potential difference, was then used to accelerate a charged particle.

An alternative device of building up a large voltage is used in the Van de Graaff accelerator. A large metal sphere is connected by an insulating belt to a source of electrical charge. The belt is rotated. The charge picked up by the belt at the source is transferred to the metal sphere. In this way, a static charge of high potential difference can be created. The voltage may then be applied to an accelerator tube in a manner similar to that of the Cockcroft-Walton accelerator.

Spontaneous fission is also observed in this region.

Binding energy may be increased by several kinds of nuclear reactions:
1. α-particle emission
2. K-electron capture
3. β^+ emission
4. β^- emission
5. neutron emission

The Cockcroft-Walton generator and the Van de Graff generator are used to accelerate charged particles to extremely high voltages.

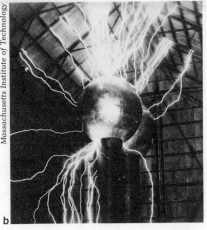

Argonne National Laboratory

Massachusetts Institute of Technology

a

b

FIGURE 23-15. The Cockcroft-Walton accelerator (a) and the Van de Graaff accelerator (b) were early devices used to accelerate charged particles.

23:12 Linear Accelerators

Further research required particles of higher and higher energy. This need led to more sophisticated devices. Both the Cockcroft-Walton and Van de Graaff accelerators were "one shot" devices. A device was needed which would boost the energy of a particle several times as it sped along. One such device was the linear accelerator. By continuing the alternation of charges on a long series of tubes, an electron can be accelerated to a very high energy. However, as the electron picks up speed, the tubes must be longer and longer, and the switching circuits must operate faster and faster. This can also be accomplished by using a radio wave traveling down the tube to impart energy to the electron.

Linear accelerators make use of alternation of charge to speed charged particles.

a

b

F. W. Hoffman, AEC Oak Ridge Operations Office

Stanford University

FIGURE 23-16. Electrons are accelerated in the wave tube (a) of this linear accelerator (b) which produces neutrons for research studies on new sources of energy.

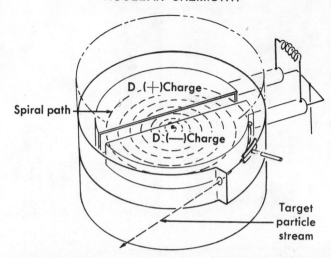

FIGURE 23-17. The cyclotron accelerates charged particles to high speeds and energies.

23:13 Circular Accelerators

Cyclotrons make use of magnetic fields and electrostatic charges to accelerate charged particles.

The concept of bending the path of the accelerated particle led to the development of the *cyclotron* (SI kluh trahn). A diagram of a cyclotron is shown in Figure 23–17. A moving particle with a charge is affected by a magnetic field, as well as by electrostatic charges. The cyclotron takes advantage of both properties to accelerate particles. The two D-shaped halves (D's) are alternately given positive and negative charges which either repel or attract the particle. By increasing the speed of the alternation of the charges on the D's, the particle can be made to pass from one to the other at greater and greater speeds. Above and below the D-shaped chambers are the poles of a very powerful magnet. As the particle is accelerated, the field of the magnet causes the particle to take a spiral path within the particle chamber. Finally, an auxiliary field causes the particle to pass through a window and to hit a target. Since it is almost impossible to accelerate a single particle, in actual practice a stream of particles is accelerated. By observing the change in the target material, particularly the products of any change, the scientist is able to investigate the nucleus of the atoms of the target.

Nuclei of atoms can be investigated by using a stream of charged particles from an accelerator.

Cyclotrons, too, had their drawbacks. As the velocity of the particle increased, the radius of its path also increased. The next improvement in accelerators was to bend the path of the particle into a circle of constant radius. The outward spiral of the particle in the cyclotron had to be overcome. A new device was developed in which

FIGURE 23-18. An aerial view of a zero-gradient synchrotron.

Argonne National Laboratory

the strength of the magnetic field was increased as the speed of the particle was increased. The result was to circularize the path of the particle. The increase in field strength had to be synchronized with the increase in speed. This device was thus called the *synchrotron* (SIHN kruh trahn).

Further refinements in synchrotron technology have led to the development of the National Accelerator Laboratory in the United States. This facility is located at Batavia, Illinois. The protons to be accelerated are given their first boost in energy by a Cockcroft-Walton-type device. Upon leaving this stage the particles have an energy of 750 KeV. They then enter a linear accelerator 150 meters long. The linear accelerator raises the energy of the protons to 200 MeV. The third stage is a synchrotron of 150 meter diameter. Here the particles are raised to 8 GeV energy. Finally, they enter the main accelerator, 6.5 kilometers in circumference! After about 70,000 laps around the main ring, they have acquired an energy of 200 GeV. It is hoped that with future improvements the energy production of the Batavia site will approach 500 GeV.

Another device used to investigate nuclear structure is the *nuclear reactor*. It is possible to study the reaction of many target materials to radiation by placing the materials in a reactor. Particles without a charge, such as neutrons, cannot be accelerated in a device using electrical and magnetic fields. However, many neutral particles are emitted in the decay of atoms in a reactor. Most of the research done using neutrons as bombarding particles has been carried out in a nuclear reactor.

The synchrotron is another device used to accelerate charged particles.

FIGURE 23-19. This is a "swimming pool" type of nuclear reactor. It is named for the large pool of water which surrounds it and acts as a radiation shield.

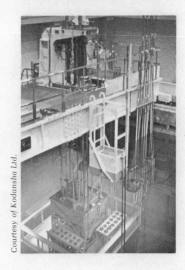

Courtesy of Kodansha Ltd.

NUCLEAR REACTIONS

23:14 Transmutations

Nuclear reactors can be used in bombardment studies with uncharged particles.

Nuclear reactions can result in the change of one element into another, because these reactions can change the number of protons in the nucleus. This change is called *transmutation* (trans myoo TAY shuhn). In natural uranium, the most common isotope is ^{238}U. Uranium-238 decays by emitting an alpha particle. The resulting atom contains two less protons and two less neutrons than uranium-238. Thus, it has an atomic number of 90 and an atomic mass of 234. This new atom is an atom of thorium, $^{234}_{90}Th$. By a natural process, uranium will transmute to thorium-234. Thorium-234 decays by emitting a beta particle. Since the mass of an electron is negligible, the new atom also has the mass number 234, but has one more positive charge than before. Thus, its atomic number is 91. The new atom is $^{234}_{91}Pa$. The uranium series of disintegrations ends with lead ($^{206}_{82}Pb$) which is a stable nuclide.

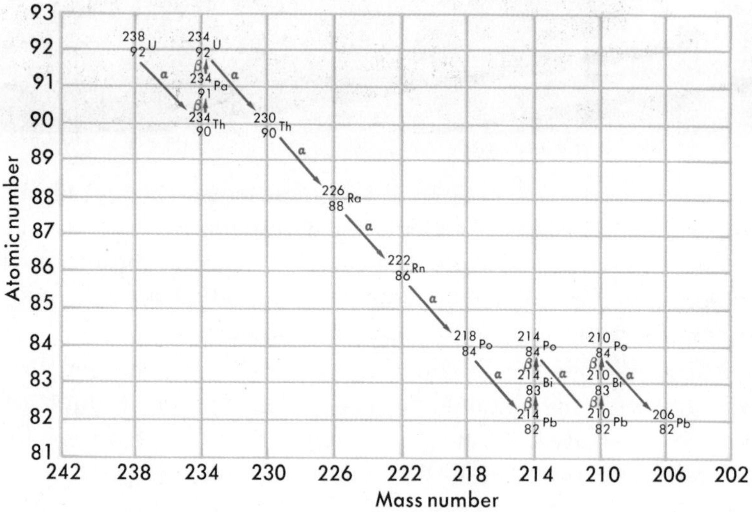

FIGURE 23-20. The nuclear decay of uranium-238 is the first step in a series of nuclear disintegrations which ends with the formation of stable lead-206.

Some elements undergo natural transmutation.

The early alchemists' goal was to find the "philosopher's stone." Our multimillion dollar accelerators now make the alchemist's dream a reality.

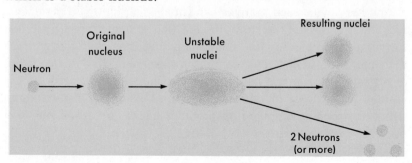

FIGURE 23-21. Fission is the splitting of the nucleus of a heavy atom.

The earliest artificial transmutation was performed by Lord Rutherford in 1911. Rutherford bombarded nitrogen-14 with alpha particles, and obtained oxygen (^{17}O) and protons as products. These two transmutations can be represented in equation form:

$$^{238}_{92}\text{U} \rightarrow \ ^{234}_{90}\text{Th} + \ ^{4}_{2}\text{He} \ (\text{natural})$$

$$^{14}_{7}\text{N} + \ ^{4}_{2}\text{He} \rightarrow \ ^{17}_{8}\text{O} + \ ^{1}_{1}\text{H} \ (\text{artificial})$$

23:15 Fission

If a very heavy nucleus becomes too unstable, it breaks into two approximately equal parts, with the release of a large amount of energy. This process is called *fission* (FISH uhn). A nucleus can be made unstable by bombardment with a number of particles, including neutrons. Nuclear reactors operate on fission reactions.

The heaviest elements are the only ones which exhibit the phenomenon of fission. When a heavy nucleus breaks up, one or more neutrons are emitted, in addition to the production of the two heavy fragments. It is possible for the neutrons emitted to produce a *chain reaction*. One atom splits, due to bombardment by a neutron. In the process of splitting, the atom gives off a neutron, which in turn can cause a second atom to split. This continues until a very large number of the atoms present have reacted. Since a large energy change is involved in the fission process, a chain reaction can serve as an energy source for various purposes. A nuclear reactor is a device for controlling nuclear fission. Reactors can be designed to produce heat for electric power generation plants, or for propulsion units in ships and submarines. In nuclear reactors, the rate of the chain reaction is

FIGURE 23-22. Nuclear energy in the form of three capsules of plutonium-238 powers this nine-pound refrigerator designed to supercool systems to $-200°\text{C}$. The nuclear fuel for this unit would last about 87 years.

Fission is the breakup of a heavy nucleus into two approximately equal parts.

Suggestion: Refer students to page 525, Figure 23-13. This graph indicates the variation in binding energy per particle.

Fission results in the release of very large amounts of energy.

FIGURE 23-23. A nuclear reactor provides energy for this electric power plant (a) and for the propulsion unit in this submarine (b).

In a nuclear reactor, the rate of the reaction is regulated with control rods.

very carefully controlled by rods which can be inserted in the reactor to absorb neutrons if the reaction becomes too rapid.

The requirements for energy sources in the United States have outstripped our ability to produce new installations. Worldwide resources of fossil fuels (petroleum and coal) appear to be sufficient only for a few decades. Although we have begun to utilize fission reactors as a source of electrical power, they represent only a few percent of the total power production facilities in operation. In the next few years, the percentage is expected to grow to about 25%. Fission reactors do not represent an unlimited source of energy. However, they do offer a source of energy for the immediate future. As with other energy sources, there are problems associated with their use. For example, what is to be done with the highly radioactive waste material? The future of fission power reactors will have to be carefully considered by all citizens.

23:16   Synthetic Elements

Some transuranium elements have been produced in nuclear reactors by bombarding plutonium-239 with neutrons.

All of the transuranium elements thus far synthesized have been produced by converting a lighter element into a heavier one by increasing the number of protons in the nucleus. One of the processes of synthetic transmutation occurs as follows. A nuclear reactor produces a high concentration of neutrons which are "packed" into the nucleus of an element, plutonium-239. As the mass number builds up, a beta particle is emitted. When this happens, a neutron is converted into a proton with no significant loss of mass. This process produces an element with an atomic number greater than the original element:

$$^{239}_{94}\text{Pu} + ^{1}_{0}\text{n} \rightarrow ^{240}_{94}\text{Pu}$$

$$^{240}_{94}\text{Pu} + ^{1}_{0}\text{n} \rightarrow ^{241}_{94}\text{Pu}$$

$$^{241}_{94}\text{Pu} \rightarrow ^{241}_{95}\text{Am} + ^{0}_{-1}\text{e}$$

This element in turn can be used as a target to produce another element with a higher atomic number. Fermium-256 ($^{256}_{100}\text{Fm}$) is the element with the highest atomic number reached in this manner.

A second method of synthesizing transuranium elements makes use of nuclear explosions which produce vast amounts of neutrons. Some neutrons are captured by uranium atoms. Successive electron emissions produce new elements. Fermium-256 is the element with the highest atomic number produced in this way.

Glenn T. Seaborg, who received credit for discovery of several transuranium elements, actually applied for and received a patent for elements he has produced. He assigned rights to these patents to the United States Government.

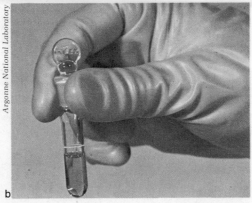

a

b

FIGURE 23-24. James Harris (a), a nuclear chemist, developed the target used to produce atoms of element-104 at the University of California at Berkeley. Plutonium (b), another man-made element, was also produced in Berkeley.

Elements with atomic numbers greater than 100 have been produced by using other elements to bombard target elements. Mendelevium ($^{256}_{101}$Md) was created by bombarding einsteinium ($^{254}_{94}$Es) with alpha particles. Nobelium, atomic number 102, was created by using carbon ions and curium. The production of lawrencium, atomic number 103, made use of boron and californium. Element 104 can be produced by the bombardment of plutonium by neon. Element 105 can be produced by the bombardment of californium with nitrogen. A heavy-ion accelerator at the University of California is being prepared to accelerate particles as heavy as bromine nuclei.

It is highly possible that elements with even greater atomic numbers can be produced. Difficulties are caused by the present low yields of transuranium elements and by their extremely short half-lives. Only a few atoms of elements 103–105 were first prepared, and these had half-lives of seconds. However, most nuclear scientists believe that prospects of producing elements with atomic numbers as high as 126 are reasonably good.

Other transuranium elements have been produced by bombarding target elements with other elements.

Eventually, it may be possible to produce synthetic elements with atomic numbers up to 126.

23:17 Fusion

The peak of the binding energy curve in Figure 23–13 occurs near the element iron, atomic number 26. We can see how both fission and the emission of small particles by atoms at the high atomic number end of the binding energy curve lead to more stable atoms. Note also that stability could be gained by the combination of the smallest nuclei into larger ones. A nuclear reaction in which two or more small nuclei combine to form one larger nucleus is called a *fusion* (FYEW zhuhn) reaction. You can see also that the slope of the binding energy curve is much greater on the low atomic number

In fusion reactions, two or more smaller nuclei combine to form a larger nucleus.

FIGURE 23-25. The fusion processes going on in the sun provide almost all of the earth's energy.

Alternate fusion reactions for the sun:

Bethe cycle for hot stars:

$$^{12}_{6}C + ^{1}_{1}H \rightarrow ^{13}_{7}N + h\nu$$

$$^{13}_{7}N \rightarrow ^{13}_{6}C + ^{0}_{+1}e + \nu$$

$$^{13}_{6}C + ^{1}_{1}H \rightarrow ^{14}_{7}N + h\nu$$

$$^{14}_{7}N + ^{1}_{1}H \rightarrow ^{15}_{8}O + h\nu$$

$$^{15}_{8}O \rightarrow ^{15}_{7}N + ^{0}_{+1}e + \nu$$

$$^{15}_{7}N + ^{1}_{1}H \rightarrow ^{12}_{6}C + ^{4}_{2}He$$

Cooler cycle:

$$^{1}_{1}H + ^{1}_{1}H \rightarrow ^{2}_{1}H + ^{0}_{1}e + h\nu$$

$$^{1}_{1}H + ^{2}_{1}H \rightarrow ^{3}_{2}He + h\nu$$

$$^{3}_{2}He + ^{3}_{2}He \rightarrow ^{4}_{2}He + 2\left(^{1}_{1}H\right) + h\nu$$

James Westwater

Fusion reactions release much larger amounts of energy than fission reactions.

side than it is on the high side. We should therefore expect fusion reactions to produce much greater amounts of energy per particle than fission reactions. This prediction is supported by observation.

Scientists have harnessed the fission reaction in a controlled process on a small scale for limited power production. If we could harness the fusion reaction for power production on a large scale, we would have a solution to energy problems for some time to come. Some of the difficult problems associated with fission reactions as a power source would also be eliminated. The availability of "fuel"

Enrico Fermi

(1901–1954)

Enrico Fermi was the first scientist to split the atom, and the first to produce an artificial element—neptunium. His work demonstrated that almost all elements undergo nuclear reactions when exposed to neutron bombardment.

Fermi's investigations were constantly interrupted during his lifetime due to political oppression. He used the occasion of his visit to Sweden to accept the Nobel Prize in 1938 as a chance to leave Italy forever.

He is chiefly known as the architect and operator of the first atomic pile, or nuclear reactor. In 1942, his reactor was put into operation, and for the first time man used energy formerly locked in the nucleus of the atom.

for nuclear fusion reactions is much greater than for fission reactions. Also, fusion reactions useful for power production do not result in radioactive waste products.

The most likely reactions for fusion power generators are the following:

$$^2_1H + {}^2_1H \rightarrow {}^3_2He + {}^1_0n$$

$$^2_1H + {}^2_1H \rightarrow {}^3_1H + {}^1_1H$$

$$^2_1H + {}^3_1H \rightarrow {}^4_2He + {}^1_0n$$

FIGURE 23-26. Dixy Lee Ray, a marine biologist, on February 6, 1973, became the first woman to head the Atomic Energy Commission.

The last of these reactions is the most promising from the standpoint of power production. However, it does have drawbacks. Tritium (^3_1H) is a radioactive nuclide which occurs naturally in only tiny amounts. It can be produced by exposing lithium-6 to the neutrons produced by the fusion reaction:

$$^6_3Li + {}^1_0n \rightarrow {}^4_2He + {}^3_1H$$

Another disadvantage is that the reactor itself will become radioactive as it is exposed to these radiations.

On the other hand, the reactions involving only deuterium (^2_1H) are radioactivity-free. Also, the supply of deuterium on the earth is huge. It has been estimated that deuterium could supply the earth with energy for as long as 10^{12} years. Extraction of deuterium from water supplies would require only a small fraction of the power output of a fusion reactor.

Present technology promises practical fusion installations within your lifetime. If certain technical problems are solved, these reactors could appear in the near future. Let us look at some of these problems.

The supply of naturally-occurring deuterium is estimated to be large enough to fuel fusion reactors for 10^{12} years.

23:18   Fusion Reactors

In order for two atomic nuclei to undergo fusion, they must come almost into contact. Recall that the nuclear force extends only about a distance equal to the diameter of the nucleus. However, since all nuclei are positively charged, they tend to repel each other strongly. In order for fusion reactions to occur, the reactants must be held in the temperature range of 10^8 to 10^9 °C for a suitable time. The length of time depends upon how closely packed the particles are during that time. At these high temperatures, of course, matter is in the form of plasma. One of the major problems of fusion reactor designers

The matter involved in fusion reactions is in the plasma state.

FIGURE 23-27. A controlled fusion device of tokamac design uses huge magnets to confine a hot, pulsing plasma of deuterium and tritium. One of these reactors is located at Princeton, New Jersey.

AEC

Fusion reactions can be contained in "magnetic bottles."

has been how to contain a substance at that temperature. Containers made from usual materials cannot be used, principally because the plasma would lose heat to them so rapidly that fusion temperatures would never be reached. Since plasmas are charged particles, they are affected by magnetic fields. By properly shaping a magnetic field, a plasma may be contained. As fusion occurs and the temperature rises, the pressure of a plasma causes it to expand. With charged particles in the plasma moving around at tremendous velocities, the plasma itself generates electric currents. Both of these effects make leakage from the magnetic "bottle" a difficult problem to solve. Achievement of proper temperature, confinement for the proper length of time, and packing enough particles in a given space are all topics of present research. Who can predict what role developments in this fascinating field will play in shaping our future!

SUMMARY

1. Radioactivity is the phenomenon of particle or quantum emission due to nuclear disintegration.
2. Radioactive decay is spontaneous; that is, it cannot be controlled.
3. The equation $E = mc^2$ indicates that, under certain conditions, mass and energy can be interconverted.
4. It has been proposed, but not established, that the nucleus is held together by "trading" or "sharing" mesons among neutrons and protons.

5. Nucleons have a "spin" property which gives some nuclei a magnetic field.

6. Nuclear magnetic resonance spectroscopy is a useful tool in investigating the structure of molecules.

7. Naturally radioactive nuclides emit three kinds of radiation: alpha (helium nuclei), beta (electrons), and gamma (quanta of energy).

8. Many subatomic particles in addition to electrons and nucleons have been discovered. Some of these are classified as antimatter.

9. Many radiation detection devices (the Geiger tube, the electroscope, the spark chamber, the cloud chamber, the bubble chamber, and photographic film) depend upon the ionizing ability of radiation for the principle of their operation.

10. Cerenkov and scintillation detectors operate on the principle that radiation causes other substances to emit light.

11. An isotope is an atom which contains the same number of protons as another atom but differs in the number of neutrons. There are three isotopes of hydrogen: protium, deuterium, and tritium.

12. Each radioactive nuclide emits a characteristic radiation. Because of this, radioactive nuclides are extremely useful in the laboratory and in industry.

13. The half-life of a radioactive substance is the length of time it takes for one-half of the atoms of a sample of the substance to disintegrate.

14. Radioactive carbon is present in all plants. By measuring the ^{14}C in plant remains, such as charcoal, it is possible to determine how long the plant has been dead. The rate of uranium decay is used in a similar way to date geological formations.

15. Binding energy is the energy needed to separate the nucleus into individual protons and neutrons.

16. The calculated mass defect of an atom indicates the transformation of some of the mass of the atom into binding energy.

17. Three relationships can be used to predict the stability of nuclides:
    (a) the binding energy per particle
    (b) the neutron-proton ratio
    (c) an even number of both protons and neutrons

18. Among particle accelerators, the "one shot" devices known as Cockcroft-Walton and Van de Graaff accelerators are still useful for low-energy particles.

19. Linear accelerators can be used for electrons or positive particles as heavy as bromine nuclei.

20. Circular accelerators began with the cyclotron. Modern synchrotrons are capable of accelerating particles to billions of electron-volt energies.

21. Bombardment of a target by neutrons is accomplished in a nuclear reactor. Since neutrons have no charge, they cannot be accelerated by electrical and magnetic devices.

22. A nuclear reactor is a device for containing and controlling a fission reaction.

23. The changing of one element into another is called transmutation.

24. Fission is the splitting of a large, unstable nucleus into two smaller, approximately equal parts.

25. Fusion is the combining of two or more small nuclei into one larger nucleus.

PROBLEMS

See Teacher's Guide at the front of this book.

1. What are the differences among the three types of natural radiation?
2. What are the tests for stability of an isotope?
3. Briefly describe the action of a radiation counter.
4. Show the formulas for the three isotopes of hydrogen.
5. What are some uses for radioactive nuclides?
6. What are the differences between fusion and fission?
7. Complete the following equations:

7. (a) $^3_1 H \rightarrow \, ^3_2 He \, + \, ^0_{-1}e$.

   (b) $^{61}_{30} Zn \rightarrow \, ^{61}_{29} Cu \, + \, ^0_{+1}e$

   (c) $^9_3 Li \rightarrow \, ^9_4 Be \, + \, ^0_{-1}e$

   (d) $^{240}_{96} Cm \rightarrow \, ^{236}_{94} Pu \, + \, ^4_2 He$

   (e) $^{199}_{84} Po \, + \, ^0_1 e \rightarrow \, ^{199}_{83} Bi$

   (a) $^3_1 H \rightarrow \, ? + \, ^0_{-1}e$

   (b) $^{61}_{30} Zn \rightarrow \, ? + \, ^0_{+1}e$

   (c) $^9_3 Li \rightarrow \, ^9_4 Be \, + \, ?$

   (d) $^{240}_{96} Cm \rightarrow \, ? + \, ^4_2 He$

   (e) $^{199}_{84} Po \, + \, ^0_{-1}e \rightarrow \, ?$ (K-capture)

ONE MORE STEP

See Teacher's Guide at the front of this book.

1. Using a Geiger counter or similar device and a radioactive source, determine (a) the change in radiation intensity with change in distance between source and detector, and (b) the shielding effect of paper, masonry, and metal.

2. Grow some plants in water which contains both the usual plant nutrient tablets and a salt containing a radioactive nuclide. Make an autoradiogram of the leaves and stems of the plant. Determine if the radioactive substance is evenly distributed in the plant or is concentrated in a specific place.

3. Make a list of radioactive nuclides presently in use in research and industry. For each nuclide, state the operation in which it is used. Much of this information can be found in your school library.

4. Determine the difference between "weak" and "strong" inter-actions between nuclear particles.

      See Teacher's Guide at the front of this book.

5. Prepare a report on the differences and similarities of the various accelerators: the cyclotron, the betatron, the synchrotron, etc.

6. What progress has been made toward large-scale production of energy by nuclear-fusion?

Suggested Readings for this chapter may be found in the Teacher's Guide at the front of this book.

Energy needs are of great concern today. Fossil fuel resources, which are of organic origin, are rapidly being depleted. Some fossil fuel deposits are so low-grade that they are not practical to use as they are found. Scientists are seeking new ways of making the best use of available fossil fuels. This HYGAS pilot plant in Chicago is designed to convert coal to a pipeline-quality synthetic natural gas equivalent. What other means are scientists studying to make better use of fossil fuels?

Organic Chemistry ——————————— 24

Chapter 24 introduces the student to organic chemistry through a systematic study of hydrocarbons and their derivatives.

Early chemists and even alchemists had observed that there were two general types of substances—those from animal and vegetable matter, and those from nonliving matter. These two types became known as organic substances and inorganic substances. It was found that all organic substances had some similar properties. Most organic compounds were found to decompose easily when heated. Most inorganic substances were observed to change very little, if any, when heated. In addition, it was thought that organic substances could be produced only by living organisms.

When chemists began to study organic substances in greater detail, they learned that nearly all organic compounds are made up of chains and rings of carbon atoms. Chemists then learned to synthesize some simple organic compounds directly from inorganic substances! This amazing discovery marked the beginning of modern organic chemistry. Today, we define organic chemistry as the chemistry of carbon compounds.

GOAL: You will gain an understanding of organic chemistry through an introductory discussion of structure, nomenclature, substituents (functional groups), and simple reactions.

The chemistry of carbon compounds is organic chemistry.

HYDROCARBONS

24:1 Classification of Hydrocarbons

One of the largest classifications of organic compounds is the group known as the *hydrocarbons*. These are compounds composed only of carbon and hydrogen. Almost all other organic compounds can be named as derivatives of the simple hydrocarbons. If the carbon atoms are linked in chains, the compounds are called *aliphatic* (al ih FAT ihk) compounds. If the atoms are linked in rings, the compounds are called *cyclic* (SI klihk).

The chain compounds may be further classified on the basis of the individual carbon-carbon bonds. A chain compound in which all carbon-carbon bonds are single bonds is called an alkane (AL kayn). This type of compound is also called a *saturated* hydrocarbon

Hydrocarbons are composed of hydrogen and carbon.

This series of compounds is often called the **paraffin** series.

Alkanes are saturated hydrocarbons.

541

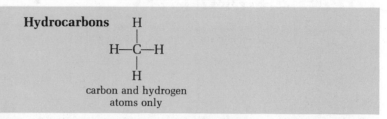

Hydrocarbons

carbon and hydrogen
atoms only

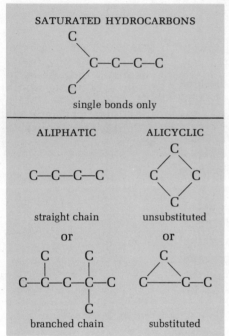

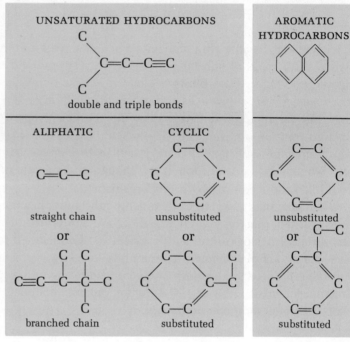

SATURATED HYDROCARBONS	UNSATURATED HYDROCARBONS	AROMATIC HYDROCARBONS
single bonds only	double and triple bonds	

ALIPHATIC	ALICYCLIC	ALIPHATIC	CYCLIC	
straight chain	unsubstituted	straight chain	unsubstituted	unsubstituted
or	or	or	or	or
branched chain	substituted	branched chain	substituted	substituted

because each carbon-carbon bond is a single bond. Thus, no more atoms can be bonded to the atoms in the compound without breaking the compound into two or more fragments.

24:2   Alkanes

The alkane family is the first in the series of families of organic compounds that we will study. The first four members of the alkane series and their formulas are: methane, CH_4; ethane, C_2H_6; propane, C_3H_8; and butane, C_4H_{10}. After butane, the members of the alkane family are named by using the Greek (sometimes the Latin) prefix for the number of carbon atoms. The ending characteristic of this family is *-ane*.

Each alkane differs from the next by a —CH_2— group. You can think of this series of compounds as being formed by removing a

Members of the alkane series differ by -CH₂-.

hydrogen atom from one of the carbon atoms, adding a $-\overset{\displaystyle H}{\underset{\displaystyle H}{C}}-$ group,
and then replacing the hydrogen. For example:

methylene group $-\overset{\displaystyle H}{\underset{\displaystyle H}{\diagdown C}}-$

$$H-\overset{\displaystyle H}{\underset{\displaystyle H}{C}}-H \; + \; -\overset{\displaystyle H}{\underset{\displaystyle H}{C}}- \;\;\rightarrow\;\; H-\overset{\displaystyle H}{\underset{\displaystyle H}{C}}-\overset{\displaystyle H}{\underset{\displaystyle H}{C}}-H$$

$$CH_4 \qquad\qquad CH_2 \qquad\qquad C_2H_6$$

Note that this equation does not represent the actual preparation of an alkane.

A series of compounds whose structures differ from each other by a specific structural unit (such as $-CH_2-$ in the case of alkanes) is called a *homologous* (hoh MAHL uh guhs) series. A general formula can be written for all of the members of a homologous series such as the alkanes. For the alkanes, the formula is C_nH_{2n+2}, where n is the number of carbon atoms in the compound.

The simplest alkane, methane, contains one carbon atom and four hydrogen atoms. The structural formula for methane is:

General formula for alkanes: C_nH_{2n+2}.

$$H-\overset{\displaystyle H}{\underset{\displaystyle H}{C}}-H$$

methane

Note: These are convention- alized diagrams. The bonds in the actual molecules are arranged around the carbon atoms in such a way that the four bonds formed by each carbon are as far apart as possible. This results in a tetrahedral distribution of bonds with a bond angle of $109°28'$.

The formulas of the next three compounds in the alkane series are:

$$H-\overset{\displaystyle H}{\underset{\displaystyle H}{C}}-\overset{\displaystyle H}{\underset{\displaystyle H}{C}}-H \qquad H-\overset{\displaystyle H}{\underset{\displaystyle H}{C}}-\overset{\displaystyle H}{\underset{\displaystyle H}{C}}-\overset{\displaystyle H}{\underset{\displaystyle H}{C}}-H \qquad H-\overset{\displaystyle H}{\underset{\displaystyle H}{C}}-\overset{\displaystyle H}{\underset{\displaystyle H}{C}}-\overset{\displaystyle H}{\underset{\displaystyle H}{C}}-\overset{\displaystyle H}{\underset{\displaystyle H}{C}}-H$$

ethane   propane   butane

If one hydrogen atom, with its associated electron, is removed from a hydrocarbon molecule, a *radical* is left:

A hydrocarbon radical is a hydrocarbon molecule from which a hydrogen atom has been removed.

$$H-\overset{\displaystyle H}{\underset{\displaystyle H}{C}}-H \qquad H-\overset{\displaystyle H}{\underset{\displaystyle H}{C}}\cdot \qquad H-\overset{\displaystyle H}{\underset{\displaystyle H}{C}}-\overset{\displaystyle H}{\underset{\displaystyle H}{C}}-\overset{\displaystyle H}{\underset{\displaystyle H}{C}}-H \qquad H-\overset{\displaystyle H}{\underset{\displaystyle H}{C}}-\overset{\displaystyle H}{\underset{\displaystyle H}{C}}-\overset{\displaystyle H}{\underset{\displaystyle H}{C}}\cdot$$

methane   methyl   propane   propyl

Radicals are named by substituting the ending -*yl* for the normal -*ane* ending of the parent compound (Table 24–1).

There are general trends in physical and chemical properties within homologous families. For instance, as the molecular mass of the compounds in a family increases, the boiling point increases. Table 24–1 lists the names of the first few members of the alkane family and some of their physical properties.

Table 24–1

Alkanes

Name of Alkane	Formula	Melting Point, °C	Boiling Point, °C	Name and Formula of Radical	
Methane	CH_4	−182	−164	Methyl	CH_3-
Ethane	C_2H_6	−183	−87	Ethyl	C_2H_5-
Propane	C_3H_8	−190	−42	Propyl	C_3H_7-
Butane	C_4H_{10}	−138	−1	Butyl	C_4H_9-
Pentane	C_5H_{12}	−130	36	Pentyl	$C_5H_{11}-$
Hexane	C_6H_{14}	−95	69	Hexyl	$C_6H_{13}-$
Heptane	C_7H_{16}	−91	98	Heptyl	$C_7H_{15}-$
Octane	C_8H_{18}	−57	126	Octyl	$C_8H_{17}-$
Nonane	C_9H_{20}	−51	151	Nonyl	$C_9H_{19}-$
Decane	$C_{10}H_{22}$	−30	174	Decyl	$C_{10}H_{21}-$
—					
Dodecane	$C_{12}H_{26}$	−10	216	Dodecyl	$C_{12}H_{25}-$
—					
Hexadecane	$C_{16}H_{34}$	+18	287	Hexadecyl	$C_{16}H_{33}-$
Heptadecane	$C_{17}H_{36}$	+22	302	Heptadecyl	$C_{17}H_{35}-$

24:3   Naming Branched Alkanes

Branched chains are numbered to give the longest chain.

For convenience in naming organic compounds, carbon atoms in a structural formula are given *position numbers*. In an unbranched chain molecule, the numbering of carbon atoms can begin at either end of the chain. For example,

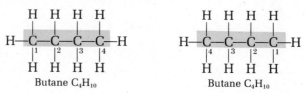

Butane C_4H_{10} Butane C_4H_{10}

Not all alkanes have unbranched chains of carbon atoms. In naming branched alkanes, we must first find the *longest* chain of carbon atoms. This chain is used as the basis of the compound name. The *parent chain* does not necessarily occur in a straight line. This compound

Alkanes are named on the basis of the longest continuous chain of carbon atoms.

Important

has hexane (C_6H_{14}) as the parent chain since the longest chain contains six carbon atoms. The carbon atoms of the longest chain are given position numbers beginning at the end of the parent chain closer to the side chain. The CH_3- group which is attached to the main chain is called a *side chain* or *substituent*. The side chain is named as a radical. We indicate, by number, the position of the carbon atom of the parent chain to which the side chain (radical) is attached. In our example, the side chain is attached to the third carbon. The side chain is a methyl radical. The parent chain is hexane. The name of this compound is 3-methylhexane. The name is written with a hyphen between the substituent position number and the substituent name. The substituent and the parent are written as one word. Numbering of the carbon atoms of the parent alkane chain always begins at the end which will give the *lowest position numbers* to the substituents.

Substituents or side chains are attached to the main chain of carbon atoms.

Carbons are numbered to give the lowest position numbers to branches.

    How do we name an alkane which has more than one side chain? Consider the example,

The parent chain is hexane. Both an ethyl group and a methyl group are attached to the parent chain. They are attached to the third carbon. The name of this alkane is 3-ethyl-3-methylhexane. Note that the radicals appear in the name in alphabetical order. Why is the name of this compound not 4-ethyl-4-methylhexane?

If there are two or more substituent groups which are alike, it is convenient to use prefixes (di-, tri-, tetra-, etc.) instead of writing each substituent separately. A comma is placed between the position numbers of the substituents which are alike. For example:

A prefix is used to indicate two or more identical substituent groups.

Note that the number of positions and the number of groups must agree.

is written 2,3-dimethylhexane. Why is the name not 4,5-dimethylhexane?

24:4 Isomers of Alkanes

Note that only one structural diagram can be drawn for methane, ethane, or propane. There are, however, two possible structures for butane:

Several empirical formulas have been developed but none of these formulas gives completely accurate predictions of the number of actual isomers.

Isomers have the same formula but different molecular structures.

butane   2-methylpropane

Each of these two structures of butane is called an *isomer* of butane (Chapter 9). Most organic compounds have isomers. There is no known way of predicting exactly how many isomers most compounds can form. Pentane (C_5H_{12}), the next member of the alkane family, has three isomers. Hexane (C_6H_{14}) has five isomers. Heptane

(C_7H_{16}) has nine. Isomers are named according to the longest chain, and not according to the total number of carbon atoms in the molecule. The second structure of butane is named 2-methylpropane.

Our work will be easier if we modify the structural formulas to a *condensed form*. There can be only one bond between carbon and hydrogen atoms. In the condensed form of a structural formula, carbon atoms are still written separately. However, the hydrogen atoms that are attached to a carbon atom are grouped with that carbon atom. Thus, the isomers of pentane may be written in the condensed form:

normal pentane

$$CH_3—CH_2—CH_2—CH_2—CH_3$$

2,2-dimethylpropane
(neopentane)

$$CH_3—\underset{\underset{CH_3}{|}}{\overset{\overset{CH_3}{|}}{C}}—CH_3$$

$$CH_3—CH_2—\underset{\underset{CH_3}{|}}{CH}—CH_3$$

2-methylbutane (isopentane)

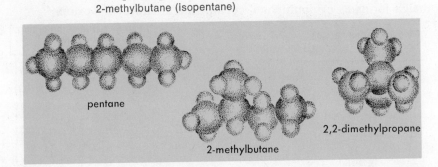

pentane

2-methylbutane

2,2-dimethylpropane

FIGURE 24-1. The three isomers of pentane.

PROBLEMS

1. Name:

a. $CH_3—\underset{\underset{}{}}{\overset{\overset{CH_3}{|}}{CH}}\!\!—\!\!\overset{\overset{CH_3}{|}}{CH}—CH_2—CH_3$ 2,3-dimethylpentane

b. $CH_3—CH_2—CH_2—CH_2—CH_2—CH_2—CH_2—CH_3$ octane

c. $CH_3—CH_2—CH_2—CH_2—\underset{\underset{CH_3}{|}}{CH}—\underset{\underset{CH_3}{|}}{\overset{\overset{CH_3}{|}}{C}}—CH_3$ 2,2,3-trimethylheptane

d. $CH_3—\overset{\overset{CH_3}{|}}{CH}—\overset{\overset{CH_3}{|}}{CH}—\overset{\overset{CH_3}{|}}{CH}—CH_2—CH_3$ 2,3,4-trimethylhexane

e. $CH_3—\underset{\underset{CH_3}{|}}{\overset{\overset{CH_3}{|}}{C}}—CH_2—CH_3$ 2,2-dimethylbutane

See Teacher's Guide at the front of this book.

2. Draw structural formulas (condensed form) for

    a. 2-methylheptane

    b. tetramethylbutane

    c. 2,2,4-trimethylpentane

    d. 3-ethyl-2-methylpentane

    e. 3-ethylhexane

3. Draw all structural formulas for the isomers of hexane.

4. Name each isomer in Question 3.

4. a. hexane
  b. 2-methylpentane
  c. 3-methylpentane
  d. 2,2-dimethylbutane
  e. 2,3-dimethylbutane

24:5 Cycloalkanes

Cycloalkanes are single-bond ring compounds.

The formation of a ring causes bond strain in all cycloalkanes except cyclohexane.

    Saturated hydrocarbons occur in three forms: straight-chain forms (alkanes), branched-chain forms (also alkanes), and cyclic forms (*cycloalkanes*). The cycloalkanes contain only single bonds. They have the general formula C_nH_{2n}. They occur in natural petroleum in such forms as cyclopropane, cyclopentane, and cyclohexane:

Ring formation causes bond strain.

No strain—puckering of ring allows a normal angle of 109°28′.

cyclopropane   cyclopentane   cyclohexane

In a structural formula for an organic molecule, a carbon atom is represented by the intersection of each pair of straight lines. All other bonds of the carbon atoms are to hydrogen atoms.

In cyclobutane, the internal angle is 100°.

    These diagrams are somewhat unwieldy. Organic chemists use stylized drawings to represent cyclic *compounds*. In the symbols for cyclic compounds, a carbon atom is understood to be at the point where each pair of straight lines meets. Each carbon atom is understood to be bonded to enough hydrogen atoms to produce a total of four bonds. The standard symbols used to represent the first five members of the *cycloalkanes* are:

cyclopropane   cyclobutane   cyclopentane   cyclohexane   cycloheptane

Some derivative compounds of the cycloalkanes are:

methylcyclopropane 1,3-dimethylcyclohexane ethylcyclopentane

24:6 Alkenes

Some hydrocarbons contain multiple bonds between carbon atoms. They may combine with other elements or compounds without breaking the carbon chain by adding on at the multiple bond. Thus, they are called *unsaturated*.

Unsaturated hydrocarbons contain multiple bonds.

This term originated because in these compounds fewer than the four possible single carbon bonds are formed; i.e., not all bonds are single bonds.

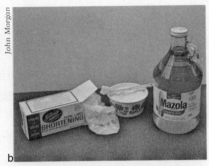

FIGURE 24-2. Unsaturated bonds are found in these common organic laboratory chemicals (a). They are also found in margarine and cooking oil, but not in lard which contains saturated bonds (b).

Unsaturated hydrocarbons containing double bonds between carbon atoms are called *alkenes* (AL keens) or *olefins* (OH leh fihns). The names of these compounds end in *-ene*. The *-ene* ending tells you that there is double bonding between carbon atoms.

Alkenes contain one double bond.

The alkenes constitute a homologous series with the general formula C_nH_{2n}. The first five members of the alkene series are ethene, C_2H_4; propene, C_3H_6; butene, C_4H_8; pentene, C_5H_{10}; and hexene, C_6H_{12}. As with the alkanes, there are general trends in the physical and chemical properties of alkenes as the molecular mass increases.

General formula for alkenes: C_nH_{2n}.

24:7 Naming Alkenes

With the introduction of double bonds, a new way of forming positional isomers is introduced. Butene in a straight chain can still have two isomers:

Alkene isomers differ in the location of their double bonds.

Compounds are named according to the longest chain with a double bond.

Compounds with double bonds, which exist in isomeric form, are named by placing the position number of the carbon atom on which the double bond begins, before the name of the parent compound. Thus:

$$\begin{array}{ccccc} H & & H & H & H \\ \diagdown & & | & | & | \\ & C=C & -C & -C & -H \\ \diagup & & | & | & | \\ H & & H & H \end{array} \quad \text{is 1-butene,}$$

and

2-Butene has two geometric isomers.

$$\begin{array}{ccccc} H & H & H & H \\ | & | & | & | \\ H-C & -C & =C & -C-H \\ | & | & | \\ H & & H \end{array} \quad \text{is 2-butene}$$

The lowest possible positional number is assigned to the first double-bonded carbon atom.

Carbon atoms in alkenes are always numbered so that the lowest possible position number is assigned to the first carbon atom to which the double bond is attached. The parent compound is named from the longest continuous chain *containing a double bond*. For example:

Compounds with two or more double bonds are not alkenes. They belong to groups called alkadienes, alkatrienes, etc. The second double bond does not have much effect on the first unless they are relatively close in the chain.

$$\overset{1}{C}H_2$$
$$2 \parallel$$
$$\overset{2}{C}H$$
$$\overset{7}{C}H_3 - \overset{6}{C}H_2 - \overset{5}{C}H_2 - \overset{4}{C}H_2 - \overset{3}{C}H - CH_2 - CH_2 - CH_3$$

is 3-propyl-1-heptene.

Geometric isomerism may result from double bonds.

The double bond also makes possible another kind of isomerism which we have already studied in Chapter 9: *geometric isomerism*.

24:8 Alkynes

Alkynes contain one triple bond.

A third family of hydrocarbons consists of molecules containing triple bonds between carbon atoms. Compounds with triple-bonded

$$H:C:::C:H$$
carbon-carbon triple bond

FIGURE 24-3. The acetylene torch is used in welding.

W. Keith Turpie

carbon atoms are called *alkynes* (AL kyns), and constitute a homologous series with the general formula C_nH_{2n-2}. They are important raw materials for industries producing synthetic materials such as plastics and fibers. Chemically, they are very reactive. The alkynes are named just as the alkenes, except the ending -*yne* replaces -*ene*. Acetylene is the common name for ethyne, the first member of this series. Acetylene is commercially the most important member of the alkyne family. The first three members of the alkyne family are ethyne, C_2H_2; propyne, C_3H_4; and butyne, C_4H_6.

General formula for alkynes: C_nH_{2n-2}.

H—C≡C—H

ethyne (acetylene)

$$H—C≡C—\overset{\displaystyle H}{\underset{\displaystyle H}{C}}—H$$

propyne

$$H—\overset{\displaystyle H}{\underset{\displaystyle H}{C}}—C≡C—\overset{\displaystyle H}{\underset{\displaystyle H}{C}}—H$$

2-butyne

Compounds with two or more triple bonds are not alkynes. They belong to groups called alkadiynes, alkatriynes, etc. The second triple bond does not have much effect on the first unless they are relatively close in the chain.

The numbering system for location of the triple bond and the substituent groups of the alkynes follows much the same pattern as was used for naming the alkenes. For example, the compound

$$CH_3—C≡C—\overset{\displaystyle CH_3}{\underset{\displaystyle CH_3}{C}}—CH_3$$

is 4,4-dimethyl-2-pentyne.

24:9 Aromatic Hydrocarbons

The benzene ring contains a conjugated system of bonds.

To an organic chemist, one of the most important organic compounds is benzene, a cyclic hydrocarbon. Its structural diagram can be written

The actual molecule is considered a resonance hybrid of these two structures.

$$
\begin{array}{c}
\text{H} \quad \text{H} \\
6\,\text{C}=\text{C}1 \\
\text{H}-5\text{C} \qquad 2\text{C}-\text{H} \qquad \leftrightarrow \qquad \text{H}-5\text{C} \qquad 2\text{C}-\text{H} \\
4\text{C}-\text{C}3 \\
\text{H} \quad \text{H}
\end{array}
$$

Usually the benzene ring is diagrammed as ⬡ or ⬡. In this structural representation, it is assumed that there is a carbon atom at each corner with one hydrogen atom attached, unless otherwise indicated. This diagram should not be confused with the symbol

⬡, which is used to represent cyclohexane, an alkane. Note that benzene has a conjugated system of double and single bonds in a continuous loop. It, therefore, possesses great stability.

Aromatic compounds are generally derived from benzene.

There are so many compounds (actually thousands) derived from benzene, that the study of benzene derivatives constitutes a whole branch of organic chemistry. Most of these compounds have rather distinctive odors. Thus, they are called *aromatic* (ayr oh MAHT ihk) compounds. Aromatic compounds are normally named as deriva-

FIGURE 24-4. Aromatic rings are found in these common organic laboratory chemicals (a). They are also a part of these familiar items (b).

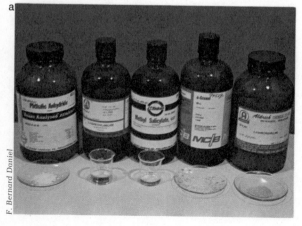

a

F. Bernard Daniel

b

John Morgan

tives of benzene. Aromatic compounds occur in small quantities in some petroleum reserves. They occur to a large extent in the coal tar which is obtained from the distillation of coal. In some compounds, several rings may be formed together in a fused system. These compounds have properties similar to benzene. An example of a fused ring compound is naphthalene:

Explain to students that it is not necessary for a compound to have a distinctive odor for it to be an aromatic compound. It is only necessary for the compound to include a benzene ring.

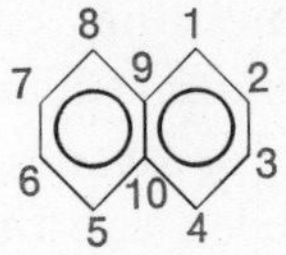

The radical formed by removing a hydrogen atom from a benzene ring is called the *phenyl* (FEEN uhl) radical.

The radical formed from a benzene ring is the phenyl radical.

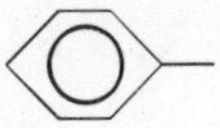

Do not confuse the phenyl radical with the benzyl radical which is

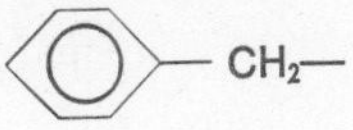

Some examples of benzene compounds are:

methylbenzene (toluene) 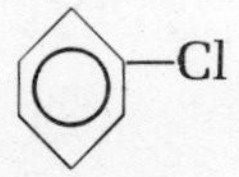   chlorobenzene (phenyl chloride) 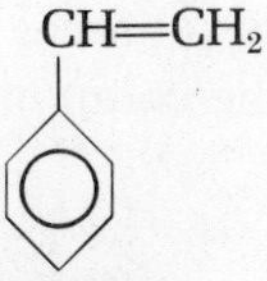   phenylethene (styrene) 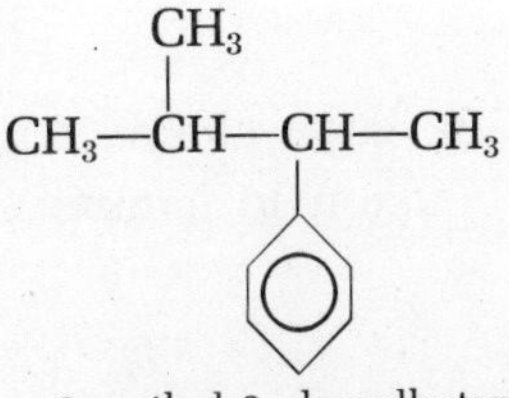   3-methyl-2-phenylbutane

DERIVATIVES OF HYDROCARBONS

24:10 Halogen Derivatives

Atoms other than carbon and hydrogen can be substituted for part of a hydrocarbon molecule. When this substitution happens, the chemical reactivity of the hydrocarbon is generally increased. The nonhydrocarbon part of the molecule is called a *functional group*. Most of the chemical reactivity of the substituted hydrocarbon is due to the functional group attached to it.

Substitutions in a hydrocarbon generally increase the reactivity.

A halogen derivative has a halogen atom substituted for a hydrogen atom.

Other well-known halogen-substituted hydrocarbons are ethyl chloride, often used as a local anesthetic, and iodoform, often used as an antiseptic

FIGURE 24-5. Some hydrocarbon derivatives are used as pesticides. These chemists are analyzing raw foods for trace amounts of pesticides.

One family of substituted hydrocarbon molecules has a halogen atom substituted for a hydrogen atom. For example, if we substitute a bromine atom for a hydrogen atom on methane, we obtain CH_3Br. The name of this compound is bromomethane. It is also possible to have more than one hydrogen atom replaced by a halogen atom. In the compound $CHCl_3$, three chlorine atoms have been substituted for three of the hydrogen atoms in a methane molecule. The name of this compound is trichloromethane. You may know this compound by its common name, chloroform. Chloroform has been widely used as a solvent. It was once used as an anesthetic. In the compound CCl_4 four chlorine atoms have been substituted for the four hydrogen atoms in a methane molecule. The name of this compound is tetrachloromethane. Its common name is carbon tetrachloride. These compounds are named as derivatives of the hydrocarbons.

$$
\begin{array}{ccc}
H & H & Cl \\
| & | & | \\
H-C-Br & Cl-C-Cl & Cl-C-Cl \\
| & | & | \\
H & Cl & Cl \\
\text{bromomethane} & \text{trichloromethane} & \text{tetrachloromethane}
\end{array}
$$

In large chains, we number the carbon atoms to avoid any confusion in naming the compounds. For example, the compound

$$
\begin{array}{cccc}
H & H & & \\
| & | & & \\
H-C-C-C=C-H & & & \\
| & | & | & | \\
H & Cl & H & Cl
\end{array}
$$

is 1,3-dichloro-1-butene.

In multisubstituted aromatic compounds, it is necessary to indicate the relative positions of the various substituent groups on the ring. If two or more substituents are attached to the benzene ring, it is necessary to assign position numbers to the carbon atoms of the ring. The atoms in the benzene ring are numbered so as to give the smallest position numbers to the substituents. For example:

Substituted hydrocarbons are named with lowest possible position numbers.

Br

Br

is 1,3-dibromobenzene, not 1,5-dibromobenzene. In the naphthalene molecule, the 1-position is next to the atom without a hydrogen atom attached. There are four 1-positions possible in each molecule of naphthalene. The 1-position which gives the lowest numbers to substituents is always used. The numbering system for naphthalene is as follows:

2-chloronaphthalene   1,3-dibromonaphthalene

Several more examples which illustrate the naming of substituted hydrocarbons are:

1-bromopropane   2-bromopropane   bromobenzene

1,3-dichlorobenzene   4-chloro-2-pentene   1-iodonaphthalene

Note that the double bond has precedence over the halogen.

24:11 Oxygen-Containing Compounds

Hundreds of thousands of organic compounds contain oxygen as well as hydrogen and carbon. Many of these compounds are familiar household items. Many more are important solvents and reactants in industry. Table 24–2 lists the names of the principal classes of oxygen-containing compounds. It also gives the general formula of the family. The symbol R— represents any hydrocarbon radical. Thus, R—OH is the general formula for alcohols. If R— represents CH_3—, the alcohol has the formula CH_3OH. This alcohol is methanol. The endings in the third column indicate the method of naming compounds of each class.

Many alcohols are important in industry as solvents and reagents.

Alcohol molecules contain a hydroxyl functional group. R-OH represents an alcohol molecule.

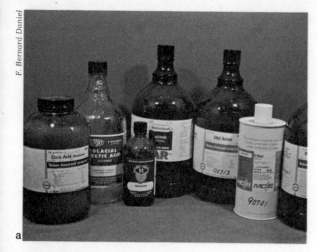

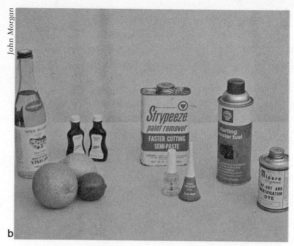

FIGURE 24-6. These compounds (from left to right) (a) represent common classes of organic compounds: acids, aldehydes, ketones, esters, ethers, and alcohols. In the home, they are contained in products such as (b) citrus fruit and vinegar, flavorings, paint remover, nail polish, engine starters, and special inks.

Table 24–2

Organic Compounds Containing Oxygen*

Class	General Formula	Ending	Example
Alcohol	R—O—H	-ol	CH_3OH methanol
Ether	R—O—R'	-oxy-	$CH_3OCH_2CH_3$ methoxyethane
Aldehyde	$R-\overset{\text{H}}{\underset{}{C}}=O$	-al	CH_3CH_2CHO propanal
Ketone	$R-\overset{O}{\overset{\|}{C}}-R'$	-one	$CH_3COCH_2CH_3$ butanone
Acid	$R-\overset{O}{\overset{\|}{C}}-O-H$	-oic acid	$CH_3CH_2CH_2CH_2COOH$ pentanoic acid
Ester	$R-\overset{O}{\overset{\|}{C}}-O-R'$	-yl -ate	$CH_3CH_2CH_2OOCCH_3$ propyl ethanoate

* R— and R'— each represent a hydrocarbon radical. The two radicals may be the same, or they may be different.

24:12   Some Nitrogen-Containing Compounds

Many organic compounds of biological importance contain nitrogen. Because nitrogen has more than one oxidation level, it can combine with organic radicals in a number of ways.

Amines (ah MEENS) are organic compounds in which a nitrogen atom is bound to alkyl groups and hydrogen atoms only. Amines are derivatives of ammonia. If only one hydrogen atom of ammonia is replaced by an alkyl group, the compound is a *primary amine*. If two hydrogen atoms are replaced, the compound is a *secondary amine*; and if all three are replaced, the compound is a *tertiary amine*. General formulas for amines are:

An amine contains nitrogen bonded to alkyl groups and/or hydrogen.

Amines are bases since the N atom possesses an unshared pair of electrons.

$$H—N—H \qquad H—N—R \qquad R—N—R' \qquad R—N—R'$$
$$\ \ \ \ |\qquad\qquad\ \ \ |\qquad\qquad\ \ \ |\qquad\qquad\ \ \ |$$
$$\ \ \ H\qquad\qquad\ \ \ H\qquad\qquad\ \ \ H\qquad\qquad\ \ R''$$

ammonia   primary amine   secondary amine   tertiary amine

Amines are usually named as derivatives of ammonia. For example, the compound

$$CH_3—CH_2—N—CH_2—CH_3$$
$$\qquad\qquad\ \ |$$
$$\qquad\qquad\ H$$

is called diethylamine. Amines may also be named as amino-substituted hydrocarbons. The compound

$$H_2N—CH_2—CH_2—CH_2—CH_2—NH_2$$

is named 1,4-diaminobutane.

FIGURE 24-7. Some laboratory organic compounds containing nitrogen are shown in (a). Important sources of nitrogen in the form of protein are shown in (b).

a

b

Other important classes of nitrogen-containing compounds are listed in Table 24–3. In this table, R— stands for a hydrocarbon radical. G— is used in place of R— with amino acids. Some amino acids have other elements in the G—. For example, G— for aspartic acid represents HOOC—CH$_2$—

Table 24–3

Organic Compounds Containing Nitrogen

Class	General Formula	Example
Amides	R—$\overset{\overset{\textstyle O}{\|\|}}{C}$—NH$_2$	CH$_3$CONH$_2$ ethanamide
Amino acids	G—$\overset{\overset{\textstyle NH_2}{\|}}{CH}$—COOH	CH$_3$CH(NH$_2$)COOH alanine (2-aminopropanoic acid)
Nitriles	R—C≡N	CH$_3$CH$_2$CH$_2$CN butanenitrile
Nitro compounds	R—NO$_2$	C$_6$H$_5$NO$_2$ nitrobenzene

ORGANIC REACTIONS

24:13 Oxidation

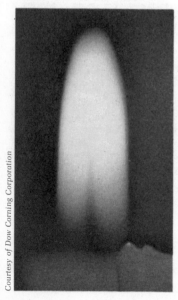

FIGURE 24-8. The products of complete oxidation of the hydrocarbons in this candle are carbon dioxide and water.

Courtesy of Dow Corning Corporation

Hydrocarbons undergo oxidation in the presence of excess oxygen to form CO$_2$ and water. However, at the high temperatures necessary for oxidation of hydrocarbons to occur, many different reactions take place at the same time. Hydrocarbon chains break into fragments. Carbon atoms change from one oxidation state to another. Oxygen atoms attach to the hydrocarbon fragments. Oxidation is complete when the only products are carbon dioxide and water.

Some hydrocarbons have very large heats of combustion. Thus, they are used commercially as fuels. Natural gas (methane) and bottled gas (butane, some propane and ethane) are used in the home for heating and cooking. Ethyne (acetylene) is used in cutting and welding torches.

The heats of combustion for a number of common organic fuels are given in Table 24–4. The values are in units of kilocalories per mole. To find out which of several fuels would be the most economical, the price must be considered. If we know the price per kilogram, we can convert the data as follows:

$$\frac{kilocalories}{mole} \left| \frac{1\ mole}{x\ grams} \right| \frac{1000\ grams}{1\ kilogram} \left| \frac{1\ kilogram}{y\ dollars} \right. = \frac{kilocalories}{per\ dollar}$$

If a gaseous fuel is being purchased and the sales unit is a unit of volume, then the temperature and pressure at which the volume is quoted must be known. Then the actual amount of matter may be computed from the ideal gas equation.

FIGURE 24-9. Bottled gas is the fuel used in this trailer (a) for heating and cooking. The fuel burned in this hot air balloon (b) is propane.

Table 24–4

Heats of Combustion of Common Organic Fuels

Fuel	Heat of Combustion (kcal/mole)	Fuel	Heat of Combustion (kcal/mole)
Benzene	782	Propane	526
Cyclohexane	938	Butane	688
Ethyne	312	Ethanol	328
Methane	211	Heptane	1150
Ethane	368	2,2,4-Trimethylpentane	1304

Products of complete combustion of a hydrocarbon are CO_2 and H_2O.

Organic chemists use the term substitution to describe the replacement of one functional group by another.

24:14 Substitution Reactions

A reaction in which a hydrogen atom of a hydrocarbon is replaced by a functional group is called a *substitution reaction*. Alkane molecules react with chlorine in the presence of sunlight to produce chloro-substituted compounds. The product is a mixture of different isomers with very similar properties. Thus, this is not a satisfactory

In substitution reactions, a hydrogen atom is replaced with a functional group.

way to prepare chlorine derivatives of alkanes. However, a number of aromatic compound substitution reactions can be controlled to produce specific products. For example, benzene reacts with nitric acid in the presence of concentrated sulfuric acid:

$$\bigcirc(l) + HNO_3(l) \xrightarrow[H_2SO_4]{conc.} \bigcirc(l) + H_2O(l)$$

The product is nitrobenzene. Alkyl groups and halogen atoms also can be easily substituted onto a benzene ring.

24:15   Addition Reactions

In addition reactions of alkenes, two species are added by breaking one bond of the double bond.

Each carbon atom contributes two electrons to a double bond. Suppose one bond is broken and the other remains intact. Each carbon atom then has available one electron to bond with some other atom. A number of substances will cause one bond of a double bond to break. An example is the addition of bromine to the double bond of ethene:

Addition reactions in more complex alkenes often lead to rearrangement of the molecule.

$$H_2C{=}CH_2(g) + Br_2(l) \rightarrow BrH_2C{-}CH_2Br(l)$$

Atoms of many substances can be added at the double bond of an alkene. Common addition agents are the halogens (except fluorine), the hydrogen halides, and sulfuric acid. The double bonds in the benzene ring of aromatic compounds are so stabilized that addition cannot be easily achieved.

Bruce Charlton

FIGURE 24-10. A bromine solution (left) can be used to test for unsaturated bonds. It does not react with an alkane (center). It loses its color in the presence of an unsaturated bond (right).

24:16 Elimination Reactions

We have seen that under certain circumstances, atoms can be "added on" to a double bond. It is also possible to remove certain atoms from a molecule to create a double bond. Such a reaction is known as an *elimination reaction*. In the most common elimination reactions, a water molecule is removed from an alcohol. A hydrogen atom is removed from one carbon atom, and a hydroxyl group is removed from the next carbon atom. For example, propene can be made from 1-propanol by the removal of water. Sulfuric acid is used as the dehydrating agent.

In elimination reactions, double bonds are created.

HCl and HNO_2 are other substances which are often eliminated.

$$H-\overset{\overset{\displaystyle H}{|}}{\underset{\underset{\displaystyle H}{|}}{C}}-\overset{\overset{\displaystyle H}{|}}{\underset{\underset{\displaystyle H}{|}}{C}}-\overset{\overset{\displaystyle H}{|}}{\underset{\underset{\displaystyle OH}{|}}{C}}-H(l) \xrightarrow{H_2SO_4} H-\overset{\overset{\displaystyle H}{|}}{\underset{\underset{\displaystyle H}{|}}{C}}-\overset{\overset{\displaystyle H}{|}}{C}=\overset{\overset{\displaystyle H}{|}}{C}-H(g) + H_2O(l)$$

24:17 Esterification and Saponification Reactions

When an alcohol reacts with either an organic acid or an organic acid anhydride, an *ester* is formed. This type of reaction is called *esterification*. For example, in the reaction between acetic acid and methanol,

The reaction of an alcohol and an organic acid produces an ester.

$$CH_3-\overset{\overset{\displaystyle O}{\|}}{C}-OH(l) + CH_3-OH(l) \rightarrow CH_3-\overset{\overset{\displaystyle O}{\|}}{C}-OCH_3(l) + H_2O(l)$$

methyl ethanoate and water are formed. Methyl ethanoate is an ester.

FIGURE 24-11. Ethyl ethanoate can be prepared by an esterification reaction (a) between ethyl alcohol and acetic acid. Soaps (b) are the products of saponification reactions.

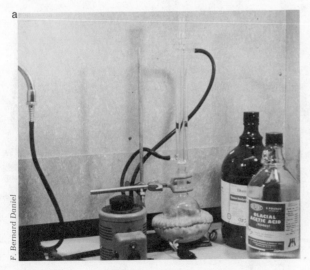

Esters are split into alcohols and salts of carboxylic acids in saponification reactions.

An ester can be split into an alcohol and a carboxylic acid by *hydrolysis* (hi DRAHL uh sihs). This would be the reverse of the reaction shown above. However, if a metallic base is used for the hydrolysis instead of water, the metallic salt of the carboxylic acid is obtained, not the acid. This process is called *saponification*. Saponification is the process used in making soaps. Since ancient times, soaps have been made from vegetable and animal oils and fats cooked in alkali bases (KOH, NaOH). Soap is a metallic salt of a fatty acid. The natural fat or oil is an ester. In this saponification reaction:

A soap is a metallic salt of a fatty acid.

$$CH_2-O-\overset{\overset{\displaystyle O}{\|}}{C}-(CH_2)_{16}-CH_3$$

$$CH-O-\overset{\overset{\displaystyle O}{\|}}{C}-(CH_2)_{16}-CH_3(amor) + 3NaOH(aq) \rightarrow$$
$$\text{base}$$

$$CH_2-O-\overset{\overset{\displaystyle O}{\|}}{C}-(CH_2)_{16}-CH_3$$

fat (a glyceride ester)

$$CH_2-CH-CH_2(l) + 3[CH_3-(CH_2)_{16}-COO^-Na^+](aq)$$
$$\;\;|\;\;\;\;\;\;|\;\;\;\;\;|$$
$$OH \;\; OH \;\; OH$$

glycerol   soap

Emil Hermann Fischer

(1852–1919)

Emil Hermann Fischer was known as the master of organic chemistry. He earned this title by his amazing amount of work on sugars. He studied not only the chemistry of sugars but also the structure of sugar molecules. He did the same kind of research with a group of nitrogen-containing compounds known as purines. For his work with sugars and purines, he was awarded the 1902 Nobel Prize.

His investigation of sugars and purines stimulated his interest in the chemistry of fermentation and in proteins and amino acids. His protein research laid the groundwork for future workers in enzyme chemistry. Curiosity also led him to the study of many other organic materials, including dyes and tannins. He was among the first of the great German organic chemists.

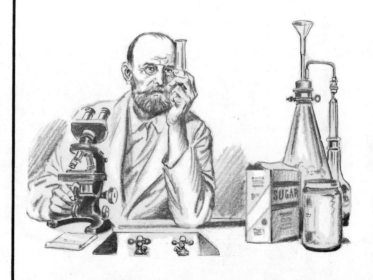

the natural fat is a *glyceride ester*. The products of the reaction are *soap* and glycerol (the alcohol of the glyceride).

A valuable by-product

Fats are esters of glycerol.

24:18   Petroleum

The chief source of organic compounds is the naturally occurring mixture called petroleum. Other important sources are coal tar, natural gas, and fermentation of natural materials. Petroleum is a mixture of hydrocarbons containing small amounts of nitrogen, oxygen, and sulfur compounds. The hydrocarbons are mainly alkanes and cycloalkanes. The initial treatment of petroleum in a refinery is a fractional distillation. This treatment separates the mixture into portions having different boiling ranges. The chief fractions are: petroleum ether (20°C–60°C), ligroin (60°C–100°C), gasoline (40–205°C), kerosene (175–325°C), gas oil (>275°C), and lubricating oil. The remainder is called asphalt.

Petroleum is the chief source of natural organic compounds.

The products from the distillation cannot be marketed as is. They must be refined to take out undesirable substances, particularly the sulfur compounds. Additives are blended with the gasoline and other products to improve their performance. Many of the by-products of the gasoline-producing stages are used as raw materials for the production of plastics and synthetic fibers and rubber.

Petroleum can be separated into portions with different boiling ranges by fractional distillation.

The yield of gasoline can be improved in a number of ways. Smaller molecules from the lower boiling fractions are joined together to form larger molecules. In another process, the larger

John Morgan

FIGURE 24-12. As Indicated on the sides of these tanks, additives have been blended with the gasoline to improve its performance.

molecules of the higher boiling fractions are broken, or "cracked," into smaller molecules.

24:19 Octane Ratings

Gasolines are rated on a scale known as *octane rating*. The basis for this scale is the property of some fuels to cause "knocking" in engines. The knocking occurs when some of the fuel explodes suddenly instead of burning evenly in a cylinder of an internal combustion engine. To rate a gasoline, a "standard" engine is required. Heptane is given an arbitrary octane rating of zero, and 2,2,4-trimethylpentane is given a rating of 100. The standard engine is run on the test fuel as well as on various mixtures of heptane and 2,2,4-trimethylpentane. When one of the mixtures of the two standards causes the same degree of knocking as the test fuel, the test is complete. The octane rating for the test fuel is the percentage of 2,2,4-trimethylpentane in the mixture with heptane.

24:20 Synthetic Rubber

The producers of synthetic substitutes for rubber have built a thriving industry based on organic chemistry. No one synthetic material can as yet replace natural rubber. However, there are many synthetics that can perform a particular job as well as or better than natural rubber. The production of synthetic rubber depends primarily upon a chemical reaction called *polymerization* (pah lihm eh ruh ZAY shuhn). In this reaction, a molecule (called a *monomer*) containing a double or triple bond adds to other similar molecules to form chains (or cross-linked chains) of very large molecular size and mass. As an example, consider two molecules of ethene:

Note: Much of the early research in synthetics was done in Germany in the period prior to and during the Second World War.

$$CH_2{=}CH_2(l) + CH_2{=}CH_2(l) \rightarrow -CH_2-CH_2-CH_2-CH_2-(amor)$$

This process can continue almost indefinitely. The bonds at the end of a chain cross-link to other chains. Gigantic molecules are formed. Such substances are called *polymers*. In this case, the polymer is named polyethene or polyethylene.

Natural rubber is a polymer of 2-methylbutadiene. The 2-methylbutadiene molecule is the monomer of natural rubber. Many types of synthetic rubber can be made from various monomers. Often they are made by polymerizing two or more substances containing double bonds.

24:21 Plastics

The production of plastics has created another important organic chemical industry. Plastics can be produced by polymerization. Some common plastics made by polymerization are polyethylene, polypropylene, polyvinyl acetate, polystyrene, and acrylics.

FIGURE 24-13. Nylon rope (a) is formed when a polymeric film formed at the interface between two immiscible liquids is lifted from the beaker. Nylon and other synthetics (b) are widely used in the home and industry.

Courtesy of Kodansha Ltd.

John Morgan

Plastics can also be made by a similar process in which both the polymer and another product, usually water, result. In this type of reaction, the molecules actually condense together. This type of reaction is called a *condensation* reaction. Other plastics such as cellophane and celluloid can be made by the chemical treatment of cellulose.

Structural diagrams for monomers and polymer units of some polymerization and condensation plastics are shown below.

Plastics may be made by condensation reactions.

An interesting exception is thiokol in which NaCl is the second product.

Polymerization plastics:

$$CH{=}CH_2(l) \rightarrow \cdots {-}CH{-}CH_2{-}CH{-}CH_2{-}CH{-}CH_2{-} \cdots$$

ethenylbenzene
or
styrene

polystyrene
(amor)

Condensation plastics:

phenol-formaldehyde (Bakelite)
(amor)

24:22 Synthetic Fibers

Most synthetic fibers are formed by condensation reactions.

Synthetic fibers are made by the same type of reactions as synthetic rubber and plastic. Most are made by condensation reactions. Nylon, for example, is a copolymer of hexanedioic acid (adipic acid) and 1,2-diaminohexane (hexamethylene diamine). In this

Synthetic fibers are giant molecules.

molecule the link between monomers is the amide link, $-\overset{\overset{\text{O}}{\|}}{\text{C}}-\overset{\overset{\text{H}}{|}}{\text{N}}-$, just as in the urea-formaldehyde plastics. Many other types of giant molecules are also produced for textile use.

A good source is the *Man-Made Fiber Fact Book* available from Man-Made Fiber Producers Association, 350 Fifth Avenue, New York, N.Y. 10001.

SUMMARY

1. Organic chemistry is the chemistry of carbon compounds.
2. Unsaturated hydrocarbons contain one or more double or triple bonds. Saturated hydrocarbons are hydrocarbons which contain only single bonds between carbon atoms.
3. Straight-chain (aliphatic) carbon compounds are formed of chains of carbon atoms covalently bound together. Cyclic carbon compounds are formed when the ends of a chain are joined together.

4. Hydrocarbons are carbon compounds which contain only carbon and hydrogen:
   (a) Alkanes are saturated hydrocarbons with chainlike molecules.
   (b) Cycloalkanes are saturated hydrocarbons with ringlike molecules.
   (c) Alkenes are chain hydrocarbons which contain a double bond between carbon atoms.
   (d) Alkynes are chain hydrocarbons which contain a triple bond between carbon atoms.
   (e) Aromatic hydrocarbons are hydrocarbons which contain a benzene ring.

5. A hydrocarbon radical is a hydrocarbon which has lost one hydrogen atom with its associated electron. It acts as a substituent to a carbon chain or ring.

6. A functional group is a nonhydrocarbon part of an organic molecule.

7. The principal classes of oxygen-containing compounds are: alcohols, ethers, aldehydes, ketones, acids, and esters.

8. The principal classes of nitrogen-containing compounds are: amines, amides, amino acids, and nitro compounds.

9. Heats of combustion can be used to calculate the cost efficiency of fuels.

10. Hydrocarbons undergo complete oxidation in the presence of excess oxygen. Carbon dioxide and water are formed.

11. In a substitution reaction, a functional group replaces a hydrogen atom of a hydrocarbon.

12. In an addition reaction, a substance "adds on" to a double bond.

13. In an elimination reaction, a substance is "split out" of a molecule, creating in its place a double bond.

14. The formation of an ester from an alcohol and an acid or acid anhydride is called esterification.

15. The splitting of an ester into the alcohol and the salt of the acid is called saponification.

16. Petroleum is the principal source of organic chemicals. It is composed mostly of hydrocarbons.

17. Gasolines are rated on their antiknock performance on the octane scale.

18. Polymerization is a reaction in which many carbon molecules containing a double or triple bond add to other similar carbon molecules to form a chain or cross-linked chains of very great molecular size and mass.

19. A condensation reaction is one in which water is eliminated between two molecules when they join. Many polymers are made by condensation methods.

PROBLEMS

5. Predict the product of the reaction between ethene and hydrogen iodide. CH_3—$CH_2I(l)$

6. Predict the structure of the copolymer of ethene and phenylethene.

6. —CH—CH$_2$—CH$_2$—CH$_2$—

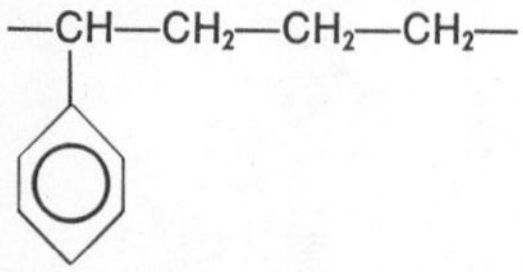

See Teacher's Guide at the front of this book.

7. Complete and balance equations for the following:
   a. chlorine + propene
   b. preparation of pentyl ethanoate
   c. complete combustion of benzene
   d. elimination of water from 1-butanol
   e. saponification of glyceryl trioctadecanoate with NaOH

8. Make a list of the names of the first thirty alkanes. Use reference books suggested by your instructor.

9. Diagram the nine isomers of heptane.

10. Find out how many isomers there are of nonane and decane.

nonane—35 isomers
decane—75 isomers

11. Name:

a. 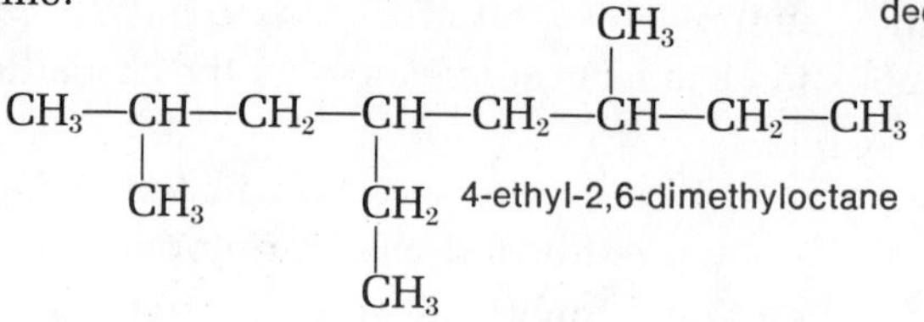
$$CH_3-\underset{\underset{CH_3}{|}}{CH}-CH_2-\underset{\underset{\underset{\underset{CH_3}{|}}{CH_2}}{|}}{CH}-CH_2-\underset{\underset{CH_3}{|}}{CH}-CH_2-CH_3$$
4-ethyl-2,6-dimethyloctane

b. 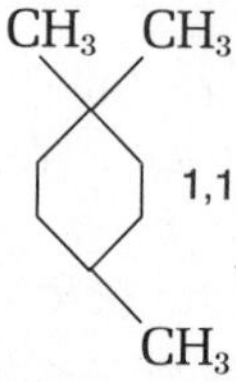
CH$_3$ CH$_3$

1,1,4-trimethylcyclohexane

CH$_3$

c. CH_3—CH=CH—CH=CH_2 1,3-pentadiene

d. 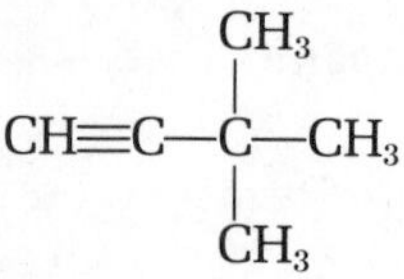
$$CH\equiv C-\underset{\underset{CH_3}{|}}{\overset{\overset{CH_3}{|}}{C}}-CH_3$$
3,3-dimethyl-1-butyne

e. 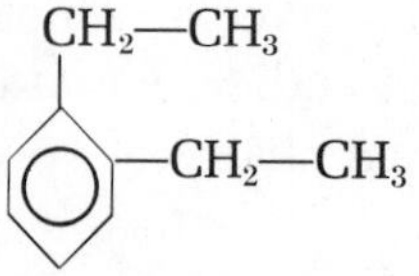
CH_2—CH_3

—CH_2—CH_3 1,2-diethylbenzene

12. Draw the structural formula (condensed form) for: See Teacher's Guide at
the front of this book.

   a. 3-ethylhexane

   b. 1,2,3,4,5,6-hexamethylcyclohexane

   c. 2-methylpropene

   d. 1-hexyne

   e. 2-methylnaphthalene

13. What is the molecular mass of the 40-carbon saturated hydrocarbon? 562

14. Name the following compounds:

   a. CH_3—CH_2—CH_2—OH 1-propanol

               OH
               |

   b. 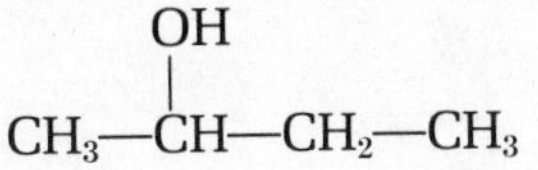 CH_3—CH—CH_2—CH_3 2-butanol

               OH
               |

   c. 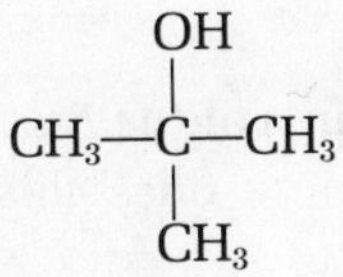 CH_3—C—CH_3 2-methyl-2-propanol
               |
              CH_3

   d. CH_3—CH_2—CH_2—CH_2—CH_2—O—CH_2—CH_2—CH_2—
                                       CH_2—CH_2—CH_3 1-pentoxyhexane

                          O
                          ‖

   e. 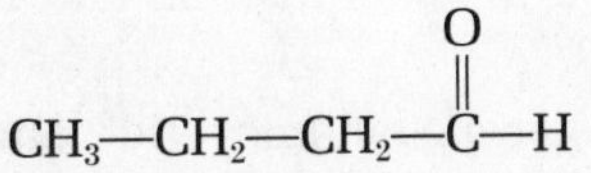 CH_3—CH_2—CH_2—C—H butanal

           O
           ‖

   f. 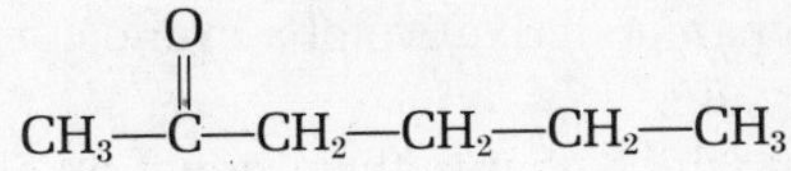 CH_3—C—CH_2—CH_2—CH_2—CH_3 2-hexanone

                      O
                     ‖

   g. 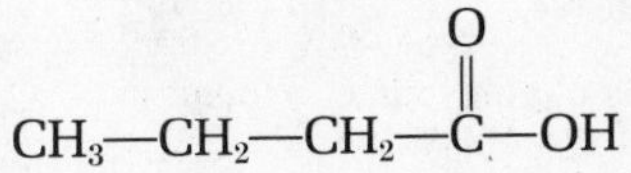 CH_3—CH_2—CH_2—C—OH butanoic acid

                                      O
                                      ‖

   h. 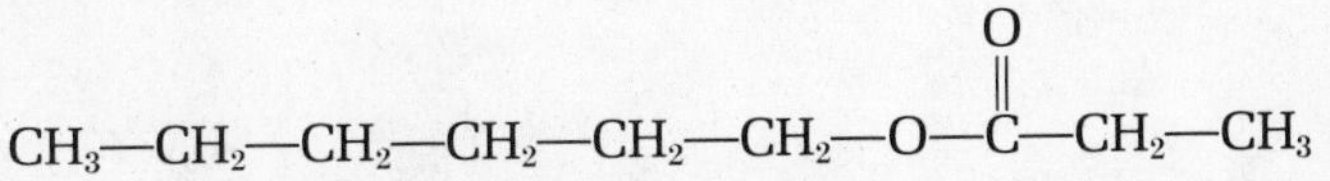 CH_3—CH_2—CH_2—CH_2—CH_2—CH_2—O—C—CH_2—CH_3 hexyl propanoate

   i. 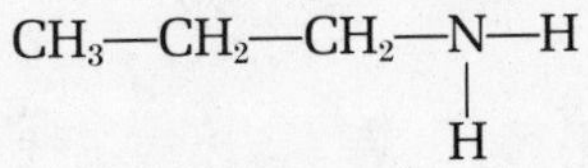 CH_3—CH_2—CH_2—N—H 1-propanamine
                     |
                     H

                    O H
                    ‖ |

   j. 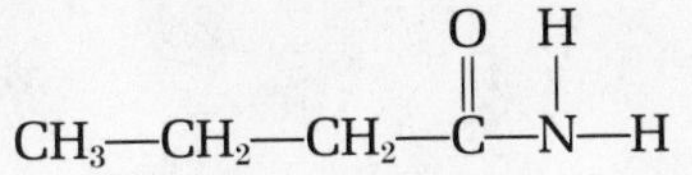 CH_3—CH_2—CH_2—C—N—H butanamide

See Teacher's Guide at the
front of this book.

15. Draw condensed structural formulas for the following compounds:
  a. 1-Butanol
  b. 2-Methyl-1-propanol
  c. 1-Propoxybutane
  d. Ethanal
  e. 3-Pentanone
  f. Propyl methanoate
  g. Trimethylamine
  h. Propanoic acid
  i. Propanamide
  j. Nitromethane

ONE MORE STEP

See Teacher's Guide at the
front of this book.

1. Make a graph of the melting and boiling points of the first twenty alkanes against their molecular masses. How does this graph illustrate homology?
2. By reference work in the library, prepare a short report to your class on the mechanism of a well known reaction in organic chemistry such as the Grignard or the Würtz reaction.
3. Prepare a report for your class on the composition and function of nucleic acids.
4. Find out what is meant by the term "heterocyclic" and try to prepare a heterocyclic compound from a noncyclic one. If this is not possible, try to prepare a derivative of a cyclic compound which is already heterocyclic.
5. Investigate the monomers which go into the production of Saran, Kodel, Acrilan, Dynel, and Mylar.

Suggested Readings for this chapter may be found in
the Teacher's Guide at the front of this book.

APPENDIX A
CHEMICAL TABLES
Table A-1. Some Properties of the Elements

Element	Symbol	Atomic Number (Z)	Atomic Mass* (M)	Melting Point (°C)	Boiling Point (°C)	Density (g/cm³)
Actinium	Ac	89	[227]	1050	3200	10.07
Aluminum	Al	13	26.98154	660	2467	2.6989
Americium	Am	95	[243]	944	2600	13.7
Antimony	Sb	51	121.75	603.5	1635	6.697
Argon	Ar	18	39.948	−189.2	−185.86	0.00178380
Arsenic	As	33	74.9216	814 (36 atm)	613 (sublimes)	5.72
Astatine	At	85	[210]	—	—	—
Barium	Ba	56	137.34	725	1637	3.6
Berkelium	Bk	97	[247]	986		14
Beryllium	Be	4	9.01218	1278	2970	1.85
Bismuth	Bi	83	208.9804	271.3	1560	9.8
Boron	B	5	10.81	2200	2550	2.34
Bromine	Br	35	79.904	−7.2	58.76	3.11
Cadmium	Cd	48	112.40	321	767	8.65
Calcium	Ca	20	40.08	843	1482	1.54
Californium	Cf	98	[251]	—	—	14
Carbon	C	6	12.011	3550	4827	2.26
Cerium	Ce	58	140.12	798	3257	6.773
Cesium	Cs	55	132.9054	28.59	690	1.90
Chlorine	Cl	17	35.453	−103	−34.6	0.003214
Chromium	Cr	24	51.996	1875	2199	7.19
Cobalt	Co	27	58.9332	1493	3100	8.90
Copper	Cu	29	63.546	1083	2582	8.94
Curium	Cm	96	[247]	1350	—	13.51
Dysprosium	Dy	66	162.50	1407	2335	8.559
Einsteinium	Es	99	[254]	—	—	—
Erbium	Er	68	167.26	1522	2510	9.045
Europium	Eu	63	151.96	826	1439	5.245
Fermium	Fm	100	[257]	—	—	—
Fluorine	F	9	18.99840	−233	−118	0.001696
Francium	Fr	87	[223]	—	—	—
Gadolinium	Gd	64	157.25	1312	3000	7.886
Gallium	Ga	31	69.72	29.8	2403	5.904
Germanium	Ge	32	72.59	937	2380	5.323

*[ ] indicates mass number of longest-lived isotope

Symbol	Atomic Radius (Å)	First Ionization Energy (eV)	Standard Reduction Potential (V) (for elements [from oxidation state indicated, or between oxidation states indicated])	Heat of Fusion (kcal/mole)	Specific Heat Capacity (cal/g-C°)	Heat of Vaporization (kcal/mole)	Abundance in Earth's Crust (%)
Ac	1.88	6.9	(3+)−2.6	2.5	—	70	trace
Al	1.26	5.98	(3+)−1.66	2.58	0.2154	70.13	8.23
Am	1.74	6.05	(3+)−2.36	2.9	—	51.7	—
Sb	1.36	8.642	(5+→3+)+0.75	4.75	0.0495	46.665	0.00002
Ar	1.88	15.76	—	0.284	0.124	1.550	0.000004
As	1.18	9.81	—	6.63	0.0785	885 (sublimes)	0.00018
At	1.4	9.5	(1−)+0.3	—	—	—	trace
Ba	2.24	5.21	(2+)−2.90	1.83	0.0362	41.74	0.0425
Bk	1.76	—	(4+→3+)+1.6	—	—	—	—
Be	1.06	9.32	(2+)−1.85	2.92	0.436	69.89	0.00028
Bi	1.82	7.287	—	2.70	0.0294	42.69	0.000017
B	0.88	8.30	—	5	0.307	90	0.001
Br	1.11	11.81	(1−)+1.0652	2.527	0.113	7.06	0.00025
Cd	1.48	8.99	(2+)−0.402	1.48	0.055	23.79	0.00002
Ca	1.96	6.11	(2+)−2.87	2.04	0.149	36.72	4.15
Cf	—	—	—	—	—	—	—
C	0.77	11.264	—	—	0.1697	170	0.02
Ce	1.82	5.65	(3+)−2.48 (4+→3+)+1.74	1.305	0.0460	99	0.006
Cs	2.65	3.894	(1+)−3.02	0.52	0.052	19.4	0.0003
Cl	0.99	12.96	(1−)+1.3595	1.531	0.114	4.878	0.0130
Cr	1.28	6.76	(2+)−0.91 (3+→2+)−0.41	4.047	0.11	82.3	0.01
Co	1.25	7.86	(2+)−0.28 (3+→2+)+1.84	3.87	0.1056	90.0	0.0025
Cu	1.35	7.72	(1+)+0.52 (2+)+0.34	3.14	0.0924	71.77	0.0055
Cm	1.75	—	—	—	—	—	—
Dy	1.78	5.93	(3+)−2.35	2.64	0.0414	55.0	0.0003
Es	—	—	—	—	—	—	—
Er	1.76	6.10	(3+)−2.30	4.76	0.0402	62.47	0.00028
Eu	1.98	5.68	(3+)−0.43 (3+→2+)−2.41	2.20	0.042	34.30	0.00012
Fm	—	—	—	—	—	—	—
F	0.64	17.42	(1−)+2.87	0.122	0.197	1.562	0.0625
Fr	2.7	4.1	—	—	—	—	—
Gd	1.80	6.16	(3+)−2.40	2.40	0.056	85.9	0.00054
Ga	1.26	6.00	(3+)−0.53	1.335	0.0977	61.46	0.0015
Ge	1.22	7.809	—	8.83	0.074	79.1	0.00015

Element	Symbol	Atomic Number (Z)	Atomic Mass* (M)	Melting Point (°C)	Boiling Point (°C)	Density (g/cm³)
Gold	Au	79	196.9665	1063	2808	19.28
Hafnium	Hf	72	178.49	2230	5200	13.29
Helium	He	2	4.00260	−272.2 (25 atm)	−268.97	0.0001785
Holmium	Ho	67	164.9304	1470	2720	8.78
Hydrogen	H	1	1.0079	−259.1	−252.7	0.0000899
Indium	In	49	114.82	157	2075	7.31
Iodine	I	53	126.9045	113.5	184.35	4.93
Iridium	Ir	77	192.22	2443	4662	22.65
Iron	Fe	26	55.847	1536.5	3000	7.8733
Krypton	Kr	36	83.80	−157.2	−152.89	0.003745
Lanthanum	La	57	138.9055	920	3454	6.166
Lawrencium	Lr	103	[256]	—	—	—
Lead	Pb	82	207.2	327.5	1744	11.34
Lithium	Li	3	6.941	180.5	1326	0.534
Lutetium	Lu	71	174.97	1675	3315	9.842
Magnesium	Mg	12	24.305	651	1110	1.74
Manganese	Mn	25	54.9380	1244	2097	7.44
Mendelevium	Md	101	[258]	—	—	—
Mercury	Hg	80	200.59	−38.87	357	13.546
Molybdenum	Mo	42	95.94	2610	5560	10.22
Neodymium	Nd	60	144.24	1016	3127	7.004
Neon	Ne	10	20.179	−248.67	−246.02	0.00090002
Neptunium	Np	93	237	639	3902	20.25
Nickel	Ni	28	58.70	1453	2730	8.908
Niobium	Nb	41	92.9064	2468	4927	8.57
Nitrogen	N	7	14.0067	−210.01	−195.79	0.0012506
Nobelium	No	102	[255]	—	—	—
Osmium	Os	76	190.2	3050	4227	22.61
Oxygen	O	8	15.9994	−218.79	−182.97	0.001429
Palladium	Pd	46	106.4	1552	2747	12.02
Phosphorus	P	15	30.97376	44.1	280.5	1.83
Platinum	Pt	78	195.09	1769.3	3827	21.45
Plutonium	Pu	94	[244]	640	3327	19.86
Polonium	Po	84	[209]	254	962	9.4
Potassium	K	19	39.098	63.7	756	0.856
Praseodymium	Pr	59	140.9077	935	3017	6.475
Promethium	Pm	61	[145]	1080	3212	6.772

*[ ] indicates mass number of longest-lived isotope

Symbol	Atomic Radius (Å)	First Ionization Energy (eV)	Standard Reduction Potential (V) (for elements from oxidation state indicated, or between oxidation states indicated)	Heat of Fusion (kcal/mole)	Specific Heat Capacity (cal/g-C°)	Heat of Vaporization (kcal/mole)	Abundance in Earth's Crust (%)
Au	1.43	9.22	(1+)+1.691 (3+)+1.498	2.955	0.03077	80.88	0.0000004
Hf	1.44	7.0	(4+)−1.70	5.75	0.0350	137	0.0003
He	0.93	24.58	—	0.002	1.241	0.020	0.0000003
Ho	1.77	6.02	(3+)−2.32	2.91	0.0414	57.6	0.00012
H	0.53	13.599	(1+) 0.000	0.028	3.44	0.219	0.14
In	1.44	5.79	(1+)−0.147 (3+)−0.338	0.78	0.058	55.4	0.00001
I	1.28	10.45	(1−)+0.5355	3.71	0.0518	9.99	0.00005
Ir	1.35	9.2	—	6.3	0.0307	146.3	0.0000001
Fe	1.26	7.90	(2+)−0.44 (3+→2+)+0.77	3.30	0.107	83.55	5.63
Kr	2.00	14.00	—	0.392	0.059	2.162	—
La	1.87	5.61	(3+)−2.52	1.481	0.0451	98.9	0.0030
Lr	—	—	—	—	—	—	0.00125
Pb	1.74	7.415	(2+)−0.126	1.147	0.032	42.5	0.00125
Li	1.52	5.392	(1+)−3.02	0.717	0.784	35.4	0.002
Lu	1.74	6.15	(3+)−2.25	4.46	0.0364	85.06	0.00005
Mg	1.40	7.64	(2+)−2.37	2.140	0.245	30.45	2.33
Mn	1.25	7.43	(2+)−1.18 (3+→2+)+1.54	2.88	0.114	54.0	0.095
Md	—	—	—	—	—	—	—
Hg	1.48	10.43	(2+)+0.854	0.548	0.033	14.172	0.000008
Mo	1.40	7.10	(3+)−0.20	6.65	0.0597	141.6	0.00015
Nd	1.82	5.49	(3+)−2.44	1.71	0.0451	65.2	0.0028
Ne	1.58	21.56	—	0.08	0.246	0.429	—
Np	1.56	5.8	(3+)−1.83	2.3	0.030	94.3	—
Ni	1.24	7.63	(2+)−0.24	4.176	0.1225	88.5	0.0075
Nb	1.47	6.883	(3+)−1.099	6.30	0.06430	163	0.0020
N	0.70	14.53	—	0.172	0.249	1.335	0.0020
No	—	—	—	—	—	—	—
Os	1.35	8.7	—	7.6	0.0309	162.0	0.0000001
O	0.66	13.618	—	0.106	0.439	1.630	46.4
Pd	1.37	8.33	(2+)+0.987	4.2	0.0584	85.4	0.000001
P	1.10	10.487	—	0.628	0.189	12.48	0.105
Pt	1.38	9.0	(2+)+1.2	4.7	0.03136	121.8	0.0000005
Pu	1.60	5.8	(3+)−2.031 (4+→3+)+0.97	0.68	0.033	82.1	—
Po	1.4	8.43	(2+)+0.65	3.0	0.0301	24.597	trace
K	2.27	4.341	(1+)−2.92	0.562	0.176	19.18	2.09
Pr	1.83	5.42	(3+)−2.47	1.65	0.0458	70.9	0.00082
Pm	—	5.55	(3+)−2.42	2.5	0.0442	—	—

Element	Symbol	Atomic Number (Z)	Atomic Mass* (M)	Melting Point (°C)	Boiling Point (°C)	Density (g/cm³)
Protactinium	Pa	91	231	1560	—	15.37
Radium	Ra	88	226	700	1140	5
Radon	Rn	86	[222]	−71	−64.99	0.00973
Rhenium	Re	75	186.207	3170	5630	21.04
Rhodium	Rh	45	102.9055	1960	3727	12.41
Rubidium	Rb	37	85.4678	38.98	688	1.532
Ruthenium	Ru	44	101.07	2310	4119	12.45
Samarium	Sm	62	150.4	1072	1900	7.536
Scandium	Sc	21	44.9559	1539	2727	2.99
Selenium	Se	34	78.96	217	684.8	4.79
Silicon	Si	14	28.086	1410	2355	2.33
Silver	Ag	47	107.868	960.8	2210	10.5
Sodium	Na	11	22.98977	97.8	883	0.9674
Strontium	Sr	38	87.62	769	1380	2.6
Sulfur	S	16	32.06	119	444.6	2.07
Tantalum	Ta	73	180.9479	2996	5427	16.654
Technetium	Tc	43	97	2170	5030	11.49
Tellurium	Te	52	127.60	450	990	6.24
Terbium	Tb	65	158.9254	1360	3041	8.234
Thallium	Tl	81	204.37	303	1457	11.85
Thorium	Th	90	232.0381	1750	4000	11.7
Thulium	Tm	69	168.9342	1545	1727	9.314
Tin	Sn	50	118.69	231.9	2260	7.28
Titanium	Ti	22	47.90	1668	3260	4.507
Tungsten	W	74	183.85	3410	5930	19.3
Uranium	U	92	238.029	1132	3818	18.97
Vanadium	V	23	50.9414	1890	3000	6.11
Xenon	Xe	54	131.30	−111.9	−107.09	0.005897
Ytterbium	Yb	70	173.04	816	1193	6.972
Yttrium	Y	39	88.9059	1509	3200	4.472
Zinc	Zn	30	65.38	419	907	7.133
Zirconium	Zr	40	91.22	1850	4377	6.506
Element 104	(Rf)	104	[257]	—	—	—
Element 105	(Ha)	105	[260]	—	—	—

*[ ] indicates mass number of longest-lived isotope

Symbol	Atomic Radius (Å)	First Ionization Energy (eV)	Standard Reduction Potential (V) (for elements from oxidation state indicated, or between oxidation states indicated)	Heat of Fusion (kcal/mole)	Specific Heat Capacity (cal/g-C°)	Heat of Vaporization (kcal/mole)	Abundance in Earth's Crust (%)
Pa	1.64	—	—	4.0	0.029	115	trace
Ra	2.20	5.28	$(2+)-2.92$	2.3	0.0288	35	trace
Rn	2.2	10.745	—	0.69	0.0244	4.0	trace
Re	1.37	7.87	$(3+)+0.3$	7.9	0.03262	171	0.0000001
Rh	1.35	7.464	$(3+)+0.80$	5.15	0.0589	118	0.0000001
Rb	2.48	4.177	$(1+)-2.99$	0.54	0.080	18.1	0.009
Ru	1.33	7.366	$(2+)+0.45$	6.2	0.0551	141	0.0000001
Sm	1.80	5.63	$(3+)-2.41$	2.06	0.0449	39.8	0.0006
Sc	1.64	6.54	$(3+)-1.88$	3.37	0.134	75.1	0.0022
Se	1.14	9.75	$(2-)-0.92$	1.25	0.0767	3.34	0.000005
Si	1.17	8.152	—	21.1	0.1597	71	28.15
Ag	1.52	7.576	$(1+)+0.7991$ $(2+\rightarrow1+)+1.980$	2.70	0.056	59.90	0.000007
Na	1.86	5.139	$(1+)-2.71$	0.622	0.292	23.43	2.36
Sr	2.14	5.696	$(2+)-2.89$	2.19	0.176	33.2	0.0375
S	1.04	10.360	$(2-)-0.447$	0.411	0.16973	2.2	0.0260
Ta	1.47	7.88	—	7.5	0.0340	182.1	0.0002
Tc	1.3	7.28	$(2+)+0.4$	5.42	0.0586	152	—
Te	1.32	9.01	$(2-)-1.143$	4.18	0.0481	13.65	0.0000002
Tb	1.78	5.98	$(3+)-2.39$	2.58	0.0437	79.1	0.00009
Tl	1.71	6.108	$(1+)-0.3363$ $(3+)+0.72$	0.98	0.0307	39.4	0.000045
Th	1.80	7.0	$(4+)-1.90$	3.85	0.0271	123.0	0.00096
Tm	1.75	6.18	$(3+)-2.28$	4.02	0.0382	45.6	0.000048
Sn	1.40	7.344	$(2+)-0.136$ $(4+\rightarrow2+)+0.15$	1.67	0.0530	70.8	0.0002
Ti	1.46	6.82	$(2+)-1.628$ $(3+\rightarrow2+)-0.369$	3.7	0.13	100.6	0.57
W	1.41	7.98	—	8.46	0.0321	197.0	0.00015
U	1.57	6.08	$(3+)-1.80$ $(4+\rightarrow3+)-0.607$	2.036	0.02778	110.9	0.00027
V	1.35	6.74	$(2+)-1.186$ $(3+\rightarrow2+)-0.256$	5.00	0.120	108.0	0.0135
Xe	2.17	12.130	—	0.548	0.0378	3.021	—
Yb	1.94	6.25	$(3+)-2.27$	1.83	0.0355	30.8	0.0003
Y	1.81	6.379	$(3+)-2.37$	2.724	0.0731	86.8	0.0033
Zn	1.31	9.394	$(2+)-0.762$	1.765	0.0928	27.62	0.007
Zr	1.45	6.837	$(4+)-1.529$	4.0	0.0664	139	0.0165
(Rf)	—	—	—	—	—	—	—
(Ha)	—	—	—	—	—	—	—

Table A-2. Major Formal Oxidation States of the Elements

(See also Table 4-3 in Chapter 4.)

1+
Copper(I)
Francium
Gold(I)
Indium(I)
Iridium(I)
Mercury(I)
Rhodium(I)

2+
Americium(II)
Beryllium
Californium(II)
Chromium(II)
Einsteinium(II)
Europium(II)
Fermium(II)
Germanium(II)
Mendelevium(II)
Molybdenum(II)
Niobium(II)
Nobelium(II)
Palladium(II)
Platinum(II)
Radium
Silicon(II)
Tin(II)
Titanium(II)
Vanadium(II)
Ytterbium(II)

3+
Actinium
Americium(III)
Antimony(III)
Arsenic(III)
Berkelium(III)
Boron
Californium(III)
Chromium(III)
Cobalt(III)
Curium(III)
Dysprosium
Einsteinium(III)
Erbium
Europium(III)
Fermium(III)
Gadolinium
Gallium
Gold
Holmium
Indium(III)
Iridium(III)
Lanthanum
Lutetium
Manganese(III)
Mendelevium(III)
Molybdenum(III)

Neodymium
Neptunium(III)
Nobelium(III)
Osmium(III)
Platinum(III)
Plutonium(III)
Praseodymium
Promethium
Protactinium
Rhodium(III)
Ruthenium(III)
Samarium
Scandium
Terbium
Thallium(III)
Thorium(III)
Thulium
Titanium(III)
Uranium(III)
Vanadium(III)
Ytterbium(III)
Yttrium

4+
Americium(IV)
Berkelium(IV)
Cerium(IV)
Chromium(IV)
Curium(IV)
Germanium(IV)
Hafnium(IV)
Iridium(IV)
Lead(IV)
Manganese(IV)
Molybdenum(IV)
Neptunium(IV)
Niobium(IV)
Osmium(IV)
Palladium(IV)
Platinum(IV)
Plutonium(IV)
Protactinium(IV)
Rhenium(IV)
Rhodium(IV)
Ruthenium(IV)
Selenium(IV)
Sulfur(IV)
Tantalum(IV)
Technetium(IV)
Tellurium(IV)
Terbium(IV)
Thorium(IV)
Tin(IV)
Titanium(IV)
Tungsten(IV)
Uranium(IV)
Vanadium(IV)
Zirconium(IV)

5+
Americium(V)
Antimony(V)
Arsenic(V)
Bismuth(V)
Chromium(V)
Manganese(V)
Molybdenum(V)
Neptunium(V)
Niobium(V)
Plutonium(V)
Protactinium(V)
Rhenium(V)
Tantalum(V)
Technetium(V)
Uranium(V)
Vanadium(V)

6+
Americium(VI)
Chromium(VI)
Iridium(VI)
Manganese(VI)
Molybdenum(VI)
Neptunium(VI)
Osmium(VI)
Platinum(VI)
Plutonium(VI)
Rhodium(VI)
Ruthenium(VI)
Selenium(VI)
Sulfur(VI)
Tellurium(VI)
Tungsten(VI)
Uranium(VI)

7+
Manganese(VII)
Neptunium(VII)
Plutonium(VII)
Rhenium(VII)
Technetium(VII)

8+
Osmium(VIII)
Plutonium(VIII)
Ruthenium(VIII)

1−
Astatide

2−
Telluride

3−
Antimonide
Arsenide

4−
Silicide

Table A-3. Ionization Constants

Substance	Ionization Constant	Substance	Ionization Constant
CH_3COOH	1.76×10^{-5}	HSO_4^-	1.20×10^{-2}
$CH_2ClCOOH$	1.40×10^{-3}	H_2CrO_4	1.8×10^{-1}
$CHCl_2COOH$	3.32×10^{-2}	$HCrO_4^-$	3.20×10^{-7}
CCl_3COOH	2×10^{-1}	$HSeO_4^-$	1.2×10^{-2}
$HOOCCOOH$	5.90×10^{-2}	H_2SeO_3	3.5×10^{-3}
$HOOCCOO^-$	6.40×10^{-5}	$HSeO_3^-$	5×10^{-8}
CH_3CH_2COOH	1.34×10^{-5}	$HBrO$	2.06×10^{-9}
C_6H_5COOH	6.46×10^{-5}	H_2TeO_3	3×10^{-3}
NH_3	1.77×10^{-5}	$HTeO_3^-$	2×10^{-8}
HF	3.53×10^{-4}	HIO	2.3×10^{-11}
HCN	4.93×10^{-10}	HIO_3	1.69×10^{-1}
H_2CO_3	4.30×10^{-7}	HIO_4	2.3×10^{-2}
HCO_3^-	5.61×10^{-11}	H_2NOH	1.1×10^{-8}
HNO_2	4.6×10^{-4}	H_2S	1×10^{-7}
H_3PO_4	7.52×10^{-3}	HS^-	1.2×10^{-13}
$H_2PO_4^-$	6.23×10^{-8}		

Table A-4. Solubility Products (at 25°C)

Substance	Solubility Product	Substance	Solubility Product
$AgBr$	7.7×10^{-13}	$BaSO_4$	1.08×10^{-10}
$AgBrO_3$	5.77×10^{-5}	$CaCO_3$	8.7×10^{-9}
Ag_2CO_3	6.15×10^{-12}	$Cu(IO_3)_2$	1.4×10^{-7}
$AgCl$	1.56×10^{-10}	CuC_2O_4	2.87×10^{-8}
Ag_2CrO_4	9×10^{-12}	FeC_2O_4	2.1×10^{-7}
$Ag_2Cr_2O_7$	2×10^{-7}	FeS	3.7×10^{-19}
AgI	1.5×10^{-16}	Li_2CO_3	1.7×10^{-3}
$AgSCN$	1.16×10^{-12}	$PbCl_2$	1.7×10^{-5}
$Al(OH)_3$	3.7×10^{-15}	PbI_2	1.39×10^{-8}
$BaCO_3$	8.1×10^{-9}	$SrCO_3$	1.6×10^{-9}

Table A-5. Specific Heat Capacities (cal/g-C° at 25°C)
(See also Table A-1 in APPENDIX A.)

Substance	Specific Heat	Substance	Specific Heat
Acetic acid	0.4911	Magnesium hydroxide	0.312
Aluminum fluoride	0.230	Magnesium sulfate	0.222
Benzene	0.4164	Phosphorus trichloride	0.209
Beryllium oxide	0.250	Potassium carbonate	0.216
Calcium sulfate	0.1712	Silicon carbide	0.164
Carbon tetrachloride	0.2046	Silicon dioxide	0.1789
Hexachloroethane	0.174	Sodium carbonate	0.273
Hydrogen iodide	0.0561	Toluene	0.431
Lithium nitrate	0.289	Zinc sulfide	0.112

Table A-6. Molal Freezing and Boiling Point Constants

Substance	Freezing Point (°C)	Molal Freezing Point Constant	Boiling Point (°C)	Molal Boiling Point Constant
Acetic Acid	16.604	−3.90 C°/mole solute/ 1000 g solvent	117.9	3.07 C°/mole solute/ 1000 g solvent
Benzene	5.48	−4.90	80.1	2.53
Nitrobenzene	5.70	−7.00	210.8	5.24
Phenol	43.0	−7.40	181.75	3.56
Water	0.00	−1.86	100	0.512

Table A-7. Solubility Rules

You will be working with water solutions, and it is helpful to have a few rules concerning what substances are soluble in water. The more common rules are listed below.

   I. All common salts of the Period IA elements and ammonium ion are soluble.

  II. All common acetates and nitrates are soluble.

 III. All binary compounds of Period VIIA elements (other than F) with metals are soluble except those of silver, mercury(I), and lead.

 IV. All sulfates are soluble except those of barium, strontium, lead, calcium, silver, and mercury(I).

  V. Except for those in Rule I, carbonates, hydroxides, oxides, and phosphates are insoluble.

Table A-8. Thermodynamic Properties

ΔH_f° = enthalpy of formation in standard states (cal/mole)
ΔG_f° = free energy of formation in standard states (cal/mole)
S° = entropy in standard states (cal/mole-K°)

	ΔH_f°	ΔG_f°	S°
O_2	0	0	49.003
H_2	0	0	31.208
$H_2O(l)$	$-68,315$	$-56,687$	16.71
$H_2O(g)$	$-57,796$	$-54,634$	45.104
H_2O_2		$-28,780$	26.2
Cl_2	0	0	53.288
Br_2	0	0	36.384
HBr	-8700	$-12,770$	47.463
I_2	0	0	27.757
HI	6330	410	49.351
S	0	0	7.60
SO_2	$-70,944$	$-71,748$	59.30
H_2SO_3	$-145,510$	$-128,560$	55.5
H_2SO_4	$-217,320$	$-177,970$	4.8
N_2	0	0	45.77
NO	21,570	—	50.347
NO_2	7930	12,260	57.35
NH_3	$-11,020$	-3940	45.97
NH_4Br	$-64,730$	$-41,900$	27
H_3PO_2	$-144,500$	—	—
H_3PO_3	$-230,500$	—	—
H_3PO_4	$-305,700$	$-267,500$	26.41
Bi	0	0	13.56
Bi_2S_3	$-34,200$	$-33,600$	47.9
CO	$-26,416$	$-32,780$	47.219
CO_2	$-94,051$	$-94,258$	51.06
CH_4	$-17,880$	$-12,130$	44.492
C_2H_6	$-20,240$	-7860	54.85
C_4H_{10}	$-29,812$	-3754	74.10
CS_2	21,440	15,600	36.17
$PbCl_2$	$-85,900$	$-75,080$	32.5
$PbBr_2$	$-66,600$	$-62,600$	38.6

Table A-8. Thermodynamic Properties (Cont.)

	ΔH_f°	ΔG_f°	S°
Hg_2Cl_2	$-63,390$	$-50,377$	46.0
Hg_2SO_4	$-177,610$	$-149,589$	47.96
$HgCl_2$	$-55,000$	$-42,200$	—
CuI	$-16,200$	$-16,620$	23.1
CuS	$-11,600$	$-11,700$	15.9
Cu_2S	$-19,000$	$-20,600$	28.9
$CuSO_4$	$-184,000$	$-158,200$	27.1
CoO	$-57,200$	$-51,000$	10.5
$CoCO_3$	$-172,700$	$-155,360$	—
$FeCl_3$	$-96,800$	—	—
FeO	$-63,700$	$-58,400$	21.9
Fe_2O_3	$-196,500$	$-177,100$	21.5
MnO_2	$-124,500$	$-111,400$	12.7
Cr_2O_3	$-269,700$	$-250,200$	19.4
Ti	0	0	7.24
TiO_2	—	$-203,800$	12.01
Be	0	0	2.28
Be_3N_2	$-135,700$	$-122,400$	—
Ca	0	0	9.95
$Ca(OH)_2$	$-235,800$	$-214,330$	—
LiBr	$-83,730$	—	—
Na	0	0	12.24
NaOH	$-101,720$	—	—
NaCl	$-98,230$	$-91,790$	17.30
NaBr	$-86,030$	—	—
Na_2SO_4	$-330,900$	$-302,780$	35.73
$Na_2Cr_2O_7$	$-136,000$	$-129,300$	14.0
K	0	0	15.34
KBr	$-93,730$	$-90,630$	23.05
KOH	$-101,520$	—	—
$KMnO_4$	$-194,400$	$-170,600$	41.04
F_2	0	0	48.44
HF	$-64,800$	$-65,300$	41.508
HCl	$-22,062$	$-22,774$	44.646
SO_3	$-108,630$	$-88,190$	12.5
H_2S	-4930	-8020	49.16
Ag	0	0	10.20
AgCl	$-30,370$	$-26,244$	23.0

Table A-9. Standard Reduction Potentials (25 °C, 1 atm, 1 M solutions with unit activity)

(See also Table A-1 in APPENDIX A.)

Half-Reaction	Volts
$H_2AlO_3^- + H_2O + 3e^- \rightleftharpoons Al + 4OH^-$	-2.35
$H_2 + 2e^- \rightarrow 2H^-$	-2.23
$UO_2^{2+} + 4H^+ + 6e^- \rightarrow U + 2H_2O$	-0.82
$Cr^{3+} + 3e^- \rightleftharpoons Cr$	-0.74
$H_3PO_3 + 2H^+ + 2e^- \rightarrow H_3PO_2 + H_2O$	-0.50
$2CO_2 + 2H^+ + 2e^- \rightarrow H_2C_2O_4$	-0.49
$2H^+ (10^{-7} M) + 2e^- \rightarrow H_2$	-0.414
$In^{3+} + 2e^- \rightarrow In^+$	-0.40
$PbSO_4 + 2e^- \rightarrow Pb + SO_4^{2-}$	-0.356
$H_3PO_4 + 2H^+ + 2e^- \rightarrow H_3PO_3 + H_2O$	-0.276
$Fe^{3+} + 3e^- \rightarrow Fe$	-0.036
$AgCN + e^- \rightarrow Ag + CN^-$	-0.02
$2H^+ + 2e^- \rightarrow H_2$	0.0000
$UO_2^{2+} + e^- \rightarrow UO_2^+$	0.062
$Cu^{2+} + e^- \rightarrow Cu^+$	0.158
$SO_4^{2-} + 4H^+ + 2e^- \rightarrow H_2SO_3 + H_2O$	0.20
$UO_2^{2+} + 4H^+ + 2^- \rightarrow U^{4+} + 2H_2O$	0.334
$VO^{2+} + 2H^+ + e^- \rightarrow V^{3+} + H_2O$	0.337
$H_2SO_3 + 4H^+ + 4e^- \rightarrow S + 3H_2O$	0.45
$I_3^- + 2e^- \rightarrow 3I^-$	0.5338
$UO_2^+ + 4H^+ + e^- \rightarrow U^{4+} + 2H_2O$	0.62
$Hg_2^{2+} + 2e^- \rightarrow 2Hg$	0.7961
$2NO_3^- + 4H^+ + 2e^- \rightarrow N_2O_4 + 2H_2O$	0.81
$O_2 + 4H^+ (10^{-7} M) + 4e^- \rightarrow 2H_2O$	0.815
$2Hg^{2+} + 2e^- \rightarrow Hg_2^{2+}$	0.905
$NO_3^- + 3H^+ + 2e^- \rightarrow HNO_2 + H_2O$	0.94
$NO_3^- \quad 4H^+ + 3e^- \rightarrow NO + 2H_2O$	0.96
$VO_2^+ + 2H^+ + e^- \rightarrow VO^{2+} + H_2O$	1.00
$O_2 + 4H^+ + 4e^- \rightarrow 2H_2O$	1.229
$Tl^{3+} + 2e^- \rightarrow Tl^+$	1.247
$Au^{3+} + 2e^- \rightarrow Au^+$	1.29
$Cr_2O_7^{2-} + 14H^+ + 6e^- \rightarrow 2Cr^{3+} + 7H_2O$	1.33
$Rh^{4+} + e^- \rightarrow Rh^{3+}$	1.43
$MnO_4^- + 8H^+ + 5e^- \rightarrow Mn^{2+} + 4H_2O$	1.491
$PbO_2 + SO_4^{2-} + 4H^+ + 2e^- \rightarrow PbSO_4 + 2H_2O$	1.685

APPENDIX B

DEFINITIONS OF STANDARDS

1 meter is equal to 1,650,763.73 times the wavelength of the orange-red light of ^{86}Kr at 1 atmosphere and 15°C. The transition is $2p_{10}5d_5$.

1 liter is equal to 1000.027 cm^3

1 second is equal to 9,192,631,770 periods of the natural electromagnetic oscillation during that transition of cesium-133 which is designated (F=4, m_F=0)$\leftrightarrow$(F=3, m_F=0).

speed of light = 2.9979250×10^{10} cm/sec

Avogadro's number = 6.022169×10^{23}/mole

Faraday's Constant = 96,486.70 coulombs/faraday

Planck's Constant = 6.626196×10^{-27} erg/hertz

1 calorie = 4.184000 joule = 4.184000×10^7 erg

1 electronvolt = 1.60219×10^{-19} joule

ideal gas constant = 0.082053 liter-atm/mole-K° = 1.9872 cal/mole-K°

ideal gas volume at STP = 22.4136 liters

APPENDIX C
LOGARITHMS OF NUMBERS

N	0	1	2	3	4	5	6	7	8	9
10	0000	0043	0086	0128	0170	0212	0253	0294	0334	0374
11	0414	0453	0492	0531	0569	0607	0645	0682	0719	0755
12	0792	0828	0864	0899	0934	0969	1004	1038	1072	1106
13	1139	1173	1206	1239	1271	1303	1335	1367	1399	1430
14	1461	1492	1523	1553	1584	1614	1644	1673	1703	1732
15	1761	1790	1818	1847	1875	1903	1931	1959	1987	2014
16	2041	2068	2095	2122	2148	2175	2201	2227	2253	2279
17	2304	2330	2355	2380	2405	2430	2455	2480	2504	2529
18	2553	2577	2601	2625	2648	2672	2695	2718	2742	2765
19	2788	2810	2833	2856	2878	2900	2923	2945	2967	2989
20	3010	3032	3054	3075	3096	3118	3139	3160	3181	3201
21	3222	3243	3263	3284	3304	3324	3345	3365	3385	3404
22	3424	3444	3464	3483	3502	3522	3541	3560	3579	3598
23	3617	3636	3655	3674	3692	3711	3729	3747	3766	3784
24	3802	3820	3838	3856	3874	3892	3909	3927	3945	3962
25	3979	3997	4014	4031	4048	4065	4082	4099	4116	4133
26	4150	4166	4183	4200	4216	4232	4249	4265	4281	4298
27	4314	4330	4346	4362	4378	4393	4409	4425	4440	4456
28	4472	4487	4502	4518	4533	4548	4564	4579	4594	4609
29	4624	4639	4654	4669	4683	4698	4713	4728	4742	4757
30	4771	4786	4800	4814	4829	4843	4857	4871	4886	4900
31	4914	4928	4942	4955	4969	4983	4997	5011	5024	5038
32	5051	5065	5079	5092	5105	5119	5132	5145	5159	5172
33	5185	5198	5211	5224	5237	5250	5263	5276	5289	5302
34	5315	5328	5340	5353	5366	5378	5391	5403	5416	5428
35	5441	5453	5465	5478	5490	5502	5514	5527	5539	5551
36	5563	5575	5587	5599	5611	5623	5635	5647	5658	5670
37	5682	5694	5705	5717	5729	5740	5752	5763	5775	5786
38	5798	5809	5821	5832	5843	5855	5866	5877	5888	5899
39	5911	5922	5933	5944	5955	5966	5977	5988	5999	6010
40	6021	6031	6042	6053	6064	6075	6085	6096	6107	6117
N	0	1	2	3	4	5	6	7	8	9

LOGARITHMS OF NUMBERS

N	0	1	2	3	4	5	6	7	8	9
40	6021	6031	6042	6053	6064	6075	6085	6096	6107	6117
41	6128	6138	6149	6160	6170	6180	6191	6201	6212	6222
42	6232	6243	6253	6263	6274	6284	6294	6304	6314	6325
43	6335	6345	6355	6365	6375	6385	6395	6405	6415	6425
44	6435	6444	6454	6464	6474	6484	6493	6503	6513	6522
45	6532	6542	6551	6561	6571	6580	6590	6599	6609	6618
46	6628	6637	6646	6656	6665	6675	6684	6693	6702	6712
47	6721	6730	6739	6749	6758	6767	6776	6785	6794	6803
48	6812	6821	6830	6839	6848	6857	6866	6875	6884	6893
49	6902	6911	6920	6928	6937	6946	6955	6964	6972	6981
50	6990	6998	7007	7016	7024	7033	7042	7050	7059	7067
51	7076	7084	7093	7101	7110	7118	7126	7135	7143	7152
52	7160	7168	7177	7185	7193	7202	7210	7218	7226	7235
53	7243	7251	7259	7267	7275	7284	7292	7300	7308	7316
54	7324	7332	7340	7348	7356	7364	7372	7380	7388	7396
55	7404	7412	7419	7427	7435	7443	7451	7459	7466	7474
56	7482	7490	7497	7505	7513	7520	7528	7536	7543	7551
57	7559	7566	7574	7582	7589	7597	7604	7612	7619	7627
58	7634	7642	7649	7657	7664	7672	7679	7686	7694	7701
59	7709	7716	7723	7731	7738	7745	7752	7760	7767	7774
60	7782	7789	7796	7803	7810	7818	7825	7832	7839	7846
61	7853	7860	7868	7875	7882	7889	7896	7903	7910	7917
62	7924	7931	7938	7945	7952	7959	7966	7973	7980	7987
63	7993	8000	8007	8014	8021	8028	8035	8041	8048	8055
64	8062	8069	8075	8082	8089	8096	8102	8109	8116	8122
65	8129	8136	8142	8149	8156	8162	8169	8176	8182	8189
66	8195	8202	8209	8215	8222	8228	8235	8241	8248	8254
67	8261	8267	8274	8280	8287	8293	8299	8306	8312	8319
68	8325	8331	8338	8344	8351	8357	8363	8370	8376	8382
69	8388	8395	8401	8407	8414	8420	8426	8432	8439	8445
70	8451	8457	8463	8470	8476	8482	8488	8494	8500	8506
N	0	1	2	3	4	5	6	7	8	9

APPENDIX C

LOGARITHMS OF NUMBERS

N	0	1	2	3	4	5	6	7	8	9
70	8451	8457	8463	8470	8476	8482	8488	8494	8500	8506
71	8513	8519	8525	8531	8537	8543	8549	8555	8561	8567
72	8573	8579	8585	8591	8597	8603	8609	8615	8621	8627
73	8633	8639	8645	8651	8657	8663	8669	8675	8681	8686
74	8692	8698	8704	8710	8716	8722	8727	8733	8739	8745
75	8751	8756	8762	8768	8774	8779	8785	8791	8797	8802
76	8808	8814	8820	8825	8831	8837	8842	8848	8854	8859
77	8865	8871	8876	8882	8887	8893	8899	8904	8910	8915
78	8921	8927	8932	8938	8943	8949	8954	8960	8965	8971
79	8976	8982	8987	8993	8998	9004	9009	9015	9020	9025
80	9031	9036	9042	9047	9053	9058	9063	9069	9074	9079
81	9085	9090	9096	9101	9106	9112	9117	9122	9128	9133
82	9138	9143	9149	9154	9159	9165	9170	9175	9180	9186
83	9191	9196	9201	9206	9212	9217	9222	9227	9232	9238
84	9243	9248	9253	9258	9263	9269	9274	9279	9284	9289
85	9294	9299	9304	9309	9315	9320	9325	9330	9335	9340
86	9345	9350	9355	9360	9365	9370	9375	9380	9385	9390
87	9395	9400	9405	9410	9415	9420	9425	9430	9435	9440
88	9445	9450	9455	9460	9465	9469	9474	9479	9484	9489
89	9494	9499	9504	9509	9513	9518	9523	9528	9533	9538
90	9542	9547	9552	9557	9562	9566	9571	9576	9581	9586
91	9590	9595	9600	9605	9609	9614	9619	9624	9628	9633
92	9638	9643	9647	9652	9657	9661	9666	9671	9675	9680
93	9685	9689	9694	9699	9703	9708	9713	9717	9722	9727
94	9731	9736	9741	9745	9750	9754	9759	9763	9768	9773
95	9777	9782	9786	9791	9795	9800	9805	9809	9814	9818
96	9823	9827	9832	9836	9841	9845	9850	9854	9859	9863
97	9868	9872	9877	9881	9886	9890	9894	9899	9903	9908
98	9912	9917	9921	9926	9930	9934	9939	9943	9948	9952
99	9956	9961	9965	9969	9974	9978	9983	9987	9991	9996
N	0	1	2	3	4	5	6	7	8	9

INDEX

Boldface numbers refer to definitions. *Italic numbers* refer to biographical and historical entries.

Electrode reaction, 489-491, 494, 495, 500, 505, 506

Electrolysis, 489-491, **492,** 493; Faradays' law of, 505, 506; predicting the product of, 499, 500, 501

Electrolyte, **425, 489**

Electrolytic conduction, **493**

Electron, 112-114; acceleration of, 527-529; annihilated, 516; capture of, 517; charge on, 505; delocalized, **229;** free, **211;** location of, 140, 141; mass of, 114, 116, 117; momentum of, 140, 141; motion of, 138-141, 150, 211, 212, 493; orbit of, 123, 124, 127; and photoelectric effect, 130, 131; quantum numbers of, 145-150; quantum theory of, 126-129; in redox reaction, 463-467, 470, 471; spin of, 150; van der Waals force on, 252-254; wave particle nature of, 138-144; wavelength of, 137

Electron acceptor, 499; *table,* 498

Electron affinity, **199;** *table,* 197

Electron cloud, 143, 144; collision of, 406, 407, 408, 410; shape of, 217-233; size and shape of, 148, 149; van der Waals radius of, 209, 210; *illus.,* 148; 149; shape, 218, 219, 221, 222, 223, 224, 225, 226, 227, 228, 229, 230; van der Waals radii, 210; *table,* bond angle, 220

Electron configuration, 145-154; diagonal rule of, 152, 153; effect on ionization energy, 195-197; effect on metallic bonding, 211, 212, 487; and periodic properties, 163, 167-172; *illus.,* 148; 149; 153; 154; *table,* 154; 165; 166

Electron donor, 499; *table,* 498

Electron dot diagram, 154; *table,* 154

Electron level, 145-154; *illus.,* 146; 147

Electron pair, multiple, 220; repulsion of, 217-220, 230, 231

Electron-pair acceptor, 428, 429

Electron-pair donor, 428, 429

Electron pump, 488, 489, 491

Electron shielding, 148, 181, 187, 197, 198

Electron sublevel, 146-154; filling of, 167-172; *illus.,* 146; 147; *See also* Orbital

Electronegativity, 199-202, **200;** and acid-base formation, 431, 432; and hydrogen bonding, 305, 306; and oxidation number, 468-470; and polar bonds, 240, 241; and van der Waals force, *253; table,* 201

Electronvolt, **196,** 529

Electrophoresis, **395**

Electroplating, 505-507

Electroscope, 513

Element, **44,** 46, 47; actinide series of, 170; classification of, 47; half-life of, 521-523, 533; lanthanide series of, 170; octet rule of, 171; oxidation number of, 59, **60,** 61, 250, **467**-470; periodic classification of, 159-190; stability of, 523-526; stable, 171, 174; strongest, 212; symbols of, 57, 58; synthetic, 532, 533; tracer, 520, 521; transition, 168, 169, 173, 178, 251; transuranium, 532, 533; *table,* actinide series, 170; atomic masses, 121; covalent radii, 207; electron configuration, 165, 166; electronegativity, 201; half-life, 532; lanthanide series, 169; periodic table, 164; symbols, 58

Elementary particle, 516

Elimination reaction, 561

Emission spectrum, 125

Empirical formula, **65,** 83, 84

Endothermic reaction, **71,** 98, 99, 101, 361, 362, 379

Endpoint, **455**

Energy, **9, 10;** activation, 72, **406,** 407, 409, 411; binding, 523-526, 533; change in, 367, 368; and chemical change, 71, 72; conservation of, 11, 94, 99, 100;

2 3 4 5 6 7 8 9 10 11 12 13 14 15-80 79 78 77 76 75

PERIODIC CLASSIFICATION OF THE ELEMENTS
(BASED ON $^{12}C = 12.0000$)

Light Metals

Transition Metals

Nonmetals

IA	IIA	IIIB	IVB	VB	VIB	VIIB	VIIIB	VIIIB	VIIIB	IB	IIB	IIIA	IVA	VA	VIA	VIIA	VIIIA
1 **H** 1.0079																	2 **He** 4.00260
3 **Li** 6.941	4 **Be** 9.01218											5 **B** 10.81	6 **C** 12.011	7 **N** 14.0067	8 **O** 15.9994	9 **F** 18.99840	10 **Ne** 20.179
11 **Na** 22.98977	12 **Mg** 24.305											13 **Al** 26.98154	14 **Si** 28.086	15 **P** 30.97376	16 **S** 32.06	17 **Cl** 35.453	18 **Ar** 39.948
19 **K** 39.098	20 **Ca** 40.08	21 **Sc** 44.9559	22 **Ti** 47.90	23 **V** 50.9414	24 **Cr** 51.996	25 **Mn** 54.9380	26 **Fe** 55.847	27 **Co** 58.9332	28 **Ni** 58.70	29 **Cu** 63.546	30 **Zn** 65.38	31 **Ga** 69.72	32 **Ge** 72.59	33 **As** 74.9216	34 **Se** 78.96	35 **Br** 79.904	36 **Kr** 83.80
37 **Rb** 85.4678	38 **Sr** 87.62	39 **Y** 88.9059	40 **Zr** 91.22	41 **Nb** 92.9064	42 **Mo** 95.94	43 **Tc** 97	44 **Ru** 101.07	45 **Rh** 102.9055	46 **Pd** 106.4	47 **Ag** 107.868	48 **Cd** 112.40	49 **In** 114.82	50 **Sn** 118.69	51 **Sb** 121.75	52 **Te** 127.60	53 **I** 126.9045	54 **Xe** 131.30
55 **Cs** 132.9054	56 **Ba** 137.34	71 **Lu** 174.97 *	72 **Hf** 178.49	73 **Ta** 180.9479	74 **W** 183.85	75 **Re** 186.207	76 **Os** 190.2	77 **Ir** 192.22	78 **Pt** 195.09	79 **Au** 196.9665	80 **Hg** 200.59	81 **Tl** 204.37	82 **Pb** 207.2	83 **Bi** 208.9804	84 **Po** 209	85 **At** 210	86 **Rn** 222
87 **Fr** 223	88 **Ra** 226	103 **Lr** 256 **	104 257	105 260													

* Lanthanide series	57 **La** 138.9055	58 **Ce** 140.12	59 **Pr** 140.9077	60 **Nd** 144.24	61 **Pm** 145	62 **Sm** 150.4	63 **Eu** 151.96	64 **Gd** 157.25	65 **Tb** 158.9254	66 **Dy** 162.50	67 **Ho** 164.9304	68 **Er** 167.26	69 **Tm** 168.9342	70 **Yb** 173.04
** Actinide series	89 **Ac** 227	90 **Th** 232.0381	91 **Pa** 231	92 **U** 238.029	93 **Np** 237	94 **Pu** 244	95 **Am** 243	96 **Cm** 247	97 **Bk** 247	98 **Cf** 251	99 **Es** 254	100 **Fm** 257	101 **Md** 258	102 **No** 255